SERIES IN PLASMA PHYSICS

N C. BROWN, ADVISORY EDITOR
LABORATORY OF ELECTRONICS
SETTS INSTITUTE OF TECHNOLOGY

L · COLLISION PHENOMENA IN IONIZED GASES

COLLISION PHENOMENA

IN IONIZED GASES

WILE

SANBO
RESEARCH
MASSACHU

MCDANIE

COLLISION PHENOMENA

IN IONIZED GASES

EARL W. McDANIEL

PROFESSOR OF PHYSICS AND ELECTRICAL ENGINEERING
GEORGIA INSTITUTE OF TECHNOLOGY
AND CONSULTANT CONTROLLED THERMONUCLEAR DIVISION
OAK RIDGE NATIONAL LABORATORY

JOHN WILEY & SONS, INC., NEW YORK · LONDON · SYDNEY

THIS BOOK IS DEDICATED TO MY SON KEITH,
DAUGHTER LINDA, AND WIFE FRANCES

PREFACE

This book is the evolutionary product of notes I have used in teaching plasma physics and gaseous electronics in the Physics and Electrical Engineering Departments of the Georgia Institute of Technology during the last seven years. It is designed as a text at about the first-year graduate level and as a reference for researchers whose work is concerned with atomic collisions and transport phenomena. Its scope is outlined at the beginning of the first chapter.

An effort has been made to make this book as nearly self-contained as practicable. By doing so I have tried to make it comprehensible, not only to physics students, but also to engineers, whose background in collision mechanics and kinetic theory is generally not substantial. My own experience has indicated that engineering students who have taken an undergraduate course in modern physics have no particular difficulty with the bulk of the material presented here. Most of the book's sections are rather straightforward, although others deal with complicated topics at an advanced level. I have found, however, that the advanced areas can be covered satisfactorily after the more elementary work has been thoroughly discussed.

I have included detailed descriptions of experimental methods and large amounts of data which have already proved useful as reference material in our laboratories at Georgia Tech.; I can only hope that they will also be useful elsewhere.

During the preparation of the manuscript I had the good fortune to obtain constructive criticism from a number of experts in the field of atomic collisions. C. F. Barnett, L. M. Branscomb, R. W. Crompton, A. Dalgarno, D. E. Kerr, D. W. Martin, E. A. Mason, M. R. C. McDowell, J. W. McGowan, and G. J. Schulz were particularly helpful, and I cannot adequately express my appreciation to them. Special thanks go to my colleague Professor J. W. Hooper (may his tribe increase!) for his invaluable assistance in the preparation of Chapter 12 and to Mr. W. C. Lineberger, one of our graduate students, who did much of the work on Chapter 13 and Appendix I. Also, I am deeply indebted to Professor S. C. Brown of the Massachusetts Institute of Technology for his continuing support and for his review of the entire manuscript. Finally, I wish to express my sincere appreciation to Dean J. W. Mason of the College of Engineering at the Georgia Institute of Technology for his encouragement and for making available funds for the preparation of the manuscript.

This book contains references to work reported up to the end of 1963. A large number of references are made to papers presented at the *Sixth International Conference on Ionization Phenomena in Gases*, Paris, July 1963, and the *Third International Conference on the Physics of Electronic and Atomic Collisions*, London, July 1963. The Proceedings of these conferences will be published in 1964 by S. E. R. M. A. (Paris) and North-Holland Publishing Company (Amsterdam), respectively.

EARL W. McDANIEL

Atlanta, Georgia
February 1964

CONTENTS

1

FUNDAMENTAL CONCEPTS

The discovery of X rays in 1895 marked the beginning of quantitative studies of ionized gases. These investigations have made important contributions to the growth of physics, both in the development of experimental apparatus and techniques and in the formulation of modern theory. They have also led to many practical applications which are too well known to require enumeration.

In spite of the concentration of effort in this area for more than half a century, many of the long-recognized problems have been only partly solved. In addition, recent studies of atmospheric and astrophysical phenomena have revealed that ionized gases play a much more important role in nature than was previously suspected, and present knowledge is insufficient to explain many of the observations. Finally, it may be pointed out that the world's conventional energy resources, including fissionable materials, are expected to be largely exhausted within a few centuries. The development of techniques for the controlled fusion of light nuclei in thermonuclear plasmas appears to offer the greatest hope for the long-range solution of our fuel problem. These considerations explain the continuing and growing interest in ionized gases and the fact that the research effort in this area is as vigorous and extensive as that in any other field of physics today.

1-1. THE SCOPE OF THE STUDY OF IONIZED GASES

The phenomena of interest in ionized gases are of two basically different types: *noncollective processes*, which involve binary or ternary collisions of the particles composing the gas with one another and with surfaces, and *collective phenomena* based on the simultaneous interaction of a large number of particles and the interaction of the ionized gas with externally applied fields. In the first category lie such topics as elastic scattering, excitation, ionization, dissociation, charge transfer, electron attachment, drift velocities, energy distributions, diffusion, recombination, and secondary and photoemission. The noncollective processes are thus seen to fall mainly within the realms of atomic collisions and transport phenomena. The second category encompasses electrical discharges, space charge effects, plasma oscillations and waves, and magnetohydrodynamics. Collective phenomena usually are significant only if the ionized gas is a true *plasma*, that is, if its dimensions are large compared with its debye shielding length.* Our attention is centered here on the noncollective phenomena, which are important in plasmas and in ordinary ionized gases.

Since our major interest here is in atomic collisions and in the transport phenomena interpreted in terms of such impacts, it is appropriate at the outset to discuss certain basic aspects of collisions. The remainder of this chapter is devoted largely to this purpose.

1-2. LABORATORY AND CENTER-OF-MASS COORDINATES AND THE ASYMPTOTIC ASPECTS OF NONRELATIVISTIC ELASTIC COLLISIONS

Two different coordinate systems are commonly used in discussions of collision problems, the laboratory (Lab) and the center-of-mass (CM). The Lab system is the frame of reference of a laboratory observer; the CM system moves with respect to the Lab system so that its origin is always coincident with the center of mass of the colliding particles. It is obviously convenient to make physical measurements in the Lab system, but, as we show in Chapter 3, the mathematical analysis of a collision is considerably simpler in the CM frame. Therefore it is desirable to

---

* The debye length is a measure of the distance over which deviations from charge neutrality can occur in an ionized gas. It is also a measure of the thickness of the sheaths which develop at plasma boundaries. The debye length is directly proportional to the square root of the energy and inversely proportional to the square root of the number density of the charged particles in the ionized gas. The expression for the debye length is derived in Appendix I, where the differences between plasmas and ordinary ionized gases are more fully explored.

establish general relationships between the two systems so that transformations from one to the other may be easily made. *All of the transformations we shall obtain apply only to the special case in which one of the
collision partners is initially at rest in the Lab system.** This condition
holds, at least approximately, in most studies of collision events.

   To derive the desired relationships, we shall consider a nonrelativistic
elastic collision between two particles and focus our attention on its

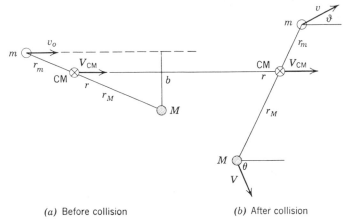

(a) Before collision   (b) After collision

FIG. 1-2-1. Asymptotic views of an elastic collision in the Lab system. In each of the
figures the distance between the particles r is much greater than the range of the interaction between the particles; m and M are at distances r_m and r_M, respectively, from the
center of mass.

ultimate effects on the motion of the particles. We are not interested here
in the detailed nature of the interaction or in what takes place "during"
the collision. The pair of particles is first viewed long before the collision
occurs, while the separation distance is still large and the interaction
between the collision partners negligible. It is next viewed long after the
collision has taken place, as the particles recede from one another with
their final fixed velocities. The scattering angles and changes in speed are
our major concerns.

   A. VELOCITIES AND KINETIC ENERGY.   Assume that a particle of mass
m is moving with initial speed v_0 in the Lab system toward a remote
particle of mass M which is at rest in the Lab system. If the particles were
incapable of interaction, the closest distance of approach of m to M would
be b, the impact parameter, shown in Fig. 1-2-1. Long after the collision

* The same approach to be used here, namely straightforward application of the laws
of conservation of energy and momentum, is also used to obtain the transformations
when both particles are moving in the Lab system before the collision.

has occurred m is observed to be moving with constant speed v at an angle ϑ with respect to its original path, whereas M is traveling with constant speed V at an angle θ with respect to the original direction; ϑ and θ are the scattering angles of m and M, respectively, in the Lab system. In this frame of reference m may be regarded as the projectile and M as the target particle.

In the Lab system the center of mass of the two particles moves with velocity V_{CM} in a direction parallel to the initial direction of m; V_{CM} is constant in magnitude and direction before, during, and after the collision. From conservation of momentum considerations, the magnitude of V_{CM} is given by the equation*

$$(m + M)V_{\mathrm{CM}} = mv_0 \tag{1-2-1}$$

This result may be expressed in the form

$$V_{\mathrm{CM}} = v_0 \frac{M_r}{M} \tag{1-2-2}$$

where M_r is the reduced mass of the pair of particles, defined by the equation

$$M_r = \frac{mM}{m + M} \tag{1-2-3}$$

Note that the reduced mass always lies between 0.5 and 1.0 times the mass of the lighter particle.

Since kinetic energy and linear momentum are conserved in the collision,

$$\frac{mv_0{}^2}{2} = \frac{mv^2}{2} + \frac{MV^2}{2} \tag{1-2-4}$$

$$mv_0 = mv \cos \vartheta + MV \cos \theta \tag{1-2-5}$$

$$0 = mv \sin \vartheta - MV \sin \theta \tag{1-2-6}$$

It should be noted that Equations 1-2-1 to 1-2-6 are valid regardless of the form of the interaction potential between the particles, provided the collision is elastic. Equations 1-2-4 to 1-2-6 enable us to obtain the final

* Equation 1-2-1 also follows from the equation defining the instantaneous position of the center of mass. If r_m and r_M denote the distances of m and M, respectively, from CM, the position of CM is specified by the equation $mr_m = Mr_M$. From Fig. 1-2-1 it is apparent that $V_{\mathrm{CM}} = v_0(r_M)/(r_m + r_M)$. By substituting $r_M = r_m(m/M)$, we then obtain (1-2-1). The velocity of the center of mass is given by 2-2-20 when both m and M are moving before the collision in the Lab system.

velocities, v and V, in terms of the initial velocity and the scattering angles:

$$\left(\frac{v}{v_0}\right)^2 - 2\left(\frac{v}{v_0}\right)\left(\frac{m}{m+M}\right)\cos\vartheta - \left(\frac{M-m}{m+M}\right) = 0 \qquad (1\text{-}2\text{-}7)$$

$$v^2 = v_0^{\,2}\left(1 - \frac{4M_r^{\,2}}{mM}\cos^2\theta\right) \qquad (1\text{-}2\text{-}8)$$

$$V = 2v_0\frac{M_r}{M}\cos\theta \qquad (1\text{-}2\text{-}9)$$

Now examine the collision in the center-of-mass coordinate system (Fig. 1-2-2). In this frame of reference the velocity of the center of mass

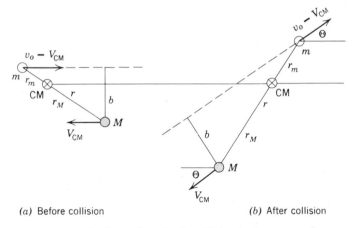

(a) Before collision　　　　　　(b) After collision

FIG. 1-2-2. Asymptotic views of an elastic collision in the center-of-mass system.

is zero. The mutual velocity of approach of the two particles is seen to be the same in the CM system as it was in the Lab system, having the value v_0.

The total linear momentum of the system in the CM frame is zero at all times. Therefore we may equate the magnitudes of the momenta of the particles and obtain the equation

$$m(v_0 - V_{\mathrm{CM}}) = MV_{\mathrm{CM}} \qquad (1\text{-}2\text{-}10)$$

The use of (1-2-2) and (1-2-3) shows that each particle has a CM momentum equal to $v_0 M_r$. Since the linear momenta of the particles are always equal and opposite, the particles must be traveling in opposite directions to one another before and after the collision. The distinction between projectile and target vanishes, and the particles are now properly regarded as initially approaching one another. The common angle of scattering in the CM system is denoted by Θ.

Since kinetic energy is conserved (except "during" the collision, when the forces acting between the particles and, consequently, their mutual potential energy, are appreciable), each of the collision partners has the same speed in the CM system after the collision as it had initially.* The total kinetic energy in the CM frame before and after the collision is given by

$$T_{CM} = \frac{m}{2}(v_0 - V_{CM})^2 + \frac{M}{2}V_{CM}{}^2 = \frac{m}{2}v_0{}^2 - \frac{(m+M)}{2}V_{CM}{}^2 \quad (1\text{-}2\text{-}11)$$

Thus the total CM kinetic energy is the initial Lab energy of m minus the energy corresponding to the motion of the center of mass in the Lab system. Again using (1-2-2), we see that

$$T_{CM} = \tfrac{1}{2}M_r v_0{}^2 \quad (1\text{-}2\text{-}12)$$

Here we have a relationship between the total CM kinetic energy, the reduced mass of the system, and the mutual velocity of approach of the collision partners.†

B. ANGULAR MOMENTUM AND MOMENT OF INERTIA.   Since no external torques act on the pair of particles, the angular momentum, J, of the system is constant before, during, and after the collision. The angular momentum about the center of mass in the CM coordinates is

$$J_{CM} = m(v_0 - V_{CM})\frac{r_m}{r_m + r_M}b + MV_{CM}\frac{r_M}{r_m + r_M}b \quad (1\text{-}2\text{-}13)$$

This result may also be expressed as

$$J_{CM} = M_r v_0 b \quad (1\text{-}2\text{-}14)$$

The moment of inertia, I, of the system about the center of mass is

$$I = mr_m{}^2 + Mr_M{}^2 \quad (1\text{-}2\text{-}15)$$

Making use of the fact that

$$mr_m = Mr_M = M_r r \quad (1\text{-}2\text{-}16)$$

where r is the total separation distance between m and M, we may write

$$I = M_r r^2 \quad (1\text{-}2\text{-}17)$$

* If the CM speed of m after the collision differed from its initial value by some factor α, the speed of M would also have to change by the same factor as the result of the collision. This would mean that the total kinetic energy of the system would have to change in violation of the principle of conservation of energy.

† This result actually applies regardless of the initial motion of the particles in the Lab system. In the preceding development we assumed the target particle to be initially at rest in the Lab frame of reference.

C. SCATTERING ANGLES.   Relationships between the scattering angles may be obtained by vector addition of the velocities of Fig. 1-2-1b to those of Fig. 1-2-2b to obtain Fig. 1-2-3.   An immediate result is

$$\theta = \tfrac{1}{2}(\pi - \Theta) \tag{1-2-18}$$

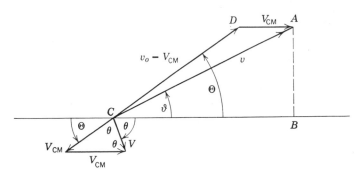

FIG. 1-2-3. Vector addition of the respective velocities of the particles in the CM system to the velocity of the center of mass in the Lab system to obtain the velocities of the particles in the Lab system and the relationships between the CM and Lab scattering angles: $v_0 - V_{CM}$ is the final velocity of m in the CM system, and V_{CM} is the velocity of CM in the Lab frame.   The sum of these vectors must equal v, the final velocity of m in the Lab system.   Likewise, the vector sum of the final velocity of M in the CM frame and the velocity of CM in the Lab frame must yield V, the final velocity of M in the Lab system.

Another relationship is obtained by examination of the triangle ABC:

$$\tan \vartheta = \frac{AB}{BC} = \frac{(v_0 - V_{CM})\sin \Theta}{V_{CM} + (v_0 - V_{CM})\cos \Theta} \tag{1-2-19}$$

or

$$\tan \vartheta = \frac{\sin \Theta}{\gamma + \cos \Theta} \tag{1-2-20}$$

where

$$\gamma = \frac{m}{M} = \frac{V_{CM}}{v_0 - V_{CM}} \tag{1-2-21}$$

Also, consideration of the line segment AB in Fig. 1-2-3 shows that

$$v \sin \vartheta = v_0 \frac{M_r}{m} \sin \Theta \tag{1-2-22}$$

Finally, we note three useful relationships between ϑ and Θ for three special values of the ratio m/M.

$$\text{If}\quad m \ll M,\quad \vartheta \approx \Theta \tag{1-2-23}$$

The Lab and CM systems are almost identical; ϑ increases monotonically from 0 to π as Θ increases from 0 to π.

$$\text{If}\quad m = M,\quad \vartheta = \frac{\Theta}{2} \tag{1-2-24}$$

ϑ varies from 0 to $\pi/2$ as Θ varies from 0 to π. No particles are back-scattered in the Lab system. Head-on scattering corresponds to $\Theta = \pi$, $\vartheta = \pi/2$, $\theta = 0$.

$$\text{If}\quad m \gg M,\quad \vartheta \approx \frac{M}{m} \sin \Theta \tag{1-2-25}$$

When $m > M$, ϑ first increases from 0 to a maximum value $\vartheta_{max} = \sin^{-1}(M/m)$, which is less than $\pi/2$, as Θ increases from 0 to

$$\Theta = \cos^{-1}(-M/m);$$

ϑ then decreases to 0 as Θ increases further to π, so that Θ is a double-valued function of ϑ. No particles are scattered beyond ϑ_{max} in the Lab system. We may distinguish between the two values of Θ that give a particular value of ϑ between 0 and $\sin^{-1}(M/m)$ by comparing the energies of m after scattering in the two cases—the energy is greater for the smaller Θ.

The geometrical relationships we have presented apply in a quantum mechanical collision as well as in the classical case. The reason for this is that the equations are essentially relationships of momentum vectors and are applied only in the asymptotic region, remote from the collision site, where the particle positions do not have to be precisely known and where consequently their momenta can be precisely determined.

D. RELATIONSHIP BETWEEN ELEMENTS OF SOLID ANGLE IN THE LAB AND CM SYSTEMS. A valuable relationship in the discussion of collision problems is the transformation law between elements of solid angle in the Lab and CM systems. If the scattering distribution is independent of the azimuthal angle, it can be shown that

$$d\Omega_{CM} = \frac{[(m/M)^2 + 2(m/M)\cos\Theta + 1]^{3/2}}{1 + (m/M)\cos\Theta} d\Omega_{Lab} \tag{1-2-26}$$

where $d\Omega_{CM} = \sin\Theta \, d\Theta \, d\varphi_{CM}$, $d\Omega_{Lab} = \sin\vartheta \, d\vartheta \, d\varphi_{Lab}$, and $\varphi_{Lab} = \varphi_{CM} = \varphi$. Equation 1-2-26 applies when the scattering is described by a spherically symmetric potential. More complex situations in which (1-2-26) does not hold are mentioned in Section 1-7-B.

1-3. INELASTIC AND RELATIVISTIC COLLISIONS

Section 1-2 dealt only with the nonrelativistic elastic collision, the simplest type to analyze. In an *elastic collision* the total kinetic energy of the system of colliding particles is the same before and after the collision—there are no permanent changes in the internal excitation energies of the collision partners. Linear and angular momenta are conserved at all times throughout the collision.

Another important type of collision is the *inelastic collision*, in which momentum is still conserved but in which the total kinetic energy of the system decreases (or increases) as the result of the excitation (or de-excitation) of one or both of the particles.* The analysis of this case is evidently more difficult than that of the elastic case, but the discussion in Section 1-2 immediately provides one useful and important result: the maximum amount of kinetic energy of the system that can be transferred in the collision to the form of internal excitation energy is the center-of-mass kinetic energy, which is given by (1-2-12). This fact results from the constancy of the total linear momentum of the system throughout the event.

Now let us inquire into the relation between the Lab and CM scattering angles in an inelastic collision. Suppose, as before, that a projectile of mass m with initial velocity v_0 in the Lab system strikes a target of mass M which is at rest in the Lab system. The projectile is scattered through an angle ϑ in the Lab system, and the target recoils at angle θ. If, in the collision, a quantity of energy ΔE is converted from kinetic to internal excitation energy, (1-2-20) is still valid:

$$\tan \vartheta = \frac{\sin \Theta}{\gamma + \cos \Theta} \tag{1-2-20}$$

However, γ is no longer equal to m/M but is now given by

$$\gamma = \frac{m}{M} \left(\frac{T_{\mathrm{CM}}}{T_{\mathrm{CM}} - \Delta E} \right)^{\frac{1}{2}} \tag{1-3-1}$$

(γ is still equal to the ratio of V_{CM} to the CM speed of m after the collision).

Several additional useful relationships among the energies and scattering angles may also be derived. From the laws of conservation of total energy and linear momentum, we may easily show that

$$\cos \theta = \frac{\Delta E + [1 + (M/m)]T_{\mathrm{Lab},M}}{2\sqrt{(M/m)T_{\mathrm{Lab},i}T_{\mathrm{Lab},M}}} \tag{1-3-2}$$

and

$$\cos \vartheta = \frac{T_{\mathrm{Lab},i} + T_{\mathrm{Lab},f} - (M/m)T_{\mathrm{Lab},M}}{2\sqrt{T_{\mathrm{Lab},i}T_{\mathrm{Lab},f}}} \tag{1-3-3}$$

* Many examples of inelastic collisions between particles are given in Chapters 5, 6, 8, and 12.

whereas application of the law of sines and the law of cosines to a diagram similar to that in Fig. 1-2-3 yields

$$T_{\text{Lab},f}\frac{\sin^2\vartheta}{\sin^2\Theta} = T_{\text{Lab},f} + \left(\frac{m}{m+M}\right)^2 T_{\text{Lab},i} - \frac{2m}{m+M}\sqrt{T_{\text{Lab},i}T_{\text{Lab},f}}\cos\vartheta$$

$$(1\text{-}3\text{-}4)$$

and

$$T_{\text{Lab},M}\frac{\sin^2\theta}{\sin^2\Theta} = T_{\text{Lab},M} + \frac{mMT_{\text{Lab},i}}{(m+M)^2} - \frac{2\sqrt{mM}}{m+M}\sqrt{T_{\text{Lab},i}T_{\text{Lab},M}}\cos\theta$$

$$(1\text{-}3\text{-}5)$$

In these equations $T_{\text{Lab},i}$ denotes the kinetic energy of the projectile in the Lab system before the collision and $T_{\text{Lab},f}$, the corresponding energy after the collision; $T_{\text{Lab},M}$, the kinetic energy of the recoiling target in the Lab system, is equal to $T_{\text{Lab},i} - T_{\text{Lab},f} - \Delta E$.

Further complications are presented if one or both of the colliding particles have relativistic velocities. The energetics of inelastic and relativistic collisions are treated in Ref. 1.

1-4. THE COLLISION CROSS SECTION CONCEPT

Before proceeding, it would be desirable to introduce the concept of the collision cross section. This will enable us to discuss more quantitatively the various types of reactions that can occur when collisions take place. The cross section is basically a measure of the probability that a given type of reaction will occur under given conditions. Its value depends on the nature of the particles and reaction considered, the mutual velocity of approach of the collision partners, and the impact parameter.

A. THE MICROSCOPIC ELASTIC SCATTERING CROSS SECTION,* q_s. As before, we begin our discussion with the conceptually simple case of elastic scattering. The ideas to be developed are easily generalized to other situations. Consider a parallel beam of monoenergetic projectiles approaching the origin of the laboratory coordinate system, as shown in Fig. 1-4-1. The beam is directed along the Z axis and is composed of N_p particles per "cm²-sec". Imagine these projectiles to be point particles but ascribe a finite size to the N_t target particles which are clustered at rest close to the origin O. We shall assume for the present that elastic scattering is the only reaction of which the projectiles and targets are capable. We shall further assume that there are sufficiently few targets present that

---

* The German word for cross section is *querschnitt*—hence the frequent use of the symbol q to denote this quantity.

none is shielded by another and that no projectile is scattered more than once.

Let $d\Omega_{\text{Lab}}$ represent the element of solid angle oriented in the spherical polar coordinate system by the angles ϑ and φ and let $N_s(\vartheta, \varphi)\, d\Omega_{\text{Lab}}$ be the number of projectiles scattered into $d\Omega_{\text{Lab}}$ per sec. Obviously

$$N_s(\vartheta, \varphi)\, d\Omega_{\text{Lab}} \sim N_p N_t\, d\Omega_{\text{Lab}}.$$

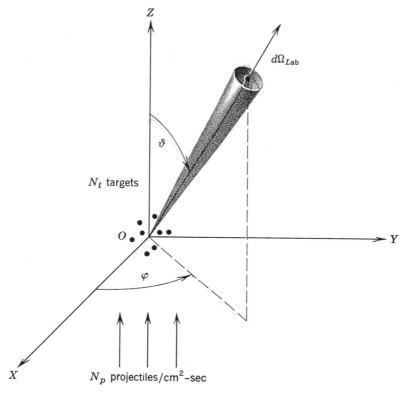

FIG. 1-4-1. The laboratory coordinate system used for discussion of the scattering of a beam of projectiles by N_t target particles clustered about the origin.

Insert a constant of proportionality $I_s(\vartheta, \varphi)$ into this expression so that

$$N_s(\vartheta, \varphi)\, d\Omega_{\text{Lab}} = I_s(\vartheta, \varphi) N_p N_t\, d\Omega_{\text{Lab}} = dI_s(\vartheta, \varphi) N_p N_t \qquad (1\text{-}4\text{-}1)$$

The quantity

$$I_s(\vartheta, \varphi)\, d\Omega_{\text{Lab}} \equiv dI_s(\vartheta, \varphi) \qquad (1\text{-}4\text{-}2)$$

is the *differential microscopic elastic scattering cross section in the Lab system.* Solving for $dI_s(\vartheta, \varphi)$, we obtain

$$dI_s(\vartheta, \varphi) = \frac{N_s(\vartheta, \varphi)\, d\Omega_{\text{Lab}}}{N_p N_t} \qquad (1\text{-}4\text{-}3)$$

which has the dimensions of cm²/target particle; $dI_s(\vartheta, \varphi)$ accordingly may be considered to be the area presented by each target particle for scattering of the projectiles into the element of solid angle $d\Omega_{\text{Lab}}$. To show that this interpretation is correct, assume that the incident beam impinges normally on a thin foil of 1 cm² area which contains N_t targets. The fraction of the incident beam scattered into $d\Omega_{\text{Lab}}$ at (ϑ, φ) with respect to the beam axis is equal to the ratio of the opaque area to the total area of the foil. Thus the number of projectiles scattered into $d\Omega_{\text{Lab}}$ per sec must be

$$N_s(\vartheta, \varphi) \, d\Omega_{\text{Lab}} = N_p \frac{I_s(\vartheta, \varphi) \, d\Omega_{\text{Lab}} N_t}{1 \text{ cm}^2}$$

But this is just what is predicted by (1-4-1), so our interpretation of $dI_s(\vartheta, \varphi)$ must be correct.

Now we define the *total microscopic elastic scattering cross section, q_s*:

$$q_s = \int dI_s(\vartheta, \varphi) = \iint I_s(\vartheta, \varphi) \, d\Omega_{\text{Lab}} = \int_0^{2\pi} \int_0^{\pi} I_s(\vartheta, \varphi) \sin \vartheta \, d\vartheta \, d\varphi \quad (1\text{-}4\text{-}4)$$

Evidently q_s represents the area presented by each of the target particles for scattering into the total solid angle, 4π steradians. The integral in (1-4-4) does not converge for all projectile-target scattering potentials. The condition for convergence is that $I_s(\vartheta, \varphi)$ increase less rapidly than $1/\vartheta^2$, for small ϑ, as ϑ decreases. The subject of convergence of the cross section integral is treated further in Chapter 3, in which techniques for calculating the scattering cross section for various assumed interaction potentials are also discussed.

Let $p(\vartheta, \varphi) \, d\Omega_{\text{Lab}}$ denote the probability that in an elastic collision the projectile is scattered into the element of solid angle $d\Omega_{\text{Lab}}$. Then the differential scattering cross section may be written

$$I_s(\vartheta, \varphi) \, d\Omega_{\text{Lab}} = q_s \, p(\vartheta, \varphi) \, d\Omega_{\text{Lab}} \quad (1\text{-}4\text{-}5)$$

It follows that

$$p(\vartheta, \varphi) = \frac{I_s(\vartheta, \varphi)}{q_s} \quad (1\text{-}4\text{-}6)$$

The symbol $\sigma_s(\vartheta, \varphi)$ is frequently used in place of $I_s(\vartheta, \varphi)$, and the total elastic scattering cross section is written as

$$\sigma_s = \int_0^{2\pi} \int_0^{\pi} \sigma_s(\vartheta, \varphi) \sin \vartheta \, d\vartheta \, d\varphi \quad (1\text{-}4\text{-}7)$$

Microscopic cross sections are usually expressed in units of cm² or in units of $\pi a_0^2 = 0.88 \times 10^{-16}$ cm², where $a_0 = 0.53 \times 10^{-8}$ cm is the radius of the first Bohr orbit of the hydrogen atom.

B. THE MACROSCOPIC SCATTERING CROSS SECTION, Q_s, AND THE SCATTER-
ING MEAN FREE PATH, λ_s.   Consider a beam of projectiles impinging
normally on a semi-infinite medium containing N stationary target
particles per cm³. Of those projectiles that penetrate to depth x in the
medium without experiencing scattering, a fraction equal to $Nq_s\,dx$ will
be scattered in passing from x to $x + dx$. This quantity is also equal to
the probability that a given projectile that reaches depth x without scattering will then suffer scattering between x and $x + dx$. If I_0 represents the
initial intensity of the incident beam in projectiles per cm²-sec and I is the
intensity of the unscattered component at depth x, then

$$dI = -INq_s\,dx \qquad (1\text{-}4\text{-}8)$$

and

$$I = I_0 e^{-Nq_s x} = I_0 e^{-Q_s x} \qquad (1\text{-}4\text{-}9)$$

where $Q_s = Nq_s$ is termed the *macroscopic or bulk scattering cross section*.
If the scattering medium is a gas of molecular weight M and density
ρ gm/cm³,

$$N = \frac{\rho N_A}{M} \qquad (1\text{-}4\text{-}10)$$

where N_A is Avogadro's number, 6.02×10^{23} molecules per mole.
Evidently Q_s represents the total effective cross-sectional area for elastic
scattering of all the target particles in 1 cm³ of the scattering medium;
Q_s has dimensions of cm⁻¹.

We now see that the probability that a given projectile will survive
scattering until it penetrates the medium at least to depth x is $e^{-Q_s x}$. As
shown above, the probability that it will then be scattered in traveling a
further distance dx is $Nq_s\,dx = Q_s\,dx$. Consequently, $\bar{x}$, the average depth
of penetration before scattering, or equivalently, the average distance
between scattering sites for a given projectile, is given by

$$\int_0^\infty x e^{-Q_s x} Q_s\,dx = \bar{x} \int_0^\infty e^{-Q_s x} Q_s\,dx \qquad (1\text{-}4\text{-}11)$$

Performing the integration, we find that

$$\bar{x} = \frac{1}{Q_s} \qquad (1\text{-}4\text{-}12)$$

Now denote by λ_s the *mean free path for elastic scattering in the medium*.
By definition

$$\lambda_s = \bar{x} \qquad (1\text{-}4\text{-}13)$$

so that

$$\lambda_s = \frac{1}{Q_s} \qquad (1\text{-}4\text{-}14)$$

It should be emphasized that in these derivations we considered the target particles to be at rest and the projectiles to constitute a parallel, mono-energetic, and homogeneous beam.

C. RELATIONSHIP BETWEEN CROSS SECTIONS IN THE LAB AND CM SYSTEMS. For a given beam and target combination, the same number of projectiles must be scattered into the Lab element of solid angle, $d\Omega_{\text{Lab}}$, as are scattered into the corresponding CM element of solid angle, $d\Omega_{\text{CM}}$. Let us assume that the scattering distribution is independent of the azimuth angle and put $\varphi_{\text{Lab}} = \varphi_{\text{CM}} = \varphi$. Then

$$I_s(\vartheta, \varphi) \, d\Omega_{\text{Lab}} = I_s(\Theta, \varphi) \, d\Omega_{\text{CM}} \qquad (1\text{-}4\text{-}15)$$

and from (1-2-26) it follows that the relationship between the cross sections in the two coordinate systems is given by

$$I_s(\vartheta, \varphi) = \frac{[(m/M)^2 + 2(m/M)\cos\Theta + 1]^{3/2}}{1 + (m/M)\cos\Theta} I_s(\Theta, \varphi) \qquad (1\text{-}4\text{-}16)$$

Evidently the total cross section must be the same in either frame of reference; that is

$$(q_s)_{\text{Lab}} = (q_s)_{\text{CM}} \qquad (1\text{-}4\text{-}17)$$

D. CROSS SECTIONS FOR REACTIONS OTHER THAN ELASTIC SCATTERING. The cross section concept obviously applies to types of reactions other than elastic scattering, and the equations in the foregoing sections may be used to describe inelastic collisions if the appropriate cross sections are used. If we now inquire about the likelihood that a given type of projectile will undergo *some* reaction, regardless of type, in traversing a medium we are led to the concept of a gross microscopic cross section

$$q = q_i + q_j + q_k + \cdots \qquad (1\text{-}4\text{-}18)$$

and a gross macroscopic cross section

$$Q = Q_i + Q_j + Q_k + \cdots \qquad (1\text{-}4\text{-}19)$$

where the subscripts serve to label the individual constituent cross sections. Evidently

$$\lambda = \frac{1}{Q} \qquad (1\text{-}4\text{-}20)$$

and

$$\frac{1}{\lambda} = \frac{1}{\lambda_i} + \frac{1}{\lambda_j} + \frac{1}{\lambda_k} + \cdots \qquad (1\text{-}4\text{-}21)$$

where λ is the gross mean free path, considering collisions of all types.

When the physical problem at hand involves the passage of a homogeneous beam through a material medium, the gross mean free path is sometimes referred to as the relaxation length. It is the distance in which the intensity of the beam is reduced to $1/e$ of its initial value, projectiles undergoing any type of reaction being considered as lost from the beam.

E. REACTION RATES AND PARTICLE FLUX FOR MONOENERGETIC PROJECTILES. Consider a monoenergetic parallel beam containing n projectiles per cm³ which passes with velocity v through a medium composed of N stationary particles per cm³. Each projectile makes, on the average, v/λ collisions per sec. Thus $nv/\lambda = Qnv$ is the average number of collisions per cm³ per sec, or the *reaction rate*.

The projectile flux is defined as

$$\varphi = nv \tag{1-4-22}$$

and has the dimensions of particles/cm²-sec. The reaction rate in this case is seen to be equal to $Q\varphi$/cm³-sec.*

The flux nv is usually described geometrically as the number of projectiles crossing 1 cm² of area per sec. This description is correct for a parallel beam of number density n and velocity v crossing a plane perpendicular to the beam axis. Under other conditions, however, this description is not correct. Suppose, for example, that the surface element is located in a medium in which the projectiles are moving isotropically in all directions. Then the number of projectiles crossing a plane surface of 1 cm² area in 1 sec is $nv/2$, not nv, as shown in Section 2-6.

F. REACTIONS INVOLVING POLYENERGETIC PROJECTILES. In our treatment of cross sections the assumption was made that all the projectiles have the same energy, but this is frequently not even approximately so in practice. Since the cross section for a particular reaction generally varies with the energy, we must extend our treatment to cover the general case.

Let $n(E)$ be the number of projectiles of energy E per cm³ per unit energy interval, so that $n(E)\,dE$ is the number per cm³ in the range E to $E + dE$. The total flux for projectiles of all energies is

$$\varphi = \int_0^\infty n(E)v\,dE = \int_0^\infty \varphi(E)\,dE \tag{1-4-23}$$

Here $\varphi(E)\,dE$ is the flux in the energy range E to $E + dE$. The reaction rate for stationary targets is

$$\int_0^\infty Q(E)\,n(E)v\,dE = \int_0^\infty Q(E)\,\varphi(E)\,dE = \bar{Q}\varphi \tag{1-4-24}$$

* In the more general case in which the motion of the target particles cannot be neglected the reaction rate is expressed by an integral containing the relative velocity of the projectiles and targets. See (2-12-2) and R. V. Meghreblian and D. K. Holmes, *Reactor Analysis*, McGraw-Hill Book Co., New York, 1960.

where $Q(E)$ is the macroscopic cross section for particles of energy E and $\bar{Q}$ is the average macroscopic cross section, given by

$$\bar{Q} = \frac{\int_0^\infty Q(E)\, n(E)v\, dE}{\int_0^\infty n(E)v\, dE} = \frac{\int_0^\infty Q(E)\, \varphi(E)\, dE}{\int_0^\infty \varphi(E)\, dE} \qquad (1\text{-}4\text{-}25)$$

The corresponding average mean free path is

$$\bar{\lambda} = \frac{\int_0^\infty \lambda(E)\, \varphi(E)\, dE}{\int_0^\infty \varphi(E)\, dE} \qquad (1\text{-}4\text{-}26)$$

In general, $\bar{\lambda}$ is not equal to the reciprocal of $\bar{Q}$, although for any E

$$\lambda(E) = \frac{1}{Q(E)} \qquad (1\text{-}4\text{-}27)$$

The importance of proper averaging techniques has been emphasized by Thompson[2] in a discussion of the formation of negative ions in oxygen by the attachment of electrons in a swarm.

G. THE PROBABILITY OF COLLISION, P, THE COLLISION FREQUENCY, ν, AND THE MEAN FREE TIME, τ.   Some writers[3] phrase the discussion of collision phenomena in terms of the probability of collision of the particles rather than of collision cross sections or mean free paths. The relationships among these quantities are expressed later.

We shall consider the target material to be gaseous and denote its number density by N. N_A denotes *Avogadro's number*, 6.02×10^{23} particles per mole, which is the number of molecules of an ideal gas contained in 22.4 liters at the standard conditions of 760 mm Hg pressure and 0°C. The *Loschmidt number* N_L is the number density at standard pressure and temperature and has the value $2.69 \times 10^{19}/\text{cm}^3$. The number density at 1 mm Hg and 0°C, $N_{1\,\text{mm}}$, equals $3.54 \times 10^{16}/\text{cm}^3$.

Let $Q_{1\,\text{mm}}$ be the macroscopic collision cross section at 1 mm pressure and 0°C. Evidently

$$Q_{1\,\text{mm}} = qN_{1\,\text{mm}} = \frac{1}{\lambda_{1\,\text{mm}}} \qquad (1\text{-}4\text{-}28)$$

where $\lambda_{1\,\text{mm}}$ is the collision mean free path at 1 mm pressure and 0°C.
The *probability of collision* P is defined as the average number of

collisions experienced by a projectile in 1 cm of path through the gas at
1 mm Hg pressure and 0°C;

$$P = \frac{1}{\lambda_{1\,mm}} = Q_{1\,mm} \tag{1-4-29}$$

It is convenient to introduce the "reduced pressure," p_0, of the gas. If we
denote the actual pressure by p mm Hg and the temperature by $T°$K and
assume ideal gas behavior, p_0 is given by the equation

$$p_0 = p\frac{273}{T} \tag{1-4-30}$$

Thus p_0 is the pressure of the gas, in mm Hg, reduced to 0°C at constant
density.

The collision mean free path is now given by

$$\lambda = \frac{1}{p_0 P} \tag{1-4-31}$$

and the *collision frequency* ν by

$$\nu = \frac{v}{\lambda} = vQ = vp_0Q_{1\,mm} = vp_0P \tag{1-4-32}$$

The *mean free time* τ is defined as the average time between successive
collisions experienced by a single projectile; τ is the reciprocal of ν:

$$\tau = \frac{1}{\nu} \tag{1-4-33}$$

The attenuation of a monoenergetic beam passing through a gas may
now be expressed by the equation

$$I = I_0 e^{-Qx} = I_0 e^{-p_0 Q_{1\,mm}x} = I_0 e^{-p_0 Px} \tag{1-4-34}$$

1-5. THE AVERAGE ENERGY LOSS AND ANGULAR SCATTERING
DISTRIBUTION IN THE CLASSICAL COLLISION
OF SMOOTH ELASTIC SPHERES

Consider two smooth elastic spheres, of masses m and M, which are
about to collide (Fig. 1-5-1). The spheres are considered to interact only
at the instant of impact; m has velocity v_0 before the collision, measured
in the Lab system; M is at rest. After the collision m rebounds with
velocity v and M moves along the impact line of centers with velocity V.*
Let D be the distance between centers when the spheres are in contact;
θ is the incidence angle and ϑ is the scattering angle of m in the Lab system.

* The collision is specular because the spheres are assumed to be smooth. The smoothness assumption guarantees that no energy goes into rotation.

The usual polar angle in the spherical coordinate system shown is θ, whereas φ is the azimuthal angle, measured in the X-Y plane; θ is obviously not constrained to lie in the Y-Z plane—it is shown in the Y-Z plane here for clarity. Evidently the scattering angular distribution will be independent of the angle φ in this example.

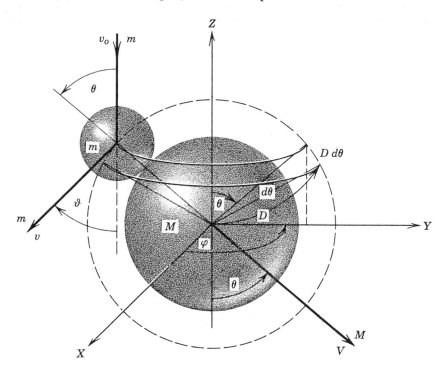

FIG. 1-5-1. The collision of elastic spheres in the Lab system. The projectile m impinges on the stationary target M with velocity v_0 at incidence angle θ and is scattered with velocity v at angle ϑ. The target recoils at angle θ with velocity V. The sum of the radii of the two elastic spheres is denoted by D.

The fractional loss of energy of m in a collision at incidence angle θ is

$$\Delta(\theta) = \frac{v_0^2 - v^2}{v_0^2} \tag{1-5-1}$$

The momentum and energy conservation equations are

$$mv_0 = mv \cos \vartheta + MV \cos \theta \tag{1-5-2}$$

$$0 = mv \sin \vartheta - MV \sin \theta \tag{1-5-3}$$

$$\frac{mv_0^2}{2} = \frac{mv^2}{2} + \frac{MV^2}{2} \tag{1-5-4}$$

Therefore

$$\Delta(\theta) = \frac{MV^2}{mv_0^2} \tag{1-5-5}$$

an expected result. The final velocity of M in the Lab system, which appears in this equation for $\Delta(\theta)$, may be expressed as

$$V = \frac{2mv_0 \cos \theta}{m + M} \tag{1-5-6}$$

(The validity of Equations 1-5-2 through 1-5-6 does not depend on the assumption of smoothness of the spheres.)

Now imagine m to be one of the projectiles in a monoenergetic beam which has uniform composition in a plane normal to the Z axis. Assuming that m undergoes a collision, let $p(\theta)\,d\theta$ be the probability that the impact occurs at an incidence angle between θ and $\theta + d\theta$. The total effective area presented for collision of m against M is πD^2. The area of the surface element defined by the cones θ and $\theta + d\theta$ is $(2\pi D \sin \theta)(D\,d\theta)$, but only a fraction, $\cos \theta$, is presented directly to projectiles approaching along $+Z$. The probability of the collision taking place between θ and $\theta + d\theta$ is therefore

$$p(\theta)\,d\theta = \begin{cases} \dfrac{2\pi D^2 \sin \theta \cos \theta\,d\theta}{\pi D^2} = \sin 2\theta\,d\theta & \left(0 \le \theta \le \dfrac{\pi}{2}\right) \\[2ex] 0 & \left(\dfrac{\pi}{2} < \theta \le \pi\right) \end{cases} \tag{1-5-7}$$

This is also the probability that the target will recoil at an angle between θ and $\theta + d\theta$ because the spheres have been assumed to be smooth.

Δ, the mean fractional loss of energy allowing for collisions at all possible angles, is then

$$\Delta = \overline{\Delta(\theta)} = \frac{\displaystyle\int_0^{\pi/2} p(\theta)\,\Delta(\theta)\,d\theta}{\displaystyle\int_0^{\pi/2} p(\theta)\,d\theta}$$

Using (1-5-4), (1-5-6), and (1-5-7), we obtain

$$\Delta = \frac{2mM}{(m + M)^2} \tag{1-5-8}$$

From (1-5-5), (1-5-6), and (1-2-18), it follows that

$$\Delta(\Theta) = \frac{2mM}{(m + M)^2}(1 - \cos \Theta) \tag{1-5-9}$$

which is a general result. In the present case of smooth elastic spheres

$$\Delta(\Theta) = \Delta(1 - \cos \Theta) \tag{1-5-10}$$

We shall now consider several special cases.

A. $m = M$.   From (1-5-8) it is apparent that here

$$\Delta = \tfrac{1}{2} \tag{1-5-11}$$

whereas (1-5-9) gives

$$\Delta(\vartheta) = \tfrac{1}{2}(1 - \cos 2\vartheta) \tag{1-5-12}$$

From the conservation equations and (1-5-6) it follows that

$$\vartheta + \theta = \frac{\pi}{2} \tag{1-5-13}$$

Therefore the spheres leave the collision site at right angles to one another in the Lab system.

Now, assuming that m suffers a collision, let $p(\vartheta)\,d\vartheta$ be the probability that m is scattered between ϑ and $\vartheta + d\vartheta$. The use of (1-5-13) in (1-5-7) yields

$$p(\vartheta)\,d\vartheta = \begin{cases} \sin(\pi - 2\vartheta)\,d\vartheta & \left(0 \le \vartheta \le \dfrac{\pi}{2}\right) \\[2mm] 0 & \left(\dfrac{\pi}{2} < \vartheta \le \pi\right) \end{cases}$$

or

$$p(\vartheta)\,d\vartheta = \begin{cases} \sin 2\vartheta\,d\vartheta & \left(0 \le \vartheta \le \dfrac{\pi}{2}\right) \\[2mm] 0 & \left(\dfrac{\pi}{2} < \vartheta \le \pi\right) \end{cases}$$

Note that

$$\int_0^{\pi/2} p(\vartheta)\,d\vartheta = \int_0^{\pi/2} \sin 2\vartheta\,d\vartheta = 1$$

All the projectiles undergoing collisions are scattered between 0 and $\pi/2$—there is no backward scattering in the Lab system.

Let $F(\vartheta)$ denote the probability per unit solid angle that if scattering occurs m will be deflected between ϑ and $\vartheta + d\vartheta$. $F(\vartheta)$ also equals the fraction of the scattered component of the beam which is deflected between ϑ and $\vartheta + d\vartheta$, per unit solid angle.

$$F(\vartheta) = \begin{cases} \dfrac{p(\vartheta)\,d\vartheta}{\displaystyle\int_0^{2\pi} d\Omega_{\text{Lab}}} = \dfrac{\sin 2\vartheta\,d\vartheta}{2\pi \sin \vartheta\,d\vartheta} = \dfrac{\cos \vartheta}{\pi} & \left(0 \le \vartheta \le \dfrac{\pi}{2}\right) \\[4mm] 0 & \left(\dfrac{\pi}{2} < \vartheta \le \pi\right) \end{cases}$$

As must be the case,

$$\int_0^{2\pi}\int_0^{\pi/2} F(\vartheta)\, d\Omega_{\mathrm{Lab}} = \int_0^{\pi/2} F(\vartheta) 2\pi \sin\vartheta\, d\vartheta = \int_0^{\pi/2} p(\vartheta)\, d\vartheta = 1$$

$F(\vartheta)\, d\Omega_{\mathrm{Lab}}$ is related to the differential microscopic scattering cross section $I_s(\vartheta)\, d\Omega_{\mathrm{Lab}}$ by the equation

$$I_s(\vartheta)\, d\Omega_{\mathrm{Lab}} = q_s\, F(\vartheta)\, d\Omega_{\mathrm{Lab}} \tag{1-5-14}$$

where

$$q_s = \pi D^2 \tag{1-5-15}$$

is the total microscopic scattering cross section.

Note that the scattering is not isotropic in the Lab system, that is,

$$I_s(\vartheta) = \begin{cases} q_s \dfrac{\cos\vartheta}{\pi} & \left(0 \le \vartheta \le \dfrac{\pi}{2}\right) \\[2ex] 0 & \left(\dfrac{\pi}{2} < \vartheta \le \pi\right) \end{cases} \tag{1-5-16}$$

is not independent of ϑ. However, the scattering is isotropic in the CM system. Equation 1-2-24 shows that when $m = M$

$$\vartheta = \frac{\Theta}{2} \tag{1-5-17}$$

where Θ is the scattering angle of m in the CM system. The use of this result in (1-2-26) gives

$$d\Omega_{\mathrm{CM}} = 4\cos\vartheta\, d\Omega_{\mathrm{Lab}} \tag{1-5-18}$$

and so by (1-4-15)

$$I_s(\Theta) = \frac{I_s(\vartheta)}{4\cos\vartheta} = \frac{q_s}{4\pi} = \frac{D^2}{4} \qquad (0 \le \Theta \le \pi) \tag{1-5-19}$$

Equation 1-5-19 holds even if $m \ne M$; $I_s(\Theta)\, d\Omega_{\mathrm{CM}}$ is the differential scattering cross section in the CM system.

We observe finally that our results are compatible with the requirement that

$$q_s = \int_0^{2\pi}\int_0^{\pi/2} I_s(\vartheta)\, d\Omega_{\mathrm{Lab}} = \int_0^{2\pi}\int_0^{\pi} I_s(\Theta)\, d\Omega_{\mathrm{CM}} \tag{1-5-20}$$

B. $m \ll M$. Equation 1-5-8 gives

$$\Delta \approx \frac{2m}{M} \tag{1-5-21}$$

another useful result, whereas ϑ and θ are now related by the equation

$$\theta \approx \frac{\pi}{2} - \frac{\vartheta}{2} \tag{1-5-22}$$

From (1-5-6) it follows that

$$V \approx \frac{2m}{M} v_0 \cos \theta \tag{1-5-23}$$

and therefore from (1-5-5)

$$\Delta(\vartheta) \approx \frac{2m}{M} (1 - \cos \vartheta) \tag{1-5-24}$$

We may also get (1-5-24) directly from (1-5-9). We also find that

$$p(\vartheta)\, d\vartheta = \sin(\pi - \vartheta) \frac{d\vartheta}{2} = \frac{\sin \vartheta}{2}\, d\vartheta \tag{1-5-25}$$

and

$$F(\vartheta) = \frac{1}{4\pi} \qquad (0 \leq \vartheta \leq \pi) \tag{1-5-26}$$

Therefore

$$I_s(\vartheta) = \frac{q_s}{4\pi} \qquad (0 \leq \vartheta \leq \pi) \tag{1-5-27}$$

and the scattering is now isotropic in the Lab system.

When $m \ll M$, $\vartheta \approx \Theta$, and the Lab and CM systems are almost identical. Consequently, the scattering is also isotropic in the CM system. All directions of motion after collision are equally probable. (Actually, the scattering of smooth elastic spheres is isotropic in the CM system regardless of the ratio of m to M.)

Attention should now be directed to the fact that according to the elastic sphere model used in this section the angular scattering distributions are all independent of the velocity of the projectiles.

C. TWO SPECIES OF PARTICLES WITH MAXWELLIAN VELOCITY DISTRIBU-
TIONS CORRESPONDING TO DIFFERENT TEMPERATURES. Cravath[4] has solved the more difficult problem of an ensemble of particles of mass m moving in a gas composed of molecules of mass M. Both types of particles are considered to be smooth elastic spheres which interact only at the instant of impact. The two species are assumed to have Maxwellian velocity distributions corresponding to temperatures T_m and T_M, respectively. It is found that

$$f = \frac{8}{3} \frac{mM}{(m + M)^2} \left(1 - \frac{T_M}{T_m}\right) \tag{1-5-28}$$

where f is the average energy lost per collision by the particles m expressed as a fraction of the average energy of these particles.

1-6. THE DIFFUSION AND VISCOSITY CROSS SECTIONS

It is now appropriate to introduce two additional cross sections: the diffusion cross section q_D and the viscosity cross section q_η; q_D is useful in discussions of the diffusion of neutral and charged particles in gases and the mobility of gaseous ions, whereas q_η appears in the treatment of the viscosity and heat conductivity of gases.[5] As we shall show in Section 2-10, the diffusion coefficient is inversely related to the diffusion cross section. The coefficients of viscosity and heat conductivity are inversely related to the viscosity cross section. These cross sections are actually of greater significance in the kinetic theory of gases than is q_s, which never appears directly in rigorous discussions of transport phenomena.

A. THE DIFFUSION CROSS SECTION, q_D. Consider a large number of particles of mass m swarming about in a gas composed of molecules of mass M and assume that the energies of the two types of particles are sufficiently low that internal excitation on impact is impossible. Thus we are dealing only with elastic collisions. Now view, in the CM system, a collision between one of the particles m and a gas molecule M. The particle has linear momentum equal to $M_r v_0$ before the collision, where M_r is the reduced mass of m and M, and v_0 is the relative velocity of approach. If the CM scattering angle is Θ, m suffers a change in its forward momentum of $M_r v_0(1 - \cos \Theta)$. The *diffusion cross section* is defined by the equation

$$q_D = \int (1 - \cos \Theta) I_s(\Theta) \, d\Omega_{CM} = 2\pi \int_0^\pi I_s(\Theta)(1 - \cos \Theta) \sin \Theta \, d\Theta$$

(1-6-1)

It is apparent that q_D is a measure of the average forward momentum lost by the particles m in collisions with the molecules M, and q_D is therefore often called the *momentum transfer cross section*.

Scattering at small angles produces only a small contribution to q_D. The quantity $(1 - \cos \Theta)$ vanishes as Θ^2 for small deflections, and for this reason the diffusion cross section often has a finite value when the total elastic cross section is (mathematically) infinite. The matter of theoretical predictions of infinitely large cross sections is discussed in Section 3-11.

The diffusion cross section q_D differs appreciably from q_s, the total elastic scattering cross section, only when the scattering is distinctly anisotropic. When the backward scattering dominates the forward scattering, $q_D > q_s$, whereas $q_D < q_s$ when the scattering is concentrated in the forward direction. If the differential elastic scattering cross section is independent of Θ, $q_D = q_s$.

Using the diffusion cross section, we may define the *momentum transfer mean free path* λ_m by the equation

$$\lambda_m = \frac{1}{Nq_{D}} \tag{1-6-2}$$

λ_m is frequently called the transport mean free path. We may also define the *collision frequency for momentum transfer* ν_m by the equation

$$\nu_m = \frac{\bar{v}_0}{\lambda_m} \tag{1-6-3}$$

where $\bar{v}_0$ is the mean velocity of the particles.

Let us now suppose that the particles of mass m moving about in the gas are electrons, which, of course, are much lighter than the gas molecules. The average energy of the electrons is assumed to be considerably greater than that of the molecules, but the assumption of elastic collisions is retained. Since, now, $m \ll M$, the fractional energy loss by an electron in a collision with a molecule which results in the electron being scattered at angle ϑ in the Lab system is

$$\Delta(\vartheta) \approx \frac{2m}{M} (1 - \cos \vartheta)$$

as seen from (1-5-24). Thus the mean fractional energy loss by the electrons per collision is

$$\Delta \approx \frac{2m}{Mq_s} \int_0^\pi \int_0^{2\pi} (1 - \cos \vartheta) I_s(\vartheta) \sin \vartheta \, d\vartheta \, d\varphi = \frac{2m}{M} \frac{q_D}{q_s} \tag{1-6-4}$$

We were able to replace the integral in the middle of (1-6-4) by q_D, since here $m \ll M$ and therefore the Lab and CM scattering angles are almost equal.

The mean fractional loss of energy experienced by an electron in traveling a distance dx through a gas containing N molecules/cm³ is then

$$\left(\frac{2m}{M} \frac{q_D}{q_s}\right) (q_s N \, dx) = \frac{2m}{M} q_D N \, dx \tag{1-6-5}$$

since $q_s N \, dx$ is the probability that m will undergo a collision in moving a distance dx. It is thus evident that electrons moving about in a gas lose energy in elastic collisions with the molecules at the rate that they would if the elastic scattering cross section were equal to q_D and the fractional energy loss per collision equal to $2m/M$.

Actually, the analysis in the foregoing paragraph does not depend much on m being very small compared with M. If we use (1-5-9) and work in CM coordinates, we get in place of (1-6-5) the result $[2mM/(m + M)^2]q_D N\,dx$, so that the energy loss in general corresponds to a cross section of q_D and a fractional energy loss per collision of $2mM/(m + M)^2$.

B. THE VISCOSITY CROSS SECTION, q_η. The *viscosity cross section* is defined by the equation

$$q_\eta = \int \sin^2 \Theta\, I_s(\Theta)\, d\Omega_{\mathrm{CM}} = 2\pi \int_0^\pi I_s(\Theta) \sin^3 \Theta\, d\Theta \qquad (1\text{-}6\text{-}6)$$

It may be noted that collisions involving CM scattering at nearly $\pi/2$ are weighted more heavily in evaluating q_η than are small-angle or backward scattering events. The physical basis for this weighting is explained by Massey and Burhop:[5] the greater the rate of collisional equalization of energy, the smaller the viscosity and heat conductivity. The energy is equalized in the collision of two identical molecules if the CM scattering angle is $\pi/2$. Collisions at angles near $\pi/2$ are therefore more effective than any others in inhibiting conductivity, hence $\sin^2 \Theta$ is the appropriate weighting factor in the integral for q_η. By contrast, diffusion is retarded most effectively by back-scattering collisions, and $(1 - \cos \Theta)$ is the proper weighting factor for q_D.

The viscosity cross section converges for the usual intermolecular force fields because $\sin^2 \Theta$ goes to 0 as Θ^2 for small deflections, as did $(1 - \cos \Theta)$ in the expression for q_D.

1-7. POTENTIAL FUNCTIONS USED TO DESCRIBE THE INTERACTION BETWEEN PARTICLES

Many different potential functions are used to describe the interaction between various types of particles. The desirability of choosing a function that realistically represents the interaction in a given problem is obvious, but it is perhaps just as obvious that in many cases realism must be sacrificed for mathematical tractability. We shall enumerate some of the potentials most frequently used in practice. These potentials are of two types—those that depend only on the distance between centers of the interacting particles and are thus angle-independent and those that contain a dependence on the relative angular orientation of the particles as well as the separation distance. Potentials involving an explicit dependence on the relative velocity are also occasionally required.

A. POTENTIALS DEPENDING ONLY ON THE SEPARATION DISTANCE. The potential V is plotted in Fig. 1-7-1 for several types of spherically symmetric interaction, each of which is discussed.

1. *Smooth elastic spheres.*

$$V(r) = \begin{cases} \infty & (r < D) \\ 0 & (r > D) \end{cases} \qquad (1\text{-}7\text{-}1)$$

Here the model consists of two rigid impenetrable spheres, the sum of whose radii is D. This potential function is crude but easy to apply in calculations.

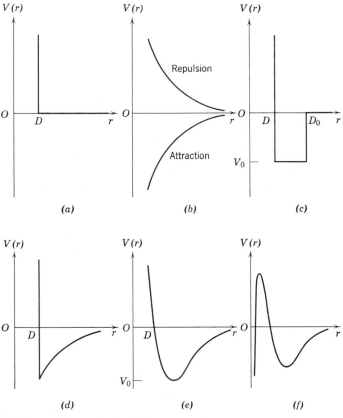

FIG. 1-7-1. Commonly used spherically symmetric potential functions: (*a*) Smooth, elastic spheres. (*b*) Point centers. (*c*) The square well. (*d*) The Sutherland potential. (*e*) The Lennard-Jones potential. (*f*) The Buckingham potential.

2. *Point centers of attraction or repulsion.*

$$V(r) = \begin{cases} \dfrac{-a}{r^n} & \text{(attraction)} \\[2mm] \dfrac{a}{r^n} & \text{(repulsion)} \end{cases} \qquad (1\text{-}7\text{-}2)$$

Here a is a positive constant, and n is the index of attraction or repulsion. When $n = 1$, we have *Coulomb interaction*. The interaction between molecules is frequently fitted by the repulsive potential of (1-7-2) with a value of n between 9 and 15. Particles assumed to repel one another according to a potential of the form $+a/r^4$ are referred to as "Maxwellian" —the r^{-4} interaction has some important special properties which were pointed out by Maxwell[6] and which are discussed in Section 1-8. The attractive r^{-4} potential is particularly important in the study of ionized gases because, as shown in Section 1-8, the point-charge-induced dipole interaction between an ion (or electron) and a neutral molecule is of this type.

The mathematical difficulty associated with the use of an r^{-n} potential depends to a considerable degree on the particular value of n chosen.

3. *The square well.*

$$V(r) = \begin{cases} \infty & (r < D) \\ -V_0 & (D < r < D_0) \\ 0 & (r > D_0) \end{cases} \qquad (1\text{-}7\text{-}3)$$

This potential function represents an impenetrable core of radius D surrounded by an attractive well of depth V_0 which extends radially out to a distance D_0. Here we have a short-range repulsion and a longer range attraction. The square-well potential is relatively easy to use.

4. *The Sutherland potential.*

$$V(r) = \begin{cases} \infty & (r < D) \\ -\dfrac{a}{r^n} & (r > D) \end{cases} \qquad (1\text{-}7\text{-}4)$$

This model applies to hard spheres of combined radius D which attract one another according to an inverse power law. It is reasonably tractable in calculations. When $n = 6$, (1-7-4) gives the *van der Waals interaction*.

5. *The Lennard-Jones potential.*

$$V(r) = \frac{a}{r^m} - \frac{b}{r^n} \qquad (1\text{-}7\text{-}5)$$

Both constants, a and b, are positive, so that the first term is repulsive and the second attractive. When the potential takes the form

$$V(r) = 4V_0\left[\left(\frac{D}{r}\right)^{12} - \left(\frac{D}{r}\right)^{6}\right] \qquad (1\text{-}7\text{-}6)$$

it is called the *Lennard-Jones* (6–12) *potential.* The inverse-sixth-power attraction represents an induced dipole-induced dipole interaction. The choice of $m = 12$ in the repulsive term is largely a matter of mathematical expediency, although it does prove to be fairly realistic for spherical nonpolar molecules.

6. *The Buckingham potentials.* The basic Buckingham potential takes the form

$$V(r) = ae^{-br} - \frac{c}{r^6} - \frac{d}{r^8} \tag{1-7-7}$$

where a, b, c, and d are constants. Its attractive terms represent the induced dipole-induced dipole and induced dipole-induced quadrupole interactions, whereas the repulsive contribution is approximated by the exponential term. The potential of (1-7-7), as well as the Buckingham-Corner potential and the modified Buckingham (6-exp) potential, are discussed in Hirschfelder, Curtiss, and Bird.[7]

7. *The 12-6-4 potential.* A reasonable model for the interaction of an ion and a molecule is obtained by the superposition of a Lennard-Jones (6-12) interaction and the interaction of a point charge with a polarizable molecule, which gives

$$V(r) = \frac{a}{r^{12}} - \frac{b}{r^6} - \frac{c}{r^4} \tag{1-7-8}$$

where a, b, and c are positive constants. The polarization attraction due to the ionic charge contributes the r^{-4} term and part of the r^{-6} term, as discussed in Section 1-8. The 12-6-4 potential has been used by Mason and Schamp in the calculation of the mobility of gaseous ions (see Section 9-2-D).

B. POTENTIALS INVOLVING THE RELATIVE ANGULAR ORIENTATION. Hirschfelder, Curtiss, and Bird[7] also treat four angle-dependent models: hard ellipsoids of revolution, spherocylindrical molecules, hard spheres in which point dipoles are embedded, and the Stockmayer model. The Stockmayer represents a superposition of a Lennard-Jones (6–12) interaction and the interaction of two point dipoles.

1-8. THE POLARIZATION ATTRACTION
OF MOLECULES BY CHARGED PARTICLES

We now wish to determine the law of force between a charged particle, which for convenience we refer to as an ion, and a neutral gas molecule. We must first calculate the dipole moment induced in a molecule by a nearby ion. Let us consider a parallel-plate capacitor and the polarization that occurs in the dielectric separating its plates. Let the surface density of free charge on the plates be σ. In the absence of a dielectric the uniform electric field intensity between the plates is $E = 4\pi\sigma$. With a gas of dielectric constant* K filling the capacitor, the field intensity is reduced to $E' = E/K$. This reduction in field intensity is due to the termination of lines of force by charges induced at the surface of the dielectric by the field. If σ' denotes the charge density induced at the surface of the dielectric, $E - E' = 4\pi\sigma'$. Then

$$\frac{E - E'}{E'} = K - 1 = \frac{4\pi\sigma'}{E'}$$

and

$$\sigma' = \frac{(K - 1)E'}{4\pi}$$

Now the electric dipole moment of all the molecules in the gas is given by the product of σ' and the area of the capacitor plate, multiplied by the plate separation, or σ' times the volume defined by the capacitor plates. Thus σ' is the total dipole moment divided by the volume, but this is just the dipole moment per cm³, or the polarization P. Consequently,

$$P = \frac{(K - 1)E'}{4\pi}$$

If N is the number of molecules per cm³, the dipole moment per molecule is

$$\mu = \frac{P}{N} = \frac{(K - 1)E'}{4\pi N}$$

In the present problem E' is the Coulomb field of an ion, $E' = e/r^2$, except at small distances. Therefore

$$\mu = \frac{(K - 1)}{4\pi N} \frac{e}{r^2} \tag{1-8-1}$$

Now the force with which a dipole of moment μ is attracted by a point charge e located at a distance r from the dipole is

$$f = \frac{2\mu e}{r^3} \cos \beta \tag{1-8-2}$$

where β is the angle between the dipole axis and the line joining the dipole and the point charge. Since the dipole here is induced by the charge, β always equals zero. Therefore the force between the ion and molecule is

$$f = \frac{(K - 1)e^2}{2\pi N r^5} \tag{1-8-3}$$

* The dielectric constant is a tensor quantity that reduces to scalar form when the medium is isotropic. Here it is a positive scalar whose magnitude is slightly greater than unity.

The mutual potential energy of the ion and molecule, accordingly, is

$$V(r) = -\int_r^\infty \frac{(K-1)e^2}{2\pi N r^5}\, dr$$

or

$$V(r) = -\frac{(K-1)e^2}{8\pi N r^4} \tag{1-8-4}$$

Equation 1-8-3 gives only an approximate expression for the force of attraction of a molecule by an ion. It is obtained by assuming that the field produced by the ion is uniform over the volume occupied by the molecule. It is possible to obtain the complete solution of the problem in the case in which the molecules are assumed to be spherical and to show that the approximate solution indeed furnishes the principal term.[8] The next term corresponds to the interaction between the charge and the quadrupole it induces in the molecule and varies as r^{-6}.[9]

The equations in this section may be expressed in terms of the polarizability of the gas α, rather than the dielectric constant K, by use of the relationship

$$\alpha = \frac{K-1}{4\pi N} \tag{1-8-5}$$

In Chapter 3 it is shown by dimensional arguments that if the interaction potential between two collision partners varies as r^{-n} the variation of the CM differential scattering cross section is given classically by the expression

$$I_s(\Theta) \sim v_0^{-4/n} \tag{1-8-6}$$

where v_0 is the relative velocity of approach. Thus the frequency at which the particles are scattered at any angle Θ for which the classical calculation is valid is proportional to

$$I_s(\Theta)v_0 \sim v_0^{1-4/n} \tag{1-8-7}$$

(Limitations of the classical scattering theory are discussed in Chapter 3.) Evidently in the present case in which $n = 4$ the collision frequency is independent of velocity, and thus the mean free time is constant. Maxwell[6,10] showed that this fact greatly simplifies many calculations and that it is possible to calculate all the transport properties for the r^{-4} potential without knowing the distribution function (see Section 2-12).

The combination of a charged point particle and a polarizable sphere is often referred to as a *constant mean free time model*. By contrast, the combination of two elastic spheres that interact only at the instant of impact is a *constant mean free path model*, since the scattering cross section in this case is independent of the velocity.

REFERENCES

1. P. Morrison, "A Survey of Nuclear Reactions," in *Experimental Nuclear Physics*, Vol. II (edited by E. Segrè), Wiley, New York, 1953, pp. 3-13. R. B. Leighton, *Principles of Modern Physics*, McGraw-Hill, New York, 1959, Chapters 1 and 14. A. M. Baldin, V. I. Gol'danskii, and I. L. Rozenthal, *Kinematics of Nuclear Reactions*, Pergamon, New York, 1961, Chapters I-III. L. D. Landau and E. M. Lifshitz, *Mechanics*, Addison-Wesley, Reading, Mass., 1960, Chapter IV. K. G. Dedrick, *Rev. Mod. Phys.* **34**, 429 (1962).
2. J. B. Thompson, *Proc. Phys. Soc. (London)* **A73**, 821 (1959).
3. See, for example, S. C. Brown, *Basic Data of Plasma Physics*, Wiley, New York, 1959, p. 2.
4. A. M. Cravath, *Phys. Rev.* **36**, 248 (1930).
5. R. D. Present, *The Kinetic Theory of Gases*, McGraw-Hill, New York, 1958, pp. 140, 146, 219. H. S. W. Massey and E. H. S. Burhop, *Electronic and Ionic Impact Phenomena*, Oxford University Press, Oxford, 1952, pp. 367-369.
6. *The Scientific Papers of James Clerk Maxwell*, Vol. II (edited by W. D. Niven) Dover, New York, 1952, pp. 26-78.
7. J. O. Hirschfelder, C. F. Curtiss, and R. B. Bird, *Molecular Theory of Gases and Liquids*, Wiley, New York, 1954, pp. 31-35.
8. P. Langevin, *Ann. Chim. Phys.* **28**, 317-321 (1903).
9. H. Margenau, *Phil. Science* **8**, 603 (1941).
10. J. H. Jeans, *The Dynamical Theory of Gases*, Dover, New York, 1954, p. 219; S. Chapman and T. G. Cowling, *The Mathematical Theory of Non-uniform Gases*, Second Edition, Cambridge University Press, London, 1952, p. 173.

2

BACKGROUND INFORMATION

FROM THE KINETIC

THEORY OF GASES

We now present for future reference some results from the kinetic theory of gases. Emphasis is placed on those topics that are of special interest in the study of ionized gases. Derivations are given for only a few of the results quoted: for derivations of the remainder and for further discussion of their physical significance the reader is referred to the standard texts on kinetic theory.[1] Particular attention is directed to the treatises by Jeans,[2] Chapman and Cowling,[3] and Hirschfelder, Curtiss, and Bird[4] for rigorous discussions of the nonequilibrium properties of gases.

2-1. THERMODYNAMIC EQUILIBRIUM AND THE SCOPE OF KINETIC THEORY

A gas is in thermodynamic equilibrium if and only if it is in mechanical, chemical, and thermal equilibrium. The first requirement necessitates a balance of mechanical forces within the gas and between the gas and its surroundings. (In the special case in which no external forces are applied, the pressure of the gas must be uniform.) The requirement of chemical equilibrium is met when a system in mechanical equilibrium does not tend to undergo a spontaneous change of internal structure; for example, by a chemical reaction or a diffusive mass transfer. The thermal equilibrium requirement implies that the gas must have a uniform temperature and that this temperature must be equal to that of the surroundings.

The kinetic theory treats gases in both equilibrium and nonequilibrium conditions. In the first instance the major concerns are the equilibrium distribution of molecular velocities and energies, molecular mean free paths and collision frequencies, effusive molecular flow, equations of state, and the electric and magnetic properties of gases. In the study of a gas that is not in thermodynamic equilibrium interest is centered about its transport properties, that is, those properties that determine the behavior of the gas as regards diffusion, thermal and electrical conduction, and viscosity. The last-mentioned are termed *transport phenomena*, and they are investigated theoretically by what is referred to as transport theory.

2-2. THE MOLECULAR VELOCITY AND ENERGY DISTRIBUTIONS OF A GAS IN THERMODYNAMIC EQUILIBRIUM

Molecules of a gas in equilibrium move about in random fashion, the trajectory of each molecule consisting of a series of line segments consecutively joined together at the points in space at which the molecule suffers collisions. The average length of the line segments is the mean free path of the molecule in the gas. The line segments are essentially straight, except near the collision sites, where the interaction between the collision partners is appreciable. The curvature of the paths due to the earth's gravitational attraction is completely negligible on the laboratory scale. (The average radius of curvature for molecules of nitrogen at room temperature is of the order of 10^7 cm, for example.)

A. A SINGLE GAS WITH NO APPLIED FIELD. The speeds of the molecules of a gas in thermodynamic equilibrium are distributed according to *Maxwell's distribution*, which may be expressed in the form

$$f(v)\, dv = N_t \left(\frac{2}{\pi}\right)^{1/2} \left(\frac{m}{kT}\right)^{3/2} v^2 e^{-mv^2/2kT}\, dv \qquad (2\text{-}2\text{-}1)$$

Here $f(v)\, dv$ is the number of molecules with speeds between v and $v + dv$ cm/sec, m is the mass of one of the molecules in grams, T is the absolute temperature in °K, and $k = 1.3806 \times 10^{-16}$ erg/°K is Boltzmann's constant. Evidently, if N_t is the total number of molecules in the gas,

$$\int_0^\infty f(v)\, dv = N_t \qquad (2\text{-}2\text{-}2)$$

The function $f(v)$ is plotted in Fig. 2-2-1; $\bar{v}$ and v_R, the mean and root-mean-square speeds, respectively, are easily calculated in terms of moments of the distribution function:

$$\bar{v} = \frac{1}{N_t} \int_0^\infty v f(v) \, dv = \left(\frac{8kT}{\pi m}\right)^{\frac{1}{2}} \tag{2-2-3}$$

$$v_R = \left[\frac{1}{N_t} \int_0^\infty v^2 f(v) \, dv\right]^{\frac{1}{2}} = \left(\frac{3kT}{m}\right)^{\frac{1}{2}} \tag{2-2-4}$$

The most probable velocity of the distribution v_p is obtained by setting

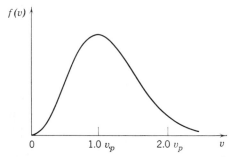

FIG. 2-2-1. The Maxwellian distribution function for the speeds of the molecules of a gas in thermodynamic equilibrium.

$d f(v)/dv$ equal to zero and solving for v:

$$v_p = \left(\frac{2kT}{m}\right)^{\frac{1}{2}} \tag{2-2-5}$$

It follows that

$$v_p/\bar{v}/v_R = 1/1.1284/1.2248 \tag{2-2-6}$$

Table 2-2-1 lists the mean velocity for a number of gases at 15°C. For comparison purposes, the muzzle velocity of a modern army rifle is about 8×10^4 cm/sec, whereas the vertical escape velocity from the earth is 1.1×10^6 cm/sec.

At 15°C the translational kinetic energies per molecule corresponding, respectively, to v_p and v_R are

$$\frac{m}{2} v_p^2 = kT = 0.025 \text{ ev} \tag{2-2-7}$$

and

$$\frac{m}{2} v_R^2 = \tfrac{3}{2}kT = 0.037 \text{ ev} \tag{2-2-8}$$

The fraction of the molecules whose speeds exceed a certain value v is

$$\frac{1}{N_t} \int_v^\infty f(v) \, dv = 1 + \left(\frac{2m}{\pi kT}\right)^{\frac{1}{2}} v e^{-mv^2/2kT} - \Phi\left[\left(\frac{m}{2kT}\right)^{\frac{1}{2}} v\right] \tag{2-2-9}$$

where

$$\Phi(x) = \frac{2}{(\pi)^{\frac{1}{2}}} \int_0^x e^{-x^2}\, dx \qquad (2\text{-}2\text{-}10)$$

is the error, or probability, integral, which is tabulated in books of mathematical tables. The sharpness of the Maxwellian distribution is

TABLE 2-2-1. Values of the mean velocity $\bar{v}$; the molecular diameter D; the mean free path λ; and the collision frequency ν, calculated from the kinetic theory for a number of common gases

Gas	Molecular Weight	v (in 10^3 cm/sec at 15°C)	D (in 10^{-8} cm)	λ (in 10^{-6} cm at 15°C, 760 mm Hg.)	ν (in 10^9 collisions/ sec at 15°C, 760 mm Hg.)
H_2	2.016	174.0	2.74	11.77	14.8
He	4.002	123.5	2.18	18.62	6.6
CH_4	16.03	61.8	4.14	5.16	12.0
NH_3	17.03	59.8	4.43	4.51	13.3
H_2O	18.02	58.2	4.60	4.18	13.9
Ne	20.18	55.0	2.59	13.22	4.2
N_2	28.02	46.7	3.75	6.28	7.4
C_2H_4	28.03	46.7	4.95	3.61	12.9
C_2H_6	30.05	45.1	5.30	3.15	14.3
O_2	32.00	43.7	3.61	6.79	6.4
HCl	36.46	40.9	4.46	4.44	9.2
A	39.94	39.1	3.64	6.66	5.9
CO_2	44.00	37.2	4.59	4.19	8.8
Kr	82.9	27.1	4.16	5.12	5.3
Xe	130.2	21.7	4.85	3.76	5.8
Electron	5.49×10^{-4}	10.5×10^3			

indicated by the fact that only 12.55% of the molecules have $v > 1.5\bar{v}$, 1.70% have $v > 2\bar{v}$, and 0.01% have $v > 3\bar{v}$.

Knowing $f(v)$, we may easily calculate the distribution function for the molecular energies:

$$f(E)\, dE = N_t \frac{2}{(\pi)^{\frac{1}{2}}(kT)^{\frac{3}{2}}} e^{-E/kT} \sqrt{E}\, dE \qquad (2\text{-}2\text{-}11)$$

$f(E)\, dE$ is the number of molecules with kinetic energy in the range E to $E + dE$.

The distribution function for the component of velocity along one direction is also of interest. The number of molecules whose X components of velocity lie between v_x and $v_x + dv_x$ is

$$f_x \, dv_x = N_t \left(\frac{m}{2\pi kT} \right)^{1/2} e^{-mv_x^2/2kT} \, dv_x \qquad (2\text{-}2\text{-}12)$$

The function f_x has the shape of an error curve. It can be shown that the root mean square of any Cartesian component of the velocity equals Newton's (isothermal) value for the speed of sound in the gas:

$$(v_i)_R = \left(\frac{p}{\rho} \right)^{1/2} \qquad (2\text{-}2\text{-}13)$$

Here p is the pressure and ρ is the density. The right-hand side of (2-2-13) should be multiplied by $(\gamma)^{1/2}$, where γ is the ratio of the specific heats, to obtain the correct speed of sound.

Each component of the velocity is distributed independently of the other components. Therefore, if $p(\mathbf{v}) \, dv_x \, dv_y \, dv_z \equiv p(v_x, v_y, v_z) \, dv_x \, dv_y \, dv_z$ is the probability that a given molecule has velocity components between v_x and $v_x + dv_x$, v_y and $v_y + dv_y$, and v_z and $v_z + dv_z$, it follows that

$$p(\mathbf{v}) \, dv_x \, dv_y \, dv_z = \frac{1}{N_t^3} f_x f_y f_z \, dv_x \, dv_y \, dv_z \qquad (2\text{-}2\text{-}14)$$

B. MIXTURES OF GASES. In a mixture of gases which is in complete equilibrium each of the species has a Maxwellian distribution characterized by the common temperature and the value of the molecular mass for that species, just as if the other constituents of the mixture were not present. We shall show that in a binary mixture of gases at the same temperature the mean value of the relative velocity of two unlike molecules $\bar{v}_0$ is given by

$$\bar{v}_0 = (\bar{v}_1^2 + \bar{v}_2^2)^{1/2} \qquad (2\text{-}2\text{-}15)$$

where $\bar{v}_1$ and $\bar{v}_2$ are the mean velocities of the two species. Evidently, if the two species are identical,

$$\bar{v}_0 = \sqrt{2}\bar{v} \qquad (2\text{-}2\text{-}16)$$

The proof of (2-2-15) which follows is taken from Present.[5] The mean value of the velocities of the type 1 molecules relative to those of type 2 is obtained by averaging v_0 over the distribution functions of both types of molecules. Thus

$$\bar{v}_0 = \iiint dv_{1x} \, dv_{1y} \, dv_{1z} \iiint dv_{2x} \, dv_{2y} \, dv_{2z} p_1(\mathbf{v}_1) \, p_2(\mathbf{v}_2) v_0 \qquad (2\text{-}2\text{-}17)$$

where

$$v_0 = [(v_{1x} - v_{2x})^2 + (v_{1y} - v_{2y})^2 + (v_{1z} - v_{2z})^2]^{1/2} \qquad (2\text{-}2\text{-}18)$$

Using (2-2-12) and (2-2-14) in (2-2-17), we have

$$\bar{v}_0 = \left(\frac{m_1}{2\pi kT}\right)^{3/2}\left(\frac{m_2}{2\pi kT}\right)^{3/2}\int_{-\infty}^{\infty}dv_{1x}\cdots\int_{-\infty}^{\infty}dv_{2z}v_0\exp-\frac{m_1v_1^2+m_2v_2^2}{2kT}$$

(2-2-19)

The computation is simplified if we transform from v_1 and v_2 to the relative velocity v_0 and the velocity of the center of mass in the Lab system V_{CM}. These velocities are given by the equations

$$\mathbf{v}_0 = \mathbf{v}_1 - \mathbf{v}_2 \qquad \mathbf{V}_{CM} = \frac{m_1\mathbf{v}_1 + m_2\mathbf{v}_2}{m_1 + m_2}$$

(2-2-20)

If we solve (2-2-20) in component form, we obtain

$$v_{1x} = V_{CMx} + \left(\frac{m_2}{m_1 + m_2}\right)v_{0x}$$

$$v_{2x} = V_{CMx} - \left(\frac{m_1}{m_1 + m_2}\right)v_{0x}$$

(2-2-21)

with similar equations for the y and z components. Therefore

$$\tfrac{1}{2}m_1v_1^2 + \tfrac{1}{2}m_2v_2^2 = \tfrac{1}{2}(m_1 + m_2)V_{CM}^2 + \tfrac{1}{2}M_rv_0^2$$

(2-2-22)

where $M_r = m_1m_2/(m_1 + m_2)$ is the reduced mass of the pair of particles. Equation 2-2-22 expresses the fact that the total kinetic energy of the particles is equal to the kinetic energy of the total mass, moving with the velocity of the center of mass in the Lab system, plus the kinetic energy of relative motion (cf. Section 1-2).

The volume elements in the two new velocity spaces are given by the equations

$$dV_{CMx}\,dV_{CMy}\,dV_{CMz} = V_{CM}^2\,dV_{CM}\sin\theta_{CM}\,d\theta_{CM}\,d\varphi_{CM}$$

$$dv_{0x}\,dv_{0y}\,dv_{0z} = v_0^2\,dv_0\sin\theta_0\,d\theta_0\,d\varphi_0$$

(2-2-23)

When (2-2-22) is substituted into the exponent in the integral in (2-2-19), the integrand is independent of the angles θ_{CM}, φ_{CM}, θ_0, and φ_0. Integration over all angles gives

$$\bar{v}_0 = (2\pi kT)^{-3}(m_1m_2)^{3/2}(4\pi)^2 I_2\left(\frac{m_1 + m_2}{2kT}\right)I_3\left(\frac{M_r}{2kT}\right)$$

(2-2-24)

where*

$$I_2\left(\frac{m_1 + m_2}{2kT}\right) = \int_0^{\infty}\exp\left[-\frac{(m_1 + m_2)V_{CM}^2}{2kT}\right]V_{CM}^2\,dV_{CM}$$

$$= \left(\frac{\pi}{2}\right)^{1/2}\left(\frac{kT}{m_1 + m_2}\right)^{3/2}$$

* See Present, Ref. 1 p. 266–267, for discussion of the relationship of I_2 and I_3 to other integrals frequently occurring in kinetic theory.

and

$$I_3\left(\frac{M_r}{2kT}\right) = \int_0^\infty e^{-M_r v_0^2/2kT} v_0^3 \, dv_0 = 2\left(\frac{kT}{M_r}\right)^2$$

Equation 2-2-24 reduces to the simple form

$$\bar{v}_0 = \left(\frac{8kT}{\pi M_r}\right)^{1/2} = \left(\frac{8kT}{\pi m_1} + \frac{8kT}{\pi m_2}\right)^{1/2} = (\bar{v}_1^2 + \bar{v}_2^2)^{1/2} \qquad (2\text{-}2\text{-}15)$$

which is the desired result.

C. A GAS IN A FORCE FIELD. The energy distribution function given in (2-2-11) does not apply for a gas in an external field of force. If the force is describable by a scalar potential, the proper distribution function is obtained by inclusion of the *Boltzmann factor*, $e^{-V/kT}$, in (2-2-11). Here V is the potential energy per molecule and is a function of position. Thus the number of molecules per cm³ with kinetic energy between E and $E + dE$ is given by

$$N(E) \, dE = N_0 \frac{2}{(\pi)^{1/2}(kT)^{3/2}} e^{-(E+V)/kT} \sqrt{E} \, dE \qquad (2\text{-}2\text{-}25)$$

where N_0 is the total number density at a point at which $V = 0$. In this case the molecules are not uniformly distributed in configuration space. The variation of the number density with position is implicitly given by the equation

$$N = N_0 e^{-V/kT} \qquad (2\text{-}2\text{-}26)$$

The temperature is uniform throughout the gas, and the *Maxwell-Boltzmann distribution* of energies (2-2-25) corresponding to this temperature holds at each point.

2-3. THE MOLECULAR DIAMETER, MEAN FREE PATH, AND COLLISION FREQUENCY

A. EQUATIONS DERIVED FROM THE ELASTIC SPHERE MODEL. Consider a gas of number density N molecules/cm³. If the molecules are assumed to be elastic spheres of diameter D whose velocities are distributed according to the Maxwellian law, it can be shown[6] that the number of collisions per cm³-sec is $(\pi/\sqrt{2})N^2D^2\bar{v}$. The free path is usually defined as the distance that a molecule travels between successive collisions. Each collision marks the end of two free paths (one for each of the two collision partners), and the total number of free paths executed per cm³-sec is $\sqrt{2}\pi N^2D^2\bar{v}$. The total length of all these free paths is $N\bar{v}$, and the average length of a free path is

$$\lambda = \frac{1}{\sqrt{2}\,\pi ND^2} \qquad (2\text{-}3\text{-}1)$$

which is designated as *Maxwell's mean free path*. This mean free path is the mean of all the paths traced out in unit time. An alternative definition leads to the *Tait mean free path*, which is the mean of all the paths being described at a given instant or the mean of all the distances traversed from a given instant to the next collision. The result of the Tait averaging procedure differs from (2-3-1) only in the substitution of the numerical factor 0.677 for $1/\sqrt{2}$, a difference of some 4%.

Note that (1-4-14) provides a value for the mean free path of a single molecule based on the assumption that all other molecules of the gas are stationary:

$$\lambda_{\text{stationary}} = \frac{1}{Q_s} = \frac{1}{Nq_s} = \frac{1}{\pi N D^2} \tag{2-3-2}$$

From the cross section point of view, the moving molecule is assumed to be a point and each of the stationary molecules is assumed to have a radius equal to the true molecular diameter D.

In a mixture of two gases the mean free path for molecules of type 1 is

$$\lambda_1 = \left[\pi N_1 D_{11}^2 (2)^{\frac{1}{2}} + \pi N_2 D_{12}^2 \left(1 + \frac{m_1}{m_2} \right)^{\frac{1}{2}} \right]^{-1} \tag{2-3-3}$$

where D_{ij} is the distance between centers of molecules of type i and j when they are in contact; that is,

$$D_{11} = D_1$$
$$D_{12} = \tfrac{1}{2}(D_1 + D_2)$$

If the particles of type 1 are light and small compared with those of type 2, (2-3-3) reduces to

$$\lambda_1 = \frac{4}{\pi N_2 D_2^2} \tag{2-3-4}$$

This equation gives the elastic sphere model prediction for the mean free path of electrons moving about in equilibrium with a gas. For reasons to be explained in Chapter 3, the elastic sphere model is unrealistic in the case of electrons and gives very poor agreement with experiment—a quantum mechanical treatment is required. The elastic sphere prediction is, however, quite good for atoms and molecules, and order-of-magnitude agreement with experiment is provided for ions in gases that are not highly ionized. With these gases consideration of the polarization attraction of the molecules by the ions (discussed in Section 1-8) leads to a reduction of the elastic sphere value for λ by about a factor of 5 and gives realistic results.

B. VARIATION OF THE MEAN FREE PATH AND COLLISION FREQUENCY WITH DENSITY AND TEMPERATURE.   The discussion in Section 2-3-A shows that the average collision frequency for a single molecule of a gas with a Maxwellian distribution is

$$\nu = \sqrt{2}\pi N D^2 \bar{v} \tag{2-3-5}$$

and that the mean free path is

$$\lambda = \frac{1}{\sqrt{2}\,\pi N D^2} \tag{2-3-1}$$

Thus, according to the elastic sphere model, the collision frequency varies directly with the density of the gas and the square root of the absolute temperature, variation with temperature arising from the proportionality of ν to $\bar{v}$. The mean free path, on the other hand, varies only with the density and is inversely proportional to it.

Models more realistic than the elastic sphere model do, however, predict a variation of the mean free path with temperature. The Sutherland model (cf. Section 1-7) gives an expression of the form[7]

$$\lambda_S = \frac{\lambda}{1 + C/T} \tag{2-3-6}$$

Here λ is the mean free path corresponding to the elastic sphere model (2-3-1) and C is a positive constant which has a different value for each gas. The reduction in the mean free path indicated by (2-3-6) is produced by the attractive field assumed in the Sutherland model.

If we let $\lambda(v)$ denote the average distance traveled by a single molecule of a particular speed v between successive collisions with molecules having a Maxwellian distribution of velocities, we find that $\lambda(v)$ is a function of v which increases monotonically from a value of 0 at $v = 0$ to a value $\sqrt{2}\lambda$ at $v = \infty$. This is made to appear reasonable by the following considerations: if the molecule is stationary, it travels zero distance before it is struck by another molecule. On the other hand, if the velocity of the single molecule approaches ∞, the other molecules may be considered stationary, and (2-3-2) applies. In this case the mean free path of the single molecule is greater than the value in (2-3-1) by the factor $\sqrt{2}$. The calculation of $\lambda(v)$ as a function of v is quite involved. It is presented in detail by Jeans.[8]

C. NUMERICAL RESULTS FOR MOLECULES IN PURE GASES.   The published values for molecular diameters and mean free paths are derived mainly from studies of viscosity, heat conductivity, diffusion rates, and equations of state. Loeb[9] has discussed in a very thorough manner all of the methods of determining these quantities. None of the models used in kinetic theory provides an exact description of any physical phenomenon, and the values deduced for the molecular diameters and mean free paths depend to some extent on the method of determination. Molecular diameters, mean free paths, and collision frequencies for a number of gases at 15°C are tabulated in Table 2-2-1. The values of λ were calculated by Kennard[10] from viscosity data, and (2-3-1) was then used to obtain D. The collision frequency ν was calculated from

$$\nu = \frac{\bar{v}}{\lambda} \tag{2-3-7}$$

The discussion in Section 1-4 shows that the probability that a molecule will travel at least a distance x through the gas between collisions is $e^{-x/\lambda}$. Thus free paths appreciably greater than λ are extremely rare—only one molecule in 148 will travel as far as 5λ between collisions and only 1 in 22,027 as far as 10λ. It should be noted that the distribution of free paths does not peak near some mean value, as does the distribution of the molecular velocities, but rather the number of free paths longer than a certain value is a decreasing exponential function of the distance.

D. THE MEAN FREE PATH OF A CHARGED PARTICLE IN A HIGHLY IONIZED GAS. The concept of the mean free path developed in Section C does not apply to a charged particle moving through a gas that contains a high concentration of ions and electrons. The reason is that the motion of the particle is influenced, in this case, more by the cumulative effect of many small-angle Coulomb scatterings than by close impacts of the type considered so far.*

2-4. THE MEAN DISTANCE BETWEEN MOLECULES IN A GAS

The mean distance d between the molecules of a gas is given by

$$d = \frac{1}{N^{1/3}} \tag{2-4-1}$$

where N is the number density. The relative values of the mean free path, the mean spacing, and the molecular diameter for a gas at various pressures are of some interest, and representative values are tabulated below. The molecular diameter is taken to be 3×10^{-8} cm. The mean free path is assumed to be 10^{-5} cm at 760 mm Hg pressure and to vary inversely with

---

* Actually we may speak of a sort of mean free path for a charged particle in a highly ionized gas, but reference is made in this case to the average depth of penetration required before multiple scattering through some large angle, usually taken to be 90° (see Appendix I).

the pressure, the temperature being held constant. A temperature of 15°C is assumed throughout.

(a) At $p = 760$ mm Hg, $\bar{d} \approx 3.3 \times 10^{-7}$ cm and $\lambda = 10^{-5}$ cm
$$\lambda/\bar{d}/D \approx 300/10/1$$

(b) At $p = 1$ mm Hg, $\bar{d} \approx 3.0 \times 10^{-6}$ cm and $\lambda = 8 \times 10^{-3}$ cm
$$\lambda/\bar{d}/D \approx 2 \times 10^{5}/100/1$$

(c) At $p = 10^{-4}$ mm Hg, $\bar{d} \approx 6.6 \times 10^{-5}$ cm and $\lambda \approx 80$ cm
$$\lambda/\bar{d}/D \approx 3 \times 10^{9}/2000/1$$

It will be noticed that at a pressure of 10^{-4} mm Hg the mean free path is comparable with the dimensions of typical laboratory apparatus.

2-5. THE RELAXATION TIME OF A GAS*

Consider a gas in which the velocity distribution is initially non-Maxwellian. Maxwell[11] calculated the rate at which the gas must approach the steady-state condition. The result[12] is that deviations from the Maxwellian distribution are damped out exponentially, with a time constant equal to $1/(\Gamma N)$, where N is the number density of the gas and Γ is a constant which depends only on the structure of the molecules. This characteristic time is called the relaxation time, and it also measures the rate at which inequalities in the pressure and shear stresses must subside.

Γ is related to the coefficient of viscosity η and the hydrostatic pressure p by the equation

$$\Gamma = \frac{p}{\eta N} \tag{2-5-1}$$

Numerical substitution into (2-5-1) shows that the relaxation time is comparable in magnitude with the mean free time for collisions in the gas, which is about 10^{-8} sec at standard conditions.

From the physical point of view the reason for the rapid approach to equilibrium is the efficient transfer of kinetic energy from one molecule to another in a collision. It was shown in Section 1-5 that a molecule transfers, on the average, half its excess energy to an identical collision partner in a single collision. Electrons, on the other hand, approach equilibrium much more slowly, since, on the average, an electron can transfer only a fraction $2m/M$ of its excess energy to a molecule in an elastic collision where m and M are the masses of the electron and

* For a good general discussion of this subject, see J. D. Lambert, "Relaxation in Gases," in *Atomic and Molecular Processes* (edited by D. R. Bates), Academic, New York, 1962.

molecule, respectively. (It is shown in Chapter 11 that when an electric field is present the electrons in a gas approach an equilibrium distribution, but it is not the Maxwell-Boltzmann distribution.)

2-6. THE NUMBER OF MOLECULES CROSSING
UNIT AREA IN A GAS PER SECOND

Let us now calculate the number of molecules of a gas in thermodynamic equilibrium that cross a surface element of unit area in the gas per unit time. Consider a small plane element of surface, dS, at an arbitrary

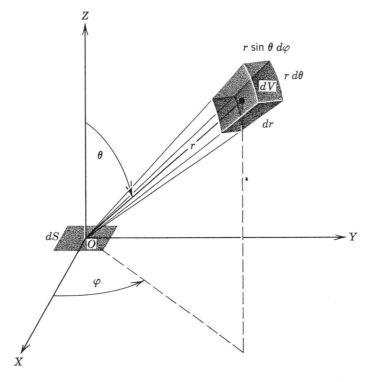

FIG. 2-6-1. The coordinate system used for calculation of the rate of scattering of molecules from volume dV through surface dS.

location within the gas and examine an element of volume, dV, located arbitrarily with respect to dS, as shown in Fig. 2-6-1. If the number density is N, there are $N\,dV$ molecules within dV. The volume of dV may be written as $r^2\,dr\,\sin\theta\,d\theta\,d\varphi$. From the form of the distribution function in (2-2-1) it is apparent that the number of molecules within dV with speeds between v and $v + dv$ is

$$n = N \left(\frac{2}{\pi}\right)^{1/2} \left(\frac{m}{kT}\right)^{3/2} v^2 e^{-mv^2/2kT} \, dv \, r^2 \, dr \sin \theta \, d\theta \, d\varphi$$

The pressure is assumed to be uniform, so N is independent of position. If the collision frequency is denoted by ν, the number of molecules leaving dV per second with speeds between v and $v + dv$ is $\nu n = \bar{v} n/\lambda$, since $\nu = \bar{v}/\lambda$. In this number, however, only those molecules scattered within the solid angle subtended at dV by dS will be headed toward dS. This fraction is given by $\cos \theta \, dS/4\pi r^2$. In this group of molecules only a fraction equal to $e^{-r/\lambda}$ will reach dS, the remainder undergoing further scattering. Thus the number leaving dV per second with speeds between v and $v + dv$ and passing directly through dS is given by

$$\frac{\bar{v} n}{\lambda} \frac{\cos \theta \, dS}{4\pi r^2} e^{-r/\lambda}$$

The total number of molecules passing through dS per second from the half-space containing dV is obtained by integrating r from 0 to ∞, θ from 0 to $\pi/2$, φ from 0 to 2π, and v from 0 to ∞. The result of this multiple integration is $(N/4)\bar{v} \, dS$. An equal number of molecules will cross dS per second from the other side, with the result that *the total number of molecules passing through an imaginary surface of unit area in the gas per second is* $(N/2)\bar{v}$.

In probe theory one is required to know the number of particles that strike the unit surface area of an object located in the gas. We see that the kinetic theory provides a value of $(N/4)\bar{v}$ for this quantity.

From the foregoing discussion it is apparent that the rate of effusion of molecules through a small hole in the vessel containing the gas is $(N/4)\bar{v}$ molecules/cm²-sec if the pressure outside the vessel is zero. Evidently this result is valid only if the hole is very small compared with the mean free path, for only under this condition is the distribution of the velocities only slightly disturbed by the effusion of the gas. As the size of the hole is increased, we eventually pass into the regime of hydrodynamic streaming.

2-7. EQUATIONS OF STATE

Many equations of state[13] have been proposed to describe the inter-relationship of the pressure, volume, and temperature of gases. Some of the most commonly used equations are listed below. The pressure, p, is measured in dyne/cm², V is the volume in cm³ of one mole of the gas, T is the absolute temperature in °K, and $R = 8.31 \times 10^7$ erg/mole-deg is the universal gas constant.

(a) $$pV = RT$$ *Ideal gas law*

Gases deviate appreciably from ideal behavior only at pressures of about 1 atm, or higher, and for this reason the ideal gas law is nearly always the equation of state used in plasma applications.

(b) $$\left(p + \frac{a}{V^2}\right)(V - b) = RT \quad \textit{van der Waals equation}$$

The constant a arises from attractive forces which the molecules exert on one another when they are reasonably close together but somewhat more that a molecular diameter apart. The constant b, on the other hand, arises from shorter range repulsive forces which come into play at a separation distance of about one molecular diameter.

(c) $$\left(p + \frac{a}{TV^2}\right)(V - b) = RT \qquad \textit{Berthelot equation}$$

(d) $$p(V - b) = RTe^{-a/RTV} \qquad \textit{Dieterici equation}$$

(e) $$p = \frac{RT}{V^2}\left(1 - \frac{c}{VT^3}\right)\left(V + B_0 - \frac{bB_0}{V}\right) - \frac{A_0}{V^2}\left(1 - \frac{a}{V}\right)$$

$$\textit{Beattie-Bridgeman equation}$$

By suitably choosing the five disposable constants in this equation, close agreement with experiment is obtained for many gases, including all of the common gases, over a wide range of pressure and temperature.

(f) $$pV = RT + \frac{B}{V} + \frac{C}{V^2} + \cdots$$

$$\textit{Virial equation of state}$$

The quantities B, $C \cdots$ in this equation are functions of temperature called the second, third, $\cdots$ virial coefficients.[*] The coefficients B, C, $\cdots$ express the magnitude of the deviations from ideal gas behavior in terms of the forces between the molecules; hence the use of the term virial. (The Latin word for forces is *vires*.)

With the exception of the ideal gas law, all the equations listed here indicate the *critical point*, at which the vapor and liquid phases are identical. Let the parameters of the system at the critical point be denoted by p_c, V_c, T_c and the "reduced coordinates" be defined as $p_r = p/p_c$, $V_r = V/V_c$,

[*] Oddly enough, pV, and not RT, is designated the first virial coefficient. See E. A. Mason and H. W. Schamp, "The Virial Equation of State," in "*Encyclopedia of Physical Chemistry and Chemical Physics*, Pergamon, London, 1964.

$T_r = T/T_c$. If the equations of state are now expressed in terms of reduced coordinates, a functional form that is the same for all substances will be obtained. (This statement holds only for two-constant equations of state. It is not true for the Beattie-Bridgeman equation, for instance, which has five disposable constants.)

2-8. DIFFUSION, VISCOSITY, AND THERMAL CONDUCTIVITY

Ordinary diffusion is a process in which there is a net spatial transport of a substance due to a gradient in the relative concentration of that substance. The diffusive flow takes place in the direction opposite that of this gradient, and the flow rate is directly proportional to the magnitude of the gradient. The constant of proportionality is called the diffusion coefficient. Diffusive flow is separate and distinct from the flow resulting from a nonuniformity of the total pressure, and entirely different techniques are used to analyze them.

There are two kinds of ordinary diffusion. *Mutual diffusion* occurs in a mixture of gases of uniform total pressure but nonuniform composition, and it continues until the inequalities in composition have been eliminated by interdiffusion of the components. In the degenerate situation, in which the components of the mixture are identical, we have the special case of *self-diffusion*. This phenomenon appears when selected molecules of a homogeneous gas diffuse through the remainder of the gas, and it may be closely approximated experimentally by the use of isotopic tracers. (Analysis of the gas is generally accomplished by mass spectrometric techniques if the isotopes are stable and by counting techniques if one or more of the isotopes are radioactive.)

A basically different type of diffusion, called *thermal*,[14] occurs when there is a temperature gradient rather than a composition* gradient in the gas. Thermal diffusion differs from ordinary diffusion in that it will always produce a state of nonuniform composition instead of leading to uniformity of composition. Thermal diffusion does, however, bring about mutual diffusion, as shown in the following example: consider a closed tube containing an initially uniform mixture of two gases. If a temperature differential is established between the ends of the tube, thermal diffusion will occur, the molecules of the heavier gas diffusing toward the cooler end of the tube as the lighter gas diffuses toward the

---

* The word "composition" rather than "concentration" is used in this discussion because "concentration" is frequently applied in the sense of mass per unit volume, which corresponds to the total number density in our nomenclature. A temperature gradient in a *pure* gas will produce a gradient in the concentration (i.e., the density will be less at the higher temperature) but not in the composition (the mole fraction is always unity).

hotter end.* As a nonuniformity of composition begins to be established by thermal diffusion, mutual diffusion sets in and tends to restore the initial uniformity. A steady state is eventually attained in which there is a gradual change in the composition along the tube, transport by mutual diffusion just balancing that produced by thermal diffusion.

The effect of thermal diffusion was predicted independently by Enskog in 1911 and Chapman in 1916 in their developments of the rigorous kinetic theory. Thermal diffusion was first demonstrated experimentally in 1916 by Dootson[3] and has been put to practical use in the separation of isotopes.

Viscosity is a process involving the transport of momentum through a moving medium because of a gradient in the velocity of that medium. The shearing stress, which is related to the transport of the momentum of flow in the direction of the velocity gradient, is proportional to the magnitude of the velocity gradient. Viscosity is a manifestation of an internal friction.

Thermal conductivity is the transport of thermal energy through a medium due to a thermal gradient in the medium. The rate of heat flow is directly proportional to the magnitude of the temperature gradient.

It is evident that all of these phenomena are closely related. Each involves the transport of some physical property of the gas. The rate of transport is directly proportional to the magnitude of the gradient that produces it, and the transport is oppositely directed to that gradient. Diffusion, viscosity, and thermal conductivity are known collectively as transport phenomena, and it is not surprising that the mathematical treatments of all three are quite similar. It is worth noting that classical theory gives sufficiently accurate results in calculations of transport coefficients except for the lightest gases at low temperatures, for which quantum theory is required (see Section 3-10).

Diffusion is the most important of the transport phenomena for our purposes, and we shall now derive an expression for the diffusion coefficient, using the so-called mean free path approach.

2-9. DERIVATION OF THE DIFFUSION COEFFICIENT
BY THE MEAN FREE PATH METHOD

Let us return to the discussion in Section 2-6 in which we calculated the number of molecules passing per unit time through unit area in a gas of uniform pressure. Now we shall assume that the pressure is non-uniform, and, specifically, that a very small density gradient exists in the

---

* This is usually, but not always, true. In ionized gases, for instance, reversals occur. Reversals in ordinary gases are also known.

Z direction, the temperature being constant throughout the gas. The macroscopic flow of the gas will be negligible, but a diffusive type of flow will occur. Calculation of the net number of molecules passing through unit area in the X-Y plane per second will provide the diffusion coefficient characterizing the flow.

Let us expand the number density N in a Taylor series about the origin:

$$N(z) = N(0) + z\left(\frac{dN}{dz}\right)_o + \frac{z^2}{2}\left(\frac{d^2N}{dz^2}\right)_o + \cdots \qquad (2\text{-}9\text{-}1)$$

The subscripts denote that the derivatives are evaluated at the origin, which is, of course, an arbitrary point within the gas. The assumption that the gradient of N is small is meant to imply that the contribution to N of terms of higher than second order is negligible within a distance equal to a mean free path, λ. The discussion in Section 2-6 indicates the method of calculating the number of molecules passing downward through unit area in the X-Y plane per second. The original expression applies here if N, which is now a function of position, is taken inside the integral. A similar expression, in which the limits of θ are $\pi/2$ and π and $\cos\theta = -|\cos\theta|$, will give the number of molecules passing upward along the Z axis per unit area per second. Subtraction of the second expression from the first gives the desired result. J, the net downward transport of molecules per unit area per second, is

$$J = \frac{\bar{v}}{4\pi\lambda} \int_0^\infty dr e^{-r/\lambda} N(z) \int_0^\pi \sin\theta\cos\theta\,d\theta \int_0^{2\pi} d\varphi$$

$$= \frac{\bar{v}}{2\lambda} \int_0^\infty dr e^{-r/\lambda} N(r\cos\theta) \int_0^\pi \sin\theta\cos\theta\,d\theta$$

$$= \frac{\bar{v}}{2\lambda} \int_0^\infty dr e^{-r/\lambda} N(r\xi) \int_{-1}^1 \xi\,d\xi \qquad (2\text{-}9\text{-}2)$$

where

$$\xi = \cos\theta$$

If the expansion for N given in (2-9-1) is substituted into (2-9-2), we obtain

$$J = \frac{\bar{v}}{2\lambda}\left[N(0) \int_0^\infty e^{-r/\lambda}\,dr \int_{-1}^1 \xi\,d\xi + \left(\frac{dN}{dz}\right)_o \int_0^\infty re^{-r/\lambda}\,dr \int_{-1}^1 \xi^2\,d\xi \right.$$

$$\left. + \frac{1}{2}\left(\frac{d^2N}{dz^2}\right)_o \int_0^\infty r^2 e^{-r/\lambda}\,dr \int_{-1}^1 \xi^3\,d\xi \right] \qquad (2\text{-}9\text{-}3)$$

The first and third terms of (2-9-3) vanish when the integration over ξ is performed. The first term indeed must vanish for physical reasons, since there can be no net transport in a uniform gas. Evaluation of the second term shows that

$$J = \frac{\bar{v}\lambda}{3}\left(\frac{dN}{dz}\right)_o \tag{2-9-4}$$

Thus, if the density increases as z increases ($dN/dz > 0$), J, as we have defined it, is positive, and there is a net flow of molecules downward along the $-Z$ axis.

The generalization to three dimensions is obvious. In this case the vector particle current density $\mathbf{J}$ is given in terms of the number density gradient by the equation

$$\mathbf{J} = -\frac{\bar{v}\lambda}{3}\nabla N \tag{2-9-5}$$

The gradient of the number density is a vector that points in the direction of most rapidly increasing number density and whose magnitude equals the spatial rate of change of N in that direction. $\mathbf{J}$ is a vector pointing in the flow direction which expresses the net number of molecules flowing through unit area normal to the flow direction per second.

Equation 2-9-5 is known as *Fick's law of diffusion*. The constant of proportionality between $\mathbf{J}$ and ∇N is the diffusion coefficient $\mathcal{D}$. Thus, according to the mean free path approach used here,

$$\mathcal{D} = \frac{\bar{v}\lambda}{3} \tag{2-9-6}$$

Equation 2-9-5 evidently applies to the case of self-diffusion. It also applies to the mutual diffusion of two dissimilar gases if the relative concentration of one of the gases is vanishingly small. Another interesting application is to the diffusion of slow neutrons through bulk matter. Here the neutrons are assumed to have a Maxwellian distribution characterized by the temperature of the medium through which they are diffusing and the nuclei of the medium are taken to be at rest.

It will be noted that the mean free path appears naturally in this approach to the diffusion problem. Similar treatments of viscosity and thermal conductivity also give results in which λ appears. For this reason these phenomena are sometimes called mean free path phenomena. However, the term is not entirely appropriate because, as we shall see, rigorous kinetic theory provides results in which the mean free path does not appear naturally.

The mean free path calculation of the molecular self-diffusion coefficient $\mathcal{D} = \mathcal{D}_{11}$ gives fair agreement with experiment. (The correct numerical coefficient is $\frac{1}{2}$ instead of $\frac{1}{3}$.) A similar calculation of the coefficient of mutual diffusion, $\mathcal{D}_{12}$, fails badly.[15] Rigorous kinetic theory, discussed in the next section, should be used for gas mixtures.

2-10. RIGOROUS EXPRESSIONS FOR THE DIFFUSION COEFFICIENT

The first rigorous calculation of the mutual diffusion coefficient was made by Maxwell[16] in 1867 for molecules interacting through a repulsive r^{-4} potential His solution was exact, an accomplishment made possible by the special properties of the r^{-4} potential discussed in Section 1-8. Maxwell's result is

$$\mathscr{D}_{12} = \frac{kT}{N M_r v_0 q_D(v_0)} = \frac{0.376 kT}{N(M_r c)^{\frac{1}{2}}} \tag{2-10-1}$$

where N is the total number density $(N_1 + N_2)$, M_r is the reduced mass of species 1 and 2, v_0 is the relative velocity, $q_D(v_0)$ is the diffusion cross section, and c is the constant relating the force between the molecules to their separation distance:

$$f = cr^{-5} \tag{2-10-2}$$

In 1872 Stefan[17] published a calculation of the mutual diffusion coefficient for hard elastic spheres, but it was not until 1905 that a general and rigorous calculation of $\mathscr{D}_{12}$ was made by Langevin.[18] Langevin's result, expressed in terms of the standard Ω collision integral of the refined theory subsequently developed by Chapman and Enskog,[19] is

$$\mathscr{D}_{12} = \frac{3kT}{16 M_r N \Omega_D} \tag{2-10-3}$$

where

$$\Omega_D = \left(\frac{kT}{2\pi M_r}\right)^{\frac{1}{2}} \int_0^\infty e^{-g^2} q_D(v_0) g^5 \, dg \tag{2-10-4}$$

and

$$g = \left(\frac{M_r v_0^2}{2kT}\right)^{\frac{1}{2}} \tag{2-10-5}$$

In the approximation used in the derivation of (2-10-3) $\mathscr{D}_{12}$ is independent of the proportions of the gas mixture, depending only on N, and not on N_1 and N_2 individually. Equation 2-10-3 is identical with the first approximation provided by the Chapman-Enskog theory, which, however, predicts a slight dependence on the composition of the gas mixture in higher approximation (cf. Section 9-2-B). The higher order corrections to (2-10-3) are small and are usually ignored.[19]

Equation 2-10-3 may be easily evaluated for the elastic sphere model. In this case q_D becomes πD_{12}^2, where $D_{12} = \frac{1}{2}(D_1 + D_2)$, D_1 and D_2 being the molecular diameters of the two species; q_D is thus independent of the velocity, and the mutual diffusion coefficient is

$$\mathscr{D}_{12} = \frac{3}{8}\left(\frac{\pi kT}{2M_r}\right)^{\frac{1}{2}} (N\pi D_{12}^2)^{-1} \tag{2-10-6}$$

In any of the foregoing expressions for $\mathscr{D}_{12}$ the self-diffusion coefficient $\mathscr{D}_{11}$ may be obtained by replacing the reduced mass M_r by half the molecular mass of the single species present.

It is important to note that the classical description of the diffusion process fails when the temperature is very low (cf. Section 3-10) or when more than one interaction potential applies, as in the diffusion of excited atoms through a gas of similar unexcited atoms and in the self-diffusion of atoms which do not have a closed shell configuration. The effect is to produce very large diffusion cross sections and small diffusion coefficients.[20] In such cases quantum theory must be used to calculate the diffusion cross section, which can then be used in the classical kinetic theory equations to obtain $\mathscr{D}_{12}$ (see Section 9-3-B).

We shall postpone further discussion of diffusion until Chapters 9 and 10. There the emphasis is on the drift velocities and geometrical distributions of electrons and ions diffusing through gases. For additional information concerning the theoretical and experimental evaluation of diffusion coefficients, the reader is referred to Chapman and Cowling,[3] Hirschfelder, Curtiss, and Bird,[4] Dalgarno,[20] and Waldmann.[21]

We now turn to a few of the fundamental topics that play an important role in rigorous treatments of neutral and ionized gases. Chapman and Cowling have presented a survey of the development of the kinetic theory, and a very detailed discussion of the theory is to be found in their book[3] and in that of Hirschfelder, Curtiss, and Bird.[4] Reference should also be made to the authoritative review of the advanced theory by Grad.[22]

2-11. PHASE SPACE AND THE LIOUVILLE THEOREM[23]

Consider a dynamical system having s degrees of freedom. The motion of this system can be described in terms of s generalized coordinates $q_1, q_2, \ldots, q_s$ and the corresponding s generalized momenta $p_1, p_2, \ldots, p_s$. A set of values of these $2s$ variables may be regarded as the coordinates of a point in a space of $2s$ dimensions, called a *phase space*, in which the generalized coordinates and momenta serve as Cartesian coordinates. A given set of initial conditions is specified by a given single point, and as the system executes some particular motion the point representing the system in phase space traces out a trajectory in that space.

Now consider a huge ensemble of noninteracting replicas of this dynamical system to be started out simultaneously with different initial conditions, that is, at different points in phase space.* The state of this entire collection of systems at any time may be described by a set of points

* Alternatively, we could imagine the same system to be started repeatedly with different initial conditions and let time be the time elapsed after starting the system in each case.

in phase space, and the histories of these systems may be represented by the motions of the various "phase points" through phase space. If the number of systems is large enough, the set of points may be represented by a continuous distribution function, $\rho(q_1, \ldots, q_s, p_1, \ldots, p_s)$, called the density in phase space. *Liouville's theorem* states that the density of such points about any one point remains constant with time. A proof of this theorem follows.

At a given instant of time the number of points in phase space representing systems which have coordinates and momenta lying in the range $\Delta q_1 \cdots \Delta q_s \Delta p_1 \cdots \Delta p_s$ at some fixed point $q_1, \ldots, q_s, p_1, \ldots, p_s$ is

$$\rho \, \Delta q_1 \cdots \Delta q_s \Delta p_1 \cdots \Delta p_s = \rho \, \Delta V$$

where ΔV is an element of volume in the $2s$-dimensional phase space. As time progresses, points will pass through each of the two sides of ΔV which are perpendicular to the q_1 axis at a rate equal to $(\rho \dot{q}_1) \Delta q_2 \cdots \Delta p_s$, where $(\rho \dot{q}_1)$ is evaluated at that side of ΔV being considered. A similar flow occurs through the opposite side, and the net outward flow from ΔV through the sides perpendicular to q_1 is given by

$$\frac{\partial(\rho \dot{q}_1)}{\partial q_1} \Delta q_1 \Delta q_2 \cdots \Delta p_s$$

if higher order terms are neglected. Now evaluate the outward flow through all remaining pairs of sides of the volume element ΔV corresponding to the remaining coordinates $q_2 \cdots p_s$. If we add all of these net outward flow rates, equate the sum to the net loss of points within ΔV, and pass to the limit of zero Δ, we obtain the differential equation for ρ:

$$-\frac{\partial \rho}{\partial t} = \sum_{i=1}^{s} \left[\frac{\partial(\rho \dot{q}_i)}{\partial q_i} + \frac{\partial(\rho \dot{p}_i)}{\partial p_i} \right]$$

Here the symbol of partial differentiation with respect to time indicates that we are fixing our attention on a given stationary point in the phase space. Expanding the derivatives, we have

$$\frac{\partial \rho}{\partial t} + \sum_{i=1}^{s} \left[\rho \left(\frac{\partial \dot{q}_i}{\partial q_i} + \frac{\partial \dot{p}_i}{\partial p_i} \right) + \dot{q}_i \frac{\partial \rho}{\partial q_i} + \dot{p}_i \frac{\partial \rho}{\partial p_i} \right] = 0$$

Hamilton's equations,

$$\dot{q}_i = \frac{\partial H}{\partial p_i}, \qquad \dot{p}_i = -\frac{\partial H}{\partial q_i} \qquad (i = 1, 2, \ldots, s) \qquad (2\text{-}11\text{-}1)$$

where H is the Hamiltonian, show that the first term in the square brackets vanishes. Thus we obtain the result

$$\frac{\partial \rho}{\partial t} + \sum_{i=1}^{s} \left(\dot{q}_i \frac{\partial \rho}{\partial q_i} + \dot{p}_i \frac{\partial \rho}{\partial p_i} \right) = 0 \qquad (2\text{-}11\text{-}2)$$

This equation expresses the fact that the total time rate of change of ρ along a trajectory in phase space is zero. The first term represents the time rate of change of ρ at a fixed point in phase space and is referred to as the local rate of change. The second term designates the time rate of change produced by flow, or streaming, in configuration space. The last term represents the change produced by streaming in momentum space.

Equation 2-11-2 is Liouville's theorem. It has the form of a continuity equation for the flow of points through phase space,

$$\frac{\partial}{\partial t}(\text{density}) + \mathbf{\nabla} \cdot (\text{density flow}) = \text{source} \qquad (2\text{-}11\text{-}3)$$

for the special case in which the source term is zero.* The theorem may be concisely written if use is made of the mobile derivative, that is, the derivative following the motion of a point. The mobile derivative in this space is defined in terms of the velocity $\mathbf{v}$, the applied force $\mathbf{f}$, and the gradient operators in s-dimensional configuration and momentum spaces, $\mathbf{\nabla}_r$ and $\mathbf{\nabla}_p$, as follows:

$$\frac{D}{Dt} = \frac{\partial}{\partial t} + \mathbf{v} \cdot \mathbf{\nabla}_r + \mathbf{f} \cdot \mathbf{\nabla}_p \qquad (2\text{-}11\text{-}4)$$

We see that Liouville's theorem may now be expressed simply as

$$\frac{D\rho}{Dt} = 0 \qquad (2\text{-}11\text{-}5)$$

This theorem is significant in kinetic theory and statistical mechanics. It shows that the volume in phase space occupied by a collection of points is constant in time—there is no tendency of the points to crowd into any particular region of phase space. The points may thus be regarded as composing an incompressible fluid. Another statement of the theorem is the following: if at some instant a point is known to lie within an infinitesimal volume of phase space, it will lie in a corresponding volume of the same size after a time t. The shape of the corresponding volume may be quite different, however.

The $2s$-dimensional phase space described in this section is not the only one that proves useful, although it does offer special advantages.[23] In the following section we utilize a phase space of six dimensions—three corresponding to spatial coordinates and three to the associated velocity

---

* Here there is no source term in the continuity equation because the systems that compose the ensemble are incapable of interaction. The phase points, each of which represents one system of the ensemble, do not collide with one another: there is no mechanism for creation or destruction of the points, and none is abruptly transferred from one region of phase space to another by an impact with another phase point.

components. A system of N particles is represented in this space by a collection of N points. Pierce[24] considers the motion of an electron beam through an arbitrary combination of applied electric and magnetic fields and shows that Liouville's theorem applies for the six-dimensional electron number density, provided the fields do not depend on the positions of the electrons; that is, in six-dimensional phase space the electron density in the vicinity of a given electron does not change as the electron moves along the beam.

2-12. THE BOLTZMANN EQUATION

The rigorous kinetic theory of gases is based on the knowledge of the distribution function $f_i(\mathbf{r}, \mathbf{v}, t)$ for each of the various species of particle present: f_i is the number density for the ith species in six-dimensional phase space. Specifically, $f_i(\mathbf{r}, \mathbf{v}, t) \, d^3r \, d^3v$ is the number of particles of type i which, at time t, lie within the volume element d^3r centered at $\mathbf{r}$ in configuration space and which have velocities within the volume element d^3v centered at $\mathbf{v}$ in velocity space. The distribution function satisfies the Boltzmann integro-differential equation. In certain cases f_i reduces to the Maxwell-Boltzmann distribution function.

The *Boltzmann equation*, which is the starting point for most rigorous calculations in kinetic theory, describes the effect of applied forces and collisions on the distribution function. It has the form of a continuity equation (2-11-3), as does the Liouville equation (2-11-2). However, the source term is no longer zero, for we now consider the interaction of particles through collisions with members of their own species and those of other species as well. Let $\mathbf{a}$ represent the acceleration produced by continuous or average forces. (If, for example, the species of particle under consideration is ionic, this acceleration may be produced by an externally applied electric field.) The effects of collisions and microscopic fluctuations are considered separately in the source, or collision, term. Thus the Boltzmann equation has the form

$$\frac{\partial f_i}{\partial t} + \mathbf{v} \cdot \mathbf{\nabla}_r f_i + \mathbf{a} \cdot \mathbf{\nabla}_v f_i = \left(\frac{\delta f_i}{\delta t} \right)_{\text{collisions}} \tag{2-12-1}$$

where $\mathbf{\nabla}_r$ is now the gradient operator in three-dimensional configuration space and $\mathbf{\nabla}_v$ is the gradient operator in the corresponding three-dimensional velocity space.

The collision term is really the sum of n integrals, where n is the number of different species present in the gas. Each of these integrals, designated by B with appropriate subscripts, gives the rate of change of the distribution function for species i caused by collisions with particles of species j

as we move along the trajectory of particles i. The collision integral B_{ij} is evidently obtained by calculating the difference between the rates of scattering of particles i into and out of the volume element d^3v_i, due to collisions with particles j. The discussion of reaction rates in Section 1-4 shows that the collision integral has the following form:

$$B_{ij}\, d^3v_i = \iint f_j(\mathbf{v}_j')f_i(\mathbf{v}_i')v_0'\, I_s(\Theta, v_0')\, d\Omega_{\mathrm{CM}}\, d^3v_j'\, d^3v_i'$$

$$-\iint f_j(\mathbf{v}_j)f_i(\mathbf{v}_i)v_0\, I_s(\Theta, v_0)\, d\Omega_{\mathrm{CM}}\, d^3v_j\, d^3v_i \quad (2\text{-}12\text{-}2)$$

$f_j(\mathbf{v}_j')\, d^3v_j'$ and $f_i(\mathbf{v}_i')\, d^3v_i'$ are the numbers of particles in position to be scattered into velocity elements d^3v_j and d^3v_i, whereas $f_j(\mathbf{v}_j)\, d^3v_j$ and $f_i(\mathbf{v}_i)\, d^3v_i$ give the numbers in position to be scattered out of d^3v_j and d^3v_i: v_0 is the relative velocity and $I_s(\Theta, v_0)\, d\Omega_{\mathrm{CM}}$ is the CM differential scattering cross section; $d\Omega_{\mathrm{CM}} = \sin \Theta\, d\Theta\, d\varphi$ is the CM element of solid angle. The integration is to be performed over all scattering angles and all velocities of the scatterers j. The collision integral is very difficult to evaluate, in general, except for the case of a constant mean free time, $v_0 I_s(\Theta, v_0) = $ constant.

Recognizing the fact that the distribution function defines a particle current in six-dimensional phase space, we may write the Boltzmann equation in the following physically meaningful form:

$$\frac{\partial f_i}{\partial t} + \nabla_r \cdot \mathbf{\gamma}_i + \nabla_v \cdot \mathbf{g}_i = \sum_{j=1}^{n} B_{ij} \quad (2\text{-}12\text{-}3)$$

Here $\mathbf{\gamma}_i$ is the component of the particle current in configuration space

$$\mathbf{\gamma}_i = \mathbf{v}f_i \quad (2\text{-}12\text{-}4)$$

and $\mathbf{g}_i$ is the component in velocity space

$$\mathbf{g}_i = \mathbf{a}f_i \quad (2\text{-}12\text{-}5)$$

The distribution function is seldom, if ever, measured, but various velocity moments can be determined experimentally. These moments are

particle number density (scalar)
$$N = \int f(\mathbf{r}, \mathbf{v}, t)\, d^3v \quad (2\text{-}12\text{-}6)$$

average energy (scalar)
$$u = \frac{m}{2N} \int v^2 f\, d^3v \quad (2\text{-}12\text{-}7)$$

drift velocity (vector)
$$\mathbf{v}_d = \frac{1}{N} \int \mathbf{v}f\, d^3v \quad (2\text{-}12\text{-}8)$$

kinetic pressure
(tensor)
$$\not{p} = m \int (\mathbf{v} - \mathbf{v}_d)(\mathbf{v} - \mathbf{v}_d) f \, d^3v \tag{2-12-9}$$

heat flow
(tensor)
$$\mathscr{H} = m \int (\mathbf{v} - \mathbf{v}_d)(\mathbf{v} - \mathbf{v}_d)(\mathbf{v} - \mathbf{v}_d) f \, d^3v \tag{2-12-10}$$

2-13. METHODS OF SOLUTION OF THE BOLTZMANN EQUATION[25]

The Boltzmann equation is quite intractable mathematically, and recourse must be made to expansion methods for its solution, except in the singular case of a constant mean free path. One of the most useful techniques is the *Chapman-Enskog method.* It applies to cases in which the system under consideration is close to thermal equilibrium, and it involves an expansion of the distribution function in powers of the perturbation parameter α, which produced the departure from equilibrium:

$$f = f^0 + \alpha f^1 + \alpha^2 f^2 + \cdots \tag{2-13-1}$$

This procedure linearizes the Boltzmann equation. The perturbed distribution function is then expanded in Sonine polynomials, and the integral equation is reduced to an infinite set of algebraic equations. This method is highly developed and well described in the literature.[26] Unfortunately, the Chapman-Enskog method is not very useful for charged particles in an electric field, since the series does not converge well in this case.

Another perturbation method is also useful, wherein the total distribution function is taken to be the sum of the function f_0, characterizing the steady-state, unperturbed system, and a small contribution f_1 caused by a perturbation:

$$f(\mathbf{r}, \mathbf{v}, t) = f_0(\mathbf{r}, \mathbf{v}, t) + f_1(\mathbf{r}, \mathbf{v}, t) \tag{2-13-2}$$

Here $f_0(\mathbf{r}, \mathbf{v}, t)$ is not necessarily Maxwellian, but it is assumed to be known or deducible from physical considerations. If (2-13-2) is substituted into the Boltzmann equation, an equation for f_1 results. If this equation is linearized by neglecting second-order terms, the following equation is obtained:

$$\frac{Df_1}{Dt} + \mathbf{a}_1 \cdot \nabla_v f_0 = -\nu f_1 \tag{2-13-3}$$

Df_1/Dt is the total time derivative of f_1 in six-dimensional phase space and $\mathbf{a}_1$ is the acceleration due to the perturbation. The right-hand side is really an integral whose integrand is linear in the perturbed distribution function. This collision integral is approximated by the term on the right-hand side of (2-13-3). The reciprocal of the effective collision frequency ν plays the role of a relaxation time—if the perturbation is removed, f_1 decays as $e^{-\nu t}$. There are numerous ways to solve (2-13-3).

One, which is particularly satisfactory for light particles moving in a medium composed of heavy particles, consists of expanding the distribution function in spherical harmonics in velocity space. This technique is frequently used for electrons in gases (see Section 11-4) and for neutrons in bulk matter of high atomic weight.

2-14. LIMITATIONS OF THE BOLTZMANN THEORY

Implicit in the use of the Boltzmann equation is the assumption that the particles of the gas move freely except "during" binary collisions whose durations are short compared with the mean free time. The Boltzmann equation is really well suited only for the treatment of problems involving relatively low density gases composed of uncharged molecules which are essentially spherically symmetric. Progress in the development of a kinetic theory for dense gases and for polyatomic molecules is described by Hirschfelder, Curtiss, and Bird.[4]

Several alternative approaches to the Boltzmann theory are applied in the study of highly ionized gases. One approach makes use of the *Fokker-Planck equation*, which phrases the problem in terms of many simultaneous long-range interactions between charged particles in the gas rather than in terms of successive short-range interactions. The Fokker-Planck method has been discussed by a number of authors, some of whom are listed in Ref. 27. Another approach is afforded by the *Vlasov, or collisionless Boltzmann, equation*.[28] In this case the collision integrals are completely neglected in the Boltzmann equation, and the result is used with Maxwell's equations for the electromagnetic field to form a set of equations which approximately describes a highly ionized gas. Still another attack on the problem employs *magnetohydrodynamics*, or hydromagnetics, which utilizes the equations of hydrodynamics together with Maxwell's equations and treats the ionized gas as a fluid.

REFERENCES

1. E. H. Kennard, *Kinetic Theory of Gases*, McGraw-Hill, New York, 1938. J. H. Jeans, *An Introduction to the Kinetic Theory of Gases*, Cambridge University Press, Cambridge, 1940. R. D. Present, *Kinetic Theory of Gases*, McGraw-Hill, New York, 1958. L. B. Loeb, *Kinetic Theory of Gases*, Third Edition, Dover, New York, 1961. T. G. Cowling, *Molecules in Motion*, Harper, New York, 1960.
2. J. H. Jeans, *The Dynamical Theory of Gases*, Dover, New York, 1954. (This book was published first by the Cambridge University Press in 1925.)
3. S. Chapman and T. G. Cowling, *The Mathematical Theory of Non-uniform Gases*, Second Edition, Cambridge University Press, London, 1952.
4. J. O. Hirschfelder, C. F. Curtiss, and R. B. Bird, *Molecular Theory of Gases and Liquids*, Wiley, New York, 1954.

5. R. D. Present, *op. cit.*, pp. 78–79.
6. J. H. Jeans, *An Introduction to the Kinetic Theory of Gases*, Chapter V.
7. E. H. Kennard, *op. cit.*, pp. 154–157.
8. J. H. Jeans, *op. cit.*, pp. 138–141.
9. L. B. Loeb, *op. cit.*, Appendix I.
10. E. H. Kennard, *op. cit.*, p. 149.
11. *The Scientific Papers of James Clerk Maxwell*, Vol II (edited by W. D. Niven), Dover, New York, 1952, pp. 26–78.
12. J. H. Jeans, *op. cit.*, p. 233.
13. E. H. Kennard, *op. cit.*, Chapter V; J. O. Hirschfelder, C. F. Curtiss, and R. B. Bird, *loc. cit.*
14. R. D. Present, *op. cit.*, Chapter 7.
15. R. D. Present, *op. cit.*, pp. 49–51.
16. J. C. Maxwell, *loc. cit.*
17. J. Stefan, *Wien. Ber.*, **65**, 323 (1872).
18. P. Langevin, *Ann. Chim. Phys.* **5**, 245 (1905). This paper is one of the classics in the literature on kinetic theory. It contains a lengthy calculation of the mobility of ions interacting with molecules through the polarization potential, as well as the general computation of the diffusion coefficient. Langevin's calculation is an excellent example of the application of the rigorous momentum transfer method of Maxwell to the solution of a difficult problem. For this reason, and because of the utility of the results obtained, the bulk of this paper is presented in translation in Appendix II at the end of this book. A similar calculation of the diffusion coefficient appears in Chapter 8 of the kinetic theory text by Present, who also gives a general discussion of the momentum transfer method in Chapter 11.
19. J. O. Hirschfelder, C. F. Curtiss, and R. B. Bird, *op. cit.*, Chapter 8. S. Chapman and T. G. Cowling, *op. cit.*, Chapter 9. A. Dalgarno and A. Williams, *Proc. Phys. Soc.* (*London*) **A-72**, 274 (1958). E. A. Mason and H. W. Schamp, *Ann. Phys.* (*New York*), **4**, 233 (1958).
20. A. Dalgarno, "Diffusion and Mobilities," in *Atomic and Molecular Processes* (edited by D. R. Bates), Academic, New York, 1962.
21. L. Waldmann, "Transporterscheinungen in Gasen von mittlerem Druck," in *Handbuch der Physik*, Vol. XII, Springer-Verlag, Berlin, 1958, pp. 295–514.
22. H. Grad, "Principles of the Kinetic Theory of Gases," in *Handbuch der Physik*, Vol. XII, Springer-Verlag, Berlin, 1958, pp. 205–294.
23. E. H. Kennard, *op. cit.*, Chapter IX; R. C. Tolman, *The Principles of Statistical Mechanics*, Oxford University Press, Oxford, 1938, Chapter III. T. L. Hill, *Statistical Mechanics*, McGraw-Hill, New York, 1956, Chapter I; L. D. Landau and E. M. Lifshitz, *Statistical Physics*, Addison-Wesley, Reading, Mass., 1958, Chapter I. G. E. Uhlenbeck and G. W. Ford, *Lectures in Statistical Mechanics*, American Mathematical Society, Providence, R.I., 1963. C. L. Longmire, *Elementary Plasma Physics*, Interscience, New York, 1963. K. Huang, *Statistical Mechanics*, Wiley, New York, 1963.
24. J. R. Pierce, *Theory and Design of Electron Beams*, Second Edition, Van Nostrand, Princeton, N. J., 1954, pp. 48–51. See also A. Arakengy, *Am. J. Phys.* **25**, 519 (1957).
25. This section is based largely on the masterly article by W. P. Allis, "Motions of Ions and Electrons," in *Handbuch der Physik*, Vol. XXI, Springer-Verlag, Berlin, 1956, pp. 383–444.
26. S. Chapman and T. G. Cowling, *loc. cit.* J. O. Hirschfelder, C. F. Curtiss, and R. B. Bird, *op. cit.*, Part 2.

27. L. Spitzer, *Physics of Fully Ionized Gases*, Second Edition, Interscience, New York, 1962, Chapter 5. W. P. Allis, *op. cit.*, pp. 429–444. S. Chandrasekhar, *Plasma Physics*, University of Chicago Press, Chicago, 1960, Chapter VII. J. G. Linhart, *Plasma Physics*, Second Edition, Interscience, New York, 1961, Chapter 6. J. L. Delcroix, *Introduction to the Theory of Ionized Gases*, Interscience, New York, 1960, pp. 116–118. A. N. Kaufman, "Plasma Transport Theory," in *La Théorie des gaz neutres et ionisés* (edited by C. de Witt and J. F. Detoeuf), Wiley, New York, 1960, pp. 293–353. J. Enoch, *Phys. Fluids* **3**, 353 (1960); A. Simon, **4**, 691 (1961). C. L. Longmire, *loc. cit.*

28. A. A. Vlasov, *Zh. Eksperim. i Teor. Fiz.* **8**, 291 (1938)—See also U.S.A.E.C. translation 2729. N. Rostoker and M. N. Rosenbluth, *Phys. Fluids*, **3**, 1 (1960). I. B. Bernstein, *Phys. Rev.* **109**, 10 (1958). *Plasma Physics* (edited by J. E. Drummond), McGraw-Hill, New York, 1961. W. B. Thompson, *An Introduction to Plasma Physics*, Addison-Wesley, Reading, Mass., 1962.

3

THE THEORY OF ELASTIC

SCATTERING IN A

CENTRAL FORCE FIELD

In this chapter we discuss the theory of mutual elastic scattering of particles interacting through a central force,* that is, a force that acts along the line of centers of the particles and whose magnitude depends only on the distance of separation. Only binary nonrelativistic collisions are treated. The classical theory is presented first and is followed by the quantum mechanical treatment. Experimental studies of elastic scattering are described in Chapter 4, which also contains results of theoretical calculations on a number of specific systems.

PART $\mathscr{A}$. THE TWO-BODY CENTRAL FORCE PROBLEM IN CLASSICAL MECHANICS

3-1. SEPARATION OF THE CENTER-OF-MASS MOTION FROM THE TOTAL MOTION

Consider two particles of masses m and M which interact with one another through a potential $V(r)$, which is a function only of the length of the vector **r** separating them. Let $\mathbf{R}_m$ and $\mathbf{R}_M$ denote the position vectors

* A reference on scattering in noncentral force fields, such as those described in Section 1-7, is J. O. Hirschfelder, C. F. Curtiss, and R. B. Bird, *Molecular Theory of Gases and Liquids*, Wiley, New York, 1954.

of the two particles in the Lab system of coordinates, so that $\mathbf{r} = \mathbf{R}_m - \mathbf{R}_M$. If no external forces are applied, Newton's second and third laws of motion for this system may be expressed as

$$\mathbf{f}_m = m\,\frac{d^2\mathbf{R}_m}{dt^2} \tag{3-1-1}$$

$$\mathbf{f}_M = M\,\frac{d^2\mathbf{R}_M}{dt^2} = -\mathbf{f}_m \tag{3-1-2}$$

The forces $\mathbf{f}_m$ and $\mathbf{f}_M$, derivable from the potential $V(r)$, act on m and M, respectively. Now introduce the vector $\mathbf{R}$, which locates the center of mass of the two particles with respect to the origin of the Lab coordinates:

$$\mathbf{R} = \frac{m\mathbf{R}_m + M\mathbf{R}_M}{m + M} \tag{3-1-3}$$

(cf. Section 1-2). If we differentiate (3-1-3) twice with respect to the time, we obtain

$$\ddot{\mathbf{R}} = \frac{m\ddot{\mathbf{R}}_m + M\ddot{\mathbf{R}}_M}{m + M} = \frac{\mathbf{f}_m + \mathbf{f}_M}{m + M} = 0 \tag{3-1-4}$$

Thus we see that the center of mass travels with a uniform rectilinear velocity.

Now we multiply (3-1-1) by M and (3-1-2) by m and subtract the second from the first. The result is

$$\mathbf{f}_m = M_r\,\frac{d^2}{dt^2}\,(\mathbf{R}_m - \mathbf{R}_M) \tag{3-1-5}$$

where M_r is the reduced mass of the pair of particles, defined by the equation

$$M_r = \frac{mM}{m + M} \tag{1-2-6}$$

Since $\mathbf{f}_m$ is in the direction of the vector $\mathbf{r} = \mathbf{R}_m - \mathbf{R}_M$, (3-1-5) for the relative motion has the same form as the equation of motion of a single particle of mass M_r in a central force field.

3-2. REDUCTION TO A TWO-BODY PROBLEM IN TWO DIMENSIONS

Let us now take the cross product of the vector $(\mathbf{R}_m - \mathbf{R}_M)$ with both sides of (3-1-5). The left side will vanish because of the central force assumption. Therefore

$$(\mathbf{R}_m - \mathbf{R}_M) \times \frac{d^2}{dt^2}\,(\mathbf{R}_m - \mathbf{R}_M) = 0$$

or

$$\frac{d}{dt}\left[(\mathbf{R}_m - \mathbf{R}_M) \times \frac{d}{dt}(\mathbf{R}_m - \mathbf{R}_M)\right] - \left[\frac{d}{dt}(\mathbf{R}_m - \mathbf{R}_M) \times \frac{d}{dt}(\mathbf{R}_m - \mathbf{R}_M)\right] = 0$$

The second term on the left side of this equation obviously equals zero. If we integrate the first term with respect to the time, we obtain

$$(\mathbf{R}_m - \mathbf{R}_M) \times \frac{d}{dt}(\mathbf{R}_m - \mathbf{R}_M) = (\mathbf{R}_m - \mathbf{R}_M) \times (\mathbf{v}_m - \mathbf{v}_M) = \mathbf{r} \times \mathbf{v}_r = \mathbf{K}$$

$$(3\text{-}2\text{-}1)$$

where $\mathbf{v}_m$ and $\mathbf{v}_M$ are the velocities of m and M, respectively, in the Lab system, $\mathbf{v}_r$ is their relative velocity,* and $\mathbf{r}$ is the directed distance from M

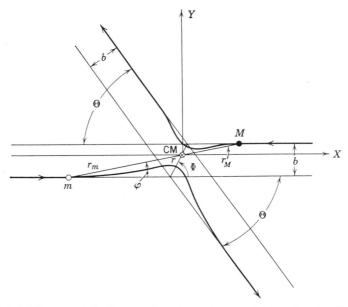

FIG. 3-2-1. The mutual elastic scattering of particles m and M as viewed in the center-of-mass system, in which the motion is two-dimensional. The motion pictured here occurs in the plane of the paper, which is perpendicular to the vectors $\mathbf{K}$ and $\mathbf{J}$. An interaction potential consisting of an attractive component and a shorter range repulsion is assumed.

to m; $\mathbf{K}$ is a vector whose magnitude and direction are constant in time. Evidently $\mathbf{K}$ is perpendicular to the plane defined by $\mathbf{r}$ and $\mathbf{v}_r$. The two particles and their center of mass thus remain in a plane perpendicular to

* The relative velocity of the collision partners at any arbitrary time is denoted by $\mathbf{v}_r$; $\mathbf{v}_0$ has been used to represent their relative velocity of approach at large r before their interaction becomes appreciable.

the vector **K** throughout the collision. Since the collision takes place in a fixed plane containing the center of mass and the motion of the center of mass is known to be uniform, only a two-dimensional problem remains to be considered.

Figure 3-2-1 shows the collision in the plane perpendicular to **K**. The impact parameter is b, and φ is the angle specifying the instantaneous orientation of the vector **r**. The particles are separated by a distance r, and r_m and r_M, the distances of m and M, respectively, from the center of mass, are in the ratio M/m. The value Φ is assumed by φ at the distance of closest approach, and Θ is the angle of scattering in the CM system. The CM trajectories of both m and M are symmetrical about the line of closest approach (the "line of apses") at the angle Φ. Proof of this statement is deferred until Section 3-5.

Let us now calculate the total kinetic energy of the particles T_{CM} in the center-of-mass system. Establish a rectangular Cartesian coordinate system X, Y, Z whose origin moves with the center of mass and whose Z axis points in the direction of the vector **K**. The X axis corresponds to $\varphi = 0$. It is evident that

$$T_{\mathrm{CM}} = \tfrac{1}{2}m(\dot{x}_m{}^2 + \dot{y}_m{}^2) + \tfrac{1}{2}M(\dot{x}_M{}^2 + \dot{y}_M{}^2) \tag{3-2-2}$$

The rectangular and polar coordinates are related by the equations

$$x_m = -\frac{M}{m+M}\, r \cos \varphi \tag{3-2-3}$$

$$y_m = -\frac{M}{m+M}\, r \sin \varphi \tag{3-2-4}$$

$$x_M = \frac{m}{m+M}\, r \cos \varphi \tag{3-2-5}$$

$$y_M = \frac{m}{m+M}\, r \sin \varphi \tag{3-2-6}$$

By substituting these relationships into (3-2-2), we may express the kinetic energy in the CM system as

$$T_{\mathrm{CM}} = \tfrac{1}{2}M_r(\dot{r}^2 + r^2\dot{\varphi}^2) \tag{3-2-7}$$

The angular momentum of the pair of particles about the center of mass is

$$\mathbf{J}_{\mathrm{CM}} = (\mathbf{r}_m \times \mathbf{p}_m) + (\mathbf{r}_M \times \mathbf{p}_M) \tag{3-2-8}$$

where $\mathbf{p}_m$ and $\mathbf{p}_M$ are the linear momenta of m and M, respectively, in the CM system. The component of $\mathbf{p}_m$ which is perpendicular to $\mathbf{r}_m$ is $mr_m\dot{\varphi}$, and a similar expression applies for M. Consequently,

$$J_{\mathrm{CM}} = r_m m r_m \dot{\varphi} + r_M M r_M \dot{\varphi} = M_r r^2 \dot{\varphi} \tag{3-2-9}$$

Now the quantity $\mathbf{r} \times \mathbf{v}_r$ was shown in (3-2-1) to be a constant. The magnitude of this quantity equals $r(r\dot\varphi) = r^2\dot\varphi$, and the angular momentum is seen to be a constant of the motion, as is the total energy.

Let v_0 be the initial relative velocity of the particles, that is, the relative velocity outside the region in which the interaction becomes appreciable.

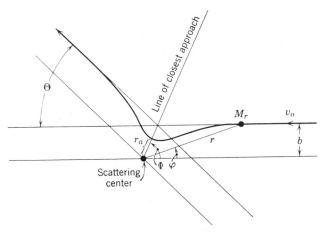

FIG. 3-2-2. The one-body problem which is dynamically equivalent to the two-body problem illustrated in Fig. 3-2-1. The center-of-mass motion of two particles m and M interacting through a potential $V(r)$ can be obtained as follows: a single hypothetical particle of mass $M_r = mM/(m + M)$ is considered to be scattered by a center of force fixed in the CM frame. The potential describing this force field is $V(r)$, where r is the separation distance between m and M. The CM velocity of M_r is considered to be equal to v_0, where v_0 is the initial relative velocity of m and M. The hypothetical particle M_r is moving toward the stationary scattering center with impact parameter b. The instantaneous distance of M_r from the scattering center is r, and M_r is scattered through an angle Θ, whose value can be calculated by (3-4-5). This angle is also the scattering angle of both m and M in the CM frame.

At some time before the collision occurs the angle $\varphi \to b/r$ and $\dot\varphi \to -b\dot r/r^2$. Then (3-2-7) and (3-2-9) show that the initial kinetic energy is $M_r v_0^2/2$ and the angular momentum is $M_r b v_0$ (cf. Section 1-2). Utilizing the constancy of the total energy and angular momentum of the system, we may then write, for any point along the trajectory,

$$\tfrac{1}{2}M_r v_0^2 = \tfrac{1}{2}M_r(\dot r^2 + r^2\dot\varphi^2) + V(r) \qquad (3\text{-}2\text{-}10)$$

$$J = M_r b v_0 = M_r r^2 \dot\varphi \qquad (3\text{-}2\text{-}11)$$

Equations 3-2-10 and 3-2-11, which are the equations of motion in the CM system, furnish a complete description of the motion in terms of the interaction potential, the initial relative velocity, and the impact parameter.

If we are given the potential, a particular trajectory may be specified by assigning values to the parameters v_0 and b or, alternatively, to the constants of motion (i.e., the total energy and the angular momentum).

Figure 3-2-2 describes the one-body problem which is dynamically equivalent to the two-body problem under discussion (cf. Equation 3-1-5). We have already shown that the equivalent single-body motion is planar and can be drawn in two dimensions. The quantities b, r, φ, Φ, and Θ are given so that their significance in the one- and two-body problems may be compared.

3-3. REDUCTION TO THE EQUIVALENT ONE-BODY PROBLEM IN ONE DIMENSION

A further conceptual reduction of the problem is possible. If we substitute the value of $\dot{\varphi}$ from (3-2-11) into (3-2-10), we may write the following expression for r as a function of time:

$$\tfrac{1}{2}M_r v_0{}^2 = \tfrac{1}{2}M_r \dot{r}^2 + V_{\text{eff}}(r) \tag{3-3-1}$$

where $V_{\text{eff}}(r)$ is the "effective potential" defined by

$$V_{\text{eff}}(r) = V(r) + \frac{M_r v_0{}^2 b^2}{2r^2} \tag{3-3-2}$$

Equation 3-3-1 contains no terms in φ. It can be regarded as describing the one-dimensional motion (along the r axis) of a particle of mass M_r with total energy $M_r v_0{}^2/2$ in an effective potential field described by $V_{\text{eff}}(r)$. The second term on the right in the expression for $V_{\text{eff}}(r)$ is equal to $J^2/2M_r r^2$ and represents the rotational kinetic energy of the system. Note that this term is a positive monotonic decreasing function of r. It can therefore be considered the source of a fictitious outwardly directed force, the "centrifugal force," and for this reason the second term on the right side of (3-3-2) is termed the "centrifugal potential." We use the symbol V_c to denote this quantity.

3-4. THE SCATTERING ANGLE IN THE CENTER-OF-MASS SYSTEM

Perhaps the most important feature of an elastic collision, from our point of view, is the angle of scattering in the center-of-mass system (see Fig. 3-2-1.) Since the CM trajectories are symmetrical about the line of closest approach, the scattering angle Θ is related to the angle Φ by the equation

$$\Theta = \pi - 2\Phi \tag{3-4-1}$$

The value, Φ, of the orientation angle φ, corresponding to the distance of closest approach, is easily calculated: dr/dt is given by (3-3-1) and $d\varphi/dt$ by (3-2-11). Hence

$$\frac{dr}{d\varphi} = \frac{dr}{dt} \bigg/ \frac{d\varphi}{dt} = \pm \frac{r^2}{b}\left[1 - \frac{V(r)}{M_r v_0^2/2} - \frac{b^2}{r^2}\right]^{1/2} \tag{3-4-2}$$

The negative sign applies for the incoming branch of the trajectory and the positive sign for the outgoing branch. At the angle of closest approach Φ we have

$$1 - \frac{V(r_a)}{M_r v_0^2/2} - \frac{b^2}{r_a^2} = 0 \tag{3-4-3}$$

The largest real root of this equation is the distance of closest approach r_a.

We should note that a real solution of (3-4-3) does not always exist. If we assume an attractive potential of the form $V(r) \sim -r^{-n}$ and further assume $n \geq 2$, there are values of the initial velocity and impact parameter for which no solution exists (see Section 3-6). The particle spirals inward until it is stopped by some repulsive force and then spirals back out. A solution always exists for a repulsive potential, however.

If a solution exists

$$\Phi = -\int_\infty^{r_a} \frac{d\varphi}{dr}\, dr = -\int_\infty^{r_a} \frac{(b/r^2)\, dr}{\left[1 - \dfrac{V(r)}{M_r v_0^2/2} - \dfrac{b^2}{r^2}\right]^{1/2}} \tag{3-4-4}$$

Equation 3-4-1 then shows Θ to be

$$\Theta(v_0, b) = \pi - 2b \int_{r_a}^{\infty} \frac{dr/r^2}{\left[1 - \dfrac{V(r)}{M_r v_0^2/2} - \dfrac{b^2}{r^2}\right]^{1/2}} \tag{3-4-5}$$

Equation 3-4-5 is of particular importance to us, since the angle of scattering is the only aspect of an elastic collision that enters into the formulas for the transport coefficients.[1] The foregoing integral has been evaluated for several potentials used to describe neutral nonpolar gases, and the results applied to the calculation of transport properties, by Hirschfelder, Curtiss and Bird.[2]

The solution of 3-4-5 for integrable power-law potentials is treated by Whittaker[3] and Goldstein,[4] among others. If the potential is assumed to be of the form $V(r) \sim \pm r^{-n}$, a solution in terms of circular functions is obtainable for $n = +2, +1$, and -2. The integral exponents $n = -6$, $-4, -1, +3, +4$, and $+6$ lead to solutions in terms of elliptic integrals. The fractional exponents $n = +\frac{1}{2}, +\frac{3}{2}, -\frac{2}{3}, +\frac{2}{3}$, and $+\frac{4}{3}$ also lead to elliptic functions.

3-5. THE SYMMETRY OF THE TRAJECTORIES IN THE CENTER-OF-MASS SYSTEM

Having obtained the differential equation of the orbit in the CM system, we may now show that the trajectory of each of the particles is symmetrical about the line of closest approach, for which $\varphi = \Phi$. To do this, let us square both sides of (3-4-2) and make the substitution $\varphi = \alpha + \Phi$. The introduction of the angle α is equivalent to counter-clockwise rotation of our polar coordinate system about the Z axis through the angle Φ, so that the line of closest approach now corresponds to $\alpha = 0$. The resulting equation is

$$\left(\frac{dr}{d\alpha}\right)^2 = \frac{r^4}{b^2}\left[1 - \frac{V(r)}{M_r v_0^2/2} - \frac{b^2}{r^2}\right] \tag{3-5-1}$$

The trajectory of each particle will be symmetrical about the line of closest approach if reflection about this line produces no change. Mathematically, this reflection is accomplished by substitution of $-\alpha$ for α. Equation 3-5-1 is obviously invariant under this substitution.

3-6. CLASSIFICATION OF THE ORBITS; ION-MOLECULE REACTIONS

A. PHYSICAL BASIS.   In Section 3-4 it was stated that a solution of (3-4-3) always exists for a repulsive potential, but not always for an attractive potential of the form $V(r) \sim -r^{-n}$, if $n \geq 2$. This statement is easily understood in terms of the effective one-dimensional motion and the centrifugal potential.

First let us consider motion in a typical repulsive potential field such as that described by the potential function $V(r)$ in Fig. 3-6-1. It has already been pointed out that if we wish to analyze the scattering problem in the single dimension r we must add to the real potential, $V(r)$, a fictitious centrifugal potential, $V_c(r)$, given in terms of the angular momentum, J, of the system by the equation

$$V_c(r) = \frac{J^2}{2M_r r^2} \tag{3-6-1}$$

This potential is plotted in Fig. 3-6-1 for some arbitrary but nonzero value of J. The total effective potential, $V_{\text{eff}}(r) = V(r) + V_c(r)$, is also shown in the figure. It is apparent that in this case the only significant effect of the centrifugal potential will be to supplement the real potential. If $V(r)$ decreases monotonically with increasing r, the effective potential will likewise, regardless of the value of the angular momentum. Hence in this one-dimensional formulation of the scattering problem a particle of total energy E will approach the scattering center and be reflected at the distance of closest approach, r_a, given by the intersection of the horizontal line at height E and the curve $V_{\text{eff}}(r)$. The radial velocity $\dot{r}$ at any point is given by the equation

$$E = \tfrac{1}{2}M_r\dot{r}^2 + V_{\text{eff}}(r) \tag{3-6-2}$$

whereas the angular motion must, of course, be such that the angular momentum is conserved throughout the scattering.

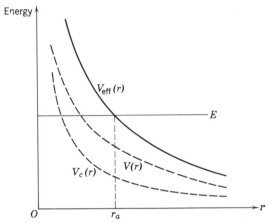

FIG. 3-6-1. The potential functions used for analysis of elastic scattering in a typical repulsive potential field.

The shape of the effective potential curve is quite different if an attractive potential is assumed. However, if $V(r) \sim -r^{-n}$ with $n < 2$, the effective potential again decreases monotonically with increasing r, at sufficiently small r, and the one-dimensional motion is similar to that in the repulsive case in regard to reflection along the r axis at some finite distance of closest approach. (This situation is illustrated in Fig. 3-6-2, in which an attractive inverse-first-power potential is assumed.) Stable orbits* are possible only for $n < 2$, and for values of E lying in the well.

If, on the other hand, the attractive potential falls off with increasing r faster than r^{-2}, the attractive potential must dominate the centrifugal potential at small r, and an effective potential of the form shown in Fig. 3-6-3 results.† (An inverse-third-power attractive potential is assumed in this illustration.) Let us consider the motion for several different values of

* A particle is said to be in a *stable orbit* if the application of a small perturbation produces a small bounded excursion from the original orbit.

† The limiting case in which $n = 2$ must be treated separately. Here the shape of $V_{\text{eff}}(r)$ is determined by the relative magnitudes of J and the coefficient of r^{-2} in the expression for $V(r)$.

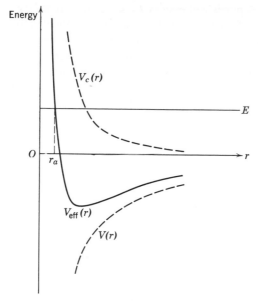

FIG. 3-6-2. The potential functions used for analysis of elastic scattering in an attractive inverse-first-power potential field.

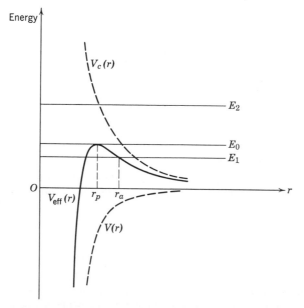

FIG. 3-6-3. The potential functions used for analysis of elastic scattering in an attractive inverse-third-power potential field.

the total energy. A particle of energy $E_1 < E_0$ starting at large r and moving toward the center of attraction will evidently be reflected at $r = r_a$ by the potential barrier shown. If, however, the total energy is $E_2 > E_0$, the particle will be able to pass over the potential barrier. It will experience a repulsion only for $r > r_p$ and will sense an attraction thereafter, as its radial distance from the scattering center decreases. When $E > E_0$, the particle actually passes through the center of attraction, which is assumed

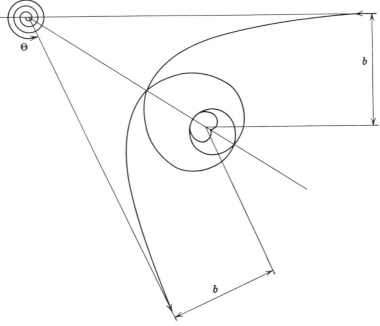

FIG. 3-6-4. An orbiting collision for which the scattering angle Θ has a large value.

to be a mathematical point in the model under consideration here.[5] A particularly interesting situation develops when the total energy just exceeds E_0, the value of $V_{\text{eff}}(r)$ at the peak of the potential curve. In this case the particle will spend a considerable time at a radial distance near the peak, where $\dot{r}$ is small by assumption, while spiraling inward toward the center. The particle is then said to "orbit" about the scattering center.* The angular motion speeds up as r decreases in order to conserve angular

* This type of collision is sometimes referred to as a "sticky collision." As a rule, however, the term *sticky collision* means an impact in which the colliding particles temporarily form a complex structure with an appreciable amount of internal excitation energy. This structure then flies apart after a lifetime which is long compared to usual collision times.

momentum, and a large number of revolutions may be made. (This is an unstable orbit, unlike those for which $n < 2$.) Under certain conditions the scattering angle may approach $-\infty$.[6] Figure 3-6-4 illustrates an orbiting collision for which Θ has a value between 6π and 7π. In this figure a long-range attractive potential and a short range, hard-core repulsive potential are assumed. A cusp appears in the trajectory when the particle is reflected from the hard core.

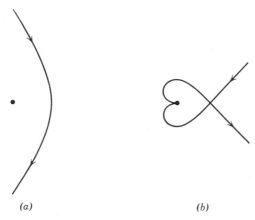

(a)   (b)

FIG. 3-6-5. Types of orbit of a particle moving in the attractive inverse-fourth-power polarization potential field:[12] (a) large angular momentum, nonspiraling orbit; (b) small angular momentum, spiraling orbit.

We see that the orbits may thus be meaningfully classified as *spiraling* or *nonspiraling*, and this distinction is frequently encountered in the literature. We shall illustrate the classification of orbits by discussing the important case of the attractive inverse-fourth-power polarization potential. The original treatment of this case by Langevin is reproduced in detail in Appendix II. The Lennard-Jones (6-12) potential has been treated similarly by Hirschfelder, Bird, and Spotz,[7] and the Buckingham (6-exp) potential, by Mason.[8]

B. CLASSIFICATION OF THE ORBITS IN THE POLARIZATION POTENTIAL FIELD. The inverse-fourth-power polarization potential has the form

$$V(r) = -\frac{\alpha e^2}{2r^4} \tag{3-6-3}$$

where e is the ionic charge and α is the electric polarizability of the molecule. Two types of orbit are possible in this potential field. The orbits corresponding to large angular momentum resemble hyperbolas (Fig. 3-6-5a), whereas for small angular momentum an inward spiraling motion takes place until some repulsive force reverses the trend (Fig. 3-6-5b).

The scattering angle for the polarization potential may be expressed as

$$\Theta = \pi - 2\Phi = \pi - 2\int_0^{\rho_0} \frac{d\rho}{\sqrt{1 - \rho^2 + e^2\alpha\rho^4/M_r v_0^2 b^4}} \tag{3-6-4}$$

in which $\rho = b/r$ and ρ_0 is the lower of the two positive roots of the polynomial in the denominator if such roots exist. If this polynomial has no real root, the integration goes from 0 to ∞. The existence of a real root is related to the nature of the orbit. If b is large enough for given v_0, a root exists, and an orbit of the type shown in Fig. 3-6-5a will result. For b less than a certain critical value b_0 no root exists, and the orbit is of the type presented in Fig. 3-6-5b. For b_0, the limiting value of b, the particles spiral into a circular orbit; b_0 is found by setting the discriminant of the square root in (3-6-4) equal to zero:

$$b_0 = \left(\frac{4e^2\alpha}{M_r v_0^2}\right)^{1/4} \tag{3-6-5}$$

Orbits for which $b < b_0$ pass through the origin if no repulsive core is present, whereas those orbits for which $b \geq b_0$ come no closer than $r_0 = b_0/\sqrt{2}$.* Several orbits of each type are accurately plotted in Fig. 3-6-6, which is a modified version of a drawing prepared by Langevin.[9] In this figure only the incoming branch of each spiraling trajectory is shown, the subsequent portion being omitted for clarity. The complete drawing appears in Fig. 4 of Appendix II.

Now let us suppose that there exists a certain critical radius r_c such that a given type of reaction between the two particles under consideration is impossible if the distance of closest approach is greater than r_c and almost certain to occur if it is less than r_c. Then, if r_c lies between 0 and $b_0/\sqrt{2}$, all collisions for which $b < b_0$ must lead to this reaction. We may therefore assume that the cross section for the reaction is the same as the *cross section for orbiting collisions*, namely

$$q_0(v_0) = \pi b_0^2 = \frac{2\pi}{v_0}\left(\frac{e^2\alpha}{M_r}\right)^{1/2} \tag{3-6-6}$$

This type of analysis has been used by Gioumousis and Stevenson,[9] and others, in calculating the rates of ion-molecule reactions.† Since b_0 for the polarization potential varies inversely as the square root of v_0, there must be some collisions at the higher velocities for which it is not true that $r_c < b_0/\sqrt{2}$. Thus this model is not realistic when applied to the calculation of the reaction cross section at high energies—it predicts that this

_____

* For a short proof of this statement see K. Yang and T. Ree, *J. Chem. Phys.* **35**, 588 (1961).

† For further discussion of such reactions see Sections 6-3, 9-6, and 9-9.

cross section should fall to zero, whereas it should actually drop to πr_c^2.

We may easily derive an alternative expression for the reaction cross section which is valid at high energies and holds for attractive or repulsive potentials of arbitrary form. Our starting point is the orbit equation (3-4-2). At the distance of closest approach r_a we have $dr/d\varphi = 0$. Thus

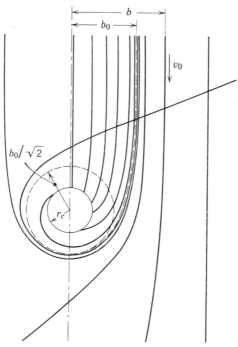

FIG. 3-6-6. Representative trajectories for the inverse-fourth-power polarization potential as a function of the impact parameter b for a given relative velocity v_0. For clarity only the incoming branch of each spiraling trajectory is shown.

(3-4-3), which is obtained from (3-4-2) by setting $dr/d\varphi = 0$, gives a relationship between the impact parameter and the distance of closest approach if we assume that the potential function and initial velocity are specified. Now let us suppose that an ion-molecule reaction is inevitable if r decreases to a value as small as r_c. The critical impact parameter b_0, which corresponds to the trajectory for which $dr/d\varphi = 0$ at $r = r_c$, is obtained by replacing r_a by r_c and b by b_0 in (3-4-3). Thus

$$1 - \frac{V(r_c)}{M_r v_0^2/2} - \frac{b_0^2}{r_c^2} = 0 \qquad (3\text{-}6\text{-}7)$$

The reaction cross section is then equal to $\pi b_0{}^2$, as is apparent from Fig. 3-6-7, and we obtain

$$q_r(v_0) = \pi r_c{}^2 \left[1 - \frac{V(r_c)}{M_r v_0{}^2/2} \right] \qquad (3\text{-}6\text{-}8)$$

We now have the cross section for the reaction in terms of only one parameter, $V(r_c)$, if $V(r)$ is known. Equation 3-6-8 applies at all energies

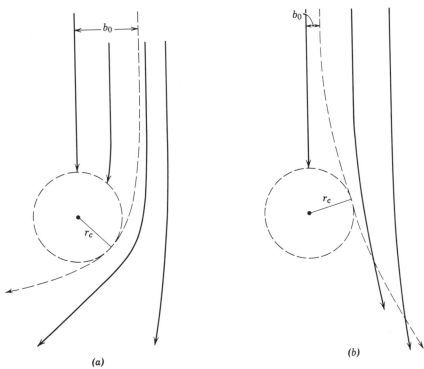

(a)   (b)

FIG. 3-6-7. (a) Attractive potential; (b) repulsive potential. Trajectories for typical attractive and repulsive potentials corresponding to a given relative velocity of approach and various impact parameters. The interparticle separation distance decreases to a value less than the critical value r_c for any trajectory whose impact parameter is less than b_0. Each of these trajectories is assumed to lead to an ion-molecule reaction so that the reaction cross section is equal to $\pi b_0{}^2$.

for attractive potentials which cannot produce orbiting and predicts a monotonic decrease from a high value at low energy toward a limiting value of $\pi r_c{}^2$ at high energies. For an attractive potential which can lead to orbiting, (3-6-8) is valid only at high energies. Equation 3-6-6 should be used for the polarization potential at low energies. Equation 3-6-8 applies in repulsive potentials only to energies above a certain threshold value, which is equal to the potential energy evaluated at the radius r_c. For repulsive potentials there is a hyperbolic increase in the reaction cross section from zero at the threshold toward a limiting value of πr_c^2 at high energies. This model was developed by Present[10] and has been applied by him and by Mason and Vanderslice[11] to the solution of specific problems.

The cross section expressed by (3-6-6) is a good approximation to the diffusion cross section for the polarization potential, the accurate value of which is given in (9-3-13). The reason[12] for this is that the final directions of the spiraling orbits are very nearly random (see Fig. 4, Appendix II), whereas the deflections associated with the nonspiraling orbits are so small that they make a negligible contribution to an integral of the type

$$q_D = \int (1 - \cos \Theta) \, I_s(\Theta) \, d\Omega_{CM} \qquad (1\text{-}6\text{-}1)$$

Vogt and Wannier[13] have also shown that the quantum mechanical description of the polarization potential is in many respects similar to the classical description.

3-7. EVALUATION OF THE SCATTERING CROSS SECTION

Let us now calculate the differential cross section $I_s(\Theta) \, d\Omega_{CM}$ for scattering into the element $d\Theta$ between the angles Θ and $\Theta + d\Theta$. The necessary and sufficient condition for scattering particles of initial relative velocity v_0 into the element of solid angle $d\Omega_{CM} = 2\pi \sin \Theta \, d\Theta$ is that the particles be incident in the annular impact ring of area $2\pi b \, db$ formed by circles of radius b and $b + db$, where b is related to Θ by (3-4-5). Hence

$$|2\pi b \, db| = |I_s(\Theta) \, 2\pi \sin \Theta \, d\Theta| \qquad (3\text{-}7\text{-}1)$$

or

$$I_s(\Theta) \, d\Omega_{CM} = \left| \frac{b}{\sin \Theta} \frac{db}{d\Theta} \right| d\Omega_{CM} \qquad (3\text{-}7\text{-}2)$$

The differential cross section in the laboratory system, $I_s(\vartheta) \, d\Omega_{Lab}$, is given in terms of $I_s(\Theta) \, d\Omega_{CM}$ by (1-4-16), and the total scattering cross section is obtained by integrating the differential cross section over the complete solid angle:

$$q_s = \int_0^{2\pi} \int_0^{\pi} I_s(\Theta) \, d\Omega_{CM} = \int_0^{2\pi} \int_0^{\pi} I_s(\vartheta) \, d\Omega_{Lab} \qquad (3\text{-}7\text{-}3)$$

These integrals diverge for potentials of infinite range, such as $V(r) \sim \pm r^{-n}$, because of a pole in the differential cross section in the forward direction, $\Theta = 0$. For potentials of this type, some deflection of the interacting particles occurs, no matter how large the impact parameter may be. Thus the effective cross sectional area of the particles appears to be infinite. This paradox is resolved in Section 3-11 by quantum mechanical considerations.

It can be seen from (3-7-2) that $I_s(\Theta)$ will become infinite if $\Theta = n\pi$ ($n = 0, 1, 2, \ldots$) for $b \neq 0$ because of the $\sin \Theta$ term in the denominator; it will also become infinite if $d\Theta/db = 0$. Both are possible for potentials that are attractive at large distances and repulsive at small distances.* Both classical scattering phenomena have optical analogues which become apparent in the quantum theory of scattering when the wave nature of the particles is explicitly introduced. The first effect is called a "glory" and the second, a "rainbow." For molecules and ions the forward and backward glories are lost in the unscattered beam, but the rainbow is observable under certain conditions (see Section 4-7-B).

3-8. COULOMB SCATTERING†

We now illustrate the use of the techniques developed above by deriving the differential cross section for *Coulomb scattering*. The potential that applies here is

$$V(r) = \frac{Zze^2}{r} \tag{3-8-1}$$

It expresses the electrostatic interaction between particles of charge Ze and ze, separated by a distance r. Either charge may be positive or negative.

Again we introduce the variable $\rho = b/r$ and define a quantity α by the equation

$$\frac{V}{M_r v_0^2/2} = \alpha\rho \tag{3-8-2}$$

so that

$$\alpha = \frac{2Zze^2}{M_r v_0^2 b} \tag{3-8-3}$$

Equation 3-4-5 then becomes

$$\Theta = \pi - 2\int_0^{\rho_0} \frac{d\rho}{\sqrt{1 - \alpha\rho - \rho^2}} \tag{3-8-4}$$

where ρ_0 is one of the roots of the equation

$$\rho^2 + \alpha\rho - 1 = 0 \tag{3-8-5}$$

* See W. L. Fite and S. Datz, "Chemical Research with Molecular Beams," *Ann. Rev. Phys. Chem.* **14** (1963), Annual Reviews, Inc., Palo Alto, Cal.

† As the reader is doubtless aware, scattering by a Coulomb field is usually referred to as *Rutherford scattering* in nuclear physics. A clear and comprehensive treatment of Rutherford scattering appears in R. D. Evans, *The Atomic Nucleus*, McGraw-Hill, New York, 1955, Appendix B.

The two roots of (3-8-5) are

$$\rho = -\frac{\alpha}{2} \pm \left(\frac{\alpha^2}{4} + 1\right)^{1/2} \tag{3-8-6}$$

and since $\rho = b/r$ it is evident that the solution containing the positive square root must be chosen.

Integrating (3-8-4), we obtain

$$\Theta = \pi - 2 \cos^{-1} \frac{\alpha}{\sqrt{\alpha^2 + 4}} \tag{3-8-7}$$

so that

$$\frac{\alpha}{\sqrt{\alpha^2 + 4}} = \cos\left(\frac{\pi}{2} - \frac{\Theta}{2}\right) = \sin\frac{\Theta}{2}$$

Thus

$$\alpha = 2 \tan\frac{\Theta}{2} = \frac{2Zze^2}{M_r v_0^2 b}$$

and

$$b = \frac{Zze^2}{M_r v_0^2 \tan(\Theta/2)} \tag{3-8-8}$$

The use of (3-7-2) then gives

$$I_s(\Theta) \, d\Omega_{CM} = \left|\frac{b}{\sin\Theta}\frac{db}{d\Theta}\right| d\Omega_{CM} = \frac{Z^2 z^2 e^4}{4M_r^2 v_0^4 \sin^4(\Theta/2)} d\Omega_{CM} \tag{3-8-9}$$

which is the desired result. It is interesting to note that precisely the same expression is obtained in the quantum mechanical treatment of Coulomb scattering (cf. Section 3-17). By dimensional analysis it can be shown[14] that if the interaction potential varies as $1/r^n$ the total scattering cross section varies as h^{2-2n}, where h is Planck's constant. Only for an inverse-first-power scattering potential does the cross section have no dependence on h, and therefore only in this case can the quantal description agree exactly with the classical description.

Because of the $\sin^4(\Theta/2)$ term in the denominator, the differential cross section expressed in (3-8-9) leads to infinite values for both the total scattering and momentum transfer cross sections. The physical basis for the divergence of the integrals expressing these quantities is the infinite range of the Coulomb potential. This difficulty is circumvented in calculations of the properties of plasmas by the use of a "shielded" Coulomb potential, a stratagem that is not only mathematically essential but also physically realistic. This matter is discussed further in Section 3-17, in Appendix I, and in all books on plasmas. The shielded Coulomb potential also accurately represents the interaction between atoms colliding at high impact energies (see Section 4-10). The differential, momentum transfer, and total collision cross sections for scattering of atomic projectiles by a Coulomb potential with exponential screening have been calculated by Everhart and his coworkers.[15]

3-9. VARIATION OF THE DIFFERENTIAL SCATTERING CROSS SECTION WITH VELOCITY

It was stated in Section 1-8 that if the interaction potential between two colliding particles varies as $V(r) \sim r^{-n}$ the variation of the center-of-mass differential scattering cross section with velocity is given classically by the expression

$$I_s(\Theta) \sim v_0^{-4/n} \tag{3-9-1}$$

where v_0 is the initial relative velocity of approach.* This statement is easily verified by dimensional considerations.

Our starting point is (3-4-2), which now assumes the form

$$\frac{dr}{d\varphi} = \pm \frac{r^2}{b}\left(1 - \frac{k}{v_0^2 r^n} - \frac{b^2}{r^2}\right)^{1/2}. \tag{3-9-2}$$

All of the constants appearing in the middle term under the radical have been lumped into the single constant k. If b, v_0, and k are specified, the trajectories of the particles are determined. Let us now scale the velocity v_0 by a factor c and then scale the distances b and r appropriately to recover an orbit equation that is formally identical to the original equation (3-9-2). Evidently, if v_0 is scaled to give a new velocity $v_0^* = cv_0$, b and r must be replaced by b^* and r^*, defined by the equations $b^* = c^{-2/n}b$ and $r^* = c^{-2/n}r$. The new orbit equation is then

$$\frac{dr^*}{d\varphi} = \pm \frac{r^{*2}}{b^*}\left(1 - \frac{k}{v_0^{*2} r^{*n}} - \frac{b^{*2}}{r^{*2}}\right)^{1/2} \tag{3-9-3}$$

and is seen to be formally identical to (3-9-2) so that the scattering angle Θ is the same as before. Since (3-7-2) shows that $I_s(\Theta)$ is proportional to b^2, it follows that

$$I_s(\Theta, cv_0) = c^{-4/n} I_s(\Theta, v_0) \tag{3-9-4}$$

Our proof is thus completed. Other proofs of the same result are given by Present and by Yang and Ree.[16]

As pointed out in Section 1-8, (3-9-1) yields the result that with elastic spheres, for which $n = \infty$, the scattering cross section is independent of the velocity. Hence the elastic sphere model is one of constant mean free path.

* The variation with scattering angle is also of interest. For a potential of the form $V(r) \sim r^{-n}$ classical theory predicts that $I_s(\Theta) \sim [\Theta^{(1+2/n)} \sin \Theta]^{-1}$ for small Θ. See E. H. Kennard, *Kinetic Theory of Gases*, McGraw-Hill, New York, 1938, pp. 119–120.

On the other hand, $n = 4$ for particles interacting through the point charge-induced dipole polarization potential, and here the differential scattering cross section varies inversely with the velocity. The collision frequency, which is proportional to $I_s(\Theta)v_0$, is then independent of v_0, and we have a constant mean free time situation. According to (3-9-1), the differential cross section is inversely proportional to v_0^4 for Coulomb scattering, in agreement with the result derived in Section 3-8.

As we shall see in Section 3-11, classical theory does not properly describe scattering at small angles in the CM system, and thus (3-9-1) cannot be used to obtain the velocity dependence of the total scattering cross section q_s.* Quantum mechanics must be used for this purpose. Massey and Mohr[17] have obtained an approximate quantal solution for an interaction potential of the form $V(r) = -Cr^{-n}$. Their result, which is derived in Section 4-7, is

$$q_s = B \left(\frac{C}{v_0}\right)^{2/(n-1)} \tag{3-9-5}$$

where B is a known constant.

PART $\mathscr{B}$. THE QUANTUM THEORY OF ELASTIC SCATTERING

We now turn to the quantal view of elastic scattering. As in Part $\mathscr{A}$ of this chapter we shall consider only nonrelativistic scattering in a spherically symmetric force field. After suitable preliminary discussion, we shall formulate the problem of elastic scattering in quantum mechanical terms and then develop methods for calculating the cross section for the case in which the collision partners are dissimilar. The mutual scattering of identical particles is then considered. The results of calculations on specific systems are discussed in Chapter 4. The material presented here is based largely on the treatments of the subject by Massey and Burhop, Mott and Massey, Schiff, Burhop, and Massey.[18] Other excellent sources of information are listed in Ref. 19.

3-10. THE INADEQUACY OF THE CLASSICAL TREATMENT OF SCATTERING

We may invoke the Heisenberg uncertainty principle to show how the classical theory fails, in general, to give an accurate description of collision processes. This principle applies to any pair of canonically conjugate

---

* It does, however, give the correct dependence of the diffusion cross section on v_0 because the small-angle contributions are suppressed by the weighting factor $(1 - \cos \Theta)$ in the integral expressing q_D.

variables* and states that the order of magnitude of the product of the uncertainties in the knowledge of the two variables must be at least as great as Planck's constant, h, divided by 2π, that is, $\hbar = h/2\pi = 1.054 \times 10^{-27}$ erg-sec. Accordingly, if the pair of variables is chosen to be the X component of position and the X component of linear momentum, the following relationship holds:

$$\Delta x \cdot \Delta p_x \geqslant \hbar \qquad (3\text{-}10\text{-}I)$$

Let us see what restrictions are thereby imposed on our knowledge of the dynamics of particles moving about in thermal equilibrium with a gas at room temperature. If we first take an argon atom and allow the uncertainty in its position along the X axis to be 10^{-8} cm, a distance approximately equal to an atomic diameter (see Table 2-2-1), we find that the X component of velocity cannot be determined with a precision greater than $\Delta v_x \approx 1.59 \times 10^3$ cm/sec. A similar calculation for a hydrogen molecule yields $\Delta v_x \geqslant 31.8 \times 10^3$ cm/sec, whereas an uncertainty of $\Delta x = 10^{-8}$ cm for an electron entails a minimum uncertainty in v_x of about 1.16×10^8 cm/sec. The mean thermal velocities of these particles at $15°C$ are 39.1×10^3, 174.0×10^3, and 1.05×10^7 cm/sec, respectively. It is apparent that the dynamics of a collision at thermal velocities are definitely hazy for an argon atom and much more so for a hydrogen molecule; for an electron the classical concept of a well-defined orbit is meaningless. At lower temperatures the classical treatment fails even more. We see that classical theory has some degree of validity in the analysis of collisions under "gas kinetic conditions" only for heavy particles or at high temperatures.

3-11. SCATTERING BY A CENTER OF FORCE OF INFINITE RANGE†

We have already remarked that an infinite value for q_s is predicted classically for scattering by any center of force of infinite range. The reason for the divergence of the cross section integral in this case is that some deflection, though perhaps small, is expected regardless of how large the impact parameter may be, and the sum of all of the contributions to the integral must therefore be infinite. In practice, the value for q_s deduced

---

* Two dynamical variables are said to be *canonically conjugate* to one another if they satisfy a conjugate pair of Hamilton's "canonical equations of motion" (2-11-1). A given rectangular Cartesian spatial coordinate and the corresponding component of linear momentum evidently constitute such a pair of variables. The total energy E and the time t are also canonically conjugate, since in the theory of relativity E is one component of the momentum four-vector and t plays the role of the corresponding spatial coordinate.

† This discussion is based on Section 1 of the chapter by Burhop which appears in the book edited by Bates, Ref. 18.

from a beam type of experiment (see Chapter 4) would then depend on the angular resolving power of the apparatus, that is, its ability to detect very small deflections of the particles from the beam. The concept of a total scattering cross section would therefore be meaningless. Consideration of the uncertainty principle shows, however, that a finite value for q_s is expected provided the potential describing the interaction between projectile and target falls off sufficiently rapidly at large r. If the apparatus has a certain minimum resolving power, this finite value for q_s can, in principle, be determined experimentally. Let us explore this matter more fully.

In a quantal analysis of scattering the projectile is represented by a wave packet which spreads as it travels through space.[20] The quantal and classical descriptions of the scattering event are basically in accord if the following two conditions are met: (1) the de Broglie wavelength of the projectile must be small compared with the distance of closest approach to the target, and (2) the deflection of the projectile must not be obscured by the spread of the wave packet.

Consider the wave packet representing a projectile traveling with velocity v_0 in the Z direction toward a fixed target located at the origin of coordinates. The packet is assumed to be moving so that it will pass at distance y from the target if undeflected. The uncertainty principle states that the width of the wave packet, Δy, and the uncertainty in the transverse component of the projectile velocity, Δv_y, are related by the equation

$$m\, \Delta y \cdot \Delta v_y \gtrsim \hbar \qquad (3\text{-}11\text{-}1)$$

where m is the mass of the projectile. The classical orbit concept will evidently be valid only if

$$y \gg \Delta y \qquad (3\text{-}11\text{-}2)$$

or, according to (3-11-1), only if

$$y \gg \frac{\hbar}{m\, \Delta v_y} \qquad (3\text{-}11\text{-}3)$$

[Note that this inequality is not an explicit statement of condition (1), since the projectile wavelength is h/mv_0, not $\hbar/m\,\Delta v_y$.] The angle of spreading of the wave packet is approximately $\Delta v_y/v_0$, so that condition (2) is satisfied only if

$$\vartheta \gg \frac{\Delta v_y}{v_0} \qquad (3\text{-}11\text{-}4)$$

where ϑ is the angle of deflection.

If we eliminate Δv_y, we see that the collision may be described classically when*

$$\vartheta y \gg \frac{\hbar}{mv_0} \qquad (3\text{-}11\text{-}5)$$

* For further discussion of the criterion for the validity of the classical description of scattering see Section 4-10.

The angle of deflection is given classically by $\vartheta \approx F_y \tau / mv_0$, where F_y is the Y component of the force on the projectile and τ is the "duration of the collision," which may be taken to be equal to y/v_0. If we put $F_y = |\partial V/\partial r| \, y/r$, we obtain $\vartheta y \approx |\partial V/\partial r| \, y^3/rmv_0^2$. Thus ϑy goes to zero as y goes to infinity (or ϑ goes to zero) if V falls off more rapidly than $1/r$ at large r. For such potentials the classical description is seen to fail at sufficiently small angles for any projectile wavelength h/mv_0. Deflections through angles smaller than some minimum angle $\vartheta_{min} \approx \hbar/mv_0 y$ are not observable, and since it is these deflections that make q_s infinite classically the quantum mechanical value for q_s may remain finite.* Improved resolution in the experimental apparatus does not lead to an indefinite increase in the measured value of the total cross section.

A problem of special interest is the elastic scattering of an electron in the static field of an atom. To first approximation, if the perturbation of the atom by the electron is ignored, the mutual potential energy at a distance r from the center of the atom is

$$V(r) = -\frac{Ze^2}{r} + 4\pi e \left[\frac{1}{r} \int_0^r \rho(r') r'^2 \, dr' + \int_r^\infty \rho(r') r' \, dr' \right] \quad (3\text{-}11\text{-}6)$$

where Ze is the nuclear charge and ρ is the charge density of atomic electrons. This energy is usually expressed as

$$V(r) = \frac{-Z_p e^2}{r} \quad (3\text{-}11\text{-}7)$$

where Z_p is the effective nuclear charge. In general, Z_p falls off exponentially with r, for large r, and a finite value for q_s results if the problem is treated quantum mechanically.

3-12. REQUIREMENTS ON ANGULAR RESOLVING POWER FOR MEASUREMENTS OF THE TOTAL ELASTIC SCATTERING CROSS SECTION

Massey and Burhop[21] stress the point that care must be taken to ensure sufficient resolution for meaningful cross section measurement. In order to obtain 1% accuracy in the measured cross section for electrons elastically scattered against molecules, the apparatus must be able to sense deflections of as little as 11° for 1-ev electrons, 6.5° for 10-ev electrons,

---

* Actually, the total cross section is finite only if $V(r)$ approaches zero more rapidly than $1/r^2$ at large r. The phase shifts (see Section 3-15) are finite if $V(r) \to 0$ faster than $1/r$, whereas the differential cross section at $\Theta = 0$ is bounded only if $V(r) \to 0$ faster than $1/r^3$. For proof of these statements see E. H. S. Burhop (D. R. Bates, Ref. 18 pp. 326–327).

2.3° for 100-ev electrons, 0.85° for 1000-ev electrons, and 0.2° for 10,000-ev electrons. These data apply to almost any type of target molecules.

The requirements are much more severe for atomic projectiles. Let ϑ_0 be the minimum angle of deflection to be counted as a collision if the error in the total cross section is not to exceed 10%. For He projectiles on He targets ϑ_0 is calculated as 3.6° for an energy of 0.0255 ev, 2.0° for 0.0862 ev, and 0.59° for 1 ev. For argon atoms on argon the corresponding minimum angles are 0.70, 0.30, and 0.11°, respectively. (Here the angles and energies are measured in the laboratory system.) The resolving power required for total cross section measurements increases roughly as the relative velocity of the collision partners, and for collisions of 100-ev protons with helium atoms deflections of less than 7 minutes of arc must be detectable in order that the measurement may be accurate within 10%.[21] Additional information on heavy particle angular scattering distributions and resolution requirements are presented in Section 4-5.

We are now in position to develop quantal expressions for the scattering cross section. The first step in this direction will be to show how the motion of the center of mass of the interacting particles may be separated from the total motion in the quantum mechanical treatment, as in the classical discussion.

3-13. SEPARATION OF THE CENTER-OF-MASS MOTION FROM THE TOTAL MOTION

The description of a pair of particles undergoing mutual scattering may be given quantum mechanically in terms of the *time-dependent* wave function $\Psi(\mathbf{R}_m, \mathbf{R}_M, t)$, where $\mathbf{R}_m = (X_m, Y_m, Z_m)$ and $\mathbf{R}_M = (X_M, Y_M, Z_M)$ are the laboratory position vectors of the particles (of mass m and M, respectively) and t is the time. The physical significance of this wave function is that $|\Psi(\mathbf{R}_m, \mathbf{R}_M, t)|^2 \, d\tau_m \, d\tau_M$ is the probability that at time t particle m will be inside the volume element $d\tau_m$ at $\mathbf{R}_m$ and M will be within the volume element $d\tau_M$ at $\mathbf{R}_M$. This wave function obeys the time-dependent Schrödinger wave equation

$$-i\hbar \frac{\partial \Psi}{\partial t} = \frac{\hbar^2}{2m} \nabla_m^2 \Psi + \frac{\hbar^2}{2M} \nabla_M^2 \Psi - V(\mathbf{R}_m, \mathbf{R}_M)\Psi \qquad (3\text{-}13\text{-}1)$$

where

$$\nabla_m^2 = \frac{\partial^2}{\partial X_m^2} + \frac{\partial^2}{\partial Y_m^2} + \frac{\partial^2}{\partial Z_m^2} \qquad (3\text{-}13\text{-}2)$$

$$\nabla_M^2 = \frac{\partial^2}{\partial X_M^2} + \frac{\partial^2}{\partial Y_M^2} + \frac{\partial^2}{\partial Z_M^2} \qquad (3\text{-}13\text{-}3)$$

and $V(\mathbf{R}_m, \mathbf{R}_M)$ is the mutual potential energy of the system when m is at $\mathbf{R}_m$ and M is at $\mathbf{R}_M$. Because of the central force assumption, $V = V(|\mathbf{R}_m - \mathbf{R}_M|)$.

Now let us put

$$(m + M)\mathbf{R} = m\mathbf{R}_m + M\mathbf{R}_M \qquad (3\text{-}13\text{-}4)$$

and

$$\mathbf{r} = \mathbf{R}_m - \mathbf{R}_M \qquad (3\text{-}13\text{-}5)$$

where $\mathbf{R} = (X, Y, Z)$ is the position vector of the center of mass of the two particles in the laboratory system and $\mathbf{r} = (x, y, z)$ is the vector joining the particles and pointing from M toward m. Then, since

$$\frac{\partial}{\partial X_m} = \frac{\partial}{\partial x} + \frac{m}{m + M}\frac{\partial}{\partial X}$$

and

$$\frac{\partial}{\partial X_M} = -\frac{\partial}{\partial x} + \frac{M}{m + M}\frac{\partial}{\partial X}$$

with similar relationships for the other coordinates and second derivatives, the operator

$$\frac{\hbar^2}{2m}\nabla_m^2 + \frac{\hbar^2}{2M}\nabla_M^2$$

transforms into the operator

$$\frac{\hbar^2}{2M_t}\nabla_R^2 + \frac{\hbar^2}{2M_r}\nabla_r^2$$

where $M_t = m + M$ is the total mass and M_r is the reduced mass. Upon this transformation, the wave equation (3-13-1) becomes

$$-i\hbar\frac{\partial\Psi}{\partial t} = \frac{\hbar^2}{2M_t}\nabla_R^2\Psi + \frac{\hbar^2}{2M_r}\nabla_r^2\Psi - V(r)\Psi \qquad (3\text{-}13\text{-}6)$$

where $\Psi = \Psi(\mathbf{r}, \mathbf{R}, t)$.

We may now separate variables and obtain a solution of the form

$$\Psi(\mathbf{r}, \mathbf{R}, t) = F(\mathbf{r}, t)\, G(\mathbf{R}, t) \qquad (3\text{-}13\text{-}7)$$

If we substitute (3-13-7) into (3-13-6), we obtain the equations

$$-i\hbar\frac{\partial F}{\partial t} = \frac{\hbar^2}{2M_r}\nabla^2 F - V(r)F + CF \qquad (3\text{-}13\text{-}8)$$

$$-i\hbar\frac{\partial G}{\partial t} = \frac{\hbar^2}{2M_t}\nabla^2 G - CG \qquad (3\text{-}13\text{-}9)$$

where C is a constant. Then, if we put

$$F(\mathbf{r}, t) = f(\mathbf{r}, t)e^{iCt/\hbar} \qquad (3\text{-}13\text{-}10)$$

and

$$G(\mathbf{R}, t) = g(\mathbf{R}, t)e^{-iCt/\hbar} \qquad (3\text{-}13\text{-}11)$$

the following equations result:

$$-i\hbar \frac{\partial f(\mathbf{r}, t)}{\partial t} = \frac{\hbar^2}{2M_r} \nabla^2 f(\mathbf{r}, t) - V(r)f(\mathbf{r}, t) \qquad (3\text{-}13\text{-}12)$$

$$-i\hbar \frac{\partial g(\mathbf{R}, t)}{\partial t} = \frac{\hbar^2}{2M_t} \nabla^2 g(\mathbf{R}, t) \qquad (3\text{-}13\text{-}13)$$

Thus we see that the wave function may be expressed as

$$\Psi(\mathbf{r}, \mathbf{R}, t) = f(\mathbf{r}, t)\, g(\mathbf{R}, t) \qquad (3\text{-}13\text{-}14)$$

where f and g satisfy (3-13-12) and (3-13-13).

Equation 3-13-12 is the wave equation that describes the behavior of the interacting particles in the center-of-mass system. As in the classical case, this motion may be regarded as that of a particle of mass M_r about a fixed scattering center. Equation 3-13-13 describes the motion of the center of mass of the particles in terms of the motion of a free particle of mass M_t in the laboratory system.

3-14. THE QUANTUM MECHANICAL FORMULATION
OF THE SCATTERING PROBLEM

From the foregoing discussion we see that we are free to formulate the scattering problem in terms of the behavior of hypothetical particles of mass M_r interacting with a fixed center of force. In the classical case we were able to determine the exact trajectory of each projectile in terms of its initial velocity v_0 and impact parameter b (or, alternatively, in terms of its total energy E and angular momentum J). According to the general principles of quantum mechanics, however, the projectile orbit is not precisely defined, and we are able to calculate only the average behavior of a large number of projectiles in their interaction with the target.

A. THE INCIDENT BEAM AND ITS WAVE FUNCTION. Let us imagine an infinitely wide beam of structureless projectiles approaching along the $-Z$ axis a structureless scattering center fixed at the origin of coordinates. A spherically symmetric force field is assumed, so that the potential energy of interaction V is a function only of the separation distance r. The incident beam is to be homogeneous and monoenergetic, and the particles in the beam are to be dissimilar to the target particle representing the scattering center. (Identical projectiles and targets require special handling in quantum mechanics and are treated separately in Section 3-18.) Furthermore, the beam intensity is to be uniform across any plane normal to the Z axis and is to be constant in time. To each projectile is ascribed a fictitious mass $M_r = mM/(m + M)$, where m and M are the true masses of the projectile and target, respectively. As is well known, the quantal representation of such a beam is a plane de Broglie wave of constant amplitude traveling in the $+Z$ direction. Let us suppose that the current density of the beam is A particles/cm²-sec, so that A particles pass through unit area normal to the beam direction per second. Some of these projectiles will experience scattering by the center of force, the number of scattered particles being directly proportional to the total elastic scattering cross section

$$q_s = \int_0^\pi \int_0^{2\pi} I_s(\Theta)\, d\Omega_{\mathrm{CM}} = 2\pi \int_0^\pi I_s(\Theta) \sin \Theta\, d\Theta \qquad (3\text{-}14\text{-}1)$$

We wish to determine the differential cross section $I_s(\Theta)\, d\Omega_{\mathrm{CM}}$, appearing in (3-14-1), as a function of angle and energy, and then obtain q_s as a function of energy by integration.

For quantitative expression of the intensity of scattering in any direction (Θ, φ) let us refer to Fig. 3-14-1. In this figure dS represents a small surface at a large distance r, in the direction (Θ, φ), from the origin. It is assumed to be normal to the radius vector. The solid angle subtended at the origin by dS is $d\Omega_{\mathrm{CM}}$. From our previous discussion of the significance of the differential cross section [cf. (1-4-1)] we see that $A\, I_s(\Theta)\, d\Omega_{\mathrm{CM}}$ equals the number of projectiles scattered through dS per second.

The plane wave representing the incident beam of particles is described by a wave function $Ce^{i(\kappa z - \omega t)}$, where C is the amplitude, κ is the wave number, and ω is the angular frequency of the wave; κ is given in terms of the de Broglie wavelength λ, the particle velocity v_0, or the initial kinetic energy T_0 by the equation

$$\kappa = \frac{2\pi}{\lambda} = \frac{M_r v_0}{\hbar} = \frac{\sqrt{2M_r T_0}}{\hbar} \qquad (3\text{-}14\text{-}2)$$

and ω is given in terms of the frequency ν, or the total energy E, by the equation

$$\omega = 2\pi\nu = \frac{E}{\hbar} \qquad (3\text{-}14\text{-}3)$$

The scattering problem we have formulated is a steady-state problem, and the energy of the incident de Broglie wave is unchanged in the process of elastic scattering. Consequently, the term $e^{-i\omega t}$ is common to all the wave functions we shall write down, so that we may drop this common time

factor and indicate only the spatial dependence of the wave functions.*
The *time-independent* wave function for the incoming plane wave is denoted
by $\psi_{inc}(r, \Theta) = Ce^{i\kappa z}$. Note that dependence of ψ_{inc} on φ is not implied,
since all aspects of the problem are independent of the azimuth angle.

We have taken the current density of the incoming beam to be A pro-
jectiles/cm²-sec. The current density may also be expressed in terms of C,

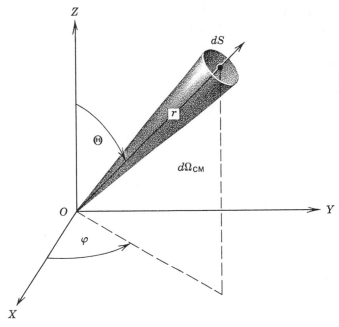

FIG. 3-14-1. The spherical polar coordinate system used in discussion of the elastic
scattering problem. The base of the cone is the surface dS referred to in the text.

the amplitude of the wave function, and thus we may obtain the relationship between A and C. We know that the average number of particles
expected to be present in unit volume at a given location in the incoming
beam is given by $\psi_{inc}^* \psi_{inc} = |\psi_{inc}|^2 = C^2$, where ψ_{inc}^* is the complex
conjugate of ψ_{inc}. Each of these particles is traveling toward the origin
along the $-Z$ axis with velocity v_0. If we now imagine a right circular
cylinder of length v_0 and unit cross-sectional area to be laid along the $-Z$
axis, it is evident that this cylinder will contain $C^2 v_0$ projectiles at any
instant and that within the next second just these projectiles, and no more,
will pass through the right-hand end of the cylinder. The current density is

* The formal separation of the space and time dependence may be accomplished by
the method used in Section 6-11-B.

then, by definition, equal to $C^2 v_0$, and A and C are thus related by the equation

$$C^2 = \frac{A}{v_0} \tag{3-14-4}$$

B. THE SCATTERED AND TOTAL WAVE FUNCTIONS. The total wave function will consist of a component associated with the incoming plane wave and another representing that portion of the incident wave which experiences scattering. The scattered wave must have the form of an outgoing spherical wave whose amplitude decreases, for large r, as $1/r$, in order that the radial current density may fall off as the inverse square of the distance from the center of force and that the number of scattered particles may thus be conserved. The wave function for the scattered wave will then have the asymptotic form

$$\psi_{\text{scatt}} \approx \frac{C}{r} f(\Theta) e^{i\kappa r} \tag{3-14-5}$$

where $f(\Theta)$ is usually called the *scattered amplitude.* We shall now establish the relation of $f(\Theta)$ to $I_s(\Theta)$, the differential elastic scattering cross section per unit solid angle. Equation 3-14-5 shows that the radial current density is equal to $v_0 |C|^2 |f(\Theta)|^2 / r^2$ for large r, and thus the number of projectiles scattered per second through the surface element dS at (Θ, φ) in Fig. 3-14-1 is

$$\frac{v_0 |C|^2}{r^2} |f(\Theta)|^2 \, dS = v_0 |C|^2 |f(\Theta)|^2 \, d\Omega_{\text{CM}} = A |f(\Theta)|^2 \, d\Omega_{\text{CM}}$$

The number of particles scattered into $d\Omega_{\text{CM}}$ per unit time is also known to equal $A I_s(\Theta) \, d\Omega_{\text{CM}}$. It then follows that

$$I_s(\Theta) = |f(\Theta)|^2 \tag{3-14-6}$$

hence it is not necessary to know $\psi(r, \Theta)$ completely to determine the differential or total cross section—we need know only the asymptotic form of the scattered wave function. (In the foregoing discussion only the scattered wave function was used to calculate the number of particles passing through dS per second. The incident beam is assumed to be collimated in such a way that its unscattered component is prevented from reaching dS, which also is assumed to be at a great distance from the scattering center. Such collimation is always provided in experimental apparatus.)

To obtain $f(\Theta)$, and thus the cross sections, we must solve the time-independent wave equation for the motion of particles of mass M_r and positive total energy ($E > 0$) in the potential field of the fixed scattering center.

The solution is required to have the asymptotic form

$$\psi = \psi_{\text{inc}} + \psi_{\text{scatt}} \approx e^{i\kappa z} + \frac{e^{i\kappa r}}{r} f(\Theta) \qquad (3\text{-}14\text{-}7)$$

where we have set the amplitude of the incoming wave equal to unity for convenience. The wave number κ was expressed in terms of the initial kinetic energy by (3-14-2). However, T_0 equals the total energy because the mutual potential energy of the particles is zero at very large r, and we may write

$$\kappa = \frac{\sqrt{2M_r E}}{\hbar} \qquad (3\text{-}14\text{-}8)$$

3-15. SOLUTION OF THE WAVE EQUATION
BY THE METHOD OF PARTIAL WAVES

The time-independent wave equation is

$$\nabla^2\psi + \frac{2M_r}{\hbar^2} [E - V(r)]\psi = 0 \qquad (3\text{-}15\text{-}1)$$

where, in spherical coordinates, the Laplacian operator is

$$\nabla^2 = \frac{1}{r^2}\frac{\partial}{\partial r}\left(r^2\frac{\partial}{\partial r}\right) + \frac{1}{r^2 \sin \Theta}\frac{\partial}{\partial \Theta}\left(\sin \Theta \frac{\partial}{\partial \Theta}\right) + \frac{1}{r^2 \sin^2 \Theta}\frac{\partial^2}{\partial \varphi^2} \qquad (3\text{-}15\text{-}2)$$

The last term in this expression vanishes in the present problem because of the lack of dependence of any of our functions on φ. Let us put

$$U(r) = \frac{2M_r V(r)}{\hbar^2} \qquad (3\text{-}15\text{-}3)$$

so that the wave equation may be written in the convenient form

$$\nabla^2\psi + [\kappa^2 - U(r)]\psi = 0 \qquad (3\text{-}15\text{-}4)$$

We seek a solution of (3-15-4), which is everywhere bounded, continuous, and single-valued and which has the asymptotic form indicated in (3-14-7).

A. SEPARATION OF THE WAVE EQUATION. Since by assumption V depends only on r, the wave equation may be separated into two equations, one of which contains only the variable r and the other only Θ. (In the more general case in which there is dependence on the azimuthal angle we would have a third equation in φ.) To perform this separation, let us write

$$\psi(r, \Theta) = L(r) Y(\Theta) \qquad (3\text{-}15\text{-}5)$$

and substitute this expression into (3-15-4). The result may be written in the form

$$\frac{1}{L}\frac{d}{dr}\left(r^2\frac{dL}{dr}\right) + r^2[\kappa^2 - U(r)] = -\frac{1}{Y}\left[\frac{1}{\sin\Theta}\frac{d}{d\Theta}\left(\sin\Theta\frac{dY}{d\Theta}\right)\right] \quad (3\text{-}15\text{-}6)$$

Note that the left side of (3-15-6) depends only on r and the right side, only on Θ. If both sides are to be equal for all values of r and Θ, both must be equal to some constant, which we shall denote as $l(l+1)$. Thus

$$\frac{1}{r^2}\frac{d}{dr}\left(r^2\frac{dL}{dr}\right) + \left[\kappa^2 - U(r) - \frac{l(l+1)}{r^2}\right]L = 0 \quad (3\text{-}15\text{-}7)$$

and

$$\frac{1}{\sin\Theta}\frac{d}{d\Theta}\left(\sin\Theta\frac{dY}{d\Theta}\right) + l(l+1)Y = 0 \quad (3\text{-}15\text{-}8)$$

Equation 3-15-8 is a special case of Legendre's equation. Because it is a second-order equation it has two linearly independent solutions, each of which may be expressed as a power series in $\cos\Theta$. Both solutions become infinite for $\Theta = 0$ unless l is zero or a positive integer, and therefore the only physically acceptable solutions of the wave equation are those corresponding to $l = 0, 1, 2, 3, \ldots$. As we shall soon see, l is a measure of the angular momentum of the projectile about the fixed scattering center. For this reason l is called the *angular momentum quantum number*. The first few acceptable solutions of (3-15-8) are

$$P_0(\cos\Theta) = 1$$
$$P_1(\cos\Theta) = \cos\Theta$$
$$P_2(\cos\Theta) = \tfrac{1}{2}(3\cos^2\Theta - 1)$$
$$P_3(\cos\Theta) = \tfrac{1}{2}(5\cos^3\Theta - 3\cos\Theta)$$

The functions $P_l(\cos\Theta)$ are the well-known Legendre polynomials.

B. EXPANSION OF THE WAVE FUNCTIONS IN PARTIAL WAVES.   We now see that the desired wave function may be written in the form

$$\psi(r, \Theta) = \sum_{l=0}^{\infty} A_l P_l(\cos\Theta) L_l(r) \quad (3\text{-}15\text{-}9)$$

where the A_l are arbitrary constants and the $L_l(r)$ are solutions of (3-15-7) for particular values of l. The terms in the foregoing sum are known as *partial waves*. Now let us assume that $U(r)$ falls off faster than $1/r$ at large r and that if $U(r)$ has a pole at the origin it is not of higher order than $1/r$. Then there are two independent solutions of (3-15-7), one of which is finite at the origin, the other being infinite there.[22] The constants A_l must be chosen so that (3-15-9) represents the sum of an incoming plane wave and an outgoing spherical scattered wave. The requirement that the solution be bounded everywhere necessitates the choice of that solution, $L_l(r)$, of (3-15-7) which is finite at the origin.

We can simplify the radial wave equation by introducing the functions $G_l(r)$ defined by the equation

$$L_l(r) = \frac{G_l(r)}{r} \qquad (3\text{-}15\text{-}10)$$

The $G_l(r)$ satisfy the equation

$$\frac{d^2 G_l(r)}{dr^2} + \left[\kappa^2 - U(r) - \frac{l(l+1)}{r^2} \right] G_l(r) = 0 \qquad (3\text{-}15\text{-}11)$$

The last two terms in the square bracket in (3-15-11) tend to zero at large r; hence we would expect the asymptotic form of any solution of (3-15-11) to be $\sin(\kappa r + \varepsilon_l)$, where ε_l is a constant. To see whether this expectation is correct, set

$$G_l(r) = u_l(r)e^{i\kappa r} \qquad (3\text{-}15\text{-}12)$$

Substitution of (3-15-12) into (3-15-11) gives the following expression for $u_l(r)$:

$$\frac{d^2 u_l}{dr^2} + 2i\kappa \frac{du_l}{dr} - \left[U(r) + \frac{l(l+1)}{r^2} \right] u_l = 0 \qquad (3\text{-}15\text{-}13)$$

For large r, $u_l(r)$ will be nearly constant, and $d^2 u_l/dr^2$ will be much smaller than $\kappa(du_l/dr)$. Neglecting $d^2 u_l/dr^2$, we can integrate (3-15-13) and obtain

$$2i\kappa \log u_l = \int^r \left[U(r) + \frac{l(l+1)}{r^2} \right] dr + \text{constant}$$

The integral converges if and only if $U(r)$ falls off faster than $1/r$ for large r, and $u_l(r)$ thus approaches a constant value as r approaches infinity for a potential of this form. This observation justifies the assumption made that $u_l(r)$ is slowly varying. Accordingly, by expressing the exponential in (3-15-12) in trigonometric form we see that for potentials which fall off faster than r^{-1} for large r, $G_l(r)$ has the asymptotic form

$$G_l(r) \approx \sin(\kappa r + \epsilon_l) \qquad (3\text{-}15\text{-}14)$$

where ϵ_l is a constant.

The solution of (3-15-7) which is finite at the origin will then have the asymptotic form

$$L_l(r) \approx \frac{1}{\kappa r} \sin\left(\kappa r - \frac{l\pi}{2} + \eta_l \right) \qquad (3\text{-}15\text{-}15)$$

where η_l is a constant for given κ and $U(r)$ called the *lth order phase shift;* η_l is the phase shift of the *l*th partial wave due to the action of the scattering potential. The term $-l\pi/2$ is inserted into (3-15-15) so that η_l will be zero if $U(r)$ is zero.

We must now determine the constants A_l in the expansion (3-15-9) so that the total wave function ψ will have the form indicated in (3-14-7). To do this, we require the expansion of the incoming plane wave $e^{i\kappa z}$ in partial waves:[23]

$$\psi_{\text{inc}} = e^{i\kappa z} = e^{i\kappa r \cos \Theta} = \sum_{l=0}^{\infty} (2l + 1) i^l \, P_l(\cos \Theta) \, j_l(\kappa r) \quad (3\text{-}15\text{-}16)$$

Here $j_l(\kappa r)$ is the spherical Bessel function which is defined in terms of the ordinary Bessel function of half-integral order by the equation

$$j_l(\kappa r) \equiv (\pi/2\kappa r)^{\frac{1}{2}} J_{l+\frac{1}{2}}(\kappa r) \quad (3\text{-}15\text{-}17)$$

The values of the first few spherical Bessel functions are

$$j_0 = \frac{\sin \kappa r}{\kappa r} \quad (3\text{-}15\text{-}18)$$

$$j_1 = \frac{\sin \kappa r}{(\kappa r)^2} - \frac{\cos \kappa r}{\kappa r} \quad (3\text{-}15\text{-}19)$$

$$j_2 = \left[\frac{3}{(\kappa r)^3} - \frac{1}{\kappa r} \right] \sin \kappa r - \frac{3}{(\kappa r)^2} \cos \kappa r \quad (3\text{-}15\text{-}20)$$

and the recurrence relation among these functions is

$$j_{l+1}(\kappa r) = \frac{2l + 1}{\kappa r} j_l(\kappa r) - j_{l-1}(\kappa r) \quad (3\text{-}15\text{-}21)$$

The asymptotic values of the spherical Bessel functions for large κr are

$$j_l(\kappa r) \approx \frac{1}{\kappa r} \sin \left(\kappa - \frac{l\pi}{2} \right) \quad (3\text{-}15\text{-}22)$$

whereas for small κr

$$j_l(\kappa r) \approx \frac{(\kappa r)^l}{1 \times 3 \times 5 \cdots (2l + 1)} \quad (3\text{-}15\text{-}23)$$

The asymptotic form of the incident plane wave for large r is then seen to be

$$\psi_{\text{inc}} = e^{i\kappa z} \approx \sum_{l=0}^{\infty} (2l + 1) i^l \, P_l(\cos \Theta) \, \frac{\sin (\kappa r - l\pi/2)}{\kappa r} \quad (3\text{-}15\text{-}24)$$

If we subtract this expression from the asymptotic expression for the total wave function

$$\psi \approx \sum_{l=0}^{\infty} A_l P_l(\cos \Theta) \frac{\sin (\kappa r - l\pi/2 + \eta_l)}{\kappa r} \qquad (3\text{-}15\text{-}25)$$

we obtain for the scattered wave

$$\psi_{scatt} = \psi - \psi_{inc} \approx \sum_{l=0}^{\infty} \frac{1}{\kappa r} P_l(\cos \Theta)\left[A_l \sin \left(\kappa r - \frac{l\pi}{2} + \eta_l \right)\right.$$

$$\left. - (2l + 1)i^l \sin \left(\kappa r - \frac{l\pi}{2} \right) \right] \qquad (3\text{-}15\text{-}26)$$

This wave function must represent an outgoing spherical wave. When (3-15-26) is expressed in terms of exponential functions by use of the equation $\sin x = (e^{ix} - e^{-ix})/2i$, the term in $e^{-i\kappa r}/r$ which appears must vanish, since it would represent an incoming spherical wave. This requirement determines the values of the constants A_l. If we express the square bracket in (3-15-26) in exponential form, we obtain

$$\frac{1}{2i} e^{i(\kappa r - l\pi/2)}[A_l e^{i\eta_l} - i^l(2l + 1)] - \frac{1}{2i} e^{-i(\kappa r - l\pi/2)}[A_l e^{-i\eta_l} - i^l(2l + 1)]$$

Evidently it is then required that

$$A_l = (2l + 1)i^l e^{i\eta_l} \qquad (3\text{-}15\text{-}27)$$

and the total wave function is seen to be

$$\psi(r, \Theta) = \sum_{l=0}^{\infty} (2l + 1)i^l e^{i\eta_l} L_l(r) P_l(\cos \Theta) \qquad (3\text{-}15\text{-}28)$$

C. THE SCATTERING CROSS SECTION.   According to (3-14-7), the scattered wave function is $(e^{i\kappa r}/r)f(\Theta)$. The right side of (3-15-26) can have this form only if

$$f(\Theta) = \frac{1}{2i\kappa} \sum_{l=0}^{\infty} (2l + 1)(e^{2i\eta_l} - 1) P_l(\cos \Theta) \qquad (3\text{-}15\text{-}29)$$

Note that $f(\Theta)$ is complex, having the form

$$f(\Theta) = A + iB \qquad (3\text{-}15\text{-}30)$$

where

$$A = \frac{1}{2\kappa} \sum_{l=0}^{\infty} (2l + 1) \sin 2\eta_l P_l(\cos \Theta) \qquad (3\text{-}15\text{-}31)$$

$$B = \frac{1}{2\kappa} \sum_{l=0}^{\infty} (2l + 1)(1 - \cos 2\eta_l) P_l(\cos \Theta) \qquad (3\text{-}15\text{-}32)$$

and i is the imaginary operator. Thus we see that

$$I_s(\Theta) = |f(\Theta)|^2 = A^2 + B^2 = \frac{1}{\kappa^2} \left| \sum_{l=0}^{\infty} (2l + 1)e^{i\eta_l} \sin \eta_l \, P_l(\cos \Theta) \right|^2$$

$$(3\text{-}15\text{-}33)$$

Integration of $I_s(\Theta)$ over the complete solid angle gives for the total elastic scattering cross section

$$q_s = \frac{4\pi}{\kappa^2} \sum_{l=0}^{\infty} (2l + 1) \sin^2 \eta_l \qquad (3\text{-}15\text{-}34)$$

To obtain (3-15-34), we use the well-known relationship

$$\int_0^{\pi} P_m(\cos \Theta) \, P_n(\cos \Theta) \sin \Theta \, d\Theta = \frac{2}{2m + 1} \, \delta_{mn} \qquad (3\text{-}15\text{-}35)$$

where δ_{mn}, the Kronecker delta, equals unity if $m = n$ and zero if $m \neq n$.

The total cross section is also directly related to $f(0)$, the scattered amplitude in the forward direction $\Theta = 0$. Since $P_l(\cos 0) = 1$ for all l,

$$f(0) = \frac{1}{2i\kappa} \sum_{l=0}^{\infty} (2l + 1)(e^{2i\eta_l} - 1)$$

Thus

$$f(0) - f^*(0) = \frac{1}{2i\kappa} \sum_{l=0}^{\infty} (2l + 1)(e^{2i\eta_l} - 1) - \frac{1}{2i\kappa} \sum_{l=0}^{\infty} (2l + 1)(e^{-2i\eta_l} - 1)$$

$$= \frac{i\kappa q_s}{2\pi}$$

so that

$$q_s = \frac{2\pi}{i\kappa} [f(0) - f^*(0)] = \frac{4\pi}{\kappa} \mathscr{I}[f(0)] \qquad (3\text{-}15\text{-}36)$$

where the symbol $\mathscr{I}$ denotes the imaginary component. This result is known as the optical theorem.

It must be emphasized that the expressions for the differential and total cross sections developed here apply only to collisions between dissimilar particles. The expressions applicable to collisions between identical particles are developed in Section 3-18. Furthermore, it must be remembered that (3-15-29) for the scattered amplitude is valid only for potentials that decrease faster than $1/r$ for large r.

The method of partial waves had its origin in Rayleigh's analysis of the scattering of sound waves by spherical obstacles.[24] The partial wave technique was first applied to atomic collisions by Faxén and Holtsmark.[25]

D. THE RELATION BETWEEN THE CLASSICAL IMPACT PARAMETER AND THE PARTIAL WAVES. In the classical treatment of scattering of projectiles from a beam incident on a fixed target particle the projectiles approach the scattering center with a random distribution of impact parameters. In a spherically symmetric force field all projectiles within the annular impact ring of inner radius b and outer radius $b + db$ are scattered between angles Θ and $\Theta + d\Theta$. The scattering angle is calculated as a function of the impact parameter (3-4-5), and the statistical angular scattering distribution is then determined by (3-7-2).

Classically, the angular momentum of the system may be written in terms of the impact parameter as

$$J = M_r v_0 b \qquad (3\text{-}2\text{-}11)$$

The angular momentum might also be expressed as

$$J = L\hbar \qquad (3\text{-}15\text{-}37)$$

where L may be zero or have *any* positive value. The impact parameter may thus be expressed in terms of the angular momentum by the equation

$$b = \frac{L\hbar}{M_r v_0} = L\lambda \qquad (3\text{-}15\text{-}38)$$

where λ denotes the de Broglie wavelength of the projectile divided by 2π. We may now visualize the incident beam as being divided into shells by cylinders that are coaxial with the line corresponding to a head-on trajectory. The radii of these cylinders are to be $l\lambda = 0$, λ, 2λ, 3λ, ..., so that the inner radius of the lth shell is $l\lambda$ and its outer radius is $(l + 1)\lambda$. Classically, all projectiles whose impact parameters lie between $l\lambda$ and $(l + 1)\lambda$ would approach the target within the lth shell, and the angular momentum of these particles would lie in the range $l\hbar$ to $(l + 1)\hbar$.

In quantum mechanics, however, the angular momentum is quantized, and it is characterized by the number $l = 0, 1, 2, 3, \ldots$, where l is now to be regarded as a quantum number. Furthermore, a group of projectiles of angular momentum quantum number l does not approach the target with a well-defined impact parameter but rather must be viewed quantally as moving mostly in the lth shell, as defined above. According to the general principles of quantum mechanics, the angular momentum of these particles is of magnitude $\sqrt{l(l + 1)}\hbar$.* Now let us examine the expansion of the

* We may show that $J = \sqrt{l(l + 1)}\hbar$ from equations that we have already derived. Equation 3-6-1 expresses the classical centrifugal potential in terms of the angular momentum as $J^2/2M_r r^2$. This quantity represents the rotational kinetic energy of the system. The term $l(l + 1)/r^2$ appearing in the radial wave equation (3-15-7) has the same dimensions as $U(r)$ and thus must represent an energy when multiplied by the factor $\hbar^2/2M_r$. The energy it represents is also evidently the rotational kinetic energy of the system. Thus, if the two terms representing this energy are equated, it follows that $J = \sqrt{l(l + 1)}\hbar$.

incoming wave in terms of the partial waves:

$$e^{i\kappa z} = \sum_{l=0}^{\infty} (2l + 1)i^l P_l(\cos \Theta) j_l(\kappa r) \qquad (3\text{-}15\text{-}16)$$

The first few spherical Bessel functions which constitute the radial part of this expansion are plotted in Fig. 3-15-1. From this figure it is seen that the first and largest maximum of $j_l(\kappa r)$ occurs near $\kappa r \equiv r/\lambda \approx 1.5l$ and

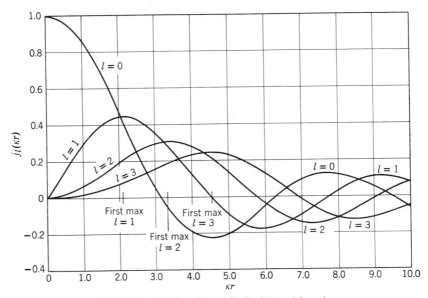

FIG. 3-15-1. The first four spherical Bessel functions.

consequently most of the projectiles whose angular momentum quantum number is l will be found somewhere within the shell whose radii are $l\lambda$ and $(l + 1)\lambda$.

Spectroscopic notation is used to designate the various values of l. Thus $l = 0$ collisions are called "s-wave collisions," $l = 1$ collisions are "p-wave collisions," $l = 2$ collisions are "d-wave collisions," etc. All wave functions associated with the s-wave are independent of angle, and s-wave scattering is consequently spherically symmetric about the scattering center.

It is interesting to note that the cross-sectional areas of the shells into which the incoming beam is divided are given by

$$\pi(l + 1)^2\lambda^2 - \pi l^2\lambda^2 = \pi(2l + 1)\lambda^2$$

This fact accounts for the weighting factor $2l + 1$ appearing in the terms of the expansion (3-15-16). The area $\pi(2l + 1)\lambda^2$ represents the upper limit on the absorption cross section* for particles in the *l*th partial wave, since no more particles can be removed from the beam than were in it originally. Equation 3-15-34 indicates, however, that the maximum cross section for elastic scattering of projectiles in the *l*th partial wave is $4\pi(2l + 1)\lambda^2$. This apparently paradoxical result is due to the diffraction of the de Broglie waves representing the beam.[26]

E. THE PHYSICAL SIGNIFICANCE OF THE PHASE SHIFTS AS ILLUSTRATED BY *s*-WAVE SCATTERING BY A SPHERICAL POTENTIAL WELL.   We may illustrate the origin and significance of the phase shifts by solving the simple problem

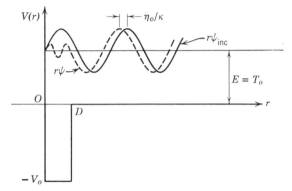

FIG. 3-15-2. Scattering of *s*-wave by a spherical potential well of radius D and depth V_0. The incident and total wave functions are multiplied by r and plotted along the horizontal axis corresponding to $V(r) = E = T_0$; $V(r)$ is the potential energy of the projectile, E is its total energy, and T_0 is its kinetic energy when $r > D$, that is, when the projectile is outside the well.

of the *s*-wave scattering of projectiles by a spherical potential well. Such a well is illustrated in Fig. 3-15-2 and described by the equations

$$V(r) = \begin{cases} -V_0 & (r < D) \\ 0 & (r > D) \end{cases}$$

(3-15-39)

If the radius D of the well is small compared with the rationalized de Broglie wavelength λ of the incident projectiles, few projectiles with non-zero angular momentum can reach the edge of the potential well. Consequently, only *s*-wave collisions are effective in the scattering, and we need consider only the first partial wave, corresponding to $l = 0$. There are many physical problems in which *s*-wave scattering predominates, and the problem treated here is one of real significance.

* An example of the absorption of particles from a beam is the attachment by gas molecules of electrons in a beam passing through the gas (Chapter 8).

If we consider only the s-wave and assume its amplitude to be unity, the wave function for the incident plane wave, is by (3-15-16),

$$\psi_{\text{inc}} = e^{i\kappa z} \approx \frac{\sin \kappa r}{\kappa r} \qquad (3\text{-}15\text{-}40)$$

where κ, the wave number of the incident wave, is given in terms of the initial kinetic energy T_0 by the equation

$$\kappa = \left(\frac{2M_r T_0}{\hbar^2}\right)^{\frac{1}{2}} \qquad (3\text{-}14\text{-}8)$$

The total wave function is the sum of the wave function for the incident wave and that for the outgoing spherical scattered wave:

$$\psi = e^{i\kappa z} + f_0 \frac{e^{i\kappa r}}{r} \qquad (3\text{-}15\text{-}41)$$

Here f_0 is the amplitude of the scattered s wave, given by (3-15-29) to be

$$f_0 = \frac{1}{2i\kappa}(e^{2i\eta_0} - 1) \qquad (3\text{-}15\text{-}42)$$

where η_0 is the phase shift for the $l = 0$ wave. Using (3-15-25) and (3-15-27), we find the asymptotic form of the total wave function to be

$$\psi \approx \frac{e^{i\eta_0}}{\kappa r} \sin (\kappa r + \eta_0) \qquad (3\text{-}15\text{-}43)$$

and the total elastic scattering cross section, according to (3-15-34), is

$$q_s = \frac{4\pi}{\kappa^2} \sin^2 \eta_0 \qquad (3\text{-}15\text{-}44)$$

We must now evaluate the phase shift for the s wave in terms of the potential. Note that (3-15-11) for the modified radial wave function $G(r)$ must be satisfied both inside and outside the well. Thus

$$\frac{d^2 G}{dr^2} + [\kappa^{*2} - U(r)]G = 0 \qquad (3\text{-}15\text{-}45)$$

where κ^* is the wave number appropriate for the region under discussion. Inside the well the solution for $G(r)$ which vanishes at the origin is

$$G(r) = A \sin \kappa_i r \qquad (3\text{-}15\text{-}46)$$

and so

$$\psi_{\text{inside}} = \frac{G(r)}{r} = \frac{A}{r} \sin \kappa_i r \qquad (3\text{-}15\text{-}47)$$

where κ_i, the wave number for $r < D$, is given by

$$\kappa_i = \left(\frac{2M_r(E - V)}{\hbar^2}\right)^{1/2} = \left(\frac{2M_r(E + V_0)}{\hbar^2}\right)^{1/2} \qquad (3\text{-}15\text{-}48)$$

The wave function (3-15-43) outside the well must now be matched to the function (3-15-47) inside the well. The standard boundary conditions are to be applied at the edge; that is, ψ and $d\psi/dr$ must be continuous at $r = D$. Then

$$\frac{e^{i\eta_0}}{\kappa} \sin(\kappa D + \eta_0) = A \sin \kappa_i D \qquad (3\text{-}15\text{-}49)$$

$$e^{i\eta_0} \cos(\kappa D + \eta_0) = A\kappa_i \cos \kappa_i D \qquad (3\text{-}15\text{-}50)$$

Dividing the first of these equations by the second, we eliminate A and obtain

$$\tan(\kappa D + \eta_0) = \frac{\kappa}{\kappa_i} \tan \kappa_i D \qquad (3\text{-}15\text{-}51)$$

or

$$\eta_0 = -\kappa D + \tan^{-1}\left(\frac{\kappa}{\kappa_i} \tan \kappa_i D\right) \qquad (3\text{-}15\text{-}52)$$

Equation 3-15-52 gives the phase shift in terms of the radius of the well and the wave numbers inside and outside the well; η_0 may also be expressed in terms of the total energy of the projectile and the depth and radius of the well, since

$$E = \frac{\kappa^2\hbar^2}{2M_r} \qquad (3\text{-}15\text{-}53)$$

and

$$V_0 = \frac{(\kappa_i^2 - \kappa^2)\hbar^2}{2M_r} \qquad (3\text{-}15\text{-}54)$$

Equation 3-15-52 shows that in general the phase shift η_0 goes to zero as the velocity of the incident particles goes to zero. The total scattering cross section given by (3-15-44) then generally has a finite limit for very slow projectiles:

$$q_s \xrightarrow[\kappa \to 0]{} 4\pi D^2 \left(\frac{\tan \kappa_0 D}{\kappa_0 D} - 1\right)^2 \qquad (3\text{-}15\text{-}55)$$

where

$$\kappa_0^2 \equiv \kappa_i^2 - \kappa^2 = \frac{2M_r V_0}{\hbar^2} \qquad (3\text{-}15\text{-}56)$$

The following exceptional cases should be noted, however. If $\kappa_0 D$ happens to equal $\tan \kappa_0 D$, the limit in (3-15-55) vanishes as the velocity goes to zero.

In addition, for $\kappa_0 D = \pi/2, 3\pi/2, 5\pi/2, \ldots$, the phase shift does not go to zero with κ, and the total scattering cross section goes to infinity as the velocity approaches zero. The infinite values for q_s which arise in the latter cases are associated with the existence of allowed energy levels within the potential well.[27]

The incident and total wave functions, multiplied by r, are shown in Fig. 3-15-2 plotted against r. The curve labeled by $r\psi_{\text{inc}}$ represents the incident wave outside the range of the interaction and its uniform extension into the well, assuming that the potential is removed. Note that the amplitude and wavelength of the solid curve are constant. The dashed curve, on the other hand, represents the actual wave function, multiplied by r, as determined by the action of the potential well. Within the well the amplitude of this curve is generally smaller than that of the unmodified curve, and its wavelength, $\lambda_i = 2\pi/\kappa_i$, is always shorter because the kinetic energy of the projectile increases when it enters the well. It is apparent that outside the well there must be a difference in phase between the modified and unmodified waves. The phase difference between the two waves outside the well is equal to the phase shift η_0, which may be represented in Fig. 3-15-2 as κ times the distance between corresponding crests of the modified and unmodified waves. For attractive potentials, such as assumed in the present example, the phase shift is positive, and the incoming wave may be regarded as *drawn in* toward the scattering center. Repulsive potentials, however, lead to a negative η_0, and the incident wave may then be thought of as *pushed out* from the scattering center.

The scattering that occurs when the amplitude of the wave function inside the potential well is very small compared with that outside the well is called *potential scattering*. It usually appears when a wave of short wavelength inside the well is to be joined to one of long wavelength outside. However, there may be certain values for the kinetic energy of the incident projectile for which the derivative of the wave function is almost zero at the edge of the well, and then the interior and exterior wave functions may be joined with substantially equal amplitudes. The scattering in this case is termed *resonance scattering*, and the cross section assumes a large value. The resonance effect is very sharp and can usually be ignored in the analysis of atomic collisions. Figure 3-15-3 shows wave functions schematically for the cases of pure potential scattering, scattering near a resonance, and pure resonance scattering.[28]

F. CALCULATION OF THE PHASE SHIFTS. Equation 3-15-29 for the scattered amplitude $f(\Theta)$ was derived on the assumption that the scattering potential $V(r)$ tends to zero faster than $1/r$. It was not necessary to assume that $V(r)$ would become negligible outside some finite radius D, but the method of partial waves is most easily applied and most useful when such a radius exists. We have pointed out that the first and largest maximum of the radial wave function $j_l(\kappa r)$ occurs near $r = 1.5l\lambda$, and for r much smaller than this value $j_l(\kappa r)$ is small and varies about as r^l, according to (3-15-23). If the radius beyond which the potential is negligible is small compared with $l\lambda$, the lth partial wave function will be small in the region in which the potential is significant, and the lth partial wave will not be appreciably affected by the scatterer. This means that the phase shift associated with this wave, and consequently the contribution of this wave to the cross section, will be small. Therefore we see that only those partial

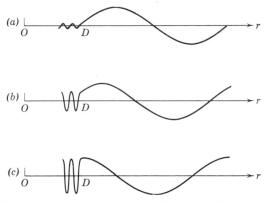

FIG. 3-15-3. Schematic representations of wave functions plotted against the distance from the center of a potential well. Curve (a) corresponds to a projectile energy between resonances; curve (b), to an energy near resonance; and curve (c), to a resonance energy.

waves associated with values of l extending from zero to some maximum value of the order of $D/\lambda = D\kappa$ need be considered in the calculation of cross sections. Since κ is proportional to the square root of the incident energy, it then follows that fewer of the laborious phase-shift calculations are required for low-energy projectiles and that the method of partial waves is most useful for low energies.

Several methods are available for calculation of the phase shifts. Clearly, by solving the differential equation (3-15-11) for $G_l(r)$, subject to the appropriate boundary conditions and comparing the solution to that when $V(r) = 0$, we can always find η_l numerically. In addition, several approximate methods are frequently used. In particular, we cite the *Born* and *Jeffreys* approximations to the phase shifts. The Born is useful when the phase shift is small and the Jeffreys when η_l is not small. Variational methods have also proved valuable. All of the methods mentioned here are treated in detail by Mott and Massey,[29] by Massey,[18] and by Bates.[30]

It should be pointed out that the Jeffreys approximation is also referred to as the Wentzel-Kramers-Brillouin (W-K-B), the classical, the phase integral, and the asymptotic approximation. A simple derivation of the Jeffreys approximation to the phase shifts which stresses physical concepts appears in Massey and Burhop.[31] We use the Jeffreys approximation to the phase shifts in Sections 4-7 and 9-3.

3-16. THE BORN APPROXIMATION

An approximate method, due to Born,[32] for the calculation of cross sections is of great importance in the study of atomic collisions. This method is valid only under certain conditions but has the virtue of permitting the cross sections to be calculated with much less labor than is required by the exact method of partial waves. We now derive the Born expression for the scattered amplitude. The reader is referred to references cited in the last section for discussion of the Born approximation to the phase shifts.

The basic assumption in the derivation is that the effect of the scattering potential is small, so that the interaction between the particles may be treated as a perturbation. A sufficient, but not necessary, condition, therefore, is that $V(r)$ be much smaller than E, the total energy of the projectiles.* This condition is evidently always obeyed for sufficiently fast projectiles. Our starting point is the wave equation

$$\nabla^2\psi + [\kappa^2 - U(r)]\psi = 0 \qquad (3\text{-}15\text{-}4)$$

and we seek a solution having the asymptotic form, for large r,

$$\psi \approx e^{i\kappa z} + \frac{e^{i\kappa r}}{r} f(\Theta) \qquad (3\text{-}14\text{-}7)$$

Mott and Massey[33] show that the most general bounded solution of the equation

$$\nabla^2\psi + \kappa^2\psi = F(x, y, z) \qquad (3\text{-}16\text{-}1)$$

is

$$\psi = G(x, y, z) - \frac{1}{4\pi} \int \frac{e^{i\kappa|\mathbf{r}-\mathbf{r}'|}}{|\mathbf{r} - \mathbf{r}'|} F(\mathbf{r}') \, d\tau' \qquad (3\text{-}16\text{-}2)$$

where G is the general solution of the equation

$$\nabla^2 G + \kappa^2 G = 0 \qquad (3\text{-}16\text{-}3)$$

* A thorough discussion of the conditions for validity of the Born approximation is given by Massey in Ref. 18.

Therefore the general solution of the wave equation (3-15-4) is

$$\psi = G - \frac{1}{4\pi} \int \frac{e^{i\kappa|\mathbf{r}-\mathbf{r}'|}}{|\mathbf{r} - \mathbf{r}'|} U(\mathbf{r}') \, \psi(\mathbf{r}') \, d\tau' \tag{3-16-4}$$

In order that this solution may have the proper asymptotic form (3-14-7), we must set $G = e^{i\kappa z}$.

Now let us assume that the scattering potential falls off sufficiently rapidly at large r' that there is an asymptotic region in which r is large in comparison with those values of r' for which there is a significant contribution to the integrand. If we let $\mathbf{n}$ represent a unit vector in the direction of $\mathbf{r}$ (see Fig. 3-16-1), we have

$$|\mathbf{r} - \mathbf{r}'| \approx r - \mathbf{n} \cdot \mathbf{r}' + \cdots \tag{3-16-5}$$

and (3-16-4) then becomes

$$\psi \approx e^{i\kappa z} - \frac{e^{i\kappa r}}{r} \frac{1}{4\pi} \int e^{-i\kappa \mathbf{n} \cdot \mathbf{r}'} U(\mathbf{r}') \, \psi(\mathbf{r}') \, d\tau' \tag{3-16-6}$$

Under the assumption that the scattering is weak, we may suppose that each point in the scattering region has a wave of full strength incident upon it. Thus we may replace the wave function $\psi(\mathbf{r}')$ in (3-16-6) by the unperturbed wave function $e^{i\kappa z'}$. Comparison of (3-14-7) and (3-16-6) then shows that

$$f(\Theta) = - \frac{1}{4\pi} \int e^{i\kappa(\mathbf{n}_0 - \mathbf{n}) \cdot \mathbf{r}'} U(\mathbf{r}') \, d\tau' \tag{3-16-7}$$

where $\mathbf{n}_0$ is a unit vector along the Z axis.

We may easily evaluate the integral in (3-16-7) by introducing the angles α and β, where α is the polar angle measured from the direction of the vector $\mathbf{n}_0 - \mathbf{n}$ and β is the corresponding azimuthal angle. Then

$$f(\Theta) = - \frac{1}{4\pi} \int_0^{2\pi} d\beta \int_0^{\pi} \sin \alpha \, d\alpha \int_0^{\infty} e^{iKr' \cos \alpha} U(r') r'^2 \, dr' \tag{3-16-8}$$

where

$$K \equiv \kappa |\mathbf{n}_0 - \mathbf{n}| = 2\kappa \sin \frac{\Theta}{2} \tag{3-16-9}$$

K is the magnitude of the momentum transferred during the collision divided by $\hbar$. If we perform the integrations over α and β and drop the dashes, we obtain

$$f(\Theta) = - \frac{2M_r}{\hbar^2} \int_0^{\infty} \frac{\sin Kr}{Kr} V(r) r^2 \, dr \tag{3-16-10}$$

which is the *Born approximation for the scattered amplitude* $f(\Theta)$.

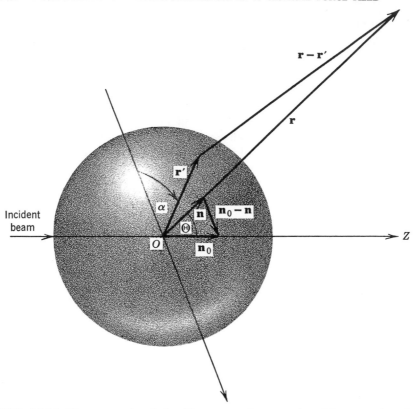

FIG. 3-16-1. The geometric relationships among the vectors used in computing the elastic scattering of particles in the Born approximation. The scattering center is located at O and is effectively localized within the spherical region shown shaded: $\mathbf{r}$ is the vector from O to the point at which the amplitude of the scattered wave is to be computed; $\mathbf{r}'$ is the vector from O to a point contributing to the scattering; α is the polar angle between $\mathbf{r}'$ and the axis through O parallel to the vector $\mathbf{n}_0 - \mathbf{n}$. The corresponding azimuthal angle β is not shown.

The approximation derived in this section is sometimes known as the *first Born approximation*. The method used here can be continued to higher approximations by an iterative procedure. For example, if

$$\psi = e^{i\kappa z} - \frac{1}{4\pi} \int \frac{e^{i\kappa|\mathbf{r}-\mathbf{r}'|}}{|\mathbf{r} - \mathbf{r}'|} U(r')e^{i\kappa z'} \, d\tau' \qquad (3\text{-}16\text{-}11)$$

is substituted for ψ in the equation

$$f(\Theta) = -\frac{1}{4\pi} \int e^{-i\kappa \mathbf{n}\cdot\mathbf{r}'} U(r') \, \psi(\mathbf{r}') \, d\tau' \qquad (3\text{-}16\text{-}12)$$

the *second Born approximation for the scattered amplitude* is obtained.

Although the formalism developed in this chapter directly applies only to elastic scattering, both the Born approximation and the method of partial waves can be used in the study of inelastic collisions as well. Examples of these applications are discussed in Chapters 5 and 6.

3-17. COULOMB SCATTERING IN THE BORN APPROXIMATION

In Coulomb scattering, for which the potential is

$$V(r) = \frac{Zze^2}{r} \tag{3-17-1}$$

the integral in (3-16-10) becomes $\int_0^\infty \sin Kr\, dr$, which is mathematically meaningless. To avoid this difficulty, let us assume for the moment that the potential has the form

$$V(r) = \frac{Zze^2}{r} e^{-\gamma r} \tag{3-17-2}$$

where γ is a positive quantity. Then the integral in (3-16-10) becomes

$$\int_0^\infty \sin Kr\, e^{-\gamma r}\, dr = \frac{K}{K^2 + \gamma^2}$$

If we now let $\gamma \to 0$, this expression goes to $1/K$, and then $f(\Theta)$ becomes

$$f(\Theta) = -\frac{2Zze^2 M_r}{\hbar^2 K^2}$$

Since $K = 2\kappa \sin(\Theta/2)$, the scattered amplitude can be written

$$f(\Theta) = -\frac{Zze^2 M_r}{2\hbar^2 \kappa^2} \frac{1}{\sin^2(\Theta/2)}$$

Now $\hbar\kappa$ is the linear momentum $M_r v_0$, so that we finally obtain for the differential scattering cross section

$$I_s(\Theta)\, d\Omega_{CM} = \frac{Z^2 z^2 e^4}{4 M_r^2 v_0^4 \sin^4(\Theta/2)}\, d\Omega_{CM} \tag{3-17-3}$$

This equation, even though obtained by an approximation method, is exactly the same as the classical result (3-8-9). It is also in exact agreement with the result obtained in an exact quantum mechanical calculation.[34]

In the foregoing derivation the inclusion of the $e^{-\gamma r}$ term to obtain the "screened Coulomb potential" in (3-17-2) was simply an *ad hoc* step of mathematical expediency. It is worth pointing out, however, that screened

Coulomb potentials are accurate representations of the true potentials in certain types of physical problems. For example, (3-17-2) gives the mutual potential energy of two charged particles in a plasma if $1/\gamma$ is taken to be the debye length of the plasma.* In this case the exponential term takes into account the shielding effect of charged particles in the neighborhood of a given ion or electron in the plasma. In atomic physics, if $1/\gamma$ is taken to be of the order of atomic dimensions, (3-17-2) may represent the potential energy of an ion or electron in the vicinity of a neutral atom. Here the screening factor allows for the shielding of the nucleus of the atom by its orbital electrons. For a discussion of scattering of particles through a screened Coulomb potential, see Section 4-10.

3-18. THE SCATTERING OF IDENTICAL PARTICLES[35]

Up to this point no mention has been made of the symmetry effects that appear when the colliding particles are identical, and we must now modify the equations for the scattering cross section to take these effects into account. Their physical basis is the fact that it is impossible to distinguish experimentally between identical projectile and target particles, and the wave function describing the system must therefore satisfy certain symmetry properties with respect to the interchange of the coordinates of the two particles. The wave function, in fact, must be symmetric or antisymmetric with respect to the interchange of the particles, depending on whether their total (combined) spin is even or odd, that is, an even or odd multiple of $\hbar$.

In order to justify the statement concerning the symmetry character of the wave function, we reason as follows. Because the collision partners are indistinguishable by assumption, the states of the system obtained from each other by simply interchanging the particles must be completely equivalent physically. This means that the wave function describing the system can change only by an unimportant phase factor as a result of a single interchange. Let $\psi(1, 2)$ represent the spatial part of the wave function of the system† before the interchange occurs. The numbers 1 and 2 refer to the two particles composing the system. The new wave function describing the system after the particles are interchanged must be given, according to what has been said, by the equation

$$\psi(2, 1) = e^{ia}\, \psi(1, 2)$$

* See Appendix I.

† When the spin in considered, the total wave function is expressed as a product of two functions, one of which depends only on the spatial coordinates and the other on the spin. The above statement concerning the symmetry or antisymmetry of the wave function refers to the spatial part of the total wave function.

where a is a real constant. If the interchange is repeated, we must recover the original wave function, that is,

$$\psi(1, 2) = e^{2ia}\, \psi(1, 2)$$

Thus $e^{2ia} = 1$ and $e^{ia} = \pm 1$, so that

$$\psi(2, 1) = \pm\psi(1, 2)$$

We see that the wave function must either be unchanged or simply undergo a change of sign if the two particles are interchanged. In the first case the wave function is said to be symmetric, whereas in the second it is anti-symmetric.

An interchange of the positions of the particles is equivalent to a reversal of the direction of the radius vector joining them. In the center-of-mass coordinate system r remains unchanged in this reversal, whereas the angle Θ becomes $\pi - \Theta$ and z becomes $-z$, since $z = r \cos \Theta$. There-fore, if we assume that the interaction potential is a function only of r, the proper asymptotic expression for the spatial part of the wave function is now

$$\psi \approx e^{i\kappa z} \pm e^{-i\kappa z} + \frac{e^{i\kappa r}}{r}\,[f(\Theta) \pm f(\pi - \Theta)] \qquad (3\text{-}18\text{-}1)$$

(with the positive sign to be used to obtain the symmetric wave function and the negative sign, the antisymmetric wave function) instead of

$$\psi \approx e^{i\kappa z} + \frac{e^{i\kappa r}}{r} f(\Theta) \qquad (3\text{-}14\text{-}7)$$

which is correct in the absence of symmetry. The wave function in (3-18-1) contains two incident plane waves of equal amplitude traveling in opposite directions, and the outgoing spherical wave takes into account the scattering of both waves. The differential cross section per unit solid angle is given by the square of the coefficient of the term $e^{i\kappa r}/r$ and is related to the prob-ability that *either* of the particles will be scattered into the element of solid angle at Θ. Thus, if the total spin of the particles is even, the differ-ential cross section per unit solid angle is

$$(I_s)_{\text{sym}} = |f(\Theta) + f(\pi - \Theta)|^2 \qquad (3\text{-}18\text{-}2)$$

and for odd total spin

$$(I_s)_{\text{anti}} = |f(\Theta) - f(\pi - \Theta)|^2 \qquad (3\text{-}18\text{-}3)$$

The appearance of the interference term $[f(\Theta)f^*(\pi - \Theta) \pm f^*(\Theta)f(\pi - \Theta)]$ is characteristic of quantum mechanics. This term does not appear in the classical treatment of scattering, in which the cross section per unit solid angle would be given simply by

$$(I_s)_{\text{class}} = |f(\Theta)|^2 + |f(\pi - \Theta)|^2 \tag{3-18-4}$$

In the foregoing discussion it was assumed that the total spin of the particles had some definite value, but we must as a rule consider a distribution among the possible spin states. To determine a cross section, we shall assume that all the spin states are equally probable. It can be shown that the total number of spin states is $(2s + 1)^2$ for two particles of spin s and that $s(2s + 1)$ of these states correspond to an even total spin and $(s + 1)(2s + 1)$ to an odd total spin, if s is half-integral. If s is integral, the weighting is reversed. Thus, if s is half-integral, the probability that the system will have even total spin is $s(2s + 1)/(2s + 1)^2 = s/(2s + 1)$, and the probability of odd total spin is $(s + 1)/(2s + 1)$. The differential cross section per unit solid angle is therefore

$$(I_s)_{\text{FD}} = \frac{s}{2s + 1} (I_s)_{\text{sym}} + \frac{s + 1}{2s + 1} (I_s)_{\text{anti}} \tag{3-18-5}$$

for half-integral s. By a similar analysis we can show that for integral s the appropriate expression is

$$(I_s)_{\text{BE}} = \frac{s}{2s + 1} (I_s)_{\text{anti}} + \frac{s + 1}{2s + 1} (I_s)_{\text{sym}} \tag{3-18-6}$$

The subscripts FD and BE in (3-18-5) and (3-18-6) are abbreviations for *Fermi-Dirac* and *Bose-Einstein*. In relativistic quantum mechanics it is shown that particles with half-integral spin obey Fermi-Dirac statistics, hence (3-18-5) applies to the scattering of particles of this type, which are called fermions. Equation 3-18-6 applies to particles of integral spin, which obey Bose-Einstein statistics and are called bosons. Electrons, positrons, protons, neutrons, and nuclei of odd mass number are fermions, and nuclei of even mass number (such as deuterons and alpha particles) are bosons.

It is now of interest to write down the expressions for the cross section in terms of the phase shifts for particles obeying these types of statistics. For distinguishable particles we know that

$$I_s(\Theta) = \frac{1}{4\kappa^2} \left| \sum_{l=0}^{\infty} (2l + 1)(e^{2i\eta_l} - 1) P_l(\cos \Theta) \right|^2 \tag{3-18-7}$$

which is just the square of the expression given in (3-15-29) for the scattered amplitude. Two changes are required, however, when we write the corresponding expressions for identical particles. First of all we must multiply I_s by a factor of 2, since we cannot distinguish between the scattered waves representing the two collision partners. Second, assuming for the moment that the total spin has a definite even value, terms of odd l must be excluded from the sum because $P_l(\cos \Theta)$ is odd for all odd l. Thus for even total spin

$$(I_s)_{\text{sym}} = \frac{1}{2\kappa^2} \left| \sum_{\text{even } l} (2l + 1)(e^{2i\eta_l} - 1) P_l(\cos \Theta) \right|^2 \tag{3-18-8}$$

and, similarly, for odd total spin

$$(I_s)_{\text{anti}} = \frac{1}{2\kappa^2} \left| \sum_{\text{odd } l} (2l + 1)(e^{2i\eta_l} - 1) P_l(\cos \Theta) \right|^2 \tag{3-18-9}$$

Equations 3-18-5 and 3-18-6 are to be used with these equations to obtain the scattering distributions when there is a mixture of spin states.

REFERENCES

1. J. O. Hirschfelder, C. F. Curtiss, and R. B. Bird, *Molecular Theory of Gases and Liquids*, Wiley, New York, 1954, p. 50 and Section 7-4.
2. *Ibid*, Sections 8-3, 8-4, and 8-5.
3. E. T. Whittaker, *A Treatise on the Analytical Dynamics of Particles and Rigid Bodies*, Fourth Edition, Cambridge University Press, Cambridge, 1937 (also Dover, New York, 1944), Chapter IV.
4. H. Goldstein, *Classical Mechanics*, Addison-Wesley, Reading, Mass., 1950, Chapter 3.
5. See T. Kihara, M. H. Taylor, and J. O. Hirschfelder, *Phys. Fluids* **3**, 715 (1960). The behavior of the particle at the origin depends on the details of the scattering model assumed. The model under discussion here is the "transparent core model" of Kihara, Taylor, and Hirschfelder. These authors also treat the "rigid core model," which is the limit $D \to 0$ of the Sutherland potential (1-7-4), and the "random scattering model," which produces random scattering of the trajectories of the particles reaching the origin. Failure to recognize the effects of different assumed boundary conditions at the origin has led to discrepancies in published values of collision integrals.
6. M. A. Eliason, D. E. Stogryn, and J. O. Hirschfelder, *Proc. Nat. Acad. Sci. (U.S.A.)* **42**, 546 (1956). H. M. Mott-Smith, *Phys. Fluids* **3**, 721 (1960).
7. J. O. Hirschfelder, R. B. Bird, and E. L. Spotz, *J. Chem. Phys.* **16**, 968 (1948).
8. E. A. Mason, *J. Chem. Phys.* **22**, 169 (1954).
9. G. Gioumousis and D. P. Stevenson, *J. Chem. Phys.* **29**, 294 (1958).
10. R. D. Present, *Proc. Nat. Acad. Sci. (U.S.A.)* **41**, 415 (1955). *Kinetic Theory of Gases*, McGraw-Hill, New York, 1958, pp. 152–153.
11. E. A. Mason and J. T. Vanderslice, *J. Chem. Phys.* **28**, 253, 1070 (1958).
12. G. H. Wannier, *Bell System Tech. J.* **32**, 170 (1953).
13. E. Vogt and G. H. Wannier, *Phys. Rev.* **95**, 1190 (1954).
14. E. J. Williams, *Rev. Mod. Phys.* **17**, 217 (1945). See also L. D. Landau and E. M. Lifshitz, *Quantum Mechanics, Non-relativistic Theory*, Addison-Wesley, Reading, Mass., 1958, p. 416.
15. E. Everhart, Gerald Stone, and R. J. Carbone, *Phys. Rev.* **99**, 1287 (1955); G. H. Lane and E. Everhart, **117**, 920 (1960).

16. R. D. Present, *Kinetic Theory of Gases*, McGraw-Hill, 1958, pp. 113–114. K. Yang and T. Ree, *J. Chem. Phys.* **35,** 588 (1961).

17. H. S. W. Massey and C. B. O. Mohr, *Proc. Roy. Soc. (London)* **A-144,** 188 (1934).

18. H. S. W. Massey and E. H. S. Burhop, *Electronic and Ionic Impact Phenomena*, Oxford University Press, Oxford, 1952. N. F. Mott and H. S. W. Massey, *The Theory of Atomic Collisions*, Second Edition, Oxford University Press, Oxford, 1952. L. I. Schiff, *Quantum Mechanics*, Second Edition, McGraw-Hill, New York, 1955. E. H. S. Burhop, "Theory of Collisions," in *Quantum Theory, Vol. I— Elements* (edited by D. R. Bates), Academic, New York, 1961. H. S. W. Massey, "Theory of Atomic Collisions," in *Handbuch der Physik*, Vol. XXXVI, Springer-Verlag, Berlin, 1956.

19. A Messiah, *Quantum Mechanics*, Interscience, New York, Vol. I (1961), Vol. II (1962). L. D. Landau and E. M. Lifshitz, *Quantum Mechanics, Non-relativistic Theory*, Addison-Wesley, Reading, Mass., 1958. E. Merzbacher, *Quantum Mechanics*, Wiley, New York, 1961. T. Y. Wu and T. Ohmura, *Quantum Theory of Scattering*, Prentice-Hall, Englewood Cliffs, N.J., 1962. K. W. Ford and J. A. Wheeler, *Ann. Phys., N.Y.*, **7,** 259, 287 (1959).

20. N. F. Mott and H. S. W. Massey, *op. cit.*, pp. 14–18.

21. H. S. W. Massey and E. H. S. Burhop, *op. cit.*, pp. 5, 391–392, 491–492.

22. N. F. Mott and H. S. W. Massey, *op. cit.*, Chapter VI.

23. N. F. Mott and H. S. W. Massey, *op. cit.*, pp. 20–22.

24. Lord Rayleigh, *The Theory of Sound*, Dover, New York 1945 (published first by Macmillan, London, 1894). Also see P. M. Morse, *Vibration and Sound*, Second Edition, McGraw-Hill, New York, 1948, Chapter VII. This reference contains a summary of the properties of the spherical Bessel functions.

25. H. Faxén and J. Holtsmark, *Z. Physik* **45,** 307 (1927).

26. H. S. W. Massey and C. B. O. Mohr, *Proc. Roy. Soc. (London)* **A-141,** 434 (1933). N. F. Mott and H. S. W. Massey, *op. cit.*, pp. 38–40. J. M. Blatt and V. F. Weisskopf, *Theoretical Nuclear Physics*, Wiley, New York, 1952, pp. 318–325.

27. N. F. Mott and H. S. W. Massey, *op. cit.*, pp. 30–31. E. H. S. Burhop (D. R. Bates, *op. cit.*, pp. 314–316).

28. J. M. Blatt and V. F. Weisskopf, *op. cit.*, p. 382.

29. N. F. Mott and H. S. W. Massey, *op. cit.*, Chapter VII.

30. *Quantum Theory* (edited by D. R. Bates), Academic, New York, 1961; *Atomic and Molecular Processes* (edited by D. R. Bates), Academic, New York, 1962.

31. H. S. W. Massey and E. H. S. Burhop, *op. cit.*, pp. 111–112.

32. M. Born, *Z. Physik*, **38,** 803 (1926).

33. N. F. Mott and H. S. W. Massey, *op. cit.*, Chapter VI, Section 4.

34. N. F. Mott and H. S. W. Massey, *op. cit.*, Chapter III.

35. L. D. Landau and E. M. Lifshitz, *op. cit.*, Chapter IX; R. M. Eisberg, *Fundamentals of Modern Physics*, Wiley, New York, 1961, Chapter 12.

4

MEASUREMENT AND

CALCULATION OF ELASTIC

SCATTERING CROSS SECTIONS

This chapter is devoted to experimental studies of elastic scattering of electrons and heavier particles in gases and to theoretical calculations made on specific projectile-target systems. In Part $\mathscr{A}$ we shall be concerned solely with electrons; ions, atoms, and molecules are treated collectively in Part $\mathscr{B}$. Although there are certain features common to the scattering of electrons and the heavier particles, the differences in their scattering behavior are so pronounced that different types of apparatus and techniques of theoretical analysis are required for their study. Thus division of our discussion of elastic scattering into two distinct parts is appropriate. Inelastic collisions are considered in later chapters.

PART $\mathscr{A}$. THE ELASTIC SCATTERING OF ELECTRONS

We have already demonstrated in Section 1-5 that the mean fractional amount of energy lost by an electron in elastic collisions with molecules initially at rest is approximately

$$\Delta \approx \frac{2m}{M} \tag{1-5-21}$$

where m and M are the electronic and molecular masses, respectively.

Since the indicated mass ratio is always less than 10^{-3}, practical interest in the elastic scattering of electrons usually does not center about the attendant loss of energy. Rather, as a rule, it is the change in direction experienced by the scattered electrons that is the important aspect of the collision. The simple calculation in Section 1-5 indicates that the scattering should be isotropic in the Lab system as well as in the CM. This prediction, being based on the ultrasimplified classical elastic sphere model, could hardly be expected to be correct. However, both experiment and more realistic calculations show that *large-angle scattering is very pronounced*, and this fact must be carefully considered in the design of apparatus utilizing electron beams. Large-angle scattering is particularly prominent at low energies but cannot be ignored even at high energies.*

Certain integrals of the differential cross section for elastic scattering are also of great interest. The unweighted integral over all angles, that is, the total scattering cross section, is evidently related to the total probability of collision. An even more important quantity is the cross section for momentum transfer, defined in Section 1-6, which determines the rate of diffusion of electrons and also the rate at which they drift through a gas under the influence of an electric field.

We now begin a more detailed discussion of electron scattering. The range of electron energies of principal interest to us in this chapter (and throughout the remainder of the book as well) extends from zero up to about 1000 ev.

4-1. MEASUREMENT OF THE TOTAL ELASTIC SCATTERING CROSS SECTION

The first studies of slow electron scattering were conducted by Lenard[1] in 1903, but quantitative measurements were not made until 1921, when Ramsauer[2] introduced his method of determining electron cross sections. We shall discuss only studies performed since that date. The earlier measurements are treated by Brode,[3] Townsend,[4] Kollath,[5] Brown,[6] and

---

* An interesting illustration of the large-angle scattering of electrons is furnished by cloud-chamber photographs of beta-ray tracks. Similar photographs of tracks made by alpha particles show that heavy particle scattering is confined, by contrast, almost entirely to extremely small angles about the forward direction. (Examples of such photographs are presented by E. Rutherford, J. Chadwick, and C. D. Ellis, *Radiations from Radioactive Substances*, Cambridge University Press, Cambridge, 1951, Plates III and VIII.) Of course, the path of a particle shown in a cloud-chamber photograph is not determined solely by elastic scattering. Some of the deflections experienced by the particle are produced by inelastic events, but the angular scattering distributions of electrons and heavy particles differ in much the same way in inelastic scattering as they do in elastic collisions.

Massey and Burhop,[7] whose works are cited as general references for this chapter. Other useful sources of information on the elastic scattering of electrons are the reviews of Craggs and Massey[8] and Huxley and Crompton.[9]

We shall subdivide our discussion of the cross section measurements according to the general type of experimental technique used. The first class of experiments to be considered involves the passage of a sharply defined nearly monoenergetic beam of electrons through a gas and direct observation of the scattering that occurs. Then we shall take up studies in which cross sections are deduced from observation of the diffusion of electrons through a gas in a uniform electric field. Microwave investigations are considered next, and then the determination of cross sections from electron drift velocity measurements. Finally we shall treat "crossed-beam" experiments, which are now playing a vital role in the study of many kinds of collision phenomena.

A. DIRECT SINGLE-BEAM MEASUREMENTS.* Ramsauer's method of electron cross section measurement is discussed in some detail here as an example of techniques employing single electron beams. Other similar methods are treated in Refs. 3, 5, 6, and 7.

Ramsauer's scattering apparatus is shown schematically in Fig. 4-1-1. Electrons are produced photoelectrically at the zinc plate P and accelerated to the desired energy by a potential difference between P and the first slit S_1. A properly adjusted, uniform magnetic field perpendicular to the plane of the drawing causes some of these electrons to travel in circular paths through S_1 and the other collimating slits, S_2–S_7, and into the Faraday cage F, if they do not undergo collisions in their passage through the apparatus. Any electrons experiencing elastic scattering through angles greater than the angular aperture of the system will fail to reach F. Also, any electrons that suffer even slight reductions in their velocity as the result

---

* Several recent studies of the elastic scattering of electrons have been made and should be mentioned here because of their special importance. A sharp resonance in helium at 19.3 $\pm$ 0.1 ev has been observed by G. J. Schulz, *Phys. Rev. Letters* **10**, 104 (1963) with a high resolution double electrostatic analyzer (see Section 5-9-D). At the Third International Conference on the Physics of Electronic and Atomic Collisions (London, 1963) Schulz also reported resonances below the first electronically excited state for neon atoms and N_2, CO, and N_2O molecules. Similar work on helium and neon was described by J. A. Simpson at the same conference and discussed by J. A. Simpson and U. Fano, *Phys. Rev. Letters* **11**, 158 (1963). The resonance at 19.3 ev in helium has also been observed with lower resolution by R. J. Fleming and G. S. Higginson, *Proc. Phys. Soc.* **81**, 974 (1963). Also, at the London conference, R. H. Neynaber, S. M. Trujillo, L. L. Marino, and E. W. Rothe described measurements of the total cross section for scattering of electrons by metastable helium in the 2^3S state at impact energies near 1 ev.

of inelastic encounters will thenceforth travel in orbits of smaller radius and be prevented from reaching F.

Now consider the beam of nearly monoenergetic electrons which remain unscattered before entry into the collector region C. Any of the electrons that experience collisions before passage through S_7 will be collected by C; the remainder is received by the Faraday cage F. It then follows that if the pressure and the arc length between S_6 and S_7 are known, the total collision cross section can be determined by measuring the currents to C and F and using the relationship in (1-4-9).

It is important in beam experiments that a given projectile avoid multiple collisions with target particles; otherwise it might be deflected out of the beam in the first impact but scattered into the collector in a subsequent collision. Multiple collisions will occur to a negligible extent if the

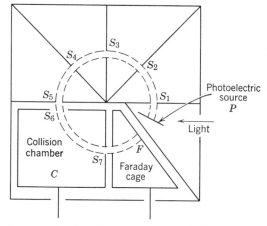

FIG. 4-1-1. Ramsauer's apparatus for the measurement of electron collision probabilities.

product of the target pressure and thickness is so low that the probability of even a single impact is small. Experimental checks are made to establish that the desired "thin target" conditions prevail by determining whether the collected currents vary linearly with the target gas pressure. In Ramsauer's apparatus rather high gas pressures (up to about 10^{-2} mm Hg) were used, but the flight path of the electrons was short enough that only single collisions occurred in most cases. In the apparatus shown in Fig. 4-1-1 the mean diameter of the path of the unscattered electrons was 20 mm. The beam was 1 mm wide and 8 mm high.

It must be emphasized that the measured cross section will equal the total elastic scattering cross section only if the electron energy is lower than the energy for excitation of any of the levels of the target gas molecules.

Otherwise, inelastic collisions make a contribution to the measured cross section. In Ramsauer's experiments provision was not made for separating the contributions of inelastic and elastic scattering. However, most of his work was done at energies low enough that inelastic collisions did not play a major role. In certain other types of apparatus[7] the scattered electrons are analyzed in energy by retarding potential techniques or deflection in electric or magnetic fields, so that only elastically scattered electrons are detected in the collector.

It is obvious that since any apparatus has a finite resolving power the cross sections that are measured correspond to scattering through angles greater than some finite minimum angle and cannot refer to the true total values. This is not so serious a matter in electron measurements as it is in the study of the scattering of heavy particles, since the scattering is not nearly so strongly peaked in the forward direction.

Brode[3] has collected data obtained in single-beam experiments on a large number of gases and vapors and has averaged the results. His curves are presented in Fig. 4-1-2.* References to the original papers from which Brode's data were drawn are cited in his review. The differences between Brode's curves and the data of the individual investigators were seldom as large as 10%, except at very low energies. This fact, coupled with the general agreement of these results with those obtained by other methods, indicates that the curves are reliable over most of the energy range.

Brode has expressed his results in terms of the probability of collision P_c, which is the average number of collisions experienced by a projectile in 1 cm of path through the target gas at 1 mm pressure and 0°C (Section 1-4-G). The cross section is given in terms of the probability of collision by the equation

$$q_s = 0.283 \times 10^{-16} P_c \text{ (in cm}^2) = 0.322 P_c (\text{in } \pi a_0^2) \qquad (4\text{-}1\text{-}1)$$

P_c is related to λ_{1mm}, the scattering mean free path at 1 mm Hg, by the equation

$$P_c = \frac{1}{\lambda_{1mm}} \qquad (4\text{-}1\text{-}2)$$

In Fig. 4-1-2 the quantity plotted along the abscissa is the electron velocity in units of $(\text{volt})^{1/2}$. The electron energy at any point along the abscissa is obtained in ev by squaring the value of the abscissa at that point. If E represents the energy in ev, the electron velocity is given by the equation

$$v = 5.93 \times 10^7 (E)^{1/2} \text{ cm/sec} \qquad (4\text{-}1\text{-}3)$$

The most striking feature of Fig. 4-1-2 is the rapid variation of P_c with electron velocity in most of the gases. Of particular interest are the curves

* Similar curves for many other gases are collected in Brown.[6]

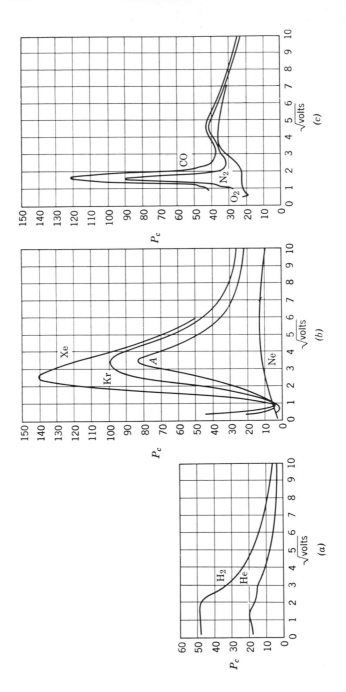

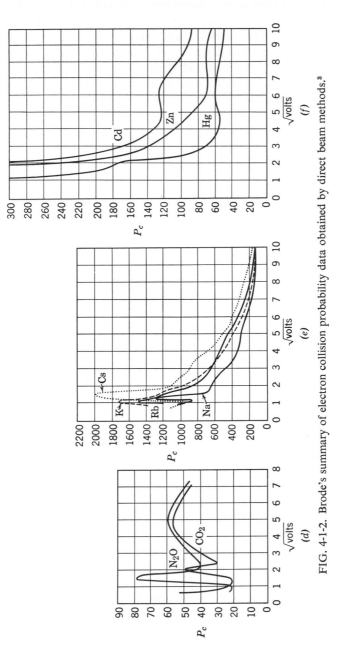

FIG. 4-1-2. Brode's summary of electron collision probability data obtained by direct beam methods.[3]

in Fig. 4-1-2b for the heavier noble gases. It will be noticed that in xenon, krypton, and argon the cross section falls to a very low value in the vicinity of 1 ev.* This marked transparency in a narrow range of energy, observed in certain other gases as well, was discovered by Ramsauer[3] and independently by Townsend and Bailey,[10] who used a diffusion method. The *Ramsauer-Towsend effect* was in violent disagreement with the classical theory of scattering, which predicted a monotonic increase in the cross section with decreasing electron energy. Quantum theory was required for the explanation of the observed scattering (Section 4-4), and, indeed, the necessity of explaining the scattering behavior of slow electrons provided a powerful impetus to the development of the quantum theory of atomic collisions.

The potential field of the outer electrons of the target particles is the major factor in determining the probability of collision. The polarizability of the molecules, and thus the distortion of the potential field by the incident electrons, is also important. Consequently, there is close similarity within a chemically similar group of gases, but large differences are observed as we go from one group to another. It is particularly interesting to note the enormous difference in the collision probabilities for the noble gases and the alkalis. For example, at 2 ev P_c is about 40 times as large for cesium as for xenon, which lies adjacent to cesium in the periodic table. The small values for the noble gases are due to the compact structure of the atoms, which have closed outer electron shells, whereas the huge values for the alkalis are a reflection of the diffuse structure of these atoms, each of which possesses one loosely bound valence electron. Interesting general trends may be noted among the monatomic elements of Fig. 4-1-2: for electron energies of about 100 ev the collision probability is inversely proportional to the ionization potential and directly proportional to the polarizability of the atoms. At high energies the cross section drops off about as $1/v$. This behavior is indicative that polarization attraction is the determining factor in the scattering at high energy.

A few general comments about beam methods for determining elastic scattering cross sections are in order. An advantage offered by these methods is the direct nature of the measurements they permit. However, the usual difficulties associated with the use of very low energy beams of charged particles (due principally to stray fields, contact potentials, and mutual electrostatic repulsion) prevent the extension of these methods to energies much below 1 ev. In beam experiments on elastic scattering

---

* The curve for argon appears to be slightly inaccurately drawn in the low-energy region. The early experiments indicated that the minimum cross section for argon actually occurs at an energy of about $\frac{1}{4}$ ev, and this result has been substantiated by various investigators in recent years.

extreme gas purity is usually not so essential as it is in certain other types of measurements, such as those of electron attachment cross sections, in which the impurities may have cross-sections orders of magnitude larger than those of the main target gas. However, insulating surface layers of condensable impurities can cause trouble by acquiring electric charge, particularly at beam slits. It is thus necessary to guard against the entry of pump oil vapor into the collision chamber by careful baffling and cold-trapping of the pumps, and a bakeable system that permits the elimination of layers which are formed in spite of all precautions is desirable. Coating the critical surfaces with an inert metal such as gold also helps greatly. (Silver is a poor choice.) Good electrostatic and magnetic shielding of the collision volume is an obvious necessity. The only solution to the problem of mutual electrostatic repulsion is to operate with low beam currents and to make sure that the measured cross sections are independent of the beam current.

B. DIFFUSION METHODS. Measurements at extremely low energies are made possible by various methods that involve the diffusion of electrons through a gas. These valuable methods were first employed by Townsend and Bailey[11] and further developed and used by Huxley and others.[9,12] We are not in a position to discuss the details of the diffusion techniques until we reach Chapter 11, so only a brief outline of the original method of Townsend and Bailey is presented here. Two separate measurements were required in these studies. The first was a determination of the lateral spread of a diffuse stream, or shower, of electrons moving a few centimeters through the gas in a weak axial electric field. (The gas pressures were of the order of 20 mm Hg, and the field strength of the order of a few volts/cm.) The second measurement was of the lateral deflection of the shower in a perpendicular uniform magnetic field. From these measurements the average kinetic energy of the electrons and the mean drift velocity could be deduced. This made it possible to calculate the mean free path of the electrons, whose energies were distributed about the measured mean value of the energy, which quantity could be varied by changing E/p, the ratio of the field strength to the pressure. The mean free path was defined to correspond to collisions of such an average character that the electrons after a collision have zero mean velocity in their original direction.

The results obtained by diffusion methods are in fair agreement with those obtained by other techniques. Some of the observed differences in the published values may be ascribed to differences in the definitions of the measured quantities. The peaks observed in the diffusion experiments are not so sharp as those in the direct beam experiments because the electrons are not even approximately monoenergetic.

Diffusion experiment results obtained before 1940 were collected and discussed by Healey and Reed.[13] Some of the work done since that time is cited in Ref. 12.

C. MICROWAVE METHODS.   Several microwave techniques have been developed for determining the electron collision probability, most of the work having been done by Brown and his colleagues at the Massachusetts Institute of Technology.   The various methods used are summarized by Brown[6] and Wharton.[14]   Microwave experiments are especially important because they can cover the energy range extending from thermal values up to several ev.   The quantity they yield is the collision probability for momentum transfer P_m, which is the reciprocal of the mean free path for momentum transfer at 1 mm Hg, defined in Section 1-6.   At energies up to several ev, P_m differs at most only slightly from P_c, so that the microwave data may be compared readily with results of other types of experiments. In some cases the lack of agreement among the low-energy results is pronounced.   It is currently believed that some of the microwave data might be faulty because the electrons were not in thermal equilibrium with the gas, as had been assumed.[15]   Also, serious discrepancies are to be expected among the results of beam experiments at energies below about 1 ev for reasons discussed earlier in this section.

Let us now sketch one of the microwave methods—that used by Phelps, Fundingsland, and Brown.[16]   Consider electrons oscillating in a gas of uniform pressure with a radian frequency ω under the influence of an electric field of intensity $E = E_0 e^{i\omega t}$.   Because of collisions, the molecules may be considered to exert a continuous viscous damping force on the electrons.   According to Newton's second law, the average motion of the electrons may be described by the equation

$$f = -cv_d - eE_0 e^{i\omega t} = \frac{d(mv_d)}{dt} \tag{4-1-4}$$

where f denotes the total force on an electron, c is the damping constant, v_d is the average velocity of the electrons,* and m is the electronic mass. A physically realistic choice for the damping constant is mv_m, where v_m is the collision frequency for momentum transfer, given in terms of the total collision frequency v, and the center-of-mass scattering angle Θ by the equation

$$v_m = v\overline{(1 - \cos \Theta)} \tag{4-1-5}$$

---

* v_d is usually called the "drift velocity" of the electrons and is given in terms of the velocity distribution function by (2-12-8).

We shall assume here that v_m is independent of v_d, so that the solution of (4-1-4) for v_d is

$$v_d = \frac{-e/m}{i\omega + v_m} E \tag{4-1-6}$$

Now the electronic current density J_e is given by

$$J_e = -nev_d \tag{4-1-7}$$

where n is the number density of the electrons; thus the complex conductivity is

$$\sigma_c = \sigma_r + i\sigma_i = \frac{J_e}{E} = \frac{ne^2/m}{i\omega + v_m} \tag{4-1-8}$$

The real and imaginary components, σ_r and σ_i, respectively, of the complex conductivity are seen to be equal to

$$\sigma_r = \frac{ne^2}{m\omega} \frac{v_m/\omega}{(v_m/\omega)^2 + 1} \tag{4-1-9}$$

and

$$\sigma_i = \frac{-ne^2}{m\omega} \frac{1}{(v_m/\omega)^2 + 1} \tag{4-1-10}$$

The ratio of the real and imaginary components is thus

$$\left| \frac{\sigma_r}{\sigma_i} \right| = \frac{v_m}{\omega} \tag{4-1-11}$$

It follows that in principle the collision frequency, and thus the collision probability, for momentum transfer can be determined by measuring the complex conductivity in a microwave discharge, if the pressure and applied frequency are known. The analysis presented here is a drastic oversimplification of the difficult analysis actually required in practice. Two sources of complication are the dependence of the collision frequency on the velocity and the fact that the velocity distribution of the electrons must be taken into account.

A block diagram of the apparatus used by Phelps, Fundingsland, and Brown[16] to determine the conductivity ratio in (4-1-11) is shown in Fig. 4-1-3. A 10-cm pulsed magnetron is used to break down periodically the gas contained at a few mm Hg pressure in the resonant cavity shown at the extreme right and thus provide a plasma whose conductivity is to be measured. The change in the cavity impedance due to the presence of the free electrons is measured by using a continuous-wave tunable magnetron and a standing-wave detector which is sensitive only for a period of a few microseconds during the afterglow.* The transient standing-wave detector

* The *afterglow* is the period following the removal of the source of excitation during which the gas remains ionized to an appreciable extent.

consists of a calibrated waveguide-beyond-cut-off attenuator followed by a superheterodyne receiver whose local oscillator frequency is controlled by a delayed sweep from a single sweep oscilloscope. The output of the receiver is observed on the oscilloscope, and the standing-wave ratio is determined by adjusting the calibrated attenuator to maintain constant amplitude at the output of the receiver. The delay circuit for the oscilloscope and the modulator for the pulsed magnetron are synchronized by a trigger generator operating at 60 cps. A cavity wavemeter and a bolometer monitor the

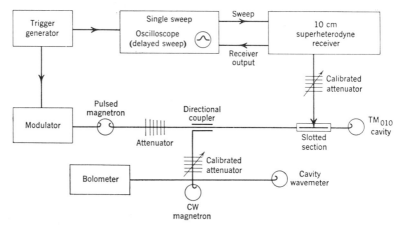

FIG. 4-1-3. Apparatus for determination of the momentum transfer collision probability for electrons by the measurement of the microwave conductivity.[16]

output of the continuous-wave magnetron. The power incident on the cavity is controlled by a calibrated variable attenuator.

Some of the data obtained by Phelps, Fundingsland, and Brown on the noble gases are presented in the next section in comparison with data derived from drift velocity measurements. Chen and Raether[17] have applied microwave interferometry techniques[14] to obtain momentum transfer cross sections for electrons of thermal energies (mean energies of about 0.06 to 0.071 ev) with cesium atoms. Their values for the probability of momentum transfer in collisions of electrons against Cs atoms can be represented by the equation

$$P_m = (997/E - 4810/E^{1/2} + 7230)/cm \qquad (4\text{-}1\text{-}12)$$

where E is the electron energy in ev. These results approach the values obtained by Brode at higher electron energies.*

* Excellent agreement with experiment has been obtained in recent calculations by W. R. Garrett and R. A. Mann, *Phys. Rev.*, **130**, 658 (1963).

D. THE DRIFT VELOCITY METHOD.   Rigorous transport theory shows that the momentum transfer cross section may be determined as a function of electron energy from measurements of the average velocity of electronic drift through a gas in a dc electric field, provided the electron energy distribution is known. Using apparatus described in Section 11-2-B, Pack, Voshall, and Phelps[18] made very careful determinations of the electronic drift velocity in a number of atomic and molecular gases. They then used the data that corresponded to the lower electronic energies, for which the energy distribution is the same as that of the gas, to determine cross sections consistent with the measured drift velocities. Their results are shown in Figs. 4-1-4 and 4-1-5, in which they are compared with the results obtained by other investigators. The data of Pack, Voshall, and Phelps are among the most reliable of all those available in the indicated energy range.

It may be noted that the momentum transfer cross section in helium is constant over the range 0.003–0.05 ev, having the value 5.3×10^{-16} cm^2. Pack and Phelps[18] state that the cross section in helium probably rises by

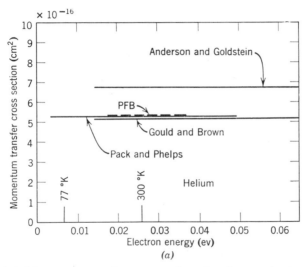

FIG. 4-1-4. Momentum transfer cross sections for electrons in the noble gases, as derived from drift velocity and microwave experiments. (a) The temperatures indicated are the electron-volt equivalents of kT. (b) The three solid curves drawn for argon, krypton, and xenon correspond to various choices of power series expansions used in the theoretical analysis. Drift velocity measurements: J. L. Pack and A. V. Phelps, *Phys. Rev.* **121,** 798 (1961); J. L. Pack, R. E. Voshall, and A. V. Phelps, *Phys. Rev.* **127,** 2084 (1962). Microwave measurements: A. V. Phelps, O. T. Fundingsland, and S. C. Brown, *Phys. Rev.,* **84,** 559 (1951); L. Gould and S. C. Brown, *Phys. Rev.* **95,** 897 (1954); J. M. Anderson and L. Goldstein, *Phys. Rev.* **102,** 933 (1956).

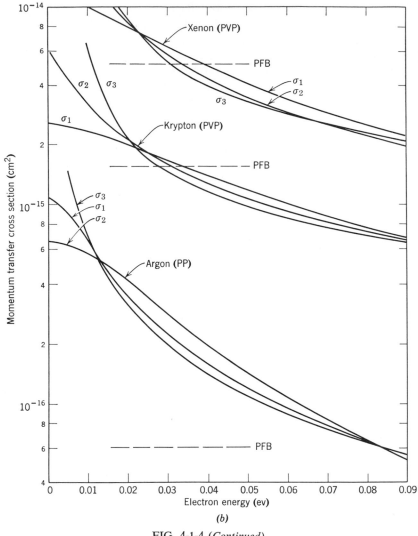

FIG. 4-1-4 *(Continued)*

20% as the electron energy is increased to 1 ev. The cross section is dependent on the energy in the other gases investigated. The triads of solid
curves drawn for argon, krypton, xenon and ammonia correspond to
various choices of power series expansions used in the theoretical analysis.
Figure 4-1-4b indicates that the microwave data reported for argon by
Phelps, Fundingsland, and Brown[16] were obtained for electrons that were
not in thermal equilibrium with the gas. On the other hand, Pack, Voshall,

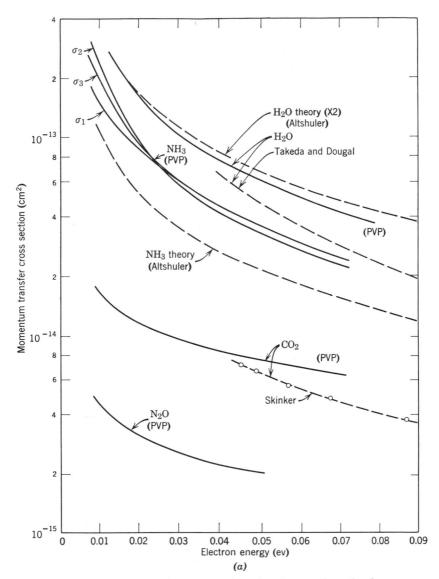

FIG. 4-1-5a. Momentum transfer cross sections for electrons in molecular gases, as derived from drift velocity measurements by Pack, Voshall, and Phelps. Data from other sources are presented for comparison. J. L. Pack, R. E. Voshall, and A. V. Phelps, *Phys. Rev.* **127**, 2084 (1962); M. F. Skinker, *Phil. Mag.* **44**, 994 (1922); S. Takeda and A. A. Dougal, *J. Appl. Phys.* **31**, 412 (1960); S. Altshuler, *Phys. Rev.* **107**, 114 (1957).

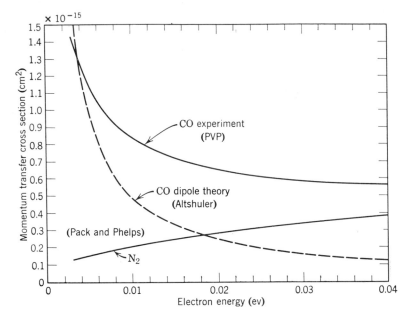

FIG. 4-1-5*b*. The difference between CO and N_2 in their ability to scatter electrons is very interesting. In most properties, the two molecules are very similar, and the very small dipole moment of CO can usually be ignored. These results indicate that here the dipole moment is of over-riding importance, despite its small magnitude.

and Phelps obtained good agreement in krypton and xenon with PFB, who assumed the cross section to be constant in their analysis. If the data of Phelps, Fundingsland, and Brown are reanalyzed with the correct energy dependence, their cross sections agree within experimental error with those obtained by Pack, Voshall, and Phelps[18] for krypton and xenon over the energy range 0.015–0.06 ev.

Drift velocity data for electrons at higher energies can also be analyzed to provide cross sections at these energies. These determinations require the solution of the Boltzmann equation for the electron energy distribution appropriate to the higher values of E/p used in these measurements. Inelastic collisions must be considered in the case of molecular gases. Momentum transfer cross sections have been obtained for hydrogen and nitrogen in this manner by Frost and Phelps,[19] who used the following approach:

Rotational excitation and momentum transfer cross sections for low-energy electrons in hydrogen and nitrogen were obtained from a comparison of theoretical and experimental values for the mobility and diffusion coefficients (see Chapters 9 to 11.) The theoretical values of the transport coefficients were derived by calculating accurate electron energy distribution functions, using an assumed set of elastic and inelastic cross sections. The discrete nature of the energy loss occurring in a rotational or vibrational excitation collision was included in the theory, as were collisions of the second kind* with thermally excited molecules. The resulting values of drift velocity and characteristic energy $\mathscr{D}/\mathscr{K}$ (cf. Section 11-2-A) were compared with experimental data, and adjustments were made in the assumed cross sections until good agreement was obtained.

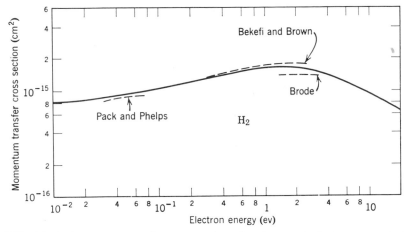

FIG. 4-1-6. Momentum transfer cross sections for electrons in hydrogen, as derived by Frost and Phelps[19] (solid curve). Also shown are data of J. L. Pack and A. V. Phelps, *Phys. Rev.* **121,** 798 (1961); G. Bekefi and S. C. Brown, *Phys. Rev.* **112,** 159 (1958); and R. B. Brode, *Rev. Mod. Phys.* **5,** 257 (1933).

The momentum transfer cross sections found in this manner are plotted in Figs. 4-1-6 and 4-1-7, which also show data obtained by other investigators. The inelastic cross sections which Frost and Phelps[19] obtained for electrons in hydrogen will be presented in Section 5-10-F. The technique described here is also being used to study other molecular gases.†

* A "collision of the second kind" is one in which internal excitation energy of one particle is transferred to another particle in the form of kinetic energy. The energy transfer is in the opposite direction, that is, from the kinetic to the potential form, in a collision of the first kind.

† The work of Frost and Phelps[19] on H_2 has been extended to higher energies and to D_2 by A. G. Engelhardt and A. V. Phelps, *Phys. Rev.* **131,** 2115 (1963). Cross sections for momentum transfer, rotational, vibrational, and electronic excitation, and ionization were investigated. Phelps and his co-workers have also obtained preliminary values of elastic and inelastic cross sections for A, Cs, N_2, O_2, CO, and CO_2 (unpublished).

E. CROSSED-BEAM METHODS.   The study of collisions between electrons and chemically unstable systems, such as hydrogen atoms, is very difficult and usually requires the use of special crossed-beam techniques if direct measurements are to be made. Some of these techniques were introduced around 1930.[7] They have been greatly extended and improved in recent years and are now being used in many laboratories for various types of experiments. In this section we shall describe first the crossed-beam apparatus used by Neynaber and his colleagues for electron scattering studies and present some of the experimental data obtained on the elastic

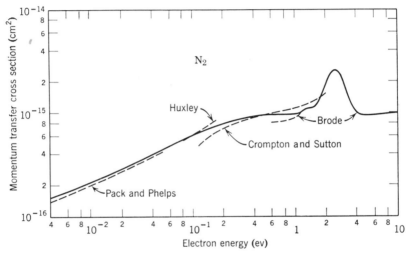

FIG. 4-1-7. Momentum transfer cross sections for electrons in nitrogen, as derived by Frost and Phelps[19] (solid curve). Also shown are data of J. L. Pack and A. V. Phelps, *Phys. Rev.* **121**, 798 (1961); L. G. H. Huxley, *Australian J. Phys.* **9**, 44 (1956) and *J. Atmospheric Terrest. Phys.* **16**, 46 (1959); R. W. Crompton and D. J. Sutton, *Proc. Roy. Soc.* (London) **A-215**, 467 (1952); and R. B. Brode, *Rev. Mod. Phys.* **5**, 257 (1933).

scattering of electrons by atomic hydrogen, oxygen, and nitrogen. Then we shall describe the atomic beam recoil techniques used by Bederson's group for studies of electron scattering by alkali atoms.

The technique used by Neynaber et al.[20] for measuring the scattering cross sections of atoms normally present in molecular form is the following. The number of electrons scattered from a region defined by the intersection of a dc electron beam and a modulated (i.e., mechanically interrupted) molecular beam is compared with the number scattered when the beam is partially dissociated. The molecular dissociation is accomplished in a radio-frequency discharge, and the degree of dissociation (typically about 30%) is measured with a mass spectrometer. From the scattering and dissociation data, the ratios of the atomic to molecular scattering cross sections are obtained at various energies. The absolute atomic values are calculated by multiplying these ratios by the molecular cross sections obtained by other investigators who used single-beam methods.

A schematic diagram of the apparatus is shown in Fig. 4-1-8. Not shown is the vacuum envelope, which is made of cadmium-plated mild

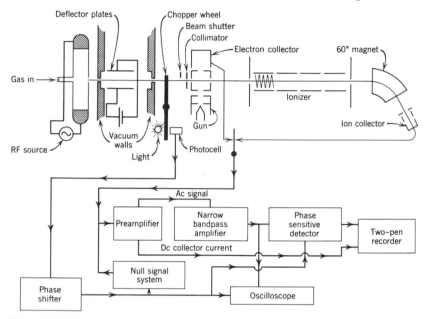

FIG. 4-1-8. The crossed-beam apparatus used by Neynaber, Marino, Rothe, and Trujillo.[20] The scattering occurs in the electron gun. The distance from the rf source to the electron gun is 21 cm.

steel in order to minimize stray magnetic fields. A neutral beam consisting entirely of molecules may be produced by the effusive flow of a molecular gas through a hole in the side of an unexcited discharge tube located in the first of three vacuum chambers. Alternatively, a partially dissociated beam may be obtained by striking a discharge within the source. The pure or mixed beam passes through a bulkhead slit into an intermediate chamber whose primary function is to provide vacuum isolation from the source. Here, also, any charged particles present in the beam are removed by a pair of oppositely charged deflector plates. As the beam emerges into the scattering chamber, it is chopped by a slotted rotating wheel at 101.8 cps, and it is further collimated by a slit just in front of the electron gun mount. It may be interrupted by a beam shutter, if desired. The neutral beam proceeds through the electron gun, where it intersects the electron beam and scatters electrons at the chopping frequency. The attenuation of the electron beam due to scattering by the neutral beam is measured as an ac signal. Finally the neutral beam enters a mass spectrometer where it is partially ionized so that the degree of dissociation of the original beam may be determined.

Typical pressures in the scattering chamber are 6×10^{-7} and 2×10^{-7} mm Hg with the gas flow on and off, respectively. The presence of background gas in the collision region dictates the use of a modulated neutral beam, since a pressure as low as 6×10^{-7} mm Hg corresponds to a number density of about 2×10^{10} molecules/cm³. If the neutral beam is run in the dc mode, it is impossible to distinguish between electrons scattered from the beam and from the background gas. With mechanical interruption of the beam, however, only scattering at the modulation frequency enters into the cross section calculation, and the dc contribution due to the background gas may be eliminated.

The gun that supplies the low-energy electrons for the scattering from the molecular beam is constructed of stainless steel parts, except for the filament which is thoriated tungsten. The gun is surrounded by a stainless steel oven which allows it to be outgassed at 250°C in order that its surfaces may be cleaned. The electron gun is normally degassed for about two hours, and then its temperature is lowered to 200°C, where it is held while measurements are being made. Electron beam currents of several micro-amperes are employed.

The relative cross section at each accelerating voltage is obtained from a ratio of ac electron currents measured at the collector with the rf discharge inactive and then active. In principle, the two intersecting beams should be the same size. The electron beam, by definition, consists only of electrons reaching the collector. If any part of the electron beam fails to pass through the neutral beam, the currents will not be appropriate for the calculation of this ratio. If the neutral beam is too large, then some electrons may be deflected into the collector, decreasing the angular resolution. Alignment difficulties necessitate the use of a molecular beam height larger than the electron beam diameter, which is about 0.10 in. However, variations of the neutral beam height from 1.8 to 2.4 times greater than the electron beam diameter produce no observable change in the relative cross section obtained. The normal molecular beam height is about 0.20 in. and its width is about 0.10 in.

The energy of the electrons, as well as the energy spread, is determined by applying retarding potentials (V) to the collector and observing the collector currents (I). The energy spread (defined as the width at half-maximum of dI/dV versus V) is 0.45 ev at 11 ev and 0.33 ev at 2.3 ev. The angular resolution of the gun is calculated to be 25°. This is the scattering angle for which the efficiency of detection of scattering is 50%. Most of the scattered electrons are detected, and the total cross section can be obtained directly from the measurements. By contrast, in the apparatus used earlier by Brackmann, Fite, and Neynaber[21] to determine the total scattering cross section for atomic hydrogen, only about 10% of the scattered electrons are collected, and the use of a theoretical angular distribution was required to project the data into a total collision cross section.

The electron collector circuitry involves conventional phase-sensitive narrow-bandpass amplification, with certain modifications described by Neynaber and his colleagues.[20] Although the sensitivity of the electronics is about 10^{-14} amp, electron gun noise limits detection to about 10^{-13} amp. The reader should refer to the papers of Neynaber and his associates for a discussion of the various tests and checks they performed in order to establish the validity of their results.

The apparatus shown in Fig. 4-1-8 has been used for measurements of the total scattering cross section for electrons on atomic hydrogen and atomic oxygen.[20] Neynaber et al.[22] have also used this apparatus with modified atom and electron sources for measurements on atomic nitrogen. These modifications were necessary because of the greater difficulty in dissociating molecular nitrogen. The results of the hydrogen measurements are displayed in Fig. 4-1-9, where they are compared with readjusted data of Brackmann, Fite, and Neynaber[21] and with various theoretical predictions.[23-29] The oxygen and nitrogen data are shown in Figs. 4-1-10 and 4-1-11, respectively. The oxygen and nitrogen experiments were motivated by an interest in the properties of high-temperature air, whereas the practical interest in the cross sections for the hydrogen atom centers about their importance in astrophysical and fusion research. These cross sections are also of great theoretical interest because they provide sensitive tests of the various approximation methods to which recourse must be made in collision theory. Since the wave functions for the hydrogen atom are completely and exactly known, many cross sections which cannot be calculated at the present time for more complex structures may be calculated for this atom.

Perel, Englander, and Bederson[30] have used the *atomic beam recoil technique* to measure the total cross sections for the scattering of electrons by lithium, sodium, and potassium in the range of about 1 to 10 ev. In this method an atomic beam is cross-fired by a modulated electron beam, and the total scattering is observed by measuring the decrease in atomic-beam intensity in the forward direction, caused by momentum transfer during the scattering process. A phase-sensitive lock-in amplifier is used to detect the atomic scattering signal, which is obtained at the modulation frequency from a continuously oxygenated surface ionization detector.

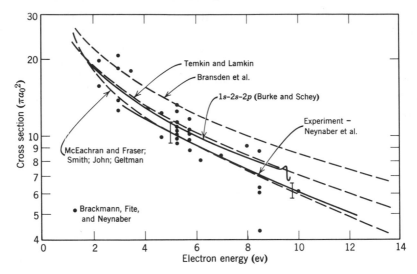

FIG. 4-1-9. Elastic scattering cross sections for electrons on atomic hydrogen, taken from the paper by Burke and Schey.[29] The experimental data of Neynaber and his co-workers[20] refer to elastic scattering only at electron energies below the first excitation energy of the hydrogen atom, 10.15 ev. The solid dots denote cross sections computed by Neynaber et al. from measurements by Brackmann et al.[21] The remaining data represent the results of theoretical calculations: Bransden, Dalgarno, John, and Seaton[23] employed a variational calculation containing both s- and p-wave scattering. Temkin and Lamkin[24] calculated s-, p-, and d-wave scattering by the method of polarized orbitals. McEachran and Fraser,[25] Smith,[26] and John[27] employed numerical methods with exchange approximations (see end of Section 4-4). Geltman[28] used a variational method in which a trial function allowed for the virtual excitation of the 2s and 3s states. Burke and Schey[29] utilized a close-coupling approximation in which the total wave function is expanded in hydrogen eigenstates, and only terms corresponding to the 1s, 2s, and 2p states are retained. Note the resonance at 9.61 ev shown on the curve of Burke and Schey. For a general discussion of the scattering of low-energy electrons by hydrogen atoms, see P. G. Burke and K. Smith, *Rev. Mod. Phys.* **34,** 458 (1962).

The principal limitation to the recoil method is the relatively poor detection efficiency for most neutral atoms. However, the alkalis can be detected with exceptionally high efficiency by using surface ionization (see Section 13-6). This method possesses certain advantages over the method described above, in which observations are made on the scattered electron beam. In the recoil method one is not concerned with the trajectories of the scattered electrons, and consequently it is not necessary to use a highly collimated electron beam. This fact permits the use of a simple electron gun design, as well as an axial magnetic field to confine the beam. Also, the problems associated with stray electric fields at low energies are

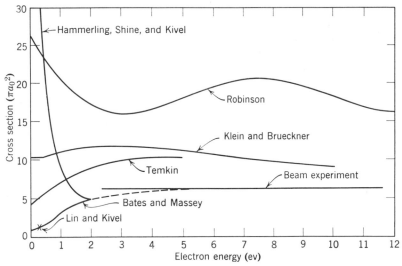

FIG. 4-1-10. Total collision cross sections for electrons scattered by atomic oxygen, taken from the paper by Neynaber et al.[20] The curve designated "beam experiment" represents the experimental data of Neynaber and his colleagues. The point marked "Lin and Kivel" denotes the result obtained from a shock tube experiment; the remaining curves refer to the results of theoretical calculations in which various approximations were employed. For references, see the paper by Neynaber et al.[20] Additional calculations on atomic oxygen, and C, Cl, and F, as well, are described by J. W. Cooper and J. B. Martin, *Phys. Rev.*, **126**, 1482 (1962).

diminished, since the trajectories of the scattered neutral atoms are unaffected by these fields. The results obtained by Perel, Englander, and Bederson on sodium and potassium are in good agreement with Brode's values (Section 4-1-A). Brode did not study lithium because of the experimental difficulties associated with the high temperatures required to obtain a suitably dense lithium target and because of the serious corrosive action of hot lithium vapor.

4-2. MEASUREMENT OF THE ANGULAR DISTRIBUTION OF ELASTICALLY SCATTERED ELECTRONS

Ramsauer and Kollath[31] were among the first to study the angular dependence of the elastic scattering of electrons. Their "zone" apparatus, shown in Fig. 4-2-1, was used for measurements at very low electron energies on several simple gases. The apparatus had an over-all length of about 20 cm, and pressures of the order of 10^{-3} mm Hg were used in the scattering chamber. Electrons from an oxide-coated filament entered the collision volume at the center of the sphere defined by the curved metal plates, and

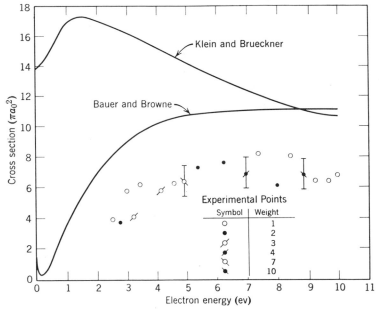

FIG. 4-1-11. Total collision cross sections for electrons scattered by atomic nitrogen. The experimental data were obtained by Neynaber et al.[22] The curves show the results of theoretical calculations by M. M. Klein and K. A. Brueckner, *Phys. Rev.* **111**, 1115 (1958) and by E. G. Bauer and H. N. Browne, whose work has not yet been published but is discussed by Neynaber et al.[22]

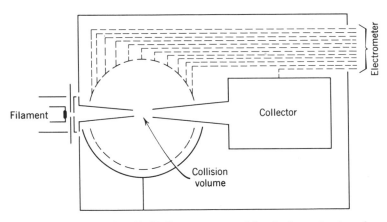

FIG. 4-2-1. Ramsauer and Kollath's "zone apparatus" for the determination of angular scattering distributions.[31]

the angular scattering distribution was determined by measuring the electron currents to each of the 11 plates. There was cylindrical symmetry about the axis of the electron beam so that the reduction of the experimental data could be effected in a straightforward manner.

Inelastic scattering becomes significant at energies above those studied by Ramsauer and Kollath, but the elastic contribution to the total scattering may be separated out if retarding potential techniques or some other form of energy selection are employed to reject inelastically scattered electrons. Several of these schemes are discussed by Massey and Burhop.*

Figure 4-2-2 shows Massey and Burhop's summary of some of the angular distribution data obtained during the 1930's in investigations of elastic scattering. (Similar figures that present inelastic contributions appear in Section 5-6, in which references to the original experiments are given.) The agreement among the results of the individual measurements by various investigators was usually very good, and in many cases the data presented in Fig. 4-2-2 were obtained with a given apparatus and are not the average of those obtained in measurements made with different equipment. The most striking feature of this figure is the appearance of distinct maxima and minima, which arise from the diffraction of the electron waves by the target atom. In general, the complexity of the angular pattern increases with the atomic number of the scatterer.

The presence of the electron gun in Ramsauer and Kollath's apparatus prevents the extension of measurements to very large angles. Gagge[32] built an apparatus that permits measurements up to and including 180° (see Fig. 4-2-3). A uniform magnetic field perpendicular to the plane of the drawing causes the elections coming from the gun G to move in a circular path. After scattering, the electrons move along another circular arc, such as $P_1 S_1 S_2$, into the collector C. A definite scattering angle corresponds to each path. To permit observations at different angles, the collector and its associated slit S_2 can be moved parallel to $S_1 S_2$, with S_1 being held fixed. Evidently scattering at either point P_1 or P_2 will cause electrons to follow the indicated final trajectory and be detected in the collector; the scattering angle is the same in either case. This fact must be taken into account in the calculation of the variation of the scattering volume with angle. With this apparatus, Gagge obtained good agreement with other investigators in the angular regions where comparisons could be made.

Figure 4-2-4 shows a schematic diagram of the crossed-beam apparatus used by Gilbody, Stebbings, and Fite[33] to investigate the angular distribution of the elastic scattering of electrons by hydrogen atoms. Atomic hydrogen is produced by dissociation of hydrogen gas in a tungsten

* See p. 84–99 of Ref. 7.

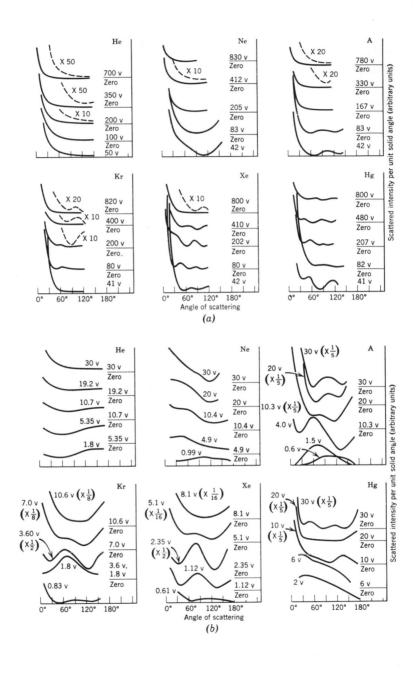

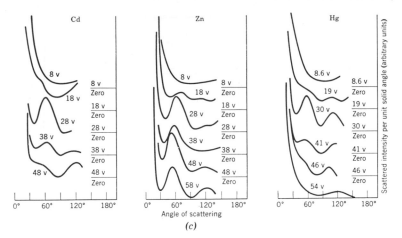

FIG. 4-2-2. Massey and Burhop's summary of data on the angular distribution of elastically scattered electrons. Studies of the elastic and inelastic differential scattering of electrons by argon atoms were recently reported by J. O. Porteus at the Third International Conference on the Physics of Electronic and Atomic Collisions, London, 1963.

furnace operated at about 2000°C. The mixed beam issuing from this furnace flows through a differentially pumped chamber, where it is interrupted at a frequency of 100 cps by a rotating chopping wheel. Any charged particles in the beam are swept aside by electrostatic deflection plates before the beam enters the high vacuum chamber, in which it is intersected by a slow-electron beam. The atomic number density in the neutral beam is of the order of $10^8–10^9/cm^3$.

The slow-electron beam crosses the atomic beam at right angles, and some of the scattered electrons enter the electron multiplier at the left, which serves as the detector. The scattering angle is scanned by rotating the electron gun assembly in the plane perpendicular to the drawing and to the atomic beam. Thus the scattering volume is determined by the cross-sectional area of the atomic beam, which is 9mm in diameter, and is constant for all scattering angles. An angle of about 10° at the scattering center is subtended by the aperture in front of the multiplier. The ac signal from the multiplier is amplified and applied to a phase-sensitive detector whose reference signal is derived from a photocell and light at the chopper. The rectified output of the

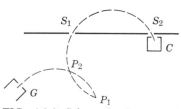

FIG. 4-2-3. Schematic diagram of Gagge's scattering apparatus.[32]

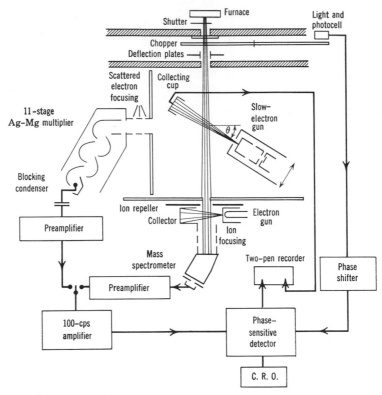

FIG. 4-2-4. The crossed-beam apparatus used by Gilbody, Stebbings, and Fite[33] for the study of the angular distribution of electrons scattered elastically from hydrogen atoms.

detector is monitored for correct phasing on an oscilloscope before integration and display on a pen recorder.

The dc slow-electron current of about 0.5 μa is monitored by a small collecting cup placed in front of the gun and rotating with it. The electron energy is determined by a retarding potential analysis of the current to this cup. Difficulties in focusing the electron beam in the presence of the stray 60-cps magnetic field from the furnace preclude measurements at energies below about 3.8 ev.

The electron gun below the collision volume ionizes a fraction of the beam from the furnace to permit analysis of the beam composition in the mass spectrometer. Molecular hydrogen is found to be the only significant impurity in the beam. The dissociation fraction as determined by the mass spectrometer is typically 90%.

The major problem in this experiment is the high noise background. At large scattering angles, the noise is due to the electrons scattered by the background gas, and at small angles imperfectly focused electrons from the gun enter the multiplier directly. This effect precludes measurements at scattering angles less than 30°. Careful screening of the exposed portions of the gun assembly is required to prevent the escape of stray electrons. All metallic surfaces in the vicinity of the slow electrons are gold-plated and capable of being heated to eliminate surface films and contact potentials. Nonmagnetic materials are used throughout.

Preliminary measurements were made with molecular hydrogen, and the angular distributions of the observed scattering were compared with

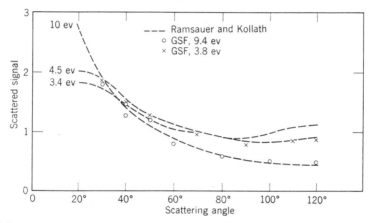

FIG. 4-2-5. Comparison of the results obtained by Gilbody, Stebbings, and Fite for elastic scattering of electrons from hydrogen molecules with the data of Ramsauer and Kollath.

those reported by Ramsauer and Kollath.[31] Good agreement was obtained, as indicated by Fig. 4-2-5. The ratio of the atomic and molecular scattering cross sections was obtained by comparing the scattered signal from a highly dissociated beam, corresponding to a high furnace temperature, with the signal obtained from the same flow of gas with the furnace at room temperature.

The experimental differential scattering cross sections for atomic hydrogen are presented in Fig. 4-2-6 for four electron energies. These cross sections, which are shown as dots, were deduced by normalization to the absolute data on molecular hydrogen published by Ramsauer and Kollath.[31] Values calculated by Burke and Schey[29] in the $1s$-$2s$-$2p$ close-coupling approximations are shown in Fig. 4-2-6 as full lines.

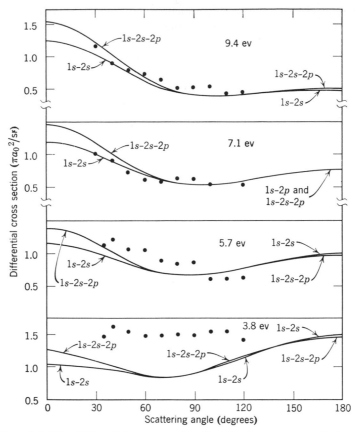

FIG. 4-2-6. The differential cross section for elastic scattering of electrons from hydrogen atoms, at four incident electron energies. The circles indicate the experimental data of Gilbody, Stebbings, and Fite.[33] The solid curves represent the values calculated by Burke and Schey.[29]

4-3. THE CALCULATION OF ELECTRON MOMENTUM TRANSFER
CROSS SECTIONS FROM DIFFERENTIAL SCATTERING DATA

The momentum transfer cross section q_D is defined in terms of the CM differential elastic scattering cross section $I_s(\Theta)\, d\Omega_{CM}$, and the CM scattering angle Θ, by the equation

$$q_D = \int (1 - \cos \Theta)\, I_s(\Theta)\, d\Omega_{CM} \qquad (1\text{-}6\text{-}1)$$

Accordingly, the momentum transfer cross section for electrons in a given gas may be obtained easily from measurements of the laboratory differential cross section for elastic scattering. Figure 4-3-1 shows the results obtained by Massey and Burhop* for electrons in helium, neon, and argon. As is apparent from (1-6-1), q_D differs significantly from the total collision cross section q_s only when the scattering is concentrated in the forward or the backward direction. At low energies these two cross sections are nearly the same for electrons.

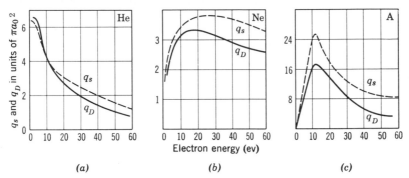

FIG. 4-3-1. Comparison of momentum transfer cross sections q_D with total collision cross sections q_s.

4-4. CALCULATIONS ON THE ELASTIC SCATTERING OF ELECTRONS

The Born approximation is not generally valid for calculations on the elastic scattering of electrons in the energy range of interest to us,[34] and computations must be made by the more laborious method of partial waves. The first calculations of this type for electron scattering were made by Holtsmark,[35] who investigated the scattering of slow electrons by argon and obtained very good agreement with experiment. Holtsmark used the Hartree potential† modified by an empirical polarization correction and evaluated the phase shifts by numerical integration of the differential equations. The polarization correction accounts for the perturbation of the atomic field by the incident electron and introduces an additional attraction between the electron and target atom. This correction was found to be necessary for the detailed explanation of the Ramsauer-Townsend effect, which was discussed in Section 4-1.

The following qualitative remarks show why the Ramsauer-Townsend effect might be expected in the heavier noble gases. Owing to the compact structure of a noble gas atom, the force it exerts on an approaching electron is short-range and strong at small r. Hence the potential field may be approximately represented by a deep, narrow potential well, such

* See p. 15 of Ref. 7.
† See D. R. Hartree, *The Calculation of Atomic Structures*, Wiley, New York, 1957.

as that shown in Fig. 3-15-2. For electrons of very low energy the radius of the potential well is small compared with the electron wavelength, and only s-wave scattering will make an important contribution to the total scattering. For certain bombarding energies the s-wave function of the incident electron may be "drawn in" by the attractive potential to just the extent that a phase shift equal to an integral multiple of π results. Then, by (3-15-34), the s-wave contribution to the scattering cross section becomes zero, and since the higher wave contributions are known to be small the total cross section falls to a very low value.* This effect may be regarded as a manifestation of the diffraction of the electron wave by the target atom.

The steepness of the wall of the potential well increases with the atomic number of the noble gas atom, so that the Ramsauer-Townsend effect is most pronounced with xenon. The effect is still strong in krypton and argon but it is not observed in neon and helium (see Fig. 4-1-2). However, the Ramsauer-Townsend effect does appear for certain other atoms and for some molecules as well.

A great deal of theoretical work has been done on electron scattering since Holtsmark's initial effort. The most useful general references to these calculations are Massey and Burhop,[7] Mott and Massey,[36] and Wu and Ohmura,[37] and the reviews by Massey,[38] Craggs and Massey,[8] and Moiseiwitsch.[39] References to the extensive recent work on electron scattering by hydrogen and oxygen atoms appear in the papers cited in Section 4-1-E, and in the comprehensive review by Burke and Smith.[40] Figures 4-4-1 through 4-4-3, which show the results obtained by Allis and Morse,[41] Fisk,[42] and Massey and Ridley,[43] indicate the essential validity of the quantal approach to the scattering problem. By contrast, classical calculations yield results that are generally in violent disagreement with experiment. There is some indication, however, that classical theory may lead to meaningful results if the binding energies and momentum distributions of the electrons in the target structure are properly considered. Gryziński[44] has introduced a classical method in which these refinements over the conventional classical theories are contained and which has produced some results in remarkably good agreement with experimental values (see Section 6-15). It is perhaps too early to assess completely the general validity of Gryziński's approach, but it will undoubtedly prove to be of considerable value in certain cases that are not amenable to quantal solution.

* Scattering by a repulsive potential cannot produce this sort of effect. With a repulsive potential, κD, the product of the wave number of the incident electron and the radius of the potential barrier, would have to be at least of the order of unity for the s-wave phase shift to be as large as $-180°$, and for a potential of this great a range higher order waves would contribute to the scattering.

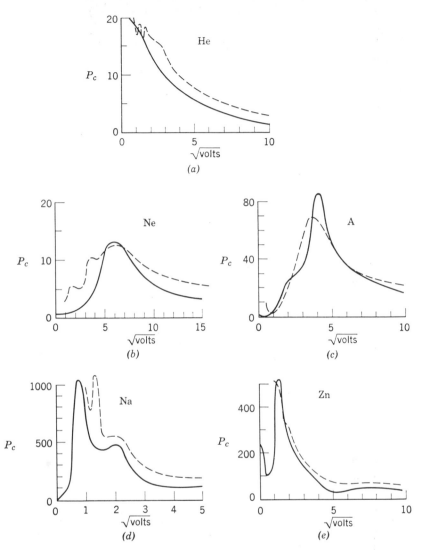

FIG. 4-4-1. Comparisons of the theoretical results of Allis and Morse (solid curves) with experimental observations (dashed curves) on electron scattering.

Although we are not giving a thorough coverage of the scattering theory, one additional point must be brought out here: the necessity of considering the possible effect of *electron exchange* on the scattering. This exchange refers to the changing of position of the incident electron with one of the orbital electrons of the target particle, which is then the one observed in the scattering. The probabilities of direct and exchange scattering cannot be added directly, since the wave amplitudes and not

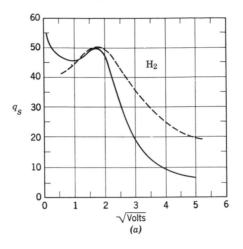

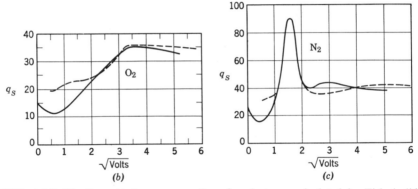

FIG. 4-4-2. Elastic scattering cross sections for electrons calculated by Fisk (solid curves) compared with experimental results (dashed curves). In this figure the cross sections are given in units of a_0^2.

the intensities are the quantities to be combined (see Section 6-13-B). For light atoms and low bombarding energies electron exchange appears to be an important effect, as shown by Fig. 4-4-3. Rubin, Perel, and Bederson[45] have performed an atomic beam recoil experiment for direct study of the exchange scattering of slow electrons by potassium atoms.

PART $\mathscr{B}$. THE ELASTIC SCATTERING OF HEAVY PARTICLES

There are several incentives for studying the elastic scattering of ions, atoms, and molecules. Perhaps the strongest comes from the possibility

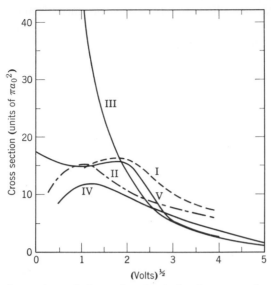

FIG. 4-4-3. Comparison of observed and calculated cross sections for scattering of electrons by molecular hydrogen: I, observed by Ramsauer method; II, observed by swarm diffusion methods; III, calculated by Massey and Ridley, ignoring exchange; IV, calculated by Massey and Ridley, including exchange; V, calculated by Fisk, using an empirical molecular scattering potential with adjustable constants.

of deducing the interaction potential between colliding particles from their scattering behavior. It is also important that cross sections for elastic scattering be available to experimentalists so that they may account for the effects of scattering in various types of experiments involving beams of heavy particles.

Several methods exist for deducing the behavior of heavy particles in elastic scattering. These methods include the analysis of data on transport processes and equations of state, thermal beam studies, and fast beam-scattering measurements. Massey and Burhop* discuss the determination of the interaction potentials between neutral molecules from diffusion, viscosity, and equation of state data. They also treat investigations of ion-molecule interactions that involve the analysis of ionic drift velocity data. Since this subject is discussed at length in Chapter 9, the present discussion is concerned only with beam-scattering studies.

The scattering of thermal beams offers a relatively direct means of investigating intermolecular forces at large separation distances. Because of the difficulty of maintaining a beam of charged particles at low energies, this technique is applicable only to the study of neutral projectiles. Most

* See Chapter VII of Ref. 7.

experiments of this type have involved oven-produced beams of particles with a Maxwellian distribution of velocities. A few investigators, however, have used mechanical velocity selectors to obtain approximately mono-energetic beams of projectiles.

Fast beam-scattering studies complement the thermal studies by providing information concerning particle interactions at close distances of approach. Furthermore, space charge difficulties become much less severe as the beam energy is increased, and it is possible to obtain well-defined beams of ions as well as neutrals at energies above a few electron volts. Fast ion beams are obtained by extracting ions from an ion source and then focusing and accelerating them to the desired energy electrostatically. The phenomenon of charge transfer (see Chapter 6) may be utilized to obtain a neutral beam. The production of such beams is discussed in Section 4-8. Since the spread in energy of the particles in a fast beam is generally small compared with the beam energy, it is not necessary to average over the velocity distribution of the projectiles, as is required in most thermal beam studies.* However, high-energy scattering experiments are difficult to analyze because of the necessity of averaging over beam width and apparatus geometry.

4-5. ANGULAR SCATTERING DISTRIBUTIONS FOR HEAVY PARTICLES

For reasons that will soon become apparent, it is better to discuss the angular distribution of elastic scattering of heavy particles before treating the experimental scattering studies. We have already pointed out in Section 3-12 that the scattering of ions, atoms, and molecules is very strongly peaked in the forward direction, in marked contrast to the behavior exhibited by electrons. This fact, which was deduced experimentally many years ago, is illustrated by a calculation made by Massey and Smith[46] in 1933. They calculated the differential elastic cross section for 110-ev protons in helium and 72-ev protons in argon, with the results shown in Table 4-5-1. Calculations were made for the Hartree field, and for the Coulomb field of the unshielded nuclei as well, to determine the screening effect of the orbital electrons. The effects of polarization and electron exchange were ignored. Massey and Smith showed that the classical theory of Section 3-7 could be used legitimately for all angles except $\Theta \approx 0$. The phase-shift treatment of Section 3-15 was applied for the forward direction. The sharp peaking of the angular distribution

---

* For discussions of these averaging procedures, see E. W. Rothe and R. B. Bernstein, *J. Chem. Phys.* **31**, 1619 (1959); S. Datz, D. R. Herschbach, and E. H. Taylor, **35**, 1549 (1961), K. Berkling, R. Helbing, K. Kramer, H. Pauly, Ch. Schlier, and P. Toschek, *Z. Physik.* **166**, 406 (1962).

TABLE 4-5-1. Differential elastic scattering cross sections per unit solid angle calculated for protons by Massey and Smith[46]

$I_s(\Theta)$ in Units of a_0^2 per Unit Solid Angle

CM Scattering Angle in Degrees	Argon (72-ev protons)		Helium (110-ev protons)	
	Hartree	Coulomb	Hartree	Coulomb
0	16×10^4	∞	9×10^3	∞
12	22.0	1.58×10^4	7.85	124.0
28	7.20	770	2.00	6.10
34	2.76	365	0.72	2.85
57	0.93	51	0.21	0.40
80	0.48	15	0.08	0.12
114	0.14	5.3	0.04	0.04
137	0.08	3.5	–	0.03
167	0.05	2.6	–	0.02

about the forward direction is indeed dramatic. The forward concentration of the scattering becomes even more pronounced as the energy increases, and Massey and Smith state that for 1000-ev protons in argon the intensity per unit solid angle at 0° is at least 10^5 times that at 10°. Massey and Smith also calculated the total elastic scattering cross sections for protons in helium and argon at several energies. Table 4-5-2 shows that their results do not differ markedly from the cross sections calculated from kinetic theory.

The foregoing discussion suggests that it is fruitless to attempt to measure accurately the total elastic cross section for heavy particles at

TABLE 4-5-2. Total elastic scattering cross sections calculated for protons by Massey and Smith.[46] These cross sections are expressed in units of πa_0^2

Gas	Proton Energy in ev	Massey and Smith's Cross Sections	Gas Kinetic Cross Sections
He	90	3.75	2.6
	800	2.0	–
A	73	16.4	7.3
	650	10.7	–

high energies. The demands on angular resolving power are impossible to meet even at energies as low as a few ev, and the resolving power required increases roughly as the velocity of the incident projectile. A better course is to make careful determinations of the angular distribution of scattering or to measure the scattering through angles greater than some minimum value that can be accurately determined. The analysis of these measurements can be conducted classically, since quantum effects become appreciable only at scattering angles comparable with the angle of resolution that would be required to measure the true total elastic cross section. Fortunately, measurement of the true total cross section is not required for interparticle force determinations—measurements of the cross section for scattering through angles greater than some known minimum angle suffice.[47] It is this cross section that is reported in the literature for heavy projectiles with energies above about 1 ev, although it is usually loosely referred to as the "total elastic scattering cross section."

The situation is more favorable at lower energies. Using the schematic angular distribution for elastic spheres derived by Massey and Mohr,[48] Massey and Burhop[49] have calculated the minimum angle of deflection ϑ_0 which must be counted as a collision in order that the measured cross section may be within 10% of the true value. If D represents the sum of the gas kinetic radii of the projectile and target particles measured in angstroms, m the molecular weight of the projectiles, and T the effective temperature of the projectiles in $°K$, then ϑ_0 is given approximately by the expression

$$\vartheta_0 \approx \frac{277}{D(mT)^{1/2}} \tag{4-5-1}$$

where ϑ_0 is measured in degrees in the laboratory system. The target is assumed here to be at rest in this coordinate system. If the resolution of the apparatus is such that a collision involving a deflection through the angle ϑ_0 can be observed, then further increase in the resolving power will lead to only a slight increase in the measured cross section. Values of ϑ_0 for various projectile-target combinations and several energies are shown in Table 4-5-3. It is shown in the next section that these demands on resolving power, although great, are not impossibly high.

4-6. TECHNIQUES USED IN THERMAL BEAM-SCATTERING STUDIES

Apparatus and techniques used in thermal beam-scattering experiments are discussed by Massey and Burhop,[50] in books and reviews on atomic and molecular beams,[51] and in numerous journal publications, some of which are cited in this section. We shall concentrate here on techniques used in recent experiments by Bernstein and his co-workers at the University of Michigan and by Neynaber's group at General Dynamics.

A. THE APPARATUS OF BERNSTEIN AND CO-WORKERS. In 1959 and 1960 Bernstein and his group conducted a series of experiments in which they measured the total collision cross sections for the interaction of atomic beams of K and Cs[52] and molecular beams of CsCl[53] with a large number

TABLE 4-5-3. Angular resolution requirements for accurate measurement of the total elastic scattering cross section of atomic projectiles on atomic targets.[49]

		ϑ_0 (degrees)							
		Projectile							
Target	Lab Energy of Projectile in ev	He	Ne	A	Li	Na	K	Rb	Cs
He	0.0255 (=300°K)	3.6	–	–	1.5	0.73	0.50	0.36	0.27
	0.0862 (=1000°K)	2.0	–	–	0.80	0.40	0.27	0.20	0.15
	1 (=11,600°K)	0.59	–	–	0.23	0.12	0.08	0.06	0.04
Ne	0.0255 (=300°K)	–	1.4	–	1.4	0.62	0.40	0.27	0.19
	0.0862 (=1000°K)	–	0.75	–	0.75	0.34	0.22	0.15	0.11
	1 (=11,600°K)	–	0.22	–	0.22	0.10	0.06	0.04	0.03
A	0.0255 (=300°K)	–	–	0.70	0.87	0.41	0.27	0.19	0.14
	0.0862 (=1000°K)	–	–	0.30	0.48	0.23	0.15	0.10	0.08
	1 (=11,600°K)	–	–	0.11	0.14	0.07	0.04	0.03	0.02

of scattering gases of varied complexity and reactivity. The apparatus they used in their atomic beam studies is shown schematically in Fig. 4-6-1. Not shown here is the vacuum envelope, which is divided by a slotted bulkhead at C into two separately pumped regions, the "oven chamber" and the "detector chamber." Typical operating pressures in these chambers, which contain large liquid nitrogen traps and baffles, are 5×10^{-7} and 1×10^{-7} mm Hg, respectively. The vacuum envelope has an 8-in. diameter and is 24 in. long.

The main components of the apparatus are a Monel oven A and slit B for production of the neutral beam, a scattering chamber F, and a Langmuir-Taylor surface ionization detector I–J for detection of the unscattered component of the beam. Oven temperatures in the vicinity of 500°K are used for production of K and Cs beams.* The oven is fitted

* Oven temperatures suitable for production of beams of various materials are tabulated on p. 372 of Ramsey.[51]

with an "ideal slit"* of width 0.0025 cm, and a similar slit D is located at the entrance to the scattering chamber for beam collimation. The effective scattering path inside this chamber is 4.44 cm. Pressures in the range of 1×10^{-6} to 2×10^{-4} mm Hg are used in the scattering chamber. These pressures are measured with a Knudsen gage.

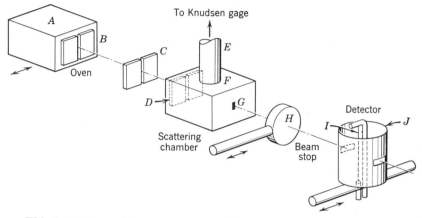

FIG. 4-6-1. Thermal beam apparatus used by Bernstein and his co-workers.[52]

A tungsten filament I about 5 cm long and 0.0025 cm in diameter is used in the surface ionization detector (the action of which is discussed in Section 13-6). The filament is heated to about 1500°K by 75 ma dc and is biased 90 v positive with respect to the ion collector J. A preamplifier and inverse-feedback dc amplifier are used to measure the ion currents, which are typically about 10^{-10} amp, corresponding to a beam intensity of 6×10^8 atoms/sec. The distance from slit B to slit D is 11.12 cm, and slit D is located 19.68 cm from I. The calculated half-width of the unscattered beam at the detector is 0.007 cm; the observed value is about twice the size. The angle subtended at midpoint of the scattering path is about 30 sec, and the over-all resolution of the apparatus is calculated to be 2 min of arc.[53]

For each projectile-target combination the beam intensity is measured for 10 to 20 values of scattering gas pressure, corresponding to 5 to 95% attenuation of the beam. The 100% transmittance level I_0 is recorded before and after each series of measurements during evacuation of the scattering chamber. Plots of the logarithm of the attenuation ratio I/I_0 versus pressure are usually linear for $I/I_0 > 0.1$. From the slope of these

* The design of this type of slit is discussed by R. C. Miller and P. Kusch, *Phys. Rev.* **99**, 1314 (1955).

plots the total cross section q_s may be calculated by means of the Rosin-Rabi equation:[54]

$$q_s = 2(\pi)^{1/2} J(z) \ln \left(\frac{I}{I_0}\right) nd \qquad (4\text{-}6\text{-}1)$$

where n is the number density of the scattering gas, d is the scattering path length, and $J(z)$ is an integral whose value is a function of the masses of the projectiles and target and the temperatures of the beam and scattering gas.

The experimental apparatus and technique used in the CsCl experiments[53] were essentially the same as those we have described. Provision was made, however, for varying the temperature of the scattering gas from 200 to 735°K, and some of the dimensions were changed so that the angular resolution was degraded to 4 min.

Hostettler and Bernstein[55] have also constructed a slotted-disk velocity selector for use in thermal beam-scattering experiments. This device has been used to study the scattering of a monoenergetic beam of lithium atoms by a crossed beam of mercury atoms at 90° incidence[56] and also the "rainbow scattering" (see Section 4-7-B) of velocity-selected K and Cs beams by a crossed Hg beam.[57] The velocity selector is 10 cm long and 16 cm in diameter and consists of six slotted aluminum alloy disks. The velocity resolution ($\Delta v/v$ for Δv at half-intensity) is 0.047, and no velocity sidebands are transmitted. The effective fractional time open to the incident beam is 0.35. At the highest rotor speed (17,000 rpm) the transmitted velocity is 1.05×10^5 cm/sec.

B. THE GENERAL DYNAMICS MODULATED-BEAM SCATTERING APPARATUS. The apparatus previously described is fairly conventional in design and is representative of that used in most of the thermal neutral-beam experiments performed. Neynaber's group at General Dynamics has recently built apparatus[58] which is similar in concept to the conventional type but which incorporates two new features. It employs a modulated beam to reduce the effects of background scattering and utilizes an electron-bombardment ionizer which permits the use of many types of neutral projectiles that cannot be detected by the surface ionization process because of their high ionization potentials. This equipment has been used to study the scattering of He, Ne, A, Kr, and Xe atoms on argon.[58]

The modulated beam apparatus, shown schematically in Fig. 4-6-2, is divided into three separately pumped vacuum chambers. Because the beam material is gaseous at normal temperatures, it is not necessary to use an oven to obtain a beam: atoms are simply allowed to effuse from the source region through a slit. The exit slit is 0.075 mm wide, and the pressure in the source region is adjusted so that the mean free path is about twice the slit width. The beam passes through the collimating slit and scattering chamber, and the undeflected component enters the detector through a 0.038-mm wide slit. The detector is the Bayard-Alpert type. The beam passes coaxially through a grid which has the form of an elliptical helix (7.5-mm major axis and 4-mm minor axis) and is bombarded by electrons over a distance of 5 cm. The electron source is an oxide-coated cathode, from which emission currents of about 40 ma are typically

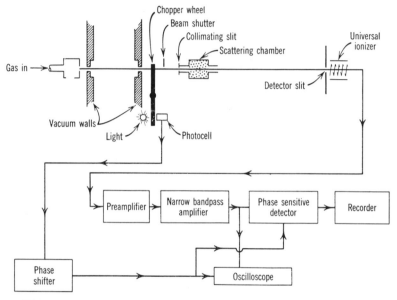

FIG. 4-6-2. The General Dynamics thermal beam scattering apparatus.[58]

drawn. The sensitivity of the ionizer to background gas is 10 μa of ion current/micron of pressure/ma emission.

The beam is chopped mechanically at 101.8 cps, and phase-sensitive detection is used. The distance from the source to the detector is about 60 cm, and the over-all angular resolution of the apparatus is calculated to be 1.5 min of arc.

Experimental values for the collision cross sections are obtained from transmitted beam intensity versus scattering gas pressure plots in the procedure outlined by Rosin and Rabi.[54] However, phase sensitive detection and the electron-bombardment ionizer (which discriminates against the faster projectiles) require a different velocity distribution for the beam particles in the calculation of the cross sections.

The General Dynamics group has also employed a mechanical velocity selector similar to that described by Hostettler and Bernstein[55] to study the scattering of lithium and potassium atoms by the noble gases.[59]

4-7. THERMAL BEAM SCATTERING—THEORY AND EXPERIMENTAL RESULTS*

A. THE TOTAL ELASTIC SCATTERING CROSS SECTION FOR AN ATTRACTIVE INVERSE-POWER-LAW POTENTIAL—THE MASSEY-MOHR THEORY. As pointed out in Section 3-9, classical theory is not applicable to the calculation of the differential scattering cross section at small angles or the total collision cross section. Quantum mechanics is required for a proper description. Here we shall derive an approximate quantum mechanical equation for the total elastic scattering cross section for two particles interacting through an attractive inverse-power-law potential. This derivation is taken from a paper by Massey and Mohr.[60]

Long-range attractive forces usually play the dominant role in determining the scattering behavior of neutral particles at low energies. It is therefore of interest to calculate the total elastic scattering cross section q_s for potentials of the form

$$V(r) \sim -Cr^{-n} \tag{4-7-1}$$

where C is a positive constant and n is a positive integer. According to (3-15-34), q_s may be expressed in terms of the phase shifts η_l as

$$q_s = \frac{4\pi}{\kappa^2} \sum_{l=0}^{\infty} (2l + 1) \sin^2 \eta_l \tag{4-7-2}$$

where

$$\kappa = \frac{M_r v_0}{\hbar} \tag{4-7-3}$$

is the wave number associated with the relative motion of the interacting particles. The reduced mass of the pair of particles is denoted by M_r, and v_0 is their relative velocity of approach at large r.

The phase shifts are given by Jeffreys' approximation (Section 3-15-F) as

$$\eta_l \approx \int_{r_0}^{\infty} \left[\kappa^2 - \frac{2M_r V(r)}{\hbar^2} - \frac{l(l + 1)}{r^2} \right]^{1/2} dr - \int_{r_0'}^{\infty} \left[\kappa^2 - \frac{l(l + 1)}{r^2} \right]^{1/2} dr \tag{4-7-4}$$

where the lower limit of each integral is the zero of the corresponding integrand. This approximation is good in the present context except at very low temperatures. Since we are dealing with heavy particles, a large number of phase shifts is required. By putting $-M_r/\hbar^2$ equal to $\alpha/2$ and

---

* An excellent review of this subject was presented by R. B. Bernstein at the Third International Conference on the Physics of Electronic and Atomic Collisions (London, 1963).

performing a binomial expansion of the square root, we have, for large l,

$$\eta_l \approx \int_{r_0'}^{\infty} \left[\kappa^2 - \frac{l(l+1)}{r^2} \right]^{\frac{1}{2}} \left[1 + \frac{\alpha V/2}{\kappa^2 - l(l+1)/r^2} + \cdots -1 \right] dr$$

$$= \int_{r_0'}^{\infty} \frac{\alpha V/2}{[\kappa^2 - l(l+1)/r^2]^{\frac{1}{2}}} dr \qquad (4\text{-}7\text{-}5)$$

The right-hand side of (4-7-5) is sometimes called the *Massey-Mohr approximation to the phase shifts*. This result is also given[46] by the Born approximation, and (4-7-5) may be used for all values of l. If $\alpha V = -Cr^{-n}$, we have, for large l,

$$\eta_l \approx \frac{C}{2} \int_a^{\infty} \left\{ r^n \left[\kappa^2 - \frac{l(l+1)}{r^2} \right]^{\frac{1}{2}} \right\}^{-1} dr = \frac{C}{2\kappa} \int_a^{\infty} [r^{n-1}(r^2 - a^2)^{\frac{1}{2}}]^{-1} dr$$

where $a = (l + \frac{1}{2})/\kappa$. (In replacing $l(l+1)$ by $(l + \frac{1}{2})^2$, we have made the *Langer modification*.) Integration gives

$$\eta_l \approx \frac{C}{2\kappa a^{n-1}} f(n) = \frac{C\kappa^{n-2}}{2(l + \frac{1}{2})^{n-1}} f(n) \qquad (4\text{-}7\text{-}6)$$

where

$$f(n) = \begin{cases} \dfrac{n-3}{n-2}\dfrac{n-5}{n-4} \cdots \dfrac{1}{2}\dfrac{\pi}{2} & (n \text{ even}) \\[3mm] \dfrac{n-3}{n-2}\dfrac{n-5}{n-4} \cdots \dfrac{2}{3} & (n \text{ odd}) \\[3mm] 1\,(n=3); \quad \dfrac{\pi}{2}(n=2) \end{cases} \qquad (4\text{-}7\text{-}7)$$

Massey and Mohr have shown that this equation holds accurately if η_l is less than 0.5, and then $\sin \eta_l \approx \eta_l$. Therefore if m denotes that value of l for which $\eta_l = 0.5$, the contribution to q_s arising from the phases $l > m$ is

$$\frac{4\pi}{\kappa^2} \sum_{l=m}^{\infty} (2l+1) \sin^2 \eta_l \approx \frac{8\pi}{\kappa^2} \sum_{l=m}^{\infty} \frac{C^2}{4} \frac{\kappa^{2n-4}}{(l + \frac{1}{2})^{2n-3}} f^2$$

$$\approx 2\pi C^2 \kappa^{2n-6} f^2 \int_m^{\infty} (l + \tfrac{1}{2})^{-2n+3} dl = \frac{2\pi C^2 \kappa^{2n-6}}{2n-4} (m + \tfrac{1}{2})^{-2n+4} f^2$$

$$= \frac{4\pi}{n-2} \frac{(m + \frac{1}{2})^2}{\kappa^2} \eta_m^2 = \frac{\pi}{n-2} \frac{(m + \frac{1}{2})^2}{\kappa^2} \qquad (4\text{-}7\text{-}8)$$

since $\eta_m = 0.5$. The contribution to q_s from waves $l < m$ is

$$\frac{4\pi}{\kappa^2} \sum_{l=0}^{m-1} (2l+1) \sin^2 \eta_l \approx 2\pi \frac{m^2}{\kappa^2} \qquad (4\text{-}7\text{-}9)$$

Therefore the total cross section is approximately equal to

$$\pi\left(2 + \frac{1}{n-2}\right)\frac{(m + \frac{1}{2})^2}{\kappa^2}$$

since m is large.* If we now use (4-7-6) and the fact that $\eta_m = 0.5$, we finally obtain the result

$$q_s = \pi\,\frac{2n-3}{n-2}\,f^{2/(n-1)}\left(\frac{C}{\kappa}\right)^{2/(n-1)} \tag{4-7-10}$$

Massey and Mohr[60] estimate that (4-7-10) should give the scattering cross section with an accuracy of about 5%. From (4-7-10) it follows that the total cross section may be written

$$q_s = B\left(\frac{C}{v_0}\right)^{2/(n-1)} \tag{4-7-11}$$

where B is a constant whose value is determined by the value of n. This result holds for potentials which fall off faster than the inverse third power of the separation distance. The differential cross section $I_s(\Theta, v_0)\,d\Omega_{CM}$ cannot be expressed in simple terms.

The Massey-Mohr expression (4-7-11) has been used by various investigators to analyze their experimental results. Before the recent work of Bernstein's group, most of the thermal molecular beam cross section measurements had been confined to a few simple targets (principally the noble gases and homonuclear diatomic gases). For these gases the long-range intermolecular interaction is identified with the attractive induced dipole-induced dipole *London dispersion force*† only. In the event that one (or both) of the colliding molecules has a permanent dipole moment,

---

* The summation (really an integration) over l can be carried out accurately—the Massey-Mohr device of splitting it in two pieces is not necessary. Equation 4-7-10 is accurate for $n = \infty$ but 7% too low for $n = 6$, as shown by use of the equation at the bottom of p. 416 of L. D. Landau and E. M. Lifshitz, *Quantum Mechanics, Non-relativistic Theory*, Addison-Wesley, Reading, Mass., 1958.

† This force arises in the following manner. At any instant the electrons in one non-polar molecule have a configuration that results in an instantaneous dipole moment. This moment induces a dipole moment in a neighboring nonpolar molecule, and these two moments interact to produce a force of attraction between the two molecules irrespective of the orientation of the instantaneous dipole in the first molecule. This type of interaction was first investigated quantum mechanically by London. The forces are called "dispersion" because they may be expressed in terms of the oscillator strengths that arise in the theory of the dispersion of light. The induced dipole-induced dipole interaction, and higher order contributions to the dispersion energy as well, is discussed at length by J. O. Hirschfelder, C. F. Curtiss, and R. B. Bird, *Molecular Theory of Gases and Liquids*, Wiley, New York, 1954, Section 3 of Chapter 1 and Part III. The influence of higher order effects on collision cross sections was discussed by P. R. Fontana at the Third International Conference on the Physics of Electronic and Atomic Collisions (London, 1963).

dipole-induced dipole (and dipole-dipole) interactions may also be significant. To a first approximation, all three types of interaction are expressible in terms of an inverse-sixth-power dependence on the separation distance at large r. Long-range forces such as those discussed here are the familiar *van der Waals forces*. They can be described rigorously in terms of the physical properties of the separated molecules. For short-range *valence* (or *chemical*) forces, on the other hand, a rigorous treatment is not possible in terms of the properties of the separated molecules. For these forces it is necessary to consider each pair of interacting molecules as a special case. The valence forces do not concern us in the present discussion—they are important only in higher energy scattering.

The experiments of Rothe and Bernstein[52] were designed to investigate the general applicability of the Massey-Mohr theory. The interaction of K beams with 77 polar and nonpolar target gases was studied, and 16 gases were used with Cs projectiles. Principally because of difficulties associated with clogging of the oven beam slit, the absolute accuracy of the measurements was only about 15%; however, relative values were obtained with about 3% accuracy. Hence the results of Rothe and Bernstein are reported as the ratio $q_s{}^*$ of the cross section for a given molecule to that of argon for the same beam projectile. These relative cross sections varied from 0.29 to 2.8. The data were correlated by using the Massey-Mohr theory, assuming an attractive interaction potential of the form $V(r) = -C'r^{-6}$. For this potential $q_s = 4.662 \times 10^{11}(C'/v_0)^{2/5}$, when cgs units are employed. The constant C' was estimated from standard formulas for the London dispersion and dipole-induced dipole forces with available refraction and dipole-moment data. The values thus calculated differ by a nearly constant factor from the experimental results; therefore the relative values are predicted with good accuracy. The discrepancy between the calculated and observed values of $q_s{}^*$ was less than $\pm 3\%$ in 57% of the gases studied and less than $\pm 10\%$ for 87% of the target molecules. Most of the large deviations occurred for the light scattering gases. The good correlation of the relative cross sections with the Massey-Mohr theory indicates that this theory provides a sound theoretical basis for discussion of thermal energy elastic scattering cross sections. However, the absolute values of the measured cross sections are about 50% higher than the predictions of the theory. Measurements made by Estermann, Foner, and Stern[61] for Cs on He with extremely high resolution (5 sec) produced an even greater discrepancy, although high resolution experiments by Pauly[62] on K-N_2 and Cs-N_2 led to values that were in fair agreement with Rothe and Bernstein's. It appears that the matter of angular resolution needs further investigation, and the theoretical estimation of $C'_{\text{dispersion}}$ should also be refined.

The work of the Michigan group was extended by Schumacher, Bernstein, and Rothe[53] to the use of cesium chloride beams, with the primary objective of observing directly the influence of dipole-dipole forces on the scattering. The temperature of the scattering gas could be varied from 200 to 735°K. For the nonpolar target gases studied the observed small temperature dependence of q_s agrees within experimental error with that expected from the temperature dependence of the relative velocity, and the relative values of the cross sections are predicted by the Massey-Mohr theory with fair accuracy. For the polar gases the measured cross sections are large, and they decrease significantly with increasing temperature. Because of the large dipole-dipole interaction, the approximate theoretical treatment (based on the limiting temperature-dependent dipole-dipole contribution to the constant C') accounts only semiquantitatively for the observations.

Other experimental investigations of value in assessing the validity of the Massey-Mohr theory for various projectile-target combinations have been made by Pauly,[63] Hostettler and Bernstein,[56] Schoonmaker,[64] Rothe et al.,[58,59] Kydd,[65] and Harrison.[66] One of the papers by Pauly[63a] is of particular interest because it contains an analysis of the effect of angular resolution on the measured cross section. Pauly showed that in the scattering of potassium atoms from He, A, N_2, and Hg about 99 % of the total cross section was obtained with an angular resolution of about 1.5 min. Additional theoretical papers of relevance here are listed at the end of the chapter.[67]

B. RAINBOW SCATTERING. In a classical analysis of molecular beam scattering Mason[68] pointed out the possibility of observing a singularity and discontinuity in the angular distribution at a critical deflection angle, which has subsequently been called the "rainbow angle" (see Section 3-7). This angle corresponds to the trajectory exhibiting maximum attraction between the interacting particles, and its determination gives directly the depth of the potential energy minimum. Using the velocity selector described in Section 4-6-A, Morse, Bernstein, and Hostettler[57] have observed rainbow scattering for potassium and cesium atoms on mercury vapor. Without velocity selection, there was no evidence of rainbow scattering.*

C. QUANTUM EFFECTS IN THERMAL BEAM SCATTERING. The partial wave analyses of scattering made by Massey and Mohr[48,60] in 1933 and 1934 indicated that quantum mechanical interference effects are to be expected

* Rainbow scattering has also been observed recently in studies of collisions of potassium atoms with krypton and hydrogen bromide—see D. Beck, *J. Chem. Phys.* **37**, 2884 (1962).

when the de Broglie wavelength of the relative motion is of the same order of magnitude as the range of the molecular interaction. However, it was not until 1960 that such quantum effects were observed. The observations were made by Hostettler and Bernstein[56] in the scattering of a mono-energetic Li beam by a crossed Hg beam. Lithium atoms were chosen as the projectiles because of their low mass and large wavelength. Figure 4-7-1 shows their data on the variation of the total cross section with the

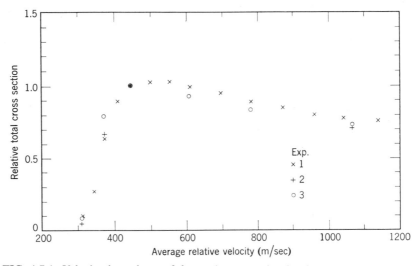

FIG. 4-7-1. Velocity dependence of the total cross section for the scattering of lithium atoms by mercury.[56]

average relative velocity. The sharp drop in the cross section as the velocity is decreased to about 450 m/sec is very unusual and is not in harmony with the Massey-Mohr formula (4-7-11). In addition, undulations are observed in the experimental plots of scattered intensity versus laboratory angle (Fig. 4-7-2). These undulations are believed to be real interference effects originating from the wave nature of the interacting beams. Similar effects were not observed in scattering of K on Hg[56] but did appear in experiments on the scattering of velocity-selected lithium atoms on xenon performed by Rothe et al.[59]

D. SCATTERING OF METASTABLE ATOMS. Several studies[69] have been made on the scattering of metastable atoms of helium in various gases. The metastable states are produced in a low voltage discharge or by bombardment of a beam of neutrals by electrons from a gun. Detection is accomplished by secondary emission from a metal surface, as described

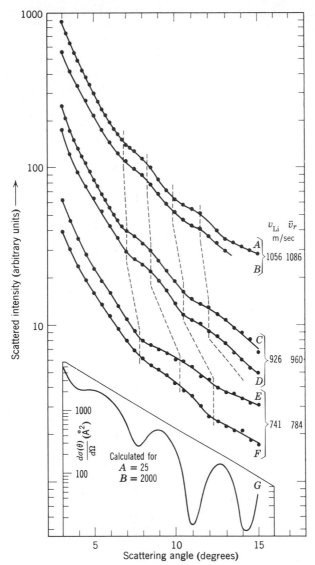

FIG. 4-7-2. Angular dependence of the scattering of Li by Hg.[56]

in Part 5 of Section 13-2-A. The cross section for scattering of the triplet atoms is greater than that for the singlets.

E. INELASTIC COLLISIONS AT THERMAL ENERGIES. Although the behavior of molecules colliding at thermal energies usually involves elastic scattering, which is determined by the long-range van der Waals forces, rotational or vibrational excitation of one or both of the collision partners is also a possibility. Furthermore, chemical reactions may occur, and, in fact, molecular beam studies have recently begun to yield important quantitative information on the nature and cross sections of chemical reactions. Most of our knowledge concerning such reactions has come from measurements of reaction rates as a function of the temperature and concentration of reacting bulk chemicals. Although this approach has been productive, it has severe limitations. The finer details are obscured by the lack of control over the energies of the molecules, by the inability to observe anything other than average behavior, and in many instances by the remote connection between the observed rate and the mechanics of the process of interest. The use of molecular beams can obviate these difficulties. In fact, molecular collisions that lead to reaction can be studied almost ideally by molecular beams, if velocity-selected beams and mass spectrometric identification of the products are employed. The application of molecular beam techniques to investigations of chemical reactions and surface phenomena has been surveyed by Datz, Taylor, and Fite.[70] Recent papers are listed in Ref. 71. Important advances are to be expected from such studies in the future.

4-8. BEAM TECHNIQUES USED FOR STUDIES OF THE ELASTIC SCATTERING OF FAST HEAVY PARTICLES

We define a fast beam as one whose particles have kinetic energies considerably in excess of normal thermal energies. The energy range of primary interest to us extends from a few ev up to about 2 kev. The lower limit is imposed by the difficulties of handling beams of slow ions,* the upper limit by the complications introduced by inelastic reactions. The work done before about 1950 is well covered by Massey and Burhop;[72] therefore we shall concentrate on recent studies. The best reference to this recent work is the excellent review by Mason and Vanderslice.[47] Of particular interest is their discussion of experimental uncertainties in beam experiments and the averaging procedures required in data analysis.

Figures 4-8-1 and 4-8-2 show schematically two types of apparatus used in beam studies of the elastic scattering of fast heavy particles and illustrate many of the techniques in current use.

A. THE APPARATUS OF CRAMER AND SIMONS. An important series of measurements[73] on the elastic scattering of positive ions in the energy

---

* This difficulty is encountered even in studies of neutral particles. Except in thermal beam experiments, it is always necessary to start with a beam of ions to obtain a beam of neutral atoms or molecules. The technique for fast neutral beam production is discussed in Section 4-8-B.

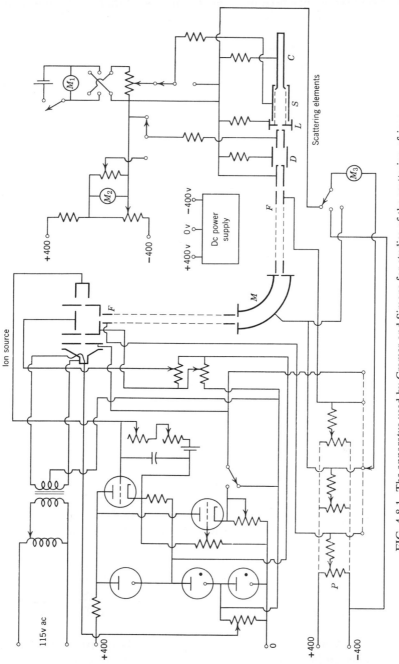

FIG. 4-8-1. The apparatus used by Cramer and Simons for studies of the scattering of ions.

range 4 to 400 ev has been made in the last few years by the group at the University of Florida. A description of one version of their apparatus follows.

The apparatus of Cramer and Simons, shown in Fig. 4-8-1, consists of a mass spectrometer, which is used to produce an ion beam, and a collision chamber and beam collector. A conventional type of ion source is employed. Electrons from a tungsten filament are accelerated to the desired energy and formed into a beam by a slit system. A jet of gas from a hydrodynamic nozzle (not shown in the figure) crosses the electron beam in a nearly field-free region. Positive ions formed here are extracted by an electric field and enter a fore chamber in which they are focused into a beam by the hollow coaxial cylinders F. The only opening between the source and the fore chamber is a 2-mm hole through which the beam passes. High-speed mercury diffusion pumps with liquid air traps are connected to this and each of the other chambers of the apparatus. The focused beam is then deflected through 90° in the magnetic field M for mass separation and again focused before passing through the defining elements D and into the collision chamber S.

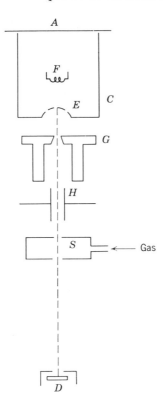

FIG. 4-8-2. A schematic drawing of the apparatus used by Amdur and his co-workers for experiments on the scattering of fast neutral particles.

The entrance to S is small enough to allow the collision chamber to be held at a pressure of about 5×10^{-3} mm Hg without an appreciable pressure rise in the mass spectrometer. The ion beam passes along the axis of S and is caught in the collector C. The dashed lines inside S represent a helical grid which is coaxial with the beam.

The diameter of the defining holes in D is 2.04 mm and that of the entrance aperture in L is 3.03 mm. The radius of the collector is 2.59 mm, and the scattering path is 35.45 mm long. From these dimensions we see that the angular aperture of the apparatus varies from about 4° at the front of the collision region to 90° at the end.

Under vacuum conditions, about 98% of the beam passes through S and is collected in C. When scattering gas is admitted to S, ions are lost from the beam both by elastic scattering and by charge transfer.* In general, these ions will be collected partly on the grid and partly on S, as the undeflected ions pass into C. An ion formed from a stationary target gas molecule by transfer of an electron between a projectile and the target molecule has a low initial kinetic energy (in the present case generally no more than about 0.25 ev). Thus, as S is made positive with respect to L and C, the ions produced by charge transfer will be repelled from S and collected on the grid. On the other hand, if S is made sufficiently negative, all scattered positive ions will be collected on S. If the currents to S and to the grid are measured as functions of the potential difference between S and the grid, it is possible to deduce values for the "total" elastic scattering and the charge transfer cross sections. Cramer and Simons show that ionization of the target gas begins to be appreciable only at the upper end of their energy range.

Apparatus of the type shown in Fig. 4-8-1 has been used in a number of studies[73] of the positive ions of hydrogen and the noble gases and for several experiments[74] on negative ions of hydrogen and oxygen as well.

B. THE NEUTRAL BEAM APPARATUS OF AMDUR AND CO-WORKERS.   Amdur and his colleagues at the Massachusetts Institute of Technology have used apparatus of the type shown schematically in Fig. 4-8-2 for an extensive series of investigations[75] of the scattering of neutral beams of hydrogen and noble gas atoms and nitrogen molecules. Ions are formed[76] in a low voltage arc between the filament F and the anode A, and some of them are extracted through the grid E mounted on the cathode C. After being accelerated to the desired energy by the ion gun G, some of these ions undergo charge transfer with neutral residual gas in the vicinity of the hole in G and become neutralized. The condenser plates H sweep aside the charged component of the mixed beam, and the remaining neutral component passes into the scattering chamber S. The unscattered neutral particles are then detected by the thermopile D. The neutral particles have almost exactly the same energy as the charged particles before neutralization, since very little energy is lost in the charge transfer process. Some energy spread is produced, however, by the uncertainty in the point of formation of the ions inside the source and the fact that some ions are neutralized between E and G before receiving the full intended acceleration. For this reason, use of the apparatus is limited to energies above about 100 ev. The highest energy at which measurements are made is 2100 ev.

4-9. RESULTS OF ELASTIC SCATTERING STUDIES WITH FAST BEAMS

A sample of the results of scattering experiments on heavy particles in the energy range 4 to 400 ev is given in Fig. 4-9-1. The shape of these

* A detailed discussion of the phenomena of charge transfer appears in Chapter 6.

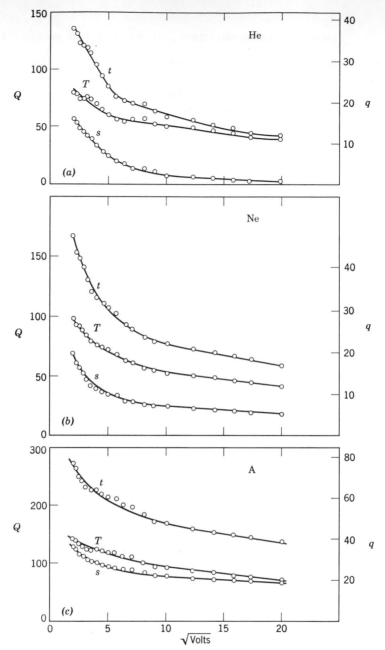

FIG. 4-9-1. Experimental values for scattering cross sections of ions in He, Ne, and A. The macroscopic cross sections Q are expressed in units of cm^{-1} and the microscopic cross sections q in units of 10^{-16} cm^2. The symbol s refers to elastic scattering, T to charge transfer, and t to the sum of s and T. (a) He^+ on He, W. H. Cramer and J. H. Simons, *J. Chem. Phys.* **26,** 1272 (1957); (b) Ne^+ on Ne, W. H. Cramer, *J. Chem. Phys.* **28,** 688 (1958); (c) A^+ on A, W. H. Cramer, *J. Chem. Phys.* **30,** 641 (1959).

curves is typical of the others obtained by Cramer and Simons.[73] The reader is directed to the references already cited for additional data on energies below several kev. Data on angular distributions at these energies are contained in Massey and Burhop[72] and papers by Berry.[77] The methods of determining the interaction potentials from scattering data are discussed by Mason and Vanderslice,[47] who also present the results thus derived from studies of many particle combinations at energies up to 5 kev.* One point stressed by Mason and Vanderslice is the following: since different models for the potential can reproduce a given set of measured cross sections, it is generally necessary to have some a priori knowledge of the form of $V(r)$ if the results are to have physical significance. If a physically realistic model is chosen, however, the potential parameters can be determined with some precision.

4-10. INVESTIGATIONS OF THE SCREENED COULOMB POTENTIAL BY SCATTERING OF 25 TO 100 kev BEAMS

Long ago it was suggested that the interaction between two atomic structures during a violent collision† may be describable to a good approximation by a *screened Coulomb potential energy function*:

$$V(r) = \frac{Z_1 Z_2 e^2}{r} e^{-r/a} \qquad (4\text{-}10\text{-}1)$$

(cf. Sections 3-8 and 3-17). The first factor is the Coulomb function which expresses the potential energy of two bare nuclei of charges $Z_1 e$ and $Z_2 e$ separated by a distance r. The exponential factor accounts for the screening of the nuclei by the orbital electrons, the spatial extent of the screening being measured by the screening length a. Bohr[78] has suggested the use of the quantity

$$a = \frac{a_0}{(Z_1^{2/3} + Z_2^{2/3})^{1/2}} \qquad (4\text{-}10\text{-}2)$$

for the screening length. Here a_0 is the radius of the first Bohr orbit in the hydrogen atom, 0.53×10^{-8} cm. A different modification of the pure Coulomb potential has also been used to describe the shielding effect of the electrons: Firsov[79] utilizes a screening factor calculated from the Thomas-Fermi statistical model of the atom.

---

* See A. A. Abrahamson, *Phys. Rev.* **130**, 693 (1963) for a recent discussion of the calculation of the potential of interaction between noble gas atoms.
† By a violent collision we mean one in which the impact parameter is small enough, for the given impact energy, that a significant change in the projectile's direction of motion results.

Recently some very interesting and important work has been done by Everhart and his students[80,81] on the scattering of ion beams at energies in the 25 to 100-kev range. Strictly speaking, most of the scattering that occurs at these high energies is inelastic, but the fraction of the projectile energy lost in a collision is so small that it has a negligible effect on the projectile trajectory. The scattering behavior of the beam is almost exactly that corresponding to elastic scattering by the projectile-target potential, and observations of the scattering distributions thus permit accurate calculation of the potential energies of interaction at small separation distances. For the moment, we shall treat these collisions as elastic; in Chapter 6 we discuss the inelastic aspects of the impacts and also describe the experimental techniques used by Everhart's group.

Everhart et al.[80,81] measured differential scattering cross sections for He$^+$ in He, Ne, and A, Ne$^+$ in Ne and A, and A$^+$ in A at beam energies of 25, 50, and 100 kev. The angular range covered (about 4 to 40° in the Lab system) was large enough to permit the calculation of $V(r)$ from the experimental data without any assumption regarding the form of $V(r)$ except that it is monotonically decreasing.[82,83] The calculations were made by classical scattering theory (see the discussion in the following paragraphs). The calculated potential curves were found to fit the Bohr form of the screened Coulomb function very nicely; the fit to the Firsov form was even better. No normalization was necessary. The potential energies corresponding to the small distances of approach (of the order of 10^{-2} Å) achieved in these high-energy experiments are in the range of 1 to 60 kev.

A classical calculation of the differential scattering cross section will be valid if (a) the de Broglie wavelength λ of the projectile is negligible compared with any significant dimension of the scattering center and (b) the collision is well defined within the limitations imposed by the uncertainty principle (cf. Section 3-11). Condition (a) requires that

$$\lambda \ll a \tag{4-10-3}$$

and

$$\lambda \ll d = \frac{Z_1 Z_2 e^2}{\frac{1}{2} M_r v_0^2} \tag{4-10-4}$$

where M_r is the reduced mass of the projectile-target combination and v_0 the initial relative velocity. The length d is known as the collision diameter; it represents the distance of closest approach in a head-on collision in the absence of screening. The collision diameter is a good measure of the size of the scattering center when d/a is small. Condition (b) leads to a lower limit, Θ^*, on the scattering angle, above which the classical calculation is valid:[78]

$$\Theta^* \approx \frac{\lambda}{2\pi a} \tag{4-10-5}$$

For most collisions between atomic structures in the energy range from about 100 ev to several hundred kev the classical calculation of the differential scattering cross section is valid except at very small angles. For example, in 50 kev neon ions on argon[84] $a = 160 \times 10^{-11}$ cm, $d = 78 \times 10^{-11}$ cm, $\lambda = 0.28 \times 10^{-11}$ cm, and $\Theta^* = 2.08 \times 10^{-4}$ radian $= 0.16°$. Thus, both conditions on the validity of a classical description are satisfied for angles greater than $0.16°$.

It is interesting to note[78,85,86] that in the regime specified by (4-10-3) and (4-10-4) the quantum mechanical Born approximation solution for the differential cross section is valid only for angles smaller than Θ^*. Thus in this regime ($\lambda \ll a$; $\lambda \ll d$) the classical and Born solutions are valid in mutually exclusive angular regions. In the regions in which $\lambda \gg d$ the Born approximation is valid for all angles and the classical solution is nowhere valid.

REFERENCES

1. P. Lenard, *Ann. Phys.* **12**, 714 (1903).
2. C. Ramsauer, *Ann. Phys.* **64**, 513 (1921); **66**, 546 (1921).
3. R. B. Brode, *Rev. Mod. Phys.* **5**, 257 (1933).
4. J. S. Townsend, *Electrons in Gases*, Hutchinson's Scientific and Technical Publications, London, 1948.
5. R. Kollath, "Durchgang langsamer Elektronen und Ionen durch Gase," in *Handbuch der Physik*, Vol. XXXIV, Springer-Verlag, Berlin, 1958, pp. 1–52.
6. S. C. Brown, *Basic Data of Plasma Physics*, Wiley, New York, 1959, Chapter 1.
7. H. S. W. Massey and E. H. S. Burhop, *Electronic and Ionic Impact Phenomena*, Oxford University Press, Oxford, 1952, Chapters I-IV.
8. J. D. Craggs and H. S. W. Massey, "The Collisions of Electrons with Molecules," in *Handbuch der Physik*, Vol. XXXVII, Springer-Verlag, Berlin, 1959, pp. 314–415.
9. L. G. H. Huxley and R. W. Crompton, "The Motions of Slow Electrons in Gases," in *Atomic and Molecular Processes* (edited by D. R. Bates), Academic, New York, 1962.
10. J. S. Townsend and V. A. Bailey, *Phil. Mag.* **43**, 593 (1922); **44**, 1033 (1922).
11. J. S. Townsend and V. A. Bailey, *Phil. Mag.* **42**, 873 (1921).
12. See for example, L. G. H. Huxley and A. A. Zaazou, *Proc. Roy. Soc. (London)* **A-196**, 402 (1949); R. W. Crompton and D. J. Sutton, **A-215**, 467 (1952); R. W. Crompton, L. G. H. Huxley, and D. J. Sutton, **A-218**, 507 (1953). B. I. H. Hall, *Australian J. Phys.* **8**, 468 (1955). L. G. H. Huxley and R. W. Crompton, *Proc. Phys. Soc. (London)* **B-68**, 381 (1955). L. G. H. Huxley, *Australian J. Phys.* **9**, 44 (1956); **10**, 118, 240 (1957); L. G. H. Huxley, R. W. Crompton, and C. H. Bagot, **12**, 303 (1959); L. G. H. Huxley, **12**, 171 (1959). L. G. H. Huxley, *J. Atmospheric*

Terrest. Phys. **16,** 46 (1959). C. A. Hurst and L. G. H. Huxley, *Australian J. Phys.* **13,** 21 (1960); L. G. H. Huxley, **13,** 578 (1960); **13,** 718 (1960).

13. R. H. Healey and J. W. Reed, *The Behavior of Slow Electrons in Gases,* Amalgamated Wireless, Ltd., Sydney (1941).
14. C. B. Wharton, "Microwave Diagnostics for Controlled Fusion Research," in *Plasma Physics* (edited by J. E. Drummond), McGraw-Hill, New York, 1961.
15. D. Formato and A. Gilardini, *Proceedings of the Fourth International Conference on Ionization Phenomena in Gases,* Uppsala, 1959, North-Holland, Amsterdam, 1960, Vol. I, p. 99. See also D. Formato and A. Gilardini, *Proceedings of the Fifth International Conference on Ionization Phenomena in Gases,* Munich, 1961, North-Holland, Amsterdam, 1962, Vol. I, p. 660.
16. A. V. Phelps, O. T. Fundingsland, and S. C. Brown, *Phys. Rev.* **84,** 559 (1951).
17. C. L. Chen and M. Raether, *Phys. Rev.* **128,** 2679 (1962).
18. J. L. Pack and A. V. Phelps, *Phys. Rev.* **121,** 798 (1961); J. L. Pack, R. E. Voshall, and A. V. Phelps, **127,** 2084 (1962).
19. L. S. Frost and A. V. Phelps, *Phys. Rev.* **127,** 1621 (1962).
20. R. H. Neynaber, L. L. Marino, E. W. Rothe, and S. M. Trujillo, O atoms. *Phys. Rev,* **123,** 148 (1961); H atoms: **124,** 135 (1961).
21. R. T. Brackmann, W. L. Fite, and R. H. Neynaber, *Phys. Rev.* **112,** 1157 (1958).
22. R. H. Neynaber, L. L. Marino, E. W. Rothe, and S. M. Trujillo, *Phys. Rev.* **129,** 2069 (1963).
23. B. H. Bransden, A. Dalgarno, T. L. John, and M. J. Seaton, *Proc. Phys. Soc.* (*London*) **A-71,** 877 (1958).
24. A. Temkin and J. C. Lamkin, *Phys. Rev.* **121,** 788 (1961).
25. R. P. McEachran and P. A. Fraser, *Can. J. Phys.* **38,** 317 (1960).
26. K. Smith, *Phys. Rev.* **120,** 845 (1960).
27. T. L. John, *Proc. Phys. Soc.* (*London*) **76,** 532 (1960).
28. S. Geltman, *Phys. Rev.* **119,** 1283 (1960).
29. P. G. Burke and H. M. Schey, *Phys. Rev.* **126,** 147 (1962); see also P. G. Burke, H. M. Schey, and K. Smith, **129,** 1258 (1963).
30. J. Perel, P. Englander, and B. Bederson, *Phys. Rev.* **128,** 1148 (1962). For further details of the experimental method see Ref. 45. More recently, experiments on A, O_2, and N_2 were described by W. Aberth, G. Sunshine, and B. Bederson at the Third International Conference on the Physics of Electronic and Atomic Collisions, London, 1963.
31. C. Ramsauer and R. Kollath, *Ann. Phys.* **12,** 529, 837 (1932).
32. A. P. Gagge, *Phys. Rev.* **44,** 808 (1933).
33. H. B. Gilbody, R. F. Stebbings, and W. L. Fite, *Phys. Rev.* **121,** 794 (1961).
34. N. F. Mott and H. S. W. Massey, *The Theory of Atomic Collisions,* Second Edition, Oxford University Press, Oxford, 1952, Chapter IX, Section 5.
35. J. Holtsmark, *Z. Phys.* **55,** 437 (1929).
36. N. F. Mott and H. S. W. Massey, *op. cit.,* Chapter X.
37. T. Y. Wu and T. Ohmura, *The Quantum Theory of Scattering,* Prentice-Hall Englewood Cliffs, N.J., 1962.
38. H. S. W. Massey, "Theory of Atomic Collisions," in *Handbuch der Physik,* Vol. XXXVI, Springer-Verlag, Berlin, 1956.
39. B. L. Moiseiwitsch, "Elastic Scattering of Electrons," in *Atomic and Molecular Processes* (edited by D. R. Bates), Academic, New York, 1962.
40. P. G. Burke and K. Smith, "The Low-energy Scattering of Electrons and Positrons by Hydrogen Atoms," *Rev. Mod. Phys.* **34,** 458–502 (1962).

41. W. P. Allis and P. M. Morse, *Z. Phys.* **70,** 567 (1931).
42. J. B. Fisk, *Phys. Rev.* **49,** 167 (1936).
43. H. S. W. Massey and R. O. Ridley, *Proc. Phys. Soc. (London)* **A-69,** 659 (1956).
44. M. Gryziński, *Phys. Rev.* **107,** 1471 (1957); **115,** 374 (1959). See also R. G. Alsmiller, Oak Ridge National Laboratory Report ORNL-3232 (1962).
45. K. Rubin, J. Perel, and B. Bederson, *Phys. Rev.* **117,** 151 (1960).
46. H. S. W. Massey and R. A. Smith, *Proc. Roy. Soc. (London)* **A-142,** 142 (1933).
47. E. A. Mason and J. T. Vanderslice, "High Energy Elastic Scattering of Atoms, Molecules, and Ions," in *Atomic and Molecular Processes* (edited by D. R. Bates), Academic, New York, 1962.
48. H. S. W. Massey and C. B. O. Mohr, *Proc. Roy. Soc. (London)* **A-141,** 434 (1933).
49. H. S. W. Massey and E. H. S. Burhop, *op. cit.,* pp. 391–392.
50. H. S. W. Massey and E. H. S. Burhop, *op. cit.,* Chapter VII.
51. See, for example, N. F. Ramsey, *Molecular Beams,* Oxford University Press, Oxford, 1956. P. Kusch and V. W. Hughes, "Atomic and Molecular Beam Spectroscopy," in *Handbuch der Physik,* Vol. XXXVII, Springer-Verlag, Berlin, 1959, pp. 1-172. H. Pauly, *Fortschr. Phys.* **9,** 613–687 (1961). J. W. Trischka, "Molecular Beams," in *Molecular Physics* (edited by D. Williams), Academic, New York, 1962, pp. 589–636.
52. E. W. Rothe and R. B. Bernstein, *J. Chem. Phys.* **31,** 1619 (1959).
53. H. Schumacher, R. B. Bernstein, and E. W. Rothe, *J. Chem. Phys.* **33,** 584 (1960).
54. S. Rosin and I. Rabi, *Phys. Rev.* **48,** 373 (1935).
55. H. U. Hostettler and R. B. Bernstein, *Rev. Sci. Instr.* **31,** 872 (1960). A similar velocity selector with extended range has been constructed by S. M. Trujillo, P. K. Rol, and E. W. Rothe, *Rev. Sci. Instr.* **33,** 841 (1962).
56. H. U. Hostettler and R. B. Bernstein, *Phys. Rev. Letters* **5,** 318 (1960).
57. F. A. Morse, R. B. Bernstein, and H. U. Hostettler, *J. Chem. Phys.* **36,** 1947 (1962); F. A. Morse and R. B. Bernstein, **37,** 2019 (1962).
58. E. W. Rothe, L. L. Marino, R. H. Neynaber, P. K. Rol, and S. M. Trujillo, *Phys. Rev.* **126,** 598 (1962).
59. E. W. Rothe, P. K. Rol, S. M. Trujillo, and R. H. Neynaber, *Phys. Rev.* **128,** 659 (1962). P. K. Rol and E. W. Rothe, *Phys. Rev. Letters* **9,** 494 (1962). E. W. Rothe, R. H. Neynaber, B. W. Scott, S. M. Trujillo, and P. K. Rol, J. Chem. Phys. **39,** 493 (1963). Additional measurements on the scattering of a velocity-selected potassium beam by neon, argon, and xenon were reported recently by H. H. Brown, K. Lulla, and B. Bederson at the Third International Conference on the Physics of Electronic and Atomic Collisions, London, 1963.
60. H. S. W. Massey and C. B. O. Mohr, *Proc. Roy. Soc. (London)* **A-144,** 188 (1934).
61. I. Estermann, S. N. Foner, and O. Stern, *Phys. Rev.* **71,** 250 (1947).
62. H. Pauly, *Z. ang. Phys.* **9,** 600 (1957).
63. (a) H. Pauly, *Z. Phys.* **157,** 54 (1959); (b) *Z. Naturforsch,* **15a,** 277 (1960); *Fortschr. Phys.* **9,** 613 (1961). (The last reference is a lengthy and valuable review.)
64. R. C. Schoonmaker, *J. Phys. Chem.* **65,** 892 (1961).
65. P. H. Kydd, *J. Chem. Phys.* **37,** 931 (1962). [H_2O and NH_3 on H_2O.]
66. Halstead Harrison, *J. Chem. Phys.* **37,** 1164 (1962). [H, He, and H_2 on H_2 and He.]
67. H. U. Hostettler and R. B. Bernstein, *J. Chem. Phys.* **31,** 1422 (1959); R. B. Bernstein, **33,** 795 (1960); R. B. Bernstein, **34,** 361 (1961); R. B. Bernstein, **36,** 1403 (1962); R. B. Bernstein, **37,** 1880 (1962), **38,** 515 (1963). Halstead Harrison and R. B. Bernstein, *J. Chem. Phys.* **38,** 2135 (1963); R. B. Bernstein and K. H. Kramer, *J. Chem. Phys.* **38,** 2507 (1963); R. B. Bernstein, *J. Chem. Phys.* **38,** 2599 (1963);

E. W. Rothe, P. K. Rol, and R. B. Bernstein, *Phys. Rev.* **130**, 2333 (1963); E. W. Rothe, P. K. Rol, R. H. Neynaber, and S. M. Trujillo, Third International Conference on the Physics of Electronic and Atomic Collisions London, 1963; D. R. Herschbach and G. H. Kwei, Third International Conference on the Physics of Electronic and Atomic Collisions London, 1963. R. B. Bernstein, A. Dalgarno, H. S. W. Massey, and I. C. Percival, *Proc. Roy. Soc.* (*London*) **A-274**, 427 (1963).

68. E. A. Mason, *J. Chem. Phys.* **26**, 667 (1957). See also K. W. Ford and J. A. Wheeler, *Ann. Phys.* **7**, 259, 287 (1959). Ch. Schlier, *Z. Phys.* **173**, 352 (1963).

69. R. F. Stebbings, *Proc. Roy. Soc.* (*London*) **A-241**, 270 (1957). J. B. Hasted, *J. Appl. Phys.* **30**, 22 (1959). J. B. Hasted and P. Mahadevan, Proc. Roy. Soc. (*London*) **A-249**, 42 (1959). G. M. Smith and E. E. Muschlitz, *J. Chem. Phys.* **33**, 1819 (1960).

70. S. Datz and E. H. Taylor, "Some Applications of Molecular Beam Techniques to Chemistry," in *Recent Research in Molecular Beams* (edited by I. Estermann), Academic, New York, 1959. W. L. Fite and S. Datz, "Chemical Research with Molecular Beams," Ann. Rev. Phys. Chem., **14** (1963), Annual Reviews, Palo Alto, Cal.

71. E. F. Greene, R. W. Roberts, and J. Ross, *J. Chem. Phys.* **32**, 940 (1960); D. R. Herschbach, **33**, 1870 (1960); D. R. Herschbach, G. H. Kwei, and J. A. Norris, **34**, 1842 (1961). D. R. Herschbach, *Discussions Faraday Soc.*, **33**, 149 (1962). D. Beck, E. F. Greene, and J. Ross, *J. Chem. Phys.* **37**, 2895 (1962). E. Gersing, E. Hundhausen, and H. Pauly, *Z. Phys.* **171**, 349 (1963). M. Ackerman, E. F. Greene, A. L. Moursund, and J. Ross, Third International Conference on the Physics of Electronic and Atomic Collisions, London, 1963. W. L. Fite and R. T. Brackmann, Third International Conference on the Physics of Electronic and Atomic Collisions, London, 1963. R. Wolfgang, Third International Conference on the Physics of Electronic and Atomic Collisions, London, 1963. S. Datz and E. H. Taylor, *J. Chem. Phys.* **39**, 1896 (1963).

72. H. S. W. Massey and E. H. S. Burhop, *op. cit.*, Chapter VIII.

73. W. H. Cramer and J. H. Simons, *J. Chem. Phys.* **26**, 1272 (1957); W. H. Cramer, **28**, 688 (1958); **30**, 641 (1959); W. H. Cramer and A. B. Marcus, **32**, 186 (1960); W. H. Cramer, **35**, 836 (1961).

74. See, for example, E. E. Muschlitz, T. L. Bailey, and J. H. Simons, *J. Chem. Phys.* **26**, 711 (1957); T. L. Bailey, C. J. May, and E. E. Muschlitz, **26**, 1446 (1957). E. E. Muschlitz, *Proceedings of the Fourth International Conference on Ionization Phenomena in Gases*, Uppsala, 1959, North-Holland, Amsterdam, 1960, Vol. I, p. 52. C. E. Baker, J. M. McGuire, and E. E. Muschlitz, *J. Chem. Phys.* **37**, 2571 (1962).

75. References to the most recent of these investigations are I. Amdur and E. A. Mason, *J. Chem. Phys.* **25**, 624, 630, 632 (1956); I. Amdur, E. A. Mason, and J. E. Jordan, **27**, 527 (1957); I. Amdur, J. E. Jordan, and S. O. Colgate, **34**, 1525 (1961); I. Amdur, M. S. Longmire, and E. A. Mason, **35**, 895 (1961); I. Amdur and R. R. Bertrand, **36**, 1078 (1962). I. Amdur, J. E. Jordan, and R. R. Bertrand, Third International Conference on the Physics of Electronic and Atomic Collisions, London, 1963.

76. The ion source used here is based on the design of the source described by E. S. Lamar and O. Luhr, *Phys. Rev.* **46**, 87 (1934).

77. H. W. Berry, *Phys. Rev.* **75**, 913 (1949); **99**, 553 (1955).

78. N. Bohr, *Kgl. Danske Videnskab. Selskab, Mat. Fys. Medd.* **18**, 8 (1948), in English.

79. O. B. Firsov, *Soviet Phys.—JETP* **6**, 534 (1958); **7**, 308 (1958).

80. E. N. Fuls, P. R. Jones, F. P. Ziemba, and E. Everhart, *Phys. Rev.* **107**, 704 (1957).

81. G. H. Lane and E. Everhart, *Phys. Rev.* **120,** 2064 (1960).
82. O. B. Firsov, *J. Exp. Theoret. Phys. (USSR)* **24,** 279 (1953), in Russian.
83. J. B. Keller, I. Kay, and J. Shmoys, *Phys. Rev.* **102,** 557 (1956).
84. E. Everhart, Gerald Stone, and R. J. Carbone, *Phys. Rev.* **99,** 1287 (1955).
85. N. F. Mott and H. S. W. Massey, *The Theory of Atomic Collisions*, Second Edition, Oxford University Press, Oxford, 1952, Chapter VII, Sections 4 and 5.
86. E. J. Williams, *Rev. Mod. Phys.* **17,** 217 (1945).

5

IONIZATION AND EXCITATION

BY ELECTRON IMPACT*

This chapter deals largely with experimental studies of the ionization and excitation of gases by electron impact. We are concerned with beam studies on targets sufficiently "thin"† that only primary ionization is significant and with swarm experiments performed at E/p low enough that electron multiplication does not occur to an appreciable extent. Thus discussion of the Townsend coefficients[1] is omitted, and thermal ionization and excitation‡ are likewise not covered. Collisional ionization and excitation by heavy projectiles are treated in Chapter 6, and photo-absorption processes are covered in Chapters 7 and 8. The discussion of theory is restricted here to a few remarks about the classical Thomson theory of ionization and various quantal calculations. A more general discussion of the quantum mechanical theory of inelastic collisions appears in Chapter 6.

* A complete bibliography on elastic and inelastic collisions involving free electrons has been compiled by L. J. Kieffer of the Joint Institute for Laboratory Astrophysics, Univ. of Colorado, Boulder, Colo. This bibliography will be published as an N. B. S. document.

† The word "thin" is used here in the same sense as in Section 4-1-A, in which beam studies of the elastic scattering of electrons were discussed.

‡ References on thermal ionization and excitation appear in the supplementary bibliography at the end of this chapter.

5-1. INTRODUCTION

The ejection of electrons from atoms and molecules by electron impact is a phenomenon of great practical interest. Most ion sources used in mass spectrometers and in apparatus for atomic collision studies are the "electron bombardment" type. In this source electrons are produced thermionically, accelerated through a suitable potential difference (usually about 100 volts), and passed through a gas to form ions in collisions with the molecules. Electron impact is also responsible for the production of electrons in rf-, glow-, and arc-discharge sources. The action of gas-filled beta-ray detectors hinges on the ionization of the counter gas by the incident electrons and their progeny. Collisional ionization and excitation are also of great importance in astrophysics, upper atmospheric phenomena, thermonuclear research, plasma physics, and gaseous electronics.* In addition, experimental data on inelastic scattering are vital to the further development of the theory of atomic collisions, for they provide tests of the assumptions and approximations that are necessarily made in calculations. Not only are data required for ordinary stable atoms and molecules; many structures of great practical and theoretical interest are ionic or are atoms that normally exist only in molecular form.

There is a vast literature on inelastic collisions of electrons.† Nearly all of the experimental work has dealt with the impact of electrons on stable targets. Reliable techniques for studying ions and chemically unstable atoms were developed only during the late 1950's, and this territory is largely unexplored. A number of excellent reviews relating to experiment and theory are available. Massey and Burhop[2] have discussed the theoretical and experimental work done before about 1950 in a comprehensive manner. The review by Massey[3] extends the coverage of inelastic impacts on atoms to about 1955, and the review by Craggs and Massey[4] covers the experimental and theoretical studies of molecular targets up to about 1958. Fite,[5] who recently surveyed the measurements of collisional ionization and excitation cross sections, emphasizes the work done since the publication of the book by Massey and Burhop.[2] Field and Franklin[6] offer a great deal of experimental data on ionization and good discussions of experimental techniques, and the works of Mott and Massey[7] and Seaton[8] present advanced discussions of the theory. Finally, a lengthy paper by Burke and Smith[9] surveys all experimental

* For a very interesting discussion of the application of ionization and excitation cross sections in these areas, see pp. 396–408, Ref. 3.
† The review of this subject presented by D. W. O. Heddle and M. J. Seaton at the Third International Conference on the Physics of Electronic and Atomic Collisions London, 1963, listed 192 papers published between January 1960 and July 1963.

and theoretical work done before the beginning of 1962 on the elastic and inelastic scattering of low-energy electrons by hydrogen atoms. One of the most valuable features of Burke and Smith's review is the description and critical analysis of the various approximations which are used in scattering theory.

PART 𝒜. IONIZATION OF ATOMS
AND MOLECULES BY ELECTRON IMPACT

5-2. GENERAL METHODS OF MEASUREMENT OF IONIZATION CROSS SECTIONS

A. SINGLE-BEAM EXPERIMENTS INVOLVING THE TOTAL COLLECTION OF RESIDUAL POSITIVE IONS; APPARENT IONIZATION CROSS SECTIONS. Most measurements of collisional ionization cross sections have been made by passing a collimated and nearly monoenergetic* beam of electrons through a gas or vapor and collecting essentially all of the positive ions formed in ionizing events. In order to obtain an accurate and meaningful value for the cross sections, we must use a "thin" target so that only a small fraction of the "primary" electrons will strike molecules of the target gas. Then an insignificant fraction of the projectiles will experience more than one collision, and an insignificant amount of ionization will be produced by electrons ejected from molecules by the beam projectiles. If i_0 denotes the incident beam current, N, the number density of the gas target, x, the effective target thickness, and i^+, the collected positive ion current, the *apparent ionization cross section* q_i will be given by the equation

$$i^+ = i_0 N q_i x \tag{5-2-1}$$

[The similarity of this equation to (1-4-8) is obvious.] Since multiply charged ions may be produced and collected, the measured cross section is really the weighted sum

$$q_i = q^+ + 2q^{2+} + 3q^{3+} + \cdots \tag{5-2-2}$$

where q^{n+} is the sum of the cross sections for all events involving ejection of n electrons from a target molecule.

Although such an experiment provides no information about the charges and masses of the residual ions, q_i does represent an unambiguous cross section for the production of free electrons. Furthermore, measurements of this type can be made with high accuracy, and they directly yield

---

* Throughout this chapter the term "monoenergetic" is used rather loosely when applied to electron beams. Strictly speaking, the term should probably be reserved for beams with half-widths of less than 0.1 ev; that is, to beams of electrons that have passed through a velocity filter of some sort.

absolute cross sections, since nondiscriminating detectors with very nearly 100% efficiency are used. Since e/m analysis of the residual ions is not attempted, all of the ions produced inside the active region of the target gas are simply swept to a negatively charged collector plate located parallel to the electron beam and bounding the active volume. The active thickness of the target may be accurately defined by the use of guard electrodes. The positive ions produced by the electron beam have low energies, and a weak electric field suffices to sweep all the ions to the collector.

Actually, the apparent cross section will equal the true cross section at electron energies below the threshold for double ionization (which is usually several times the threshold for single ionization). Furthermore, with electronic projectiles, single ionization from the outermost shell is usually much more probable than multiple ionization or inner-shell ionization, and q_i is generally nearly equal to the cross section for single electron ejection from the outer shell. (Innershell ionization is discussed by Massey and Burhop[2] and Massey.[3])

B. SINGLE-BEAM EXPERIMENTS INVOLVING e/m ANALYSIS OF RESIDUAL POSITIVE IONS; TRUE IONIZATION CROSS SECTIONS. If we wish to determine the cross section for production of ions of a given charge-to-mass ratio, e/m analysis is required. Ions may be drawn transversely from a narrow section of the target gas and analyzed by one of several different mass spectrometric techniques. If careful attention is paid to the matter of discrimination in the ion collection and detection processes, we may obtain an accurate value for the cross section for production of any particular ionic species relative to that of any other species produced in significant quantity. The difficulty of accurately determining the effective volume of the target gas and the efficiency of the mass spectrometer has led to a concentration of effort in measuring relative cross sections. Absolute values may be obtained from these data by comparison with a cross section whose absolute value is already known. Since simple stable atoms and molecules are generally used as standards, the importance of accurate absolute cross sections for such structures is evident.

In certain types of studies, however, knowledge of absolute cross sections is not important. In recent years there has been considerable theoretical interest in the variation of the cross sections for production of single ionic species in the region near threshold.* Also a great deal

---

* The threshold energy for ionization by electron impact is equal to the ionization energy of the target structure within a factor of 1 part in 10^4. If the target is stationary or moving slowly, the laboratory kinetic energy of the electronic projectile is very nearly equal to the center-of-mass energy of the projectile-target combination, and it is the latter energy that can be transferred to excitation energy in the collision (cf. Section 1-3).

of work has been done to gain information concerning the electronic states in which the ions are formed. Both types of studies are discussed further in Section 5-5. Evidently e/m analysis is required for such investigations, but absolute cross sections are not.

C. CROSSED-BEAM EXPERIMENTS ON UNSTABLE TARGET PARTICLES. Crossed modulated beam techniques have been used since 1958 for cross section measurements on unstable targets. Most of these experiments have involved the intersection of a mechanically modulated thermal beam of neutral atoms with a dc beam of electrons of variable energy in apparatus somewhat similar to that shown in Fig. 4-1-8. This approach is quite satisfactory for neutral targets, but difficulties (mainly associated with cross modulation of the dc beam) appear when both beams consist of charged particles. Dolder, Harrison, and Thonemann[10] have recently developed a technique that appears to obviate these difficulties. Their application of this technique to the study of ionization of He$^+$ ions by electrons was the first successful beam experiment with two species of charged particles. The scheme they employed intersects a fast well-collimated beam of He$^+$ ions with an electron beam of variable energy and then resolves the ion beam with respect to its charge states after it passes through the intersection region. If the incident He$^+$ beam has an energy of several kev, the momentum imparted to any of the He$^+$ ions experiencing ionization is negligible compared with their initial forward momentum, so that the He^{2+} ions thus formed remain in the beam along with the He$^+$ ions that do not lose their remaining electrons. An important factor in the success of this technique appears to be the simultaneous modulation of both the ion and the electron beams and the ability to vary the relative phase of the modulation. Dolder, Harrison, and Thonemann's apparatus is described in detail in Section 5-4, in which additional discussion of other crossed-beam ionization studies also appears.

5-3. MEASUREMENT OF IONIZATION CROSS SECTIONS FOR STABLE ATOMS AND MOLECULES

This section deals with studies of the ionization of simple gases by electron impact at electron energies ranging up to about 1000 ev. Apparent ionization cross section data are presented for a few simple gases. Additional information on polyatomic gases appears in the article by Craggs and Massey[4] and in Field and Franklin.[6] Recent high-resolution work done on simple structures near threshold is considered in Section 5-5.

The bulk of the available ionization data on monatomic and diatomic gases at energies significantly above threshold was obtained between 1925 and 1940. This fact has two implications. First, it is a testimony to the skill of the early investigators who obtained data of sufficient reliability to make it unnecessary to repeat their measurements before the recent intensification of interest in the detailed shape and fine structure of the cross section curves. Second, it signifies that the measured cross sections are relatively insensitive to impurities in the target gas, since the measurements in question were made before the advent of high-vacuum techniques.

A. APPARATUS. Here we shall discuss several types of apparatus that were used successfully for electron ionization studies around 1930.

1. *Tate and Smith's apparatus for measurement of apparent ionization cross sections.* Tate and Smith[11] used the apparatus shown in Fig. 5-3-1

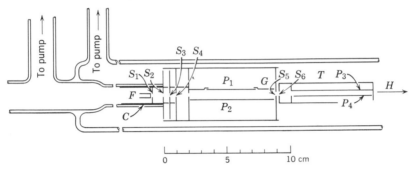

FIG. 5-3-1. Apparatus used by Tate and Smith[11] for measurement of ionization potentials and apparent ionization cross sections.

to measure the ionization potentials and apparent ionization cross sections of N_2, CO, O_2, NO, H_2, and C_2H_2. This apparatus is essentially the same as that employed earlier by Smith for studies of He, Ne, and A[12] and mercury vapor.[13] Smith's earlier apparatus was not suitable for gases that are dissociated by a hot filament. Tate and Smith's tube is divided into two compartments, each of which is separately pumped. The source of electrons is a tungsten filament F, located inside a tantalum cylinder C which is sealed into a pyrex tube. The disk in front of the filament contains a number of holes so that the region between the diaphragms S_1 and S_2 may be pumped out effectively. The only opening between the two compartments of the tube is the hole in S_2, which is 0.035 cm in diameter. Thus products of the dissociation of the gas are unable to diffuse into the other compartment of the tube, which contains the target gas at a pressure of 10^{-4} to 10^{-3} mm Hg. Constant differences of potential are maintained between F and S_1 and between S_2 and S_3, whereas a variable acceleration potential V is applied between S_3 and S_4. With this arrangement, the electron current to the trap T is independent of the magnitude of V. An axial magnetic field H of several hundred gauss produced by a solenoid surrounding the tube confines the primary electrons to a well-defined beam. Scattering of the beam electrons by gas molecules would otherwise require the use of strong electric fields to prevent these electrons from reaching the ion collector P_1 and thus cause a serious variation in the energy of the incident electrons along the beam path. Electrons scattered from the beam might also cause secondary electron emission from interior surfaces of the apparatus if magnetic confinement were not employed. Electron beam currents of about 5×10^{-8} amp were utilized by Tate and Smith. The magnetic field prevented the beam from striking the rim of any of the apertures through which it passed.

Positive ions formed within the active region of the target gas are collected on the plate P_1. Plots of collected ion current versus the potential difference applied between P_1 and P_2 showed saturation at a few volts, even at beam energies up to 4500 ev, indicating that essentially all of the ions could be collected by potential differences of this magnitude. The collector voltage generally used was 4 volts.* Guard electrodes G held at the same potential as P_1 accurately define the effective target thickness, which is 4 cm. The plates P_2 and G are connected together by means of a high resistance, the midpoint of which is connected to the slit S_5, so that the speed of the electrons is not appreciably altered by the transverse collection field.

The collimating magnetic field causes the beam electrons to travel in helices, the radii of which are determined by the electron speed and the angle at which each electron leaves the gun. Accordingly the path length of the primary electrons through the target gas is slightly uncertain, but this effect is important only at low beam energies. The maximum angle at which electrons leave the gun is determined by the size of the exit aperture. If l is the effective length of the target, d, the diameter of the exit aperture of the gun in mm, B, the magnetic flux density in gauss,

---

* Recent studies by D. Rapp and P. Englander-Golden indicate, however, that the weak sweeping field used by Tate and Smith was insufficient to collect all of the energetic ions produced in *dissociative* ionization of molecules (see Section 5-7-A). Using apparatus very similar to that of Tate and Smith, Rapp and Englander-Golden found that 4 volts was adequate to collect all the ions formed in electron impact on the atomic gas helium but that 30 volts were required at high electron energies to collect all of the energetic protons produced in dissociative ionization of molecular hydrogen. With 30 volts sweeping voltage, they obtained cross sections about 3.5 per cent higher than those of Tate and Smith for H_2 at high electron energies. This work was discussed at the Sixth International Conference on Ionization Phenomena in Gases, Paris, 1963.

and V, the energy of the beam electrons in ev, the maximum path length of a beam electron is[2]

$$l\left(1 + 1.10 \times 10^{-4}\frac{d^2B^2}{V}\right)$$

The minimum path length is, of course, l. Thus, if $d = 1$ mm, $B = 250$ gauss, and $V = 100$ ev, the maximum path length is about 6% greater than the minimum value.*

2. *Bleakney's apparatus for measurement of true electron ionization cross sections.*   Figure 5-3-2 illustrates the apparatus which Bleakney first described in 1929[14] and used to measure the appearance potentials and cross sections for production of individual ionic species in Hg,[15] H_2,[16] and He, Ne, and A.[17]   A uniform magnetic field H is used to confine a narrow

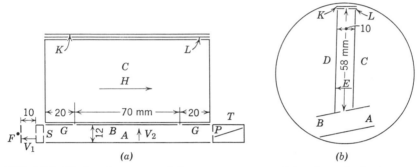

FIG. 5-3-2. Bleakney's apparatus[14] for appearance potential and true ionization cross section measurements.

beam of electrons to a straight path and also to separate the residual ions which have different values of e/m.   Electrons from a filament F are accelerated by a potential difference V_1 through a system of slits S into the target region between the plates A and B.   The beam is collected in the trap T, and secondaries are prevented from returning to the target region by a potential difference of about 90 volts between the plate P and the walls of the trap.   Beam currents of only about 3×10^{-7} amp were used, so that space charge effects were negligible.   Target gas pressures ranged from about 2×10^{-5} mm Hg to 10^{-3} mm Hg, the higher pressures being used with the smaller gas molecules.   Care was taken to ensure thin-target conditions so that the beam provided a linear source of positive ions of almost uniform density.

* Massey and Burhop's analysis of the effect of an axial magnetic field on the path length of the electrons has been superseded by recent work by R. K. Asundi, *Proc. Phys. Soc.* (*London*) **82**, 372 (1963). Asundi shows that the path length is governed primarily by the energy available to the electrons normal to the field direction and that there is a negligible increase in path length in the experiments of Tate and Smith.

The ions formed in the target gas by the electron beam are extracted from the beam region by a potential difference V_2 of several volts applied between plates A and B. Because of the presence of the magnetic field, this cross field does not appreciably affect either the velocity of the beam electrons or the position of the beam. A long narrow slit is cut in plate B parallel to the beam direction, so that a long, narrow ribbon of positive ions passes through B for e/m analysis in the analyzer shown in Fig. 5-3-2b. The magnetic field, furnished by a long solenoid, is perpendicular to the plane of the drawing. The electron beam has the form of a ribbon. This shape was secured by stretching a tungsten filament wire lengthwise in front of the first slit shown in Fig. 5-3-2a. This slit has dimensions 1×4 mm; the slit in plate B is 0.25 mm wide and 60 mm long. In the analyzer an electric field E is applied between plates C and D which is just strong enough to balance the magnetic force on the ions selected for detection. The desired ions then travel in a straight line up through the slit in plate L and are collected on plate K. Ions with different charge-to-mass ratio are deflected toward plate D. The electrodes A and B are set at a slight angle with respect to the horizontal to allow for the curvature of the ion path before it reaches the slit in B. Let us now derive the expression for the charge-to-mass ratio of the ions detected in the analyzer. Let X denote the direction perpendicular to plates C and D, and Y, the direction parallel to them. Ions moving in the crossed electric and magnetic fields E and H of the analyzer will describe trochoidal trajectories. If an ion of charge e and mass m enters the analyzer with velocity v_0 in the Y direction at time $t = 0$, the equation of its orbit in the analyzer will be

$$x = \left(\frac{mc}{eH}\right)\left(v_0 - \frac{Ec}{H}\right)\left[1 - \cos\left(\frac{eHt}{mc}\right)\right]$$

$$y = \left(\frac{Ect}{H}\right) + \left(\frac{mc}{eH}\right)\left(v_0 - \frac{Ec}{H}\right)\sin\left(\frac{eHt}{mc}\right)$$

(5-3-1)

where c denotes the velocity of light. Since x must vanish identically for ions collected by plate K, the condition for detection of a particular ionic species is

$$\frac{e}{m} = \frac{E^2 c^2}{2VH^2}$$

(5-3-2)

where V is the potential through which the ion was accelerated before it entered the analyzer.* The operational procedure fixes the values of H

---

* Equation 5-3-2 may be derived much more simply from the requirement that the electric and magnetic forces on an ion must balance in order that it may pass straight through the analyzer. Thus in MKS units, $eE = evB$, where B is the flux density, and since $mv^2/2 = eV$ we obtain the requirement that $e/m = E^2/2VB^2$.

and the potentials V_1 and V_2 and then scans the e/m spectrum by varying the electric field intensity E. The length of plate B equals the effective target thickness, so that measurement of the current of positive ions to B gives the apparent total ionization cross section. The ratios of the areas under the various peaks in the e/m spectrum indicate the relative abundances of the various species of ions produced.

An improved analyzer, shown in Fig. 5-3-3, was subsequently employed by Bleakney[18] to measure the ionization potential of molecular hydrogen

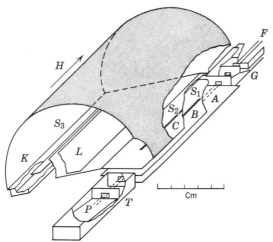

FIG. 5-3-3. Bleakney's improved analyzer.[18]

and by Bleakney and Smith[19] to obtain the cross section for double ionization of He atoms by single electron impact. They used a water-cooled solenoid 1 meter long and with a 5-in. bore that could produce a field of 1500 gauss continuously without iron in the magnetic circuit. With such a field it was possible to use a Dempster-type semicircular analyzer. Electrons from the filament F are accelerated between the first two diaphragms of the electron gun G and pass between plates A and B, as shown by the dotted lines. The electron beam is collected by the inclined plate P, which is held about 100-volt positive with respect to the rest of the trap T to prevent the escape of secondary electrons. The positive ions formed along the magnetically confined electron path are accelerated through the two slits S_1 and S_2 by a small field between A and B and a stronger one between B and C. The ions then travel along circular arcs in the magnetic field. The radius of the circle along which a given ion moves is determined by the relation

$$\frac{e}{m} = \frac{2V}{r^2 H^2} \tag{5-3-3}$$

where V is the potential difference through which the particular ion has fallen before it passes through S_2. The ions selected for detection pass through the third slit S_3 and fall on plate K, which is connected to an electrometer. Different ionic species are passed successively through S_3 by varying the accelerating potential V applied to S_2. The total ion current is measured by connecting plate L to the electrometer and setting V so that no ions pass through S_3. The entire apparatus within the

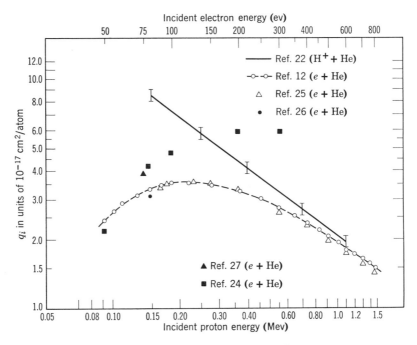

FIG. 5-3-4. Comparison of experimental apparent ionization cross sections for protons and electrons of equal velocity incident on helium.

vacuum tube is made of tantalum and tungsten with pyrex insulators and can be baked out in a furnace mounted inside the solenoid.

Apparatus somewhat similar to that shown in Fig. 5-3-3 was used by Tate and Smith[20] to measure the ionization potentials and probabilities of formation of singly and multiply charged ions in Na, K, Rb, Cs, Kr, and Xe at electron energies up to 700 ev. A preponderance of singly charged ions was observed in each gas studied. Sodium, potassium, rubidium, and cesium were introduced into the scattering chamber in the vapor phase by heating a solid sample contained in a side tube. The remaining alkali metal, lithium, was not studied because its low vapor pressure requires an inconveniently high scattering chamber temperature (about 600°C) to provide a suitably high target number density. (Lithium has been studied recently, however, by Brink, who used a crossed-beam apparatus. Brink's work on the alkalis is discussed in Section 5-4.) Tate, Smith, and Vaughan[21] also made a mass spectrum analysis of the products of ionization of nitrogen, acetylene, nitric oxide, cyanogen, and carbon monoxide.

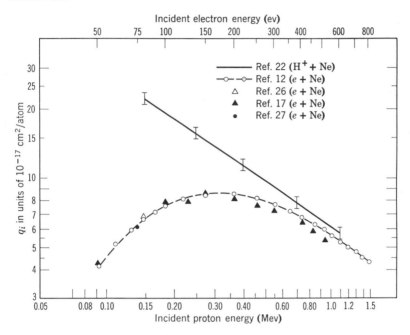

FIG. 5-3-5. Comparison of experimental apparent ionization cross sections for protons and electrons of equal velocity incident on neon.

B. EXPERIMENTAL DATA ON STABLE SYSTEMS.   Ionization cross section data for a number of simple gases are shown in Figs. 5-3-4 through 5-3-14.* The electron data on He, Ne, A, H_2, N_2, O_2, and CO presented in Figs. 5-3-4 through 5-3-10 are compared with cross sections obtained by McDaniel et al.[22] with fast incident protons. The classical Thomson theory of ionization[23] predicts that electrons and protons of equal velocity incident on a given target should have the same cross section for ionization. The same prediction is made by quantum theory, but with the important qualification that the comparison is valid only if the projectile velocities

* Data on 10 representative organic compounds at electron energies up to 12 kev have been reported by P. Kebarle and E. W. Godbole, *J. Chem. Phys.* **36**, 302 (1962).

are high, so that the Born approximation may be applied. Hooper et al.[22] have shown that the proton results do agree with the generally preferred electron ionization data on the gases displayed in Figs. 5-3-4 through 5-3-10 if the data are compared at the same projectile velocity and at electron energies above about 300 ev. Furthermore, the experimental cross sections vary with energy, at high energy, in the manner predicted by the Born approximation; that is, the cross section curves appear

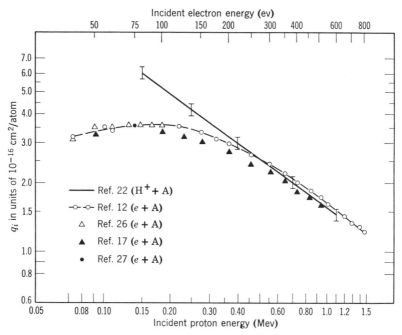

FIG. 5-3-6. Comparison of experimental apparent ionization cross sections for protons and electrons of equal velocity incident on argon.

essentially linear on a log-log plot. This electron-proton comparison is discussed further in Section 6-16.

The relevance of the comparison to the present discussion is that the agreement between the electron and proton results at high energy is an additional indication of the validity of the electron data obtained by some of the early workers, specifically Smith, Tate, and Bleakney. The results reported in 1925 by Compton and Van Voorhis[24] do not agree with the other data presented on He and H_2, probably because the technique of magnetic confinement of the electron beam had not been introduced at that time. Harrison's results[25] are in good agreement with the bulk of the other results on He, but the agreement is only fair in the case of H_2. Other comparison data provided by Tozer and Craggs[26] and Lampe, Franklin, and Field[27] pertain to electron energies too low for the proton comparison but corroborate the results of Smith, Tate, and Bleakney at lower energies.

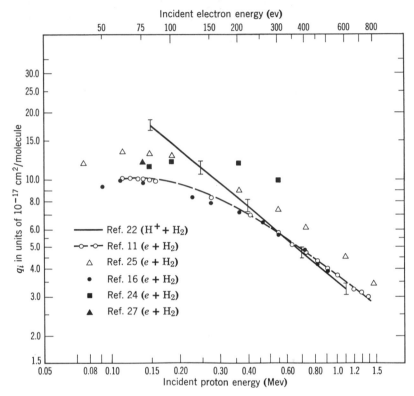

FIG. 5-3-7. Comparison of experimental apparent ionization cross sections for protons and electrons of equal velocity incident on molecular hydrogen.

Figures 5.3.11 through 5-3-14 present linear plots of the *probability of ionization,* P_i for a number of gases for which proton comparison data are unavailable; P_i equals the number of positive charges produced per incident electron per centimeter of path through the gas at 1 mm Hg pressure and 0°C and is thus seen to be the macroscopic apparent ionization cross section at 1 mm pressure. The ionization cross section in cm² is related to the probability of ionization by the expression

$$q_i = 0.283 \times 10^{-16} P_i \qquad (5\text{-}3\text{-}4)$$

These ionization curves have the typical shape—they rise steeply from

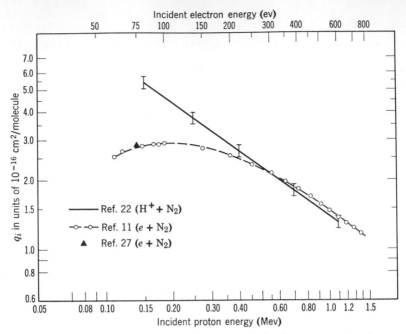

FIG. 5-3-8. Comparison of experimental apparent ionization cross sections for protons and electrons of equal velocity incident on molecular nitrogen.

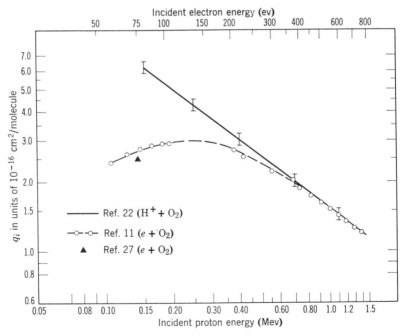

FIG. 5-3-9. Comparison of experimental apparent ionization cross sections for protons and electrons of equal velocity incident on molecular oxygen.

zero at threshold, peak at an energy several times the threshold value, and then decrease slowly at higher energy.

Data on the probability of production of specific ionic species are shown in Figs. 5-3-12 through 5-3-14. It will be noticed that single ionization occurs in the great majority of the ionizing impacts but that at high energies a significant number of multiply charged ions are produced. Most of the ejected electrons come from the outer shells.

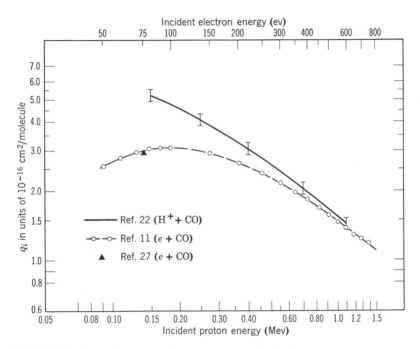

FIG. 5-3-10. Comparison of experimental apparent ionization cross sections for protons and electrons of equal velocity incident on carbon monoxide.

Additional data on the ionization (and excitation) of mercury from threshold to 100 ev were reported by Nottingham[28] in 1939. Nottingham's work was among the best done by the earlier investigators. He used a magnetic analyzer to select electrons within a narrow energy range from the larger thermal energy distribution and was thereby able to obtain a much more nearly monoenergetic beam than had been previously secured. (The energy spread of an unanalyzed beam makes it impossible to obtain accurate results at energies near threshold.) References to more recent high-resolution measurements are given in Section 5-5.

It may be of interest to point out that much of the recent work on ionization of molecules by electrons has been done with commercial mass spectrometers. Lampe, Franklin, and Field,[27] for example, used a Consolidated Electrodynamics Corporation Model 21-620 mass spectrometer, which employs crossed electric and magnetic fields and cycloidal ion

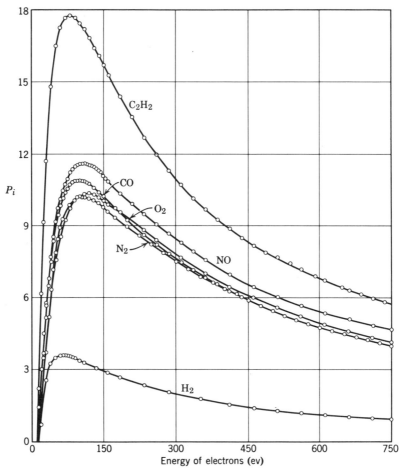

FIG. 5-3-11. The probability of ionization of N_2, CO, O_2, NO, H_2 and C_2H_2. The ordinate represents the number of positive charges per electron per cm path at 1 mm Hg pressure and 0°C. J. T. Tate and P. T. Smith, *Phys. Rev.* **39**, 270 (1932).

orbits. They obtained relative values for the cross sections at a fixed electron energy (75 ev) for a large number of gases, including argon, and converted the results to absolute data by comparison of their argon data with the absolute cross sections obtained by earlier investigators.

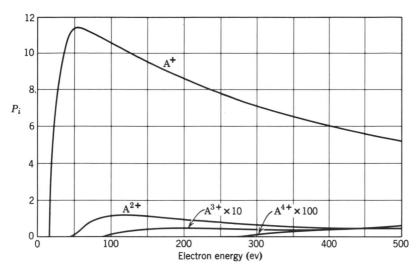

FIG. 5-3-12. The probability of ionization of argon. W. Bleakney, *Phys. Rev.* **36,** 1303 (1930).

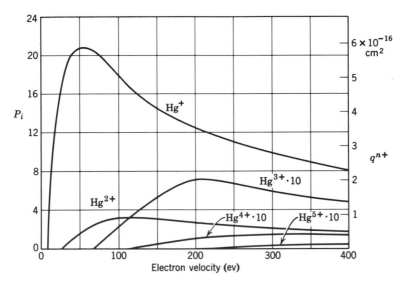

FIG. 5-3-13. Number of Hg^+, Hg^{2+}, Hg^{3+}, Hg^{4+}, and Hg^{5+} ions per electron per cm path per mm Hg pressure at $0°C$. The ionization cross section scale is shown at the right side of the figure. W. Bleakney, *Phys. Rev.* **35,** 139 (1930).

5-4. STUDIES OF THE IONIZATION OF UNSTABLE TARGETS
BY ELECTRON IMPACT: CROSSED-BEAM EXPERIMENTS

A. APPARATUS.   Recent improvements in vacuum techniques, electronic circuitry, and electron multipliers have made possible accurate studies of the ionization of chemically unstable structures. Most measurements on such systems involve crossed-beam techniques, some of which were discussed in Section 4-1-E.

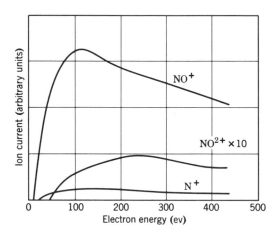

FIG. 5-3-14. The probability of ionization of nitric oxide, NO. J. T. Tate, P. T. Smith, and A. L. Vaughan, *Phys. Rev.* **48,** 525 (1935).

The first crossed-beam experiment appears to have been performed in 1930 by Funk,[29] who studied the ionization of sodium and potassium by electron impact. Funk's approach was to intersect a dc beam of atoms from an oven with a dc beam of electrons and collect the ions thus formed in a Faraday cup, in which the atomic beam itself was condensed. Since ionization of the background gas gave a contribution to the collected ion current which was about as large as that due to ionization of the beam atoms, Funk's results were not accurate. However, the improvements in instrumentation already mentioned and the development of modulated beam techniques now make it possible to achieve reliable results. The lower base pressures obtainable result in smaller contributions from background gas, and beam modulation permits discrimination of the desired signal from that due to background because the former occurs at the modulation frequency and at a particular phase with respect to the chopping signal.

The feasibility of the modulated, crossed-beam method for ionization measurements was demonstrated by Boyd and Green,[30] who made measurements on He and H_2 and obtained results compatible with the earlier, single-beam data of Tate and Smith.[11,12] The first data on unstable systems were reported by Fite and Brackmann, who studied electrons on atomic hydrogen[31] and atomic oxygen.[32] At about the same time, Boyd and Boksenberg[33] reported measurements on atomic hydrogen.

Atomic hydrogen and oxygen have been studied more recently by Rothe et al.[34] at electron energies of 100 to 750 ev for H and 100 to 500 ev for O. Their procedure was similar to that described in Section 4-1-E in connection with previous elastic scattering experiments[35] performed in the same laboratory. The apparatus used for the ionization studies differs from that shown in Fig. 4-1-8 in that the low-energy scattering gun has been replaced by an electron impact ionizer. The number of ions formed in the region defined by the intersection of the dc electron beam and the modulated molecular beam is compared with the number formed when the neutral beam is partially dissociated and the degree of dissociation is measured with a mass spectrometer. From these data the ratios of the apparent atomic to molecular ionization cross sections are obtained. The absolute atomic values are calculated by multiplying these ratios by the molecular ionization cross sections of Tate and Smith.[11]

In the same laboratory measurements have also been made of the apparent cross section for ionization of atomic nitrogen by electron impact over the energy range 25 to 750 ev.[36] Because of the difficulty of dissociating the nitrogen molecule, the rf discharge source used to produce atomic hydrogen and atomic oxygen in previous experiments was replaced by a pulsed dc discharge that delivers a beam in which about 20% of the nitrogen molecules are dissociated. An improved ionizer, shown in Fig. 5-4-1, was developed for the nitrogen experiments. The electron beam in the ionizer is ribbon-shaped so that a large electron current will pass through the neutral beam. Electrons originate from a long oxide-coated cathode and are extracted through a slit in G_1, which is maintained at a fixed potential with respect to the cathode. Acceleration to the desired final energy is accomplished between the slits in G_1 and G_2. Electron beam currents of about 100 μa are used. The beam is defined by a magnetic field of about 400 gauss applied parallel to the beam axis, so that no significant electron current is detected at G_2, G_3, or on the ion collector. The magnetic field also serves to prevent scattered electrons and electrons produced in ionizing events from reaching the ion collector. Electrons are prevented from leaving the electron collector region by the action of the magnetic field and by the potentials on the collector and repeller. The electron beam intersects the neutral beam between G_2 and G_3, and the resulting ions are collected by the application of a potential V_i (usually about 30 volts) across the ion collector. Saturation measurements indicate that all the ions are collected, including energetic ions formed in dissociative ionization. The ion collection field causes only a small uncertainty in the electron energy—less than 3 ev for a 30-volt ion collection potential. The height of the neutral beam is large enough for the entire electron beam to pass through the neutral beam.

Apparatus somewhat similar to that just described has been used by Brink[37] at the Lawrence Radiation Laboratory to measure the relative

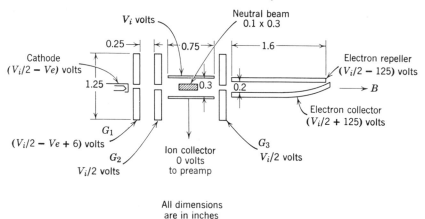

All dimensions
are in inches

FIG. 5-4-1. The ionizer used in the study of the ionization of atomic nitrogen by electron impact.[36]

ionization cross sections of lithium, sodium, and potassium by electrons with energy variable from threshold to 500 ev. An atomic beam from an oven is chopped by a rotating slotted wheel and intersected by a dc electron beam. The ions thus produced are extracted from the interaction region by a weak electric field and focused into a mass spectrometer which employs a 14-stage electron multiplier as the ion detector.

As stated earlier, some novel crossed-beam techniques have recently been introduced by Dolder, Harrison, and Thonemann[10] at Harwell. The apparatus* they used for the study of electron impact ionization of He^+ is shown in Fig. 5-4-2. Ions from the source S are accelerated through a potential difference of 5000 volts to the electrodes L and then passed through the electromagnet M_1 for e/m analysis. The resulting beam of 5 kev He^+ ions is collimated by the slit h (5 mm high) in the plate P before it enters the interaction space B. Electrons from the gun G cross this beam at right angles and are collected in the Faraday cup C_3. The electron gun,

* This apparatus has also been used to obtain cross sections for ionization of Ne^+ and N^+ by electron impact. See K. T. Dolder, M. F. A. Harrison, and P. C. Thonemann, *Proc. Roy. Soc. (London)* **A-274**, 546 (1963) and M. F. A. Harrison, K. T. Dolder, and P. C. Thonemann, *Proc. Phys. Soc. (London)* **82**, 368 (1963).

193

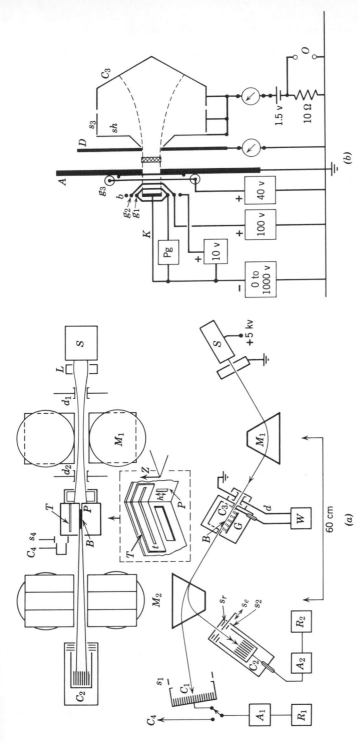

FIG. 5-4-2. Apparatus used by Dolder, Harrison, and Thonemann[10] for study of the ionization of He+ ions by electron impact. (a) Schematic views of apparatus: the upper diagram shows the side elevation and the lower the plan view. S, ion source; L, lens; d_1 and d_2, deflector plates used to align the He+ ion beam; M_1 and M_2, electromagnets; B, interaction space; G, electron gun; C_3, electron collector; C_1, C_2 and C_4, ion collectors; A_1, dc amplifier; A_2, vibrating-reed electrometer; R_1 and R_2, pen recorders. (b) The electron gun and collector viewed along the axis of the ion beam, showing the cathode (K), control grid (g_1), accelerating grid (g_2), and beam focusing wires (b). The grid g_3 draws back secondary electrons from the anode (A). Typical electrode potentials are shown. The electron beam has a rectangular cross section approximately 3.7 × 0.2 cm and is focused vertically.

shown in Fig. 5-4-2b, was designed to produce an approximately mono-energetic beam free from secondary electrons ejected from its grids and also to minimize the field penetration from the gun electrodes into the interaction space B. The momentum transferred to the He^{2+} ions which are produced in collisions of electrons with the He^+ ions is insufficient to deflect the He^{2+} ions from the beam. However, after the beam emerges from the interaction space, it is separated into its singly and doubly charged components by the analyzer magnet M_2, which deflects the He^+ ions into C_1 and the He^{2+} ions into C_2.

In terms of the experimentally measured quantities, the ionization cross section for formation of He^{2+} ions from He^+ is given by the equation

$$q^{2+} = \frac{I^{2+}}{I^+} \frac{1}{J} \frac{hevV}{2(v^2 + V^2)^{\frac{1}{2}}} F \tag{5-4-1}$$

where I^+ and J are the currents of He^+ ions and electrons, respectively, crossing the interaction space, and I^{2+} is the current of He^{2+} ions formed by electron impact. The electron and ion velocities are v and V, respectively, and e is the electronic charge. The factor F is given by the expression

$$F = \frac{\int_0^h i(z)\, dz \int_0^h j(z)\, dz}{\int_0^h i(z)\, j(z)\, dz} \tag{5-4-2}$$

where $j(z)\, dz$ and $i(z)\, dz$ are the electron and He^+ currents passing through the areas defined by the height dz and the respective beam widths. The factor F, which takes into account inhomogeneities in the beam number densities, has the value unity when either beam has uniform density; F is evaluated by lowering a slotted shutter T through the beams and simultaneously measuring the electron and He^+ currents passing through the slit t (0.5 mm high). Adjustment of the apparatus always ensures that $0.93 < F < 1.00$.

The currents measured at the collectors C_1 and C_2 do not correspond exactly to those in the interaction space because of space-charge repulsion losses of ions, mainly in the narrow gap of the magnet M_2. To restrict these losses, the He^+ beam current is kept small, typically about 3×10^{-7} amp. Electron beam currents of about 2 ma are used, and the current of He^{2+} ions measured at C_2 does not exceed 3×10^{-15} amp. In this experiment it is necessary to pulse both the electron and ion beams. Therefore the indicated currents refer to mean levels. The electron current is measured by a moving-coil meter, the current to C_1, by dc amplifier, and the He^{2+} current to C_2 by a vibrating-reed electrometer. Secondary electrons produced by ions striking the collectors are suppressed by applying negative potentials to the electrodes s_1, s_2, and s_4. The collector C_2 must be carefully insulated to avoid charge leakage and shielded to prevent the collection of stray particles. To minimize the entrance of stray particles into C_2, an adjustable entrance slit s_e is set just wide enough to accept the entire He^{2+} beam. Even so, there is a background current to C_2 of about 2×10^{-16} amp which is attributed to fast metastable helium atoms formed when the He^+ beam hits metal surfaces inside the apparatus. Some of these neutral metastables enter C_2 and rebound to release electrons on striking s_2. These electrons are accelerated back into C_2 and give a negative background current.

Dolder, Harrison, and Thonemann found it impracticable to reduce the pressure in their apparatus below 10^{-6} mm Hg, and consequently a current of He^{2+} ions was formed by charge stripping on the background gas which was comparable with the maximum current of He^{2+} produced by electron impact. The background gas pressure depends to some extent on the electron current, but when the electron current is rapidly pulsed the gas pressure does not change appreciably between pulses. Consequently the rate of charge stripping is steady. On the other hand, the current of He^{2+} arising from electron impacts is produced only during the electron pulses, and it is possible to distinguish between the two sources of the doubly charged ions. Considerations of the volume of the interaction space and the pumping speed indicate that the gas pressure cannot change appreciably in a time less than about 10^{-2} sec; therefore the electron beam is pulsed at a frequency of about 5000 cps. The He^+ beam is also deflected out of the interaction space at this same frequency by voltage pulses applied to the deflector plate d. Thus the He^+ beam current crossing the interaction space has a square waveform, and its duty cycle is set to be 50%. The electron current pulses have a shorter duration than the ion pulses, as shown in Fig. 5-4-3. In the "coincidence" mode the electron and ion beams pulses are synchronized, so that both electrons and ions cross the interaction space at the same time. In this mode He^{2+} ions are produced both by charge stripping and electron impact. In the "anticoincidence" mode the He^+ beam is "on" only when the electron beam is "off," so that electron-ion collisions cannot occur and charge stripping is the only mechanism for the formation of He^{2+}. Thus I^{2+}, the ion current produced by electron impacts, is the difference between the mean currents measured at C_2 in the "coincidence" and "anticoincidence" modes. The modulation frequency is sufficiently high that the gas pressure is steady and the rate of charge stripping is the same for both modes.

B. EXPERIMENTAL RESULTS. The data obtained by Rothe et al.[34] on atomic hydrogen and atomic oxygen are displayed in Figs. 5-4-4 and 5-4-5.

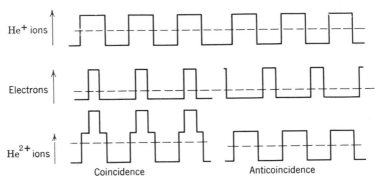

FIG. 5-4-3. The waveforms of ion and electron beam currents in the experiment of Dolder, Harrison, and Thonemann.[10] The mean levels of the pulsed currents are shown by the dashed lines.

Comparison is made, in the case of hydrogen, with the experimental results of Fite and Brackmann[31] and Boyd and Boksenberg.[33] The experiment performed by the latter investigators was a relative measurement, and their data have been normalized to the results of a Born approximation calculation, which is discussed in Ref. 8 of the paper by Rothe et al.[34] The remaining curve in Fig. 5-4-4 shows the results of an impulse

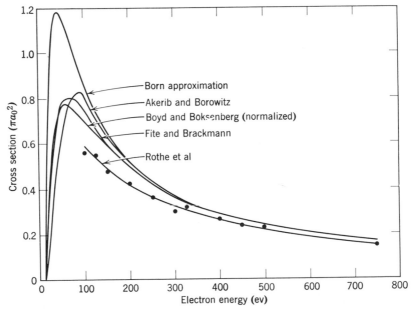

FIG. 5-4-4. Cross sections for ionization of atomic hydrogen by electron impact.[34]

approximation calculation by Akerib and Borowitz.[38] Comparison is made in Fig. 5-4-5 with experimental data on atomic oxygen obtained by Fite and Brackmann[32] and with the results of a theoretical calculation by Seaton.[39]

Figure 5-4-6 shows the experimental data obtained by Smith et al.[36] on atomic nitrogen. Also shown are the cross sections calculated by Seaton[39] for single ionization of the nitrogen atom. Seaton's values were obtained

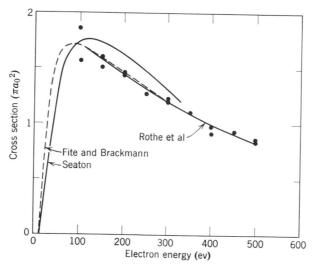

FIG. 5-4-5. Cross sections for ionization of atomic oxygen by electron impact.[34]

by use of the Bethe approximation for the relation between the electron impact ionization cross section and the photoionization cross section (see Section 7-4). The theoretical values are about 30% higher than the experimental cross sections, even though the experimental include small contributions from multiple ionization.

Dolder, Harrison, and Thonemann's results[10] on the ionization of He^+ from threshold to 1000 ev are shown in Fig. 5-4-7 on the curve labeled M. The quantity plotted along the ordinate axis is the experimental cross section multiplied by the classical scaling factor $(\chi_2/\chi_1)^2$, where χ_1 is the ionization energy of atomic hydrogen and χ_2 that for He^+ (13.6 and 54.4 ev, respectively). The electron energy is expressed in units of the ionization energy along the abscissa axis. This method of plotting the data facilitates their comparison with the data on atomic hydrogen. (According to classical theory, $(\chi_n/\chi_1)^2 q_i$ as a function of E/χ_n should be the same for all members of the sequence of ions, of atomic number n, isoelectronic to the H atom.) The curves labeled T, E, and G give estimates for He+ based on the classical calculations of Thomson,[23,40] Elwert,[41] and Gryziński.[42] The Coulomb-Born calculation made by Burgess[43] is shown by curve C. Since these calculations did not extend past 12 times threshold, the curve C has been extended, as indicated by the dashed line, by use of the plane wave Born approximation for atomic hydrogen taken from the paper by Fite and Brackmann.[31] At high energies the two approximations

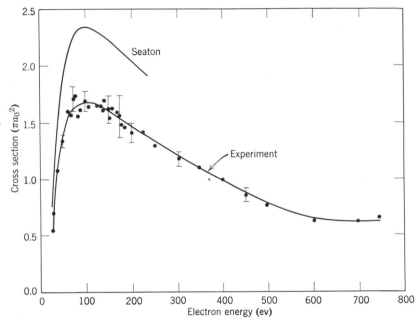

FIG. 5-4-6. Cross sections for ionization of atomic nitrogen by electron impact.[36]

coincide when the cross sections for He+ ions are scaled by the factor $(\chi_2/\chi_1)^2$. This good agreement between experiment and theory serves to corroborate the experimental results, as the Born approximation is quite accurate at high electron energies. More refined calculations recently made by Burgess and Rudge[44] are also in good agreement with the experimental results. Dolder, Harrison, and Thonemann estimate that their data are accurate to within $\pm 10\%$ at all energies above 150 ev. The effect of the ionic field of the He+ ion may be assessed by comparing the curve M with curve F, which shows Fite and Brackmann's experimental data for atomic hydrogen. The curves coincide at high energies, but the He+ cross section is higher at electron energies less than about five times threshold. This difference may be explained by the fact that at low energies a significant number of electrons are swept in toward the ions by the long-range Coulomb field, and an increase in the probability of ionization results. At high energies the ionic attraction represents only a negligible perturbation on the electronic trajectories.

Brink's relative ionization cross sections[37] for lithium, sodium, and potassium are shown in Figs. 5-4-8 through 5-4-10. The experimental energy scales have been adjusted so that the curves pass through the known

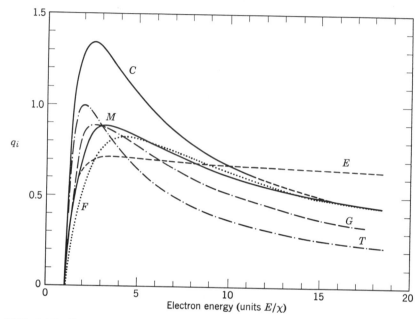

FIG. 5-4-7. Cross sections for ionization of He^+ ions by electron impact. Curve M is the experimental cross section multiplied by the scaling factor $(\chi_2/\chi_1)^2$. It is compared with the theoretical curves of Burgess (C), Gryziński (G), Elwert (E) and Thomson (T). Curve F shows Fite and Brackmann's measurements for atomic hydrogen.

ionization potentials. This process corrects for contact potentials in the apparatus; it involves a horizontal shift of the curves by about 1 ev. Doubly charged ions were observed for sodium and potassium but not for lithium. This indicates that Li^{2+} cannot have an abundance of more than a few per cent of that of Li^+. Brink's data on sodium and potassium are in general agreement with the results obtained by Tate and Smith.[20] There are no other experimental data available for comparison with Brink's data on lithium, but detailed quantum mechanical calculations have been made on this system by Peach and McDowell.[45] The theoretical cross section has a maximum value of $0.9\pi a_0^2$ and decreases as $E^{-1} \log E$ at high energies.

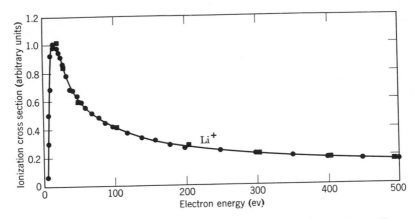

FIG. 5-4-8. Cross sections for ionization of lithium by electron impact.[37]

Brink's curves for lithium and sodium have the energy dependence expected for a simple ionization process. From 500 ev down to within 25 ev of the threshold, the lithium data lie on a straight line on a log-log plot. If the sodium data are normalized to lithium at 500 ev, they lie on the same straight line. This indicates that these cross sections have the same energy dependence over this energy range and differ only in absolute value. Brink has argued convincingly that the break in the curve for production of K^+ is due to the onset of autoionization and that similar structure observed by Tate and Smith[20] in curves for rubidium and cesium have the same origin. Figure 5-4-11 shows that the ionization of potassium can proceed by two independent processes. The simple ionization

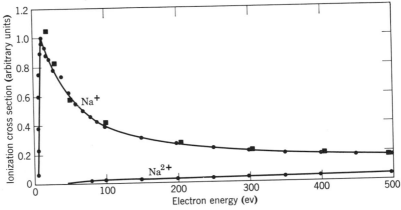

FIG. 5-4-9. Cross sections for ionization of sodium by electron impact.[37]

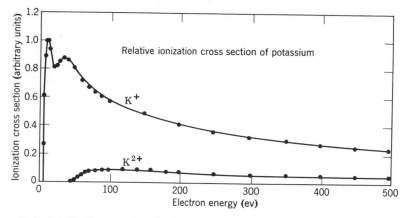

FIG. 5-4-10. Cross sections for ionization of potassium by electron impact.[37]

mechanism corresponds to a transition from the electronic ground state configuration $3p^64s$ to the ionic ground state $3p^6$, which can also be reached by the process of autoionization through the $3p^54s^2$ excited state of the atom. The threshold for this second process is about 19 ev, at which energy the upper curve in Fig. 5-4-10 shows a sharp break. A general discussion of autoionization appears in Section 8-2-A.

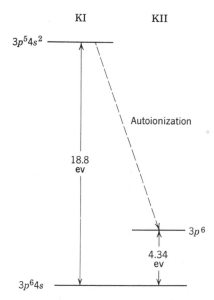

FIG. 5-4-11. Illustration of transitions involved in simple ionization and autoionization of potassium.[37]

5-5. THRESHOLD IONIZATION AND FINE STRUCTURE STUDIES

The first part of this section is concerned with experimental techniques for obtaining information about the variation of electron ionization cross sections near threshold and about the fine structure of ionization curves. The second part deals with theoretical predictions and experimental results.

A. EXPERIMENTAL TECHNIQUES.   1. *High-resolution apparatus.* The usual mass spectrometer ion source is unsatisfactory for precise ionization studies at low electron energies because of the large (in percentages) spread in the energies of the beam electrons and the uncertainty in the mean energy. The major sources of difficulty are (a) the initial distribution of energies of thermionically emitted electrons; (b) the acceleration of the electrons by an unknown contact potential difference between the cathode and the ionization chamber; and (c) an unknown acceleration of the electrons in their passage through the ionization chamber because of the presence of the electric field necessary to extract the ions. Nottingham's technique for reducing the energy spread of the electrons has already been mentioned.[28] The next noteworthy advance in high-resolution techniques came with the development of the *retarding potential difference* (RPD) *method*[46] by Fox and his co-workers in 1951.

The RPD ion source is illustrated in Fig. 5-5-1. Electrons from the filament are accelerated into the grounded ionization chamber 5 by the potential V_i. This chamber contains the target gas at a pressure of about 10^{-5} mm Hg. The electrons are distributed in energy over a range of several ev, as indicated by the dashed curve drawn near the filament. The intermediate electrode 4 is held at a negative potential V_R with respect to the filament in order to prevent the less energetic electrons in the distribution from entering the ionization chamber. However, those electrons that have kinetic energy greater than eV_R associated with their motion along the axis will not be stopped, and a beam of electrons with an energy distribution cut off sharply on the lower side will enter the chamber. If the magnitude of V_4 is now decreased by a small amount ΔV_R from V_{4M} to V_{4m}, with V_i held constant, the energy cutoff will change to admit electrons in the energy range $e \Delta V_R$ to the ionization chamber. The increase in the rate of ionization of the target gas is then attributable to these additional electrons, whose energies are closely defined within the range $e \Delta V_R$. The electron beam is collimated by a longitudinal magnetic field, and the electrons with appreciable transverse velocity components are caught by the electrode 4, whose aperture is small compared with the Larmor radius of the beam electrons. In order to obtain adequate ion currents, it is necessary to apply a weak electric field across the ionization chamber in a direction normal to the electron beam. The use of a conventional dc draw-out field would result in an inhomogeneity and uncertainty in the electron energy. To avoid this difficulty, Fox et al. pulse both the electron gun and the draw-out electrode in such a way that electrons can produce ionization only when the extraction field is zero. The draw-out voltage is applied for only a short time following each burst

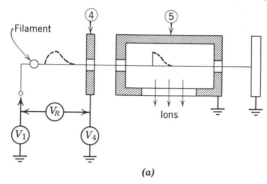

(a)

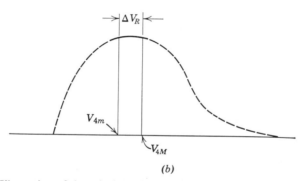

(b)

FIG. 5-5-1. Illustration of the principle of the retarding potential difference method.[46] (a) A sketch of the ion source showing the electrode structure and the voltage references. (b) A distribution in electron energy which is modified by the retarding potential to give the equivalent of a monoenergetic electron beam.

of ionization. When contact potentials are properly taken into account,[47] the maximum effective energy spread of the beam is only 0.06 ev, and the kinetic energy of the electrons is known within 0.1 ev. In addition to being used in ionization studies, the RPD method has also been applied in a number of important electron excitation studies (see Section 5-9) and investigations of negative ion formation (see Chapter 8).

Within the last decade considerable progress has also been made in reducing the energy spread of electron beams by further development of the techniques of electrostatic energy analysis. Clarke[48] built a 127° cylindrical electrostatic energy selector which provided electron beams with energy spreads as low as 0.2 ev. Improvements on Clarke's design were made by Marmet and Kerwin,[49] who have been able to produce electron beams with energy spreads of only 0.04 ev, measured at the half-height of the distribution. Marmet and Kerwin reduced the amount of electron reflection from the plates of their analyzer by covering them with curved tungsten mesh grids. These grids now define the electric field in the analyzer, and the plates behind them are biased to collect all the electrons that get through the grids. By this means the space charge within the analyzer is significantly reduced. They also covered the walls of the ionization chamber with close-packed arrays of short, fine, gold-plated copper tubes, mounted with their axes perpendicular to the chamber walls. The electron reflection coefficient of this "electron velvet" is only about 20%, and a substantial reduction of space charge within the ionization chamber results from its use. An excellent 127° analyzer recently constructed by Schulz[50] for studies of vibrational excitation of molecules is described in Section 5-9. Parallel-plate electrostatic analyzers have also proved useful, and they offer the advantage of simple construction. Such a device has been utilized by Foner and Nall[51] in their studies of threshold ionization. The properties of cylindrical analyzers have been investigated by Hughes and Rojansky[52] and Bainbridge and Jordan,[53] and the action of parallel-plate analyzers is discussed by Yarnold and Bolton[54] and Harrower.[55]

2. *Beam energy modulation.* The techniques described for obtaining high resolution in electron beam experiments have been applied to the study of fine structure in ionization cross section curves. An entirely different approach has been worked out by Morrison.[56] Electrons from a conventional type of gun are accelerated through a dc potential which is modulated by a very small ac component. This energy modulation results in a modulation of the ion current at frequencies that are harmonics of the driving frequency. To first order, the amplitude of the nth harmonic of the ion current is proportional to the nth derivative, with respect to the electron energy, of the ionization cross section averaged over the energy distribution of the electrons in the beam. Thus the structure of the ionization curves may be studied without the necessity of directly plotting the curves. Since the demands on instrumental stability and reproducibility are thereby considerably lessened, this technique shows considerable promise. The method has not yet been fully evaluated.

B. THEORETICAL PREDICTIONS AND EXPERIMENTAL RESULTS. In 1953 Wannier[57] derived a threshold law for single ionization of atoms and ions by electron impact. His prediction, which was based on an approximate classical calculation coupled with statistical mechanical arguments, was that the yield should rise as the 1.127th power of the excess electron energy for atoms, whereas for ions the exponent should lie between 1.127 and unity. Wannier stated that his derivation was not rigorous because some of the difficulties of the three-body problem were circumvented by the application of ergodicity. More recently Geltman[58] investigated the problem quantum mechanically, using a Coulomb-modified form of the Born approximation. He predicted that near threshold the cross section for production of ions of charge $+ne$ from a neutral atom should increase as the nth power of the excess energy.

Most of the measurements made in recent years on ions with no low-lying excited states appear to confirm Geltman's predictions, but some confusion exists with respect to more complicated structures.[5] Part of the difficulty may stem from imperfections remaining in the experimental techniques.

Figure 5-5-2, taken from a paper by Fox,[59] shows cross section curves for single ionization of a number of simple gases. Fox obtained the indicated absolute cross sections by comparison of his relative data with the absolute data obtained in the 1930's by Smith,[12] Tate and Smith,[11] and Nottingham.[28] The breaks in the curves shown may be attributable to the production of ions in excited states or to the onset of additional modes of ionization, such as autoionization. Further discussion of ionization near threshold appears in Ref. 60. Still more work needs to be done in this area.

5-6. ANGULAR AND ENERGY DISTRIBUTIONS
OF INELASTICALLY SCATTERED ELECTRONS

Many measurements[61] have been made of the distributions in angle and energy of electrons scattered by atoms and molecules, and although the greater part of this work was done long ago most of the results are still considered trustworthy. Data on angular distributions in elastic scattering were presented in Section 4-2; comparisons between results on elastic and inelastic scattering appear in Figs. 5-6-1 and 5-6-2, which are taken from the book by Massey and Burhop.[62] These data were obtained by standard beam-scattering techniques involving electrostatic energy analysis of the electrons scattered from the beam at selected angles. Additional data and discussions of experimental techniques are to be found in Massey and Burhop's book[62] and in the review by Massey.[63] Of particular interest is Massey and Burhop's discussion[62] of the general trends in the observed angular scattering distributions.

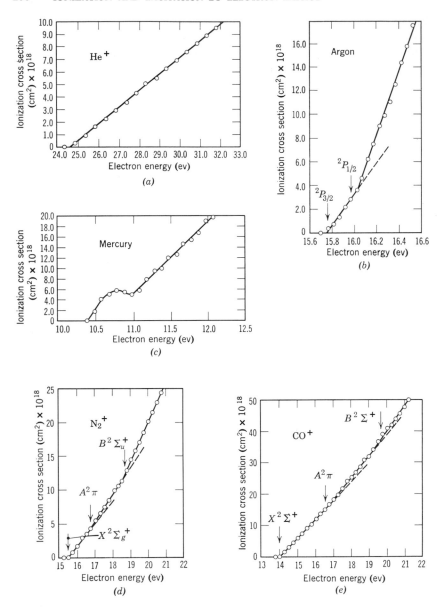

FIG. 5-5-2. Cross sections for single ionization of simple gases by electron impact.[59] (a) The ionization efficiency curve for He⁺. (b) The ionization efficiency curve for A⁺ near threshold. The arrows indicate the doublet ground states determined from spectroscopic data. (c) The ionization efficiency curve for Hg⁺ near threshold. (d) The ionization efficiency curve for N₂⁺. The arrows indicate the designated energy states of the ion determined from spectroscopic data. (e) The ionization efficiency curve for CO⁺. The spectroscopically determined energy levels are indicated by arrows.

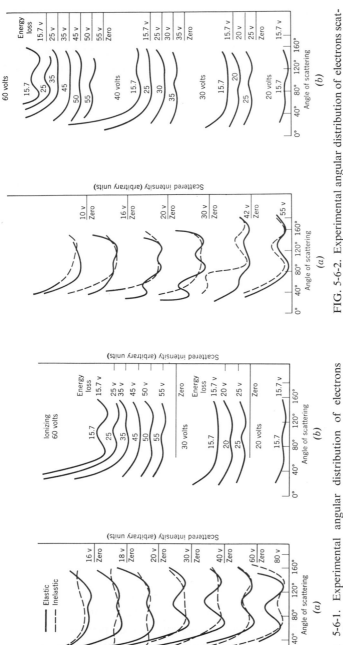

FIG. 5-6-1. Experimental angular distribution of electrons scattered by argon atoms. (a) Elastic (———) and inelastic (– – –) collisions, the latter involving excitation to the ³P₁ level, with an energy loss of 11.6 ev. (b) Ionizing collisions with different energy losses.

FIG. 5-6-2. Experimental angular distribution of electrons scattered by mercury atoms. (a) Elastic (———) and inelastic (– – –) collisions, the latter involving excitation to the 6 ³P₁ level. (b) Ionizing collisions with different energy losses.

5-7. ENERGY DISTRIBUTIONS OF IONS AND ELECTRONS
PRODUCED BY ELECTRON IMPACT

A. IONS. Only a very small amount of momentum can be transferred to an atom or molecule by electron impact, and ions produced in collisions that involve the mere stripping of electrons off the target have essentially the same kinetic energies as the original target structures. If, on the other hand, the target dissociates when ionization occurs, internal energy is transferred to the fragments in the form of kinetic energy, and the target may fly apart rather violently. The breakup of the structure is described in terms of the *Franck-Condon principle*, which states that in an electronic transition the separation and relative velocity of the nuclei of the molecule are altered only to a negligible extent. (The Franck-Condon principle is discussed at length in Refs. 4, 6, and 64. This principle also governs dissociative electron attachment to molecules, as is brought out in Section 8-1-B.)

A considerable amount of work has gone into measurement of the energy distribution of the ionic fragments produced in dissociative ionization. Apparatus of the "Lozier tube" type* was used in many of these studies,[65] and most of the remainder were performed with mass spectrometers.[66] The experimental methods employed and results obtained are fully discussed by Massey and Burhop,[64] Craggs and Massey,[4] and Field and Franklin.[6]

However, a recent paper by Dunn[67] casts serious doubt on the validity of many of the conclusions based on various types of dissociative excitation studies made both on Lozier tubes and on mass spectrometers with conventional ion sources. Both types of apparatus selectively detect particles ejected at right angles to the exciting electron beam, and Dunn shows that the angular distributions of the dissociation products are expected to be anisotropic in a majority of the cases. Dunn argues as follows: because of the great relative mass of the nuclei, when an electronic transition to an antibonding state occurs in a molecule, the dissociation normally takes place in a time that is short compared with the period of the molecular rotation. Hence, to a good approximation, the dissociation products will be moving in a direction characteristic of the vibratory motion. For this reason, if the excitation probability has a dependence on the relative orientation of the incident electron beam and some axis of the molecule, the dissociation products should have a corresponding distribution.

Anisotropies are clearly revealed in a study made by Dunn and Kieffer[68] of the angular distributions and energy profiles of protons released in

* For a description of the Lozier tube and its application to the study of electron attachment see Section 8-5-B.

dissociative ionization of hydrogen molecules. The apparatus used in this study is illustrated in Fig. 5-7-1. Electrons from a gun rigidly attached to a cylindrical rotatable collision chamber produce ionization in the target gas, and ions formed in the collision region drift out through a slot milled along the periphery of the chamber. The slot is in the plane which contains the electron beam and which is perpendicular to the axis of the chamber. Ions leaving the chamber at a selected angle drift through fixed collimating apertures into a sector field magnetic analyzer. They are then accelerated into an electron multiplier and detected. The collision chamber and the

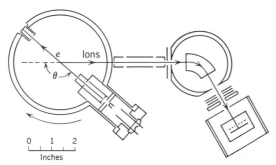

FIG. 5-7-1. Apparatus used by Dunn and Kieffer[68] to study anisotropies in the dissociative ionization of hydrogen molecules.

electrodes in the drift region are gold-plated to minimize stray electric fields, and shielding is used to reduce the magnetic field in the chamber and drift region to less than 40 mgauss. The base vacuum is about 2×10^{-7} mm Hg, and the experiments are conducted at about 2×10^{-5} mm Hg. Two types of measurements are made. First, the magnetic field in the analyzer is set to transmit protons of a selected energy, and the proton current is measured as a function of the angle θ for a given electron energy. This is done for electrons of various discrete energies and for several proton energies. Then the angle and electron energy are fixed, and the proton energy is scanned by varying the magnetic field. These measurements are made for various angles and electron beam energies.

The angular distributions that Dunn and Kieffer obtained for 8.6-ev protons are shown in Fig. 5-7-2. We may note a marked energy dependence, with a transition from forward peaking at lower electron energies to slight peaking at right angles at high energies. (The slight fore-aft asymmetry is due to a fore-aft asymmetry in the scattering chamber.) The energy dependence of the anisotropy is dramatically shown in Fig. 5-7-3, which gives the ratio of the proton current at 20° to that at right angles. The dotted vertical line represents the threshold electron energy at which

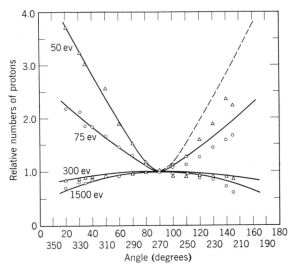

FIG. 5-7-2. Angular distribution of 8.6-ev protons produced in dissociative ionization of H_2 molecules by electrons of various energies.

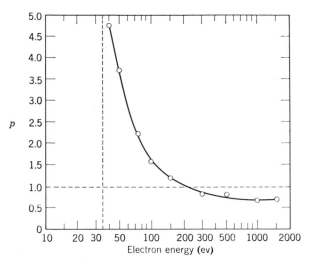

FIG. 5-7-3. The ratio p versus electron energy for 8.6-ev protons produced in dissociative ionization of H_2; p is the ratio of the number of protons received at 20° with respect to the electron beam direction to the number received at 90°.

this particular ion energy appears. The distribution changes rapidly from being strongly peaked in the forward direction near threshold to isotropic at about 200 ev. At electron energies above about 200 ev the distribution changes very slowly with energy and is slightly peaked at right angles. Figure 5-7-4 shows the proton energy distributions as measured by Lozier[69] using 75-ev electrons, as measured by Dunn and Kieffer,[68] and as predicted by the Franck-Condon principle. (The breakup of the H_2 molecule is discussed in terms of the Franck-Condon principle in Section 8-1-B.) Dunn and Kieffer's results on H_2 are seen to be in accord with the Franck-Condon rule.[70]

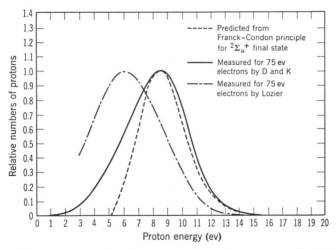

FIG. 5-7-4. Proton energy distributions for the reaction $e + H_2 \rightarrow H + H^+ + 2e$.

B. ELECTRONS.   Now we turn to consideration of the energy distribution of electrons ejected in ionization events. If the energy of the incident electrons is less than a few times the threshold energy for ionization of the target atom or molecule, all of the ejected electrons have energies of no more than a few ev. As the incident energy is increased, some secondaries of higher energy are produced, and at incident energies of several kev something like half the ejected electrons have energies greater than the threshold energy of the target. Experimentally, it is impossible to distinguish between the secondaries and the inelastically scattered incident electrons, and precise experimental information on the energy spectrum of the ejected electrons is lacking. Nevertheless, the conclusion expressed above can be drawn from laboratory observations, and theoretical studies support it. Of particular relevance are calculations[71] of the energy distributions of secondary electrons produced by proton impact, since the energy spectrum of electrons ejected by electron impact should be similar to that of secondaries ejected from the same target by protons of the same incident velocity. If we assume that this correspondence holds, the calculations of Bates, McDowell, and Omholt[71] indicate that in the ionization of neon by 1-kev electrons about 65% of the ejected electrons have energies greater than the ionization energy of atomic hydrogen (13.6 ev), 40% have energies greater than twice this amount, and 25% have energies in excess of four times this energy (see Fig. 6-7-12).

PART $\mathscr{B}$. EXCITATION OF ATOMS AND MOLECULES BY ELECTRON IMPACT

We now begin a discussion of the excitation of atoms and molecules by electron impact. We shall consider excitation to higher electronic states, which may occur both in atoms and molecules, along with vibrational and rotational excitation, which occurs only in molecules.

Experimental studies of processes involving excitation are less direct and considerably more difficult than those of ionization because of the greater difficulty of accurately measuring the signal associated with the excitation process. In ionization measurements the characteristic signal is the production of ions, which are easily collected and registered because of their electric charge. In excitation studies the task of detection is much heavier, and indeed much of the effort in such experimentation has been expended in the development of schemes for detecting the production of excitation. A number of these techniques are discussed in subsequent sections.

There is, however, a compensatory advantage associated with excitation experiments because as a rule the detection signals are unique to the state of the system to which the excitation occurs. In ionization studies we generally know only that the target has been ionized, and the state of the residual ion is usually unknown, except in some measurements near threshold (cf. Section 5-5). Excitation measurements, on the other hand, clearly pertain in most cases to specific, known states of the system. Not only is more detailed information obtained; it may also be used for "diagnostic" purposes in gaseous electronics and astrophysics. The uniqueness of the signal resulting from excitation to a state from which optical radiation to a lower state is permitted is particularly valuable: observation of the radiation emitted by the solar corona, for example, allows estimates to be made of the chemical composition and atomic concentrations of the corona, if the relevant excitation cross sections and transition probabilities are known.

5-8. GENERAL METHODS FOR EXPERIMENTAL DETERMINATION
OF EXCITATION CROSS SECTIONS

The principal methods used to obtain information about electron impact excitation processes are the following:

(a) A homogeneous beam of electrons of known and variable energy is passed through a gas, and atoms or molecules of the gas are raised to electronic states of higher energy. Measurements are made of the wavelength and intensity of the optical radiation resulting from spontaneous radiative transitions in de-excitation to lower levels, and the excitation cross sections are calculated as a function of the electron energy. Prism and grating monochromators, or gas absorption cells, may be used for spectral range selection. Photocells, photomultipliers, gas-filled photon counters, and photoelectric detectors are commonly used for detection of the photons. This method is evidently not applicable to the excitation of metastable states, from which radiative transitions are forbidden. The method has low sensitivity because the detector intercepts only a small fraction of the photons produced and because not all of the photons arriving at the detector are registered.

(b) Observations may be made of the wavelength and intensity of spectral lines emitted by an electrical discharge. Apart from the difficulty of absolute intensity measurements, the obtainment of accurate results is dependent on a knowledge of the number density and velocity distribution of the free electrons in the discharge. Radiation resulting from secondary effects may produce severe complications.

(c) Cross sections for excitation of metastable levels may be obtained by firing a beam of electrons through a gas and determining the rate of production of metastables by one of the following methods. The concentration of metastables may be deduced from measurements of selective light absorption or by observations of anomalous dispersion. Both techniques offer low sensitivity. Alternatively, measurements can be made of the number of secondary electrons ejected when the metastables collide with a metal electrode within the gas volume (see Section 13-2-A-5). Also, the metastables may be "quenched" by passing them through an electric or magnetic field which induces them to radiate their excess energy and fall to a lower state.* The radiation thus emitted is detected by the standard means. The quenching action is usually accomplished by electric fields of about 50 volts/cm or magnetic fields of several hundred gauss.

(d) A swarm of electrons is allowed to diffuse through a gas in an

---

* The possibility of quenching metastable states by high-frequency electromagnetic waves has been recently discussed by W. Zernik, *Phys. Rev.* **132**, 320 (1963).

electric field of known intensity. Analysis of data on the rate of diffusion and drift can yield information on the various scattering mechanisms, including inelastic collisions leading either to metastable or ordinary excited states.

(e) A beam of electrons is passed through a gas and inelastically scattered electrons are collected. The energy losses are characteristic of the excitation processes, and measurement of the energy spectrum of the scattered electrons will provide information on these processes. This method is applicable to metastable as well as ordinary excited states. An advantage offered by this method is the ease of signal detection, for only a current measurement is required. However, the scattered electron collector must have unusually good energy resolution in order to distinguish between closely separated energy states of the target molecule. The early work based on this method was discussed in Section 5-6; the techniques to which reference was made there are best suited to relatively high electron energies. Recent work on higher resolution apparatus, which can be used for precision work at quite low electron energies, is discussed in Section 5-9-D.

The foregoing methods are covered at length by Massey and Burhop,[2] Massey,[3] Craggs and Massey,[4] and Fite.[5] Of particular interest in connection with recent experiments is Fite's analysis of radiation detectors.

5-9. TECHNIQUES USED IN RECENT EXCITATION EXPERIMENTS

Here we shall describe some of the apparatus and techniques utilized in recent experiments on excitation by electron impact.

A. APPARATUS USED BY STEBBINGS ET AL. FOR MEASUREMENT OF THE RATIO OF CROSS SECTIONS FOR PRODUCTION OF METASTABLE HYDROGEN ATOMS AND LYMAN-α RADIATION. During the last few years a series of important and difficult experiments has been performed by Fite and his associates[72] and by Lichten and Schultz[73] on excitation of hydrogen atoms by electron impact. This work has been thoroughly discussed by Fite[5] and by Burke and Smith,[9] and the reader is referred to their works for fuller accounts of experimental details and the procedures required for analysis of the data. Here we describe only one piece of the apparatus used in these studies, this particular apparatus being chosen mainly because it vividly illustrates the techniques used in quenching metastable states by an electric field. Some of the results obtained in the hydrogen investigations are presented in Section 5-10-A.

One aspect of the excitation of atomic hydrogen which was studied by the experimenters is the production of Ly-α radiation by electron impact.

This radiation may be excited in several ways. First, it may be produced by direct excitation from the ground $1^2S_{1/2}$ state to the $2^2P_{1/2}$ and $2^2P_{3/2}$ states, from which allowed radiative transitions in the reverse direction can proceed. Second, the atom may be excited into a state for which $n > 2$, then radiate down to one of the $2P$ levels, and finally return to the ground state; Ly-α radiation is emitted in the last step of the cascade. Third, Ly-α may arise from quenching the metastable $2S_{1/2}$ state, which can be excited by electron impact on the ground-state atom. The $2^2P_{1/2}$ state in atomic hydrogen is separated from the $2^2S_{1/2}$ state only by the

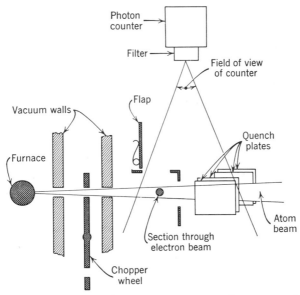

FIG. 5-9-1. Schematic representation of the apparatus used to measure the ratio of the cross sections for production of metastable atoms and Lyman-α radiation in collisions of electrons with ground-state hydrogen atoms (Stebbings et al.[72]).

amount of energy (about 4×10^{-6} ev) equal to the Lamb shift. Hence an electric field may perturb atoms in the metastable state and produce a mixture of $2^2S_{1/2}$ and $2^2P_{1/2}$ states so that radiative transitions from the $2P_{1/2}$ level to the ground state may occur. Very weak fields may induce these transitions, and stray fields must be minimized to avoid accidental quenching. In the experiment described here Stebbings, Fite, Hummer, and Brackmann[72] made use of the multiplicity of mechanisms for producing Ly-α radiation to measure the ratio of the cross sections for production of $2S$ hydrogen atoms and Lyman-α radiation.

The experimental arrangement which Stebbings et al.[72] employed is schematically illustrated in Fig. 5-9-1. Hydrogen atoms in a modulated neutral beam are excited by electrons in a perpendicular dc beam* and pass into a "quench" region, throughout which an electrostatic field of 30 volts/cm can be established. An iodine-vapor-filled ultraviolet photon counter[74] mounted on a trolley can be positioned to view either the region of beam intersection or the region between the quench plates. An oxygen absorption cell with lithium fluoride windows, positioned in front of the counter discriminates against frequencies other than that of the 1216 Å Ly-α radiation. When the counter is opposite the beam interaction region, it detects the Ly-α radiation produced in direct excitation events. (The lifetime of the excited states from which the allowed radiation is emitted is only of the order of 10^{-9} sec, so that the atoms excited to these states move only a negligible distance, about 10^{-3} cm, before they decay.) If the flap shown in the diagram is lowered, the quench field turned on, and the counter moved to view the quench region, only that radiation which arises from quenching metastables produced upstream in the interaction region can be detected. Since the lifetime of an undisturbed $2S$ hydrogen atom is of the order of 10^{-3} sec,[75] few of the metastables decay spontaneously before they reach the quench region. The desired cross section ratio can be determined by comparing the counter output signals produced by direct excitation and by metastable quenching. Procedures for obtaining absolute cross sections from this ratio and other excitation data are discussed by Fite[5] and by Burke and Smith.[9] Some of the results appearing in the original journal publications have been amended to take proper account of the angular distribution and polarization of the emitted radiation. The radiation produced by the quench field was initially considered by Stebbings et al. to be 100% polarized parallel to the electric field and to have the angular distribution of an electric dipole radiator oriented with its axis parallel to the quench field. However, a later analysis by Lichten[76] showed that the radiation is completely unpolarized and that the angular distribution is isotropic.

B. THE SECONDARY ELECTRON DETECTION METHOD FOR THE STUDY OF EXCITATION TO METASTABLE STATES. In 1942 Dorrestein[77] reported cross sections for the excitation of metastable states of helium and neon. His method was one in which the metastable atoms are detected by their ability to eject secondary electrons from a metallic surface whose work function is lower than the metastable excitation energy. More recently this same method has been used in refined form by Schulz and Fox[78] for high-resolution experiments on the excitation of metastable levels in helium near threshold.

* An axial magnetic field of 50 gauss used to confine the electron beam and the scattered electrons is not strong enough to have an appreciable effect on the lifetime of the metastable atoms. A much stronger field, 575 gauss, was used for quenching in the experiment of Lichten and Schultz.[73]

The excitation tube used by Schulz and Fox is shown schematically in Fig. 5-9-2. Electrons are emitted from a tungsten filament F, accelerated into the collision chamber C, and collected on the electrode E. The retarding potential difference method (cf. Section 5-5-A) is used to reduce the effective energy spread of the beam to about 0.1 ev. The electrodes P_1, P_2, and P_3 in the electron gun are used for this purpose. An axial magnetic field of about 100 gauss prevents defocusing of the beam by the retarding field. The collision chamber, which contains the target gas at a pressure in the range 10^{-4} to 10^{-2} mm Hg, is surrounded by two concentric

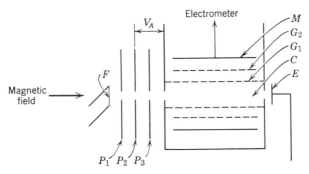

FIG. 5-9-2. Apparatus for study of excitation of metastables, with an RPD electron gun and secondary electron detector for the metastables.[78]

grids, G_1 and G_2, made of mesh which is 90% transparent. The diameters of these grids are 6.3 and 8.4 mm, respectively. A concentric solid cylinder M serves as the detector of the metastables produced by electron impact in the collision chamber. As in all of the apparatus described in this section, the components of the tube are gold-plated to reduce contact potentials.

Metastable atoms created along the axis of C move out of the collision chamber with thermal velocities, since their mean free paths are longer than the dimensions of the tube. Some of these metastables reach the cylinder M, where they eject secondary electrons* which are then accelerated to the grid G_2 by a potential difference of about 15 volts. A vibrating reed electrometer is connected through a 10^{10} ohm resistor to M. Measurement of the secondary electron current from M gives a measure of the number of metastables arriving at the collector M. The experimental data are the differences in secondary electron current observed when the potential of the retarding electrode P_2 is varied with respect to that of the

---

* Atoms raised to ordinary excited states might also eject secondary electrons from M if they could reach the detector before they are de-excited, but their short lifetime against spontaneous radiation prevents them from doing so.

filament. Using Stebbings' value of 0.29 for the efficiency of ejection of secondary electrons from a gold surface by metastable helium impact,[79] Schulz and Fox obtained absolute excitation cross sections as well as highly resolved relative excitation curves. Their results are presented in Section 5-10-B.

C. SCHULZ'S TRAPPED-ELECTRON METHOD. A very important new method for studying inelastic electron collisions has been developed by

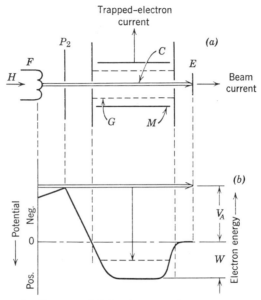

FIG. 5-9-3. Schematic diagram of Schulz's trapped-electron apparatus for studying inelastic electron collision processes, showing the tube (a) and the potential distribution along the axis of the tube (b); V_A is the accelerating potential and W is the well depth. The kinetic energy of the beam electrons is $(V_A + W)$ when they are in the collision chamber. Those electrons that lose more energy than V_A in a collision inside the potential well are trapped and collected on M.

Schulz.[80] The method consists of trapping low-energy inelastically scattered electrons in an electrostatic potential well and collecting them with high efficiency. A simplified diagram of Schulz's "trapped-electron" apparatus is shown in Fig. 5-9-3a. Although the construction of the tube is identical to that used by Schulz and Fox[78] and described above, different potentials are applied to the electrodes surrounding the collision chamber and a different mode of operation is employed. The filament F emits electrons which pass through the RPD gun (only the retarding electrode P_2 is shown in Fig. 5-9-3) into the collision chamber C and then to the collector E. An axial magnetic field H provides beam confinement. Two cylindrical grids surround the collision volume, although only one of them is shown in the drawing. These grids and the entrance and exit plates are held at the same potential. A well-insulated cylindrical collector M surrounds the grids. When a positive potential is applied to M with respect to the grid G, a small part of the potential penetrates into the collision chamber C. The grids are mesh, made of 0.002-in. wires with 0.038-in. spacing, and the potential at the tube axis is of the order of 0.5% of that applied between M and G. The potential difference between the axis of the tube and the collision chamber electrodes (the grids and end plates) is the well depth W. Figure 5-9-3b shows the potential versus distance along the tube axis for the case in which the electron collector is at the potential of the collision chamber electrodes, taken to be zero volts. The electrode P_2 is at a negative potential V_A with respect to G, since the beam electrons are accelerated to their final energy between P_2 and the entrance plate, which is connected to G. The double horizontal line in Fig. 5-9-3b indicates the energy $(V_A + W)$ of the electron beam in the collision chamber, and the arrow pointing downward from the double line represents the energy lost in an inelastic collision. Although the electron beam reaching the collision chamber has an energy spread of only about 0.1 ev, it acquires a larger effective spread because of the nonrectangular shape of the potential well. Nevertheless, the resolution of the instrument is better than 0.2 ev.

An electron in the beam which makes an inelastic collision and loses an amount of energy between V_A and $(V_A + W)$, so that its residual energy is smaller than the well depth W, is trapped in its axial motion by the well. It cannot reach the collision chamber electrodes and will therefore oscillate in the well until it makes its way by multiple collisions to the trapped-electron collector M. With a fixed well depth, we can trace out the excitation function between the excitation threshold V_X and $(V_X + W)$ by varying the electron accelerating voltage V_A. At the energy $(V_X + W)$ an artificial cutoff occurs because electrons having suffered inelastic collisions now appear above the top of the well and are not trapped. The trapped-electron current is the sum of the currents produced by excitation to all levels between V_A and $(V_A + W)$, and a clear indication of the state to which the target is excited is obtained only near the threshold for excitation of the lowest excited state. Alternatively, it is possible to keep V_A fixed at a value below the first excitation potential and vary the well depth. This method offers the advantage of not having an artificial cutoff; all inelastically scattered electrons are collected at all energies. Above the ionization threshold it directly measures the cross section $(q_x + 2q^+)$, where q_x and q^+ are the excitation and single-ionization cross sections, respectively. (Here we assume that multiple ionization is not occurring.)

The trapped-electron apparatus just described was the first model used by Schulz.[80] An improved model[81] which differs from the original in several important respects was subsequently constructed. The length of the collision chamber was increased from 19 to 152 mm to improve the uniformity of the potential well, and the magnetron magnet used with the first tube was replaced with a solenoid which provides a variable and more uniform field of 300 to 1000 gauss. The double grid G was replaced by a single grid with a much more transparent structure to allow well depths

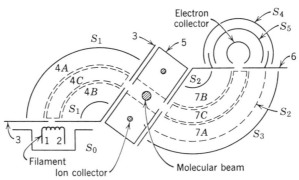

FIG. 5-9-4. Schematic diagram of Schulz's double electrostatic analyzer. Electrons are emitted by the filament, deflected by the cylindrical grids ($4A$ and $4B$) with radii of 1.0 and 1.5 cm, respectively, injected into the collision chamber 5, and analyzed by sweeping the voltage between electrodes 6 and 3. S_1, S_2, S_3, S_4, S_5 are shields to collect unwanted electrons; $4C$ and $7C$ are top and bottom grids. Typical operating voltages between the electrodes indicated: $(4A\text{-}4B) = 1.2$ v; $(7A\text{-}7B) = 1.2$ v; (filament-3) = 1.4 v; $(F\text{-}S_1) = 20$ v; $(F\text{-}S_2) = (F\text{-}S_3) = 20$ v. The electron collector is grounded. All slits are 0.5×4 mm.

up to 4 volts. (In the original apparatus the greatest feasible well depth was about 0.2 volt.) Another refinement consisted of plating the electron collector M with platinum black to reduce the secondary electron emission. (The collector is also generally held a few volts positive with respect to the collision chamber for secondary electron suppression.) Schulz[82] has also described some new sophisticated techniques for data recording in trapped-electron studies.

The trapped-electron method has been employed in a number of investigations of electronic and vibrational excitation (see Section 5-10) and negative ion formation (see Section 8-7).

D. SCHULZ'S DOUBLE ELECTROSTATIC ANALYZER. Schulz has recently constructed a double electrostatic analyzer[83] for studies of vibrational excitation of molecules by electron impact. The apparatus, shown in

Fig. 5-9-4, consists of two identical 127° electrostatic analyzers separated by a collision chamber, in which the electrons are crossed by a dc molecular beam. The analyzers are similar to the one designed by Marmet and Kerwin[49] and incorporate many of the refinements that have been introduced in the last few years. A thoria-coated iridium filament emits electrons that pass into the first analyzer, where they are deflected by the cylindrical grids 4A and 4B and focused on the exit slit. The electrons of undesired energy are collected on the "absorber shield" S_1, so that an essentially monoenergetic beam of electrons can be accelerated into the collision chamber 5, which consists of a cylindrical grid and a concentric ion collector ring. A molecular beam, originating in a 3-mm diameter tube close to the cylindrical grid, crosses the electron beam.* The energy distribution of the electrons scattered in the forward direction is analyzed by the second analyzer, from the end of which the electrons enter a highly insulated and shielded collector. The electron current to this collector is measured with a vibrating reed electrometer. The second analyzer is identical with the first except for having an additional electrode, S_3, which collects the primary electron beam when the second analyzer is tuned to an energy-loss process.

The parts of the tube nearest to the electron beam are gold-plated, and the absorber shields and electron collector are coated with platinum black to minimize the production of secondary electrons. This apparatus has extremely high energy resolution—the half-width of the energy spread of the electrons passing through a single analyzer is approximately 0.06 ev.† The accelerating voltage between the two 127° segments can be swept by a motor-driven helipot, and the collector current versus accelerating voltage plotted on an X-Y recorder. Peaks resulting from electrons which have lost discrete amounts of energy in exciting vibrational levels up to $v = 8$ are observed in experiments on nitrogen,[83] (v is the vibrational quantum number).

The double electrostatic analyzer gives the energy dependence of the cross section for excitation of any resolved level and also an estimate of the magnitude of the excitation cross section relative to the elastic scattering cross section. However, it has a low sensitivity (about 10^{-4} of that of a trapped-electron instrument), since only a small fraction of the scattered electrons enter the second analyzer.

---

* An ultrahigh vacuum system is utilized, and the tube is baked at 320°C, so that a residual pressure of 10^{-9} mm Hg is achieved. The effective pressure in the molecular beam is about 100 times the background pressure, and beam modulation is not required.
† An electrostatic analyzer with comparable energy resolution was described by J. A. Simpson at the Third International Conference on the Physics of Electronic and Atomic Collisions, London, 1963.

5-10. REVIEW OF RECENT EXCITATION EXPERIMENTS

Some of the excitation experiments performed during the last few years are now described. References to related theoretical work will be found in the papers discussed here.

A. ELECTRONIC EXCITATION OF ATOMIC HYDROGEN.   Figure 5-10-1 shows cross sections for production of $2S$ metastables from ground-state hydrogen atoms by electron impact. This figure is Fig. 18 of the paper by Burke and Smith,[9] who describe the calculations by which the theoretical curves were

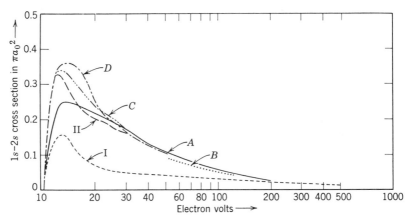

FIG. 5-10-1. Cross sections for electron impact excitation of ground-state hydrogen atoms to the metastable $2S$ state. Curves I and II are the experimental results of Stebbings et al.[72] and of Lichten and Schultz,[73] respectively. The theoretical curves were calculated as follows. *A:* Born approximation; *B:* second Born approximation; *C:* $1S$-$2S$ strong-coupling approximation; *D:* $1S$-$2S$-$2P$ approximation.

obtained and also the schemes for normalization of the experimental data. Although the shapes of the experimental curves obtained by Stebbings et al.[72] and by Lichten and Schultz[73] agree very well, their curves are in poor absolute agreement. The normalization question appears to be of crucial importance. Lichten and Schultz normalized their results to the Born approximation at 45 ev (the upper limit of their experimental energy range), and the validity of the normalization at an energy that low may be questioned. On the other hand, according to Burke and Smith[9] it is difficult to see how the theory can be made to agree with Stebbings' experimental results. This matter is also discussed by Fite.[5]

B. ELECTRONIC EXCITATION OF NOBLE GAS ATOMS.*   The excitation of helium has been studied by Schulz and Fox,[78] who used the secondary electron detection method, and by Schulz,[81] who used the trapped-electron technique. The results of these experiments are displayed in Fig. 5-10-2, both sets of the data being normalized to unity at the peak of the 2^3S metastable excitation. The optical values of the excitation energies of the lowest levels are indicated by arrows. The trapped-electron results show

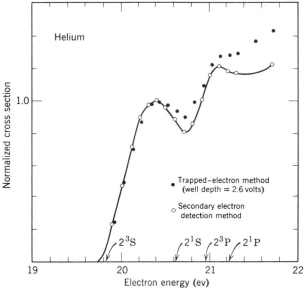

FIG. 5-10-2. The electron impact excitation function for helium near threshold.[81]

a less pronounced dip in the vicinity of the second metastable level at about 20.6 ev because of the larger energy spread of the electron beam after it enters the nonrectangular potential well. The discrepancy above 21.2 ev is thought to be the result of excitation of the 2^1P resonance level, which the secondary electron production method cannot detect. Photoelectrons ejected by energetic photons emitted in the $2^1P–1^1S$ transition will, however, contribute to the apparent metastable atom signal, although the

---

* Some recent references on electronic excitation of noble gas atoms are R. H. McFarland and E. A. Soltysik, *Phys. Rev.* **127,** 2090 (1962); **128,** 1758, 2222 (1962) **129,** 2581 (1963); R. H. McFarland, *Phys. Rev. Letters* **10,** 397 (1963); R. H. Hughes, R. B. Kay, and L. D. Weaver, *Phys. Rev.* **129,** 1630 (1963); D. W. O. Heddle and C. B. Lucas, *Proc. Roy. Soc. (London)* **A-271,** 129 (1963). Also see the papers presented by R. H. McFarland; R. M. St. John, and C. C. Lin; and D. W. O. Heddle and R. G. Keesing at the Third International Conference on the Physics of Electronic and Atomic Collisions, London, 1963.

gold surface used for metastable detection does not respond to photons emitted in the 2^3P–2^3S transition. In the trapped-electron experiment excitation to both P states is detected with the same efficiency as excitation to the metastable levels.

Schulz and Fox[78] obtained a value of 4×10^{-18} cm² ($\pm 30\%$) for the absolute cross section at the peak of the 2^3S excitation. This value is in good agreement with the corresponding cross section of 5×10^{-18} cm² obtained by Maier-Leibnitz,[84] who used a retarding potential method on electrons in a swarm experiment. Schulz was unable to obtain a reliable absolute cross section with the trapped-electron method because of the effects of elastically scattered electrons.[81] The shape of the curves in Fig. 5-10-2 is in fairly good agreement with that obtained by Dorrestein[77] with an electron beam and a secondary electron detection method. Excitation in helium has also been studied by Woudenberg and Milatz,[85] who detected the metastables by their absorption of the 10,830 Å line, and by Corrigan and Von Engel[86] in an electron swarm experiment. In addition, Smit et al.[87] have measured the excitation functions for the triplet lines (4713 and 5876 Å) of helium in experiments with low-energy electron beams. Gabriel and Heddle[88] have obtained the excitation functions for S-, P- and D-state formation and found the total inelastic cross section (excluding contributions from ionization) to be 2.9×10^{-17} cm² at an electron energy of 108 ev.

In the experiments already referred to[84] Maier-Leibnitz also measured cross sections for electronic excitation of neon and argon. His experimental method and results are described by Massey and Burhop[2] and Massey.[3]

C. ELECTRONIC EXCITATION OF MERCURY ATOMS. Several studies of the excitation of mercury have been made in the last few years. Jongerius et al.[89] measured optical excitation functions of mercury lines by passing electron beams with energy variable between 5 and 20 ev through mercury vapor and measuring the intensity of the light emitted perpendicular to the beam with a grating monochromator and photomultiplier. Schulz[80] has applied his trapped-electron method to the study of mercury excitation, and Lichten and McDermott[90] have studied the metastable states of mercury produced by electron impact, using atomic beam methods. Massey and Burhop[2] and Massey[3] give a number of other references to older work on this atom.

D. EXCITATION OF NITROGEN MOLECULES. Schulz has used both the trapped-electron method[81] and his double electrostatic analyzer[83] to study the electronic and vibrational excitation of molecular nitrogen. Figure 5-10-3 shows the trapped-electron current as a function of electron-beam energy for a well depth of 0.2 volt, under which condition only electrons with kinetic energy between 0 and 0.2 ev contribute to the trapped current.* Four distinct peaks are evident below 12 ev. The three peaks of highest energy in this range correspond to excitation of the electronic states of the molecule indicated in Fig. 5-10-3.† The lowest peak at about 2.3 ev, which had previously been observed by Haas[91] in a swarm experiment, requires a different explanation. The nitrogen molecule has no known

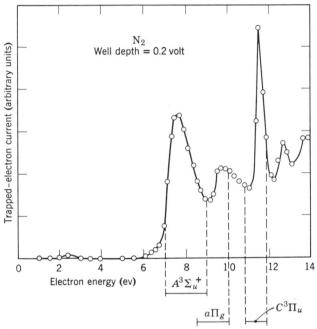

FIG. 5-10-3. The excitation spectrum of nitrogen obtained by the trapped-electron method.[81] The Franck-Condon range of a few of the states is indicated.

states of electronic excitation below 6.0 ev, and "direct" vibrational excitation of the molecule by electron impact is improbable. Only when the incoming electron remains in the vicinity of the molecule for a time that is long compared to its natural transit time can the cross section for vibrational excitation be appreciable. Accordingly, Schulz[81] advanced

* R. K. Curran, *J. Chem. Phys.* **38**, 780 (1963) has been able to reproduce this curve by measuring the energy dependence of the SF_6^- ion current in a mass spectrometer whose source contains a mixture of N_2 and SF_6. As the electrons are deactivated to zero energy in collisions with N_2 molecules, they are captured by the SF_6 to form negative ions.

† The lowest of these states is metastable, with a lifetime of about 2 sec, according to a measurement by N. P. Carleton and O. Oldenberg, *J. Chem. Phys.* **36**, 3460 (1962).

the hypothesis that the lowest energy peak involves the formation of a negative ion whose lifetime against autodetachment* is very short, so that the ion quickly decays to one of the various vibrational levels of the neutral nitrogen molecule and gives off the temporarily attached electron in the process.† The data that Schulz obtained are consistent with this hypothesis.

The relative heights of the peaks observed in the trapped-electron method depend on the well depth used in obtaining the spectrum, and the peak at 2.3 ev for the nitrogen molecule is not very pronounced at a well

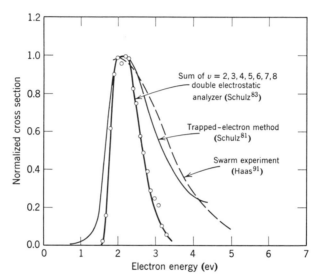

FIG. 5-10-4. Comparison of results of several experiments showing the vibrational excitation of the nitrogen molecule at an electron energy of about 2.3 ev. The points shown are the sums of all the curves of Fig. 5-10-5, normalized to unity at the peak.

depth of 0.2 volt. A well depth of 0.8 volt was used to obtain the more distinct peak marked "trapped-electron method" in Fig. 5-10-4.

The excellent energy resolution of Schulz's double electrostatic analyzer enabled him to resolve the vibrational levels excited by electron impact. By mapping the energy spectrum of the electrons scattered forward into the second analyzer, Schulz observed peaks resulting from excitation of the vibrational levels with quantum numbers $v = 2, 3, 4, 5, 6, 7,$ and 8.

---

* See Section 8-2-A.

† The theory of this mechanism was discussed by J. C. Y. Chen at the Third International Conference on the Physics of Electronic and Atomic Collisions, London, 1963.

(It was not possible to obtain data on the $v = 1$ state.*) From spectra obtained at different beam energies within the range 1.5 to 4 ev, Schulz obtained the energy dependence of the cross section for excitation of the indicated vibrational levels. These relative cross sections are shown in Fig. 5-10-5. The curve in Fig. 5-10-4 marked "double electrostatic analyzer" represents the sum of the cross sections for $v = 2$ to $v = 8$ plotted against electron energy and normalized to unity at the peak. Schulz did not obtain the absolute value of the cross section at the 2.3 ev peak; however, Haas[91] estimates this quantity to be about 15% of the cross section for elastic scattering at this energy. According to this estimate, and the data presented in Fig. 4-1-7, the excitation cross section at 2.3 ev is 1.2×10^{-16} cm².

E. EXCITATION OF OXYGEN MOLECULES. Schulz and Dowell[92] have recently applied the trapped-electron method to the study of vibrational and electronic excitation of the O_2 molecule, using a well depth of 0.16 volt. The lower sensitivity but higher resolution double electrostatic analyzer could not be used in these experiments because the low-energy inelastic cross sections in oxygen are quite small. Peaks observed in the trapped-electron current are interpreted as being due to vibrational excitation of the oxygen molecule to the states $v = 1$ to $v = 8$. Two low-lying electronic states are also excited: $^1\Delta_g$ and $^1\Sigma_g{}^+$, at 0.98 ev and 1.63 ev, respectively, above the ground state. At 0.16 ev above threshold the cross sections for excitation of these two electronic states are approximately 3×10^{-20} cm² and 6×10^{-21} cm², respectively. For electronic states above 5 ev, however, the cross sections at 0.16 ev above threshold are of the order of 10^{-18} cm², a value that is typical for most atoms and molecules.

Figure 5-10-6 shows Schulz and Dowell's plot of the excitation cross section at 0.16 ev above threshold versus the vibrational quantum number.

* Schulz's initial studies of excitation of nitrogen with a double electrostatic analyzer[83] involved collection and energy analysis of electrons scattered in the forward ($\vartheta = 0$) direction after passage through the first analyzer and collection region. This collection scheme had two deficiencies: (1) the elastically scattered electrons could not be distinguished from the primary beam, since there is very little energy loss associated with the elastic scattering, and (2) the cross section for excitation to the first vibrational level ($v = 1$) could not be measured because the residual background current from the primary beam was too high. In later studies, reported at the Sixth International Conference on Ionization Phenomena in Gases, Paris, 1963, Schulz overcame these deficiencies by analyzing the scattered electrons at another angle, arbitrarily chosen to be 72°. In this manner it was possible to study excitation to the $v = 1$ level. The cross section for this level is about 40 per cent higher than that for $v = 2$ excitation and does not fall to zero sharply at about 1.7 ev, as would be expected by comparison with the other cross sections. Schulz attributes the long tail for $v = 1$ excitation below 1.7 ev to "direct" excitation of the first vibrational level.

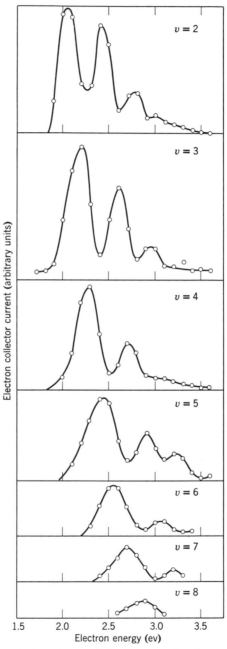

FIG. 5-10-5. The energy dependence of the cross section for excitation to various vibrational states of the nitrogen molecule. The cross sections are plotted on the same relative scale; the absolute scale is arbitrary.[83]

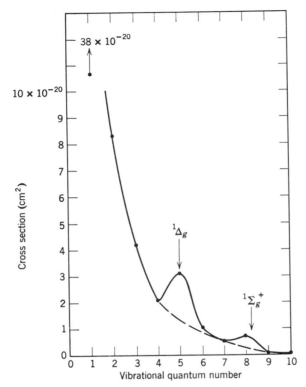

FIG. 5-10-6. The excitation cross section for O_2 at 0.16 ev above threshold versus the vibrational quantum number.[92] These data were obtained by the trapped-electron method with an effective well depth of 0.16 ev.

The relative cross sections are accurate within about 30%, although the absolute values are estimated to be accurate only within a factor of 2. The points in this figure indicate that vibrational excitation of the ground electronic state $X^3\Sigma_g^-$ takes place up to at least $v = 4$ and probably up to $v = 9$. The enhancement of the cross section at $v = 5$ can be attributed to the excitation of the $^1\Delta_g$ state in the zeroth vibrational level. The peak at $v = 8$ may be due to excitation of the $^1\Sigma_g^+$ state.

A plot of the trapped-electron current versus electron energy for energies between 4 and 12 ev is displayed in Fig. 5-10-7. The observed peaks can be correlated with optical absorption data, as indicated by the notations at the top of the drawing. The dissociation limits are marked by the vertical lines, with spectroscopic symbols indicating the dissociation products. The initial rise of the trapped-electron current at about 4.5 ev occurs near the threshold of the $^2\Sigma_u^+$ state and the next rise at the threshold for the Schumann-Runge continuum, that is, the $^3\Sigma_u^-$ state.

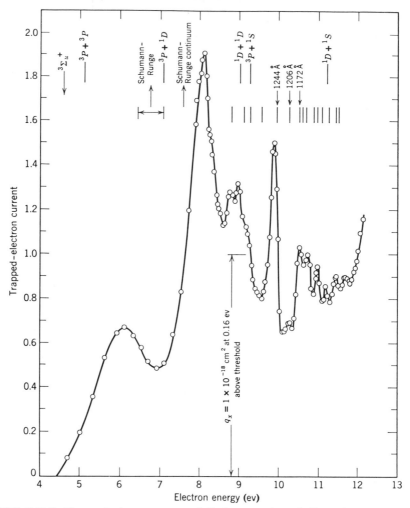

FIG. 5-10-7. The excitation spectrum of O_2 between 4- and 12-ev electron energy. Peaks observed in optical absorption are indicated.[92]

F. EXCITATION OF MOLECULAR HYDROGEN. Information on inelastic collision processes in molecular hydrogen has been obtained by Frost and Phelps[93] by analysis of experimental electron transport data.* Their procedure is (a) to assume a set of elastic and inelastic cross sections, (b) to calculate the electron energy distribution function and transport coefficients, and (c) to compare the calculated coefficients with experimental

* The work of Frost and Phelps on H_2 has been extended to higher energies and to D_2 by A. G. Engelhardt and A. V. Phelps, *Phys. Rev.* **131**, 2115 (1963).

values. The assumed cross sections are then modified and the procedure repeated until good agreement between theoretical and experimental results are achieved. Frost and Phelps's cross sections for molecular hydrogen are shown in Fig. 5-10-8. The momentum transfer cross sections

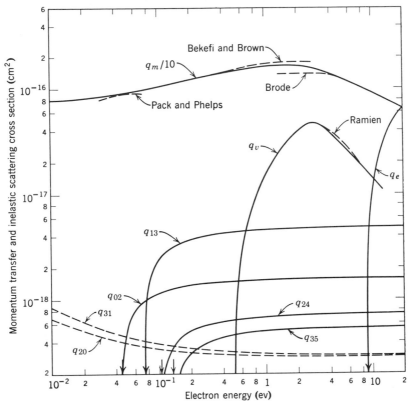

FIG. 5-10-8. Final assumed cross sections for H_2 as a function of electron energy: q_m is the momentum transfer cross section; q_{02}, q_{13}, q_{24}, q_{35}, q_{20}, and q_{31} are the cross sections for electron impact induced transitions between the rotational states indicated by the subscripts times the fraction of the molecules in the initial state (first subscript) for the gas at $300°K$; and q_v and q_e are the assumed cross sections for the excitation of the first vibrational state and the electronic states.[93]

shown here were presented in Fig. 4-1-6 and are repeated here for comparison with the inelastic data. Data on elastic and "energy exchange" collision frequencies for hydrogen, and for nitrogen as well, are presented in Section 11-5. Preliminary data on A, Cs, O_2, CO, and CO_2 have also been obtained and will be published.

Several other experiments on molecular hydrogen should be mentioned here. Corrigan and Von Engel[94] have studied the excitation and dissociation of hydrogen by an electron swarm. Schulz[80] has investigated excitation in molecular hydrogen by his trapped-electron method. Lichten has established the existence of a metastable electronic state of H_2[95] and studied the fine structure of the molecule by molecular beam techniques.[96] Kerwin, Marmet, and Clarke[97] have identified vibrational levels in the hydrogen molecular ion H_2^+. The vibrational excitation of molecular hydrogen ions is of particular interest in connection with controlled thermonuclear research. In some thermonuclear machines, such as DCX and Ogra, a beam of high-energy molecular ions is injected between two magnetic mirrors, and dissociation is produced by impact or interaction with electric and magnetic fields so that the resulting atomic ions can be trapped between the mirrors. The dissociation is facilitated if the molecular ions are in high vibrational states (see Section 6-8).

G. OTHER EXCITATION AND DE-EXCITATION STUDIES. Finally we wish to enumerate a few other recent excitation experiments of special importance. In addition to the work described earlier, Schulz has also applied his trapped-electron technique to the study of CO,[81] H_2O,[82] and N_2O.[98] Phelps and his associates[99] have used optical absorption techniques to study the diffusion and de-excitation and to measure the lifetime of metastable states of noble gas atoms and molecules in the afterglow of discharges. Phelps[100] has also analyzed the effect of the imprisonment of resonance radiation on excitation experiments. The elastic electron exchange cross section (cf. Section 4-4) in sodium has been measured by Dehmelt[101] by the *optical pumping method*. Electron exchange collisions have also been studied by Lichten and Schultz,[73] and Rubin, Perel, and Bederson[102] have studied exchange in elastic collisions of slow electrons with potassium atoms. (All of the de-excitation and exchange experiments listed here are discussed by Fite.[5]) Lichten[103] has also made electron-beam studies of the excitation of metastable states of the O_2, C_2H_2, and C_2H_4 molecules, and Foner and Hudson[104] have performed mass spectrometric studies of metastable nitrogen atoms and molecules.

REFERENCES

1. L. B. Loeb, *Basic Processes of Gaseous Electronics*, Second Edition, University of California Press, Berkeley, 1960, Chapters VIII and IX. A. N. Prasad and J. D. Craggs, "Attachment and Ionization Coefficients," in *Atomic and Molecular Processes* (edited by D. R. Bates), Academic, New York, 1962. See also Section 8-5-A.
2. H. S. W. Massey and E. H. S. Burhop, *Electronic and Ionic Impact Phenomena*, Oxford University Press, Oxford, 1952, Chapters II-IV.

3. H. S. W. Massey, "Excitation and Ionization of Atoms by Electron Impact," in *Handbuch der Physik*, Vol. XXXVI, Springer-Verlag, Berlin, 1956, pp. 307–408.

4. J. D. Craggs and H. S. W. Massey, "The Collisions of Electrons with Molecules," in *Handbuch der Physik*, Vol. XXXVII Springer-Verlag, Berlin, 1959, pp. 314–415.

5. W. L. Fite, "The Measurement of Collisional Excitation and Ionization Cross Sections," in *Atomic and Molecular Processes* (edited by D. R. Bates), Academic, New York, 1962.

6. F. H. Field and J. L. Franklin, *Electron Impact Phenomena and the Properties of Gaseous Ions*, Academic, New York, 1957.

7. N. F. Mott and H. S. W. Massey, *The Theory of Atomic Collisions*, Second Edition, Oxford University Press, Oxford, 1952.

8. M. J. Seaton, "The Theory of Excitation and Ionization by Electron Impact," in *Atomic and Molecular Processes* (edited by D. R. Bates), Academic, New York, 1962.

9. P. G. Burke and K. Smith, *Rev. Mod. Phys.* **34**, 458–502 (1962). The work described here has recently been extended to higher energies by P. G. Burke, H. M. Schey, and K. Smith, *Phys. Rev.* **129**, 1258 (1963).

10. K. T. Dolder, M. F. A. Harrison, and P. C. Thonemann, *Proc. Roy. Soc.* (*London*) A-**264**, 367 (1961).

11. J. T. Tate and P. T. Smith, *Phys. Rev.* **39**, 270 (1932).

12. P. T. Smith, *Phys. Rev.* **36**, 1293 (1930).

13. P. T. Smith, *Phys. Rev.* **37**, 808 (1931).

14. W. Bleakney, *Phys. Rev.* **34**, 157 (1929).

15. W. Bleakney, *Phys. Rev.* **35**, 139 (1930).

16. W. Bleakney, *Phys. Rev.* **35**, 1180 (1930).

17. W. Bleakney, *Phys. Rev.* **36**, 1303 (1930).

18. W. Bleakney, *Phys. Rev.* **40**, 496 (1932).

19. W. Bleakney and L. G. Smith, *Phys. Rev.* **49**, 402 (1936). (For newer data on the double ionization of helium by electron impact see H. E. Stanton and J. E. Monahan, *Phys. Rev.* **119**, 711 (1960).)

20. J. T. Tate and P. T. Smith, *Phys. Rev.* **46**, 773 (1934).

21. J. T. Tate, P. T. Smith, and A. L. Vaughan, *Phys. Rev.* **48**, 525 (1935).

22. E. W. McDaniel, J. W. Hooper, D. W. Martin, and D. S. Harmer, *Proceedings of Fifth International Conference on Ionization Phenomena in Gases*, Munich, 1961, North-Holland, Amsterdam, Vol. I, 60, 1962. J. W. Hooper, D. S. Harmer, D. W. Martin, and E. W. McDaniel, *Phys. Rev.* **125**, 2000 (1962). This work is discussed in Section 6–7.

23. J. J. Thomson and G. P. Thomson, *Conduction of Electricity Through Gases*, Third Edition, Cambridge University Press, Cambridge, Volume II, 1933.

24. K. T. Compton and C. C. Van Voorhis, *Phys. Rev.* **26**, 436 (1925).

25. H. Harrison, Ph.D. thesis, Catholic University Press, Washington, D.C., 1956.

26. B. A. Tozer and J. D. Craggs, *J. Electr. Control* **8**, 103 (1960).

27. F. W. Lampe, J. L. Franklin, and F. H. Field, *J. Am. Chem. Soc.* **79**, 6129 (1957).

28. W. B. Nottingham, *Phys. Rev.* **55**, 203 (1939).

29. H. Funk, *Ann. Phys.* **4**, 149 (1930).

30. R. L. F. Boyd and G. W. Green, *Proc. Phys. Soc.* **71**, 351 (1958).

31. W. L. Fite and R. T. Brackmann, *Phys. Rev.* **112**, 1141 (1958).

32. W. L. Fite and R. T. Brackmann, *Phys. Rev.* **113**, 815 (1959).

33. R. L. F. Boyd and A. Boksenberg, *Proceedings of Fourth International Conference on Ionization Phenomena in Gases*, Uppsala, 1959, North-Holland, Amsterdam, 1960. Vol. I, p. 529.

34. E. W. Rothe, L. L. Marino, R. H. Neynaber, and S. M. Trujillo, *Phys. Rev.* **125,** 582 (1962).
35. R. H. Neynaber, L. L. Marino, E. W. Rothe, and S. M. Trujillo, *Phys. Rev.* **123,** 148 (1961); **124,** 135 (1961).
36. A. C. H. Smith, E. Caplinger, R. H. Neynaber, E. W. Rothe, and S. M. Trujillo, *Phys. Rev.* **127,** 1647 (1962).
37. G. O. Brink, *Phys. Rev.* **127,** 1204 (1962).
38. R. Akerib and S. Borowitz, *Phys. Rev.* **122,** 1177 (1961).
39. M. J. Seaton, *Phys. Rev.* **113,** 814 (1959).
40. J. J. Thomson, *Phil. Mag.* **23,** 449 (1912).
41. G. Elwert, *Z. Naturforsch.* **7a,** 432 (1952).
42. M. Gryziński, *Phys. Rev.* **115,** 374 (1959).
43. A. Burgess, *Astrophys. J.* **132,** 503 (1960).
44. A. Burgess and M. R. H. Rudge, *Proc. Roy. Soc.* (*London*) **A-273,** 372 (1963).
45. G. Peach and M. R. C. McDowell, *Proceedings of the Third International Conference on the Physics of Electronic and Atomic Collisions,* London, 1963, North-Holland, Amsterdam, 1964.
46. R. E. Fox, W. M. Hickam, T. Kjeldaas, and D. J. Grove, *Phys. Rev.* **84,** 859 (1951). R. E. Fox, W. M. Hickam, D. J. Grove, and T. Kjeldaas, *Rev. Sci. Instr.* **26,** 1101 (1955). R. E. Fox, *Advances in Mass Spectrometry,* Pergamon, London, 1959, pp. 397–412.
47. R. E. Fox, W. M. Hickam, and T. Kjeldaas, *Phys. Rev.* **89,** 555 (1953).
48. E. M. Clarke, *Can. J. Phys.* **32,** 764 (1954).
49. P. Marmet and L. Kerwin, *Can. J. Phys.* **38,** 787 (1960).
50. G. J. Schulz, *Phys. Rev.* **125,** 229 (1962).
51. S. N. Foner and B. H. Nall, *Phys. Rev.* **122,** 512 (1961).
52. A. L. Hughes and V. Rojansky, *Phys. Rev.* **34,** 284 (1929).
53. K. T. Bainbridge and E. B. Jordan, *Phys. Rev.* **50,** 282 (1936).
54. G. D. Yarnold and H. C. Bolton, *J. Sci. Instr.* **26,** 38 (1949).
55. G. A. Harrower, *Rev. Sci. Instr.* **26,** 850 (1955).
56. J. D. Morrison, *J. Chem. Phys.* **21,** 1767 (1953), **22,** 1219 (1954). *Rev. Sci. Instr.* **25,** 291 (1954).
57. G. H. Wannier, *Phys. Rev.* **90,** 817 (1953).
58. S. Geltman, *Phys. Rev.* **102,** 171 (1956).
59. R. E. Fox, *J. Chem. Phys.* **35,** 1379 (1961).
60. W. M. Hickam, *Phys. Rev.* **95,** 703 (1954). R. E. Fox and W. M. Hickam, *J. Chem. Phys.* **22,** 2059 (1954). J. D. Morrison, *J. Appl. Phys.* **28,** 1409 (1957). J. L. Franklin, V. H. Dibeler, R. M. Reese, and M. Krauss, *J. Am. Chem. Soc.* **80,** 298 (1958). R. M. Reese, V. H. Dibeler, and J. L. Franklin, *J. Chem. Phys.* **29,** 880 (1958). V. H. Dibeler and R. M. Reese, **31,** 282 (1959). D. C. Frost and C. A. McDowell, *Advances in Mass Spectrometry,* Pergamon, London, 1959, pp. 413–430. J. D. Morrison and A. J. C. Nicholson, *J. Chem. Phys.* **31,** 1320 (1959). F. H. Dorman, J. D. Morrison, and A. J. C. Nicholson, **31,** 1335 (1959). M. Krauss, R. M. Reese, and V. H. Dibeler, *J. Research Natl. Bur. Standards* **63A,** 201 (1959). P. Marmet and L. Kerwin, *Can. J. Phys.* **38,** 972 (1960). D. C. Frost and C. A. McDowell, *Can. J. Chem.* **38,** 407 (1960). R. E. Fox, *J. Chem. Phys.* **33,** 200 (1960). F. H. Dorman and J. D. Morrison, **34,** 578 (1961). F. H. Dorman and J. D. Morrison, **34,** 1407 (1961). R. K. Curran and R. E. Fox, **34,** 1590 (1961). R. E. Fox and R. K. Curran, **34,** 1595 (1961). R. K. Curran, **34,** 2007 (1961). F. H. Dorman and J. D. Morrison, **35,** 575 (1961). P. Marmet and J. D. Morrison, **35,** 746 (1961). R. W. Kiser, **36,** 2964 (1962).

61. See, for example, E. G. Dymond, *Phys. Rev.* **29**, 433 (1927). J. H. McMillen, **36**, 1034 (1930). E. C. Bullard and H. S. W. Massey, *Proc. Roy. Soc. (London)*, **A-130**, 579 (1931). F. L. Arnot, **A-130**, 655 (1931). C. B. O. Mohr and F. H. Nicoll, **A-138**, 229, 469 (1932). A. L. Hughes and J. H. McMillen, *Phys. Rev.* **39**, 585 (1932). J. T. Tate and R. R. Palmer, **40**, 731 (1932). A. P. Gagge, **44**, 808 (1933). E. C. Childs and H. S. W. Massey, *Proc. Roy. Soc. (London)*, **A-141**, 473 (1933). F. H. Nicoll and C. B. O. Mohr, **A-142**, 320, 647 (1933). E. C. Childs and H. S. W. Massey, **A-142**, 509 (1933). J. H. McMillen, *Phys. Rev.* **46**, 983 (1934). E. B. Jordan and R. B. Brode, **43**, 112 (1933). M. Goodrich, **49**, 422 (1936), **52**, 259 (1937).

62. H. S. W. Massey and E. H. S. Burhop, *op. cit.*, pp. 84–102.

63. H. S. W. Massey, *op. cit.*, pp. 344–349.

64. H. S. W. Massey and E. H. S. Burhop, *op. cit.*, Chapter IV.

65. See, for example, W. W. Lozier, *Phys. Rev.* **36**, 1285, 1417 (1930), **44**, 575 (1933), **45**, 840 (1934), **46**, 268 (1934). J. T. Tate and W. W. Lozier, **39**, 254 (1932). E. E. Hanson, **51**, 86 (1937). R. Buchdahl, *J. Chem. Phys.* **9**, 146 (1941). J. Marriott and J. D. Craggs, E. R. A. Rept. L/T 308 (1954). J. Marriott, R. Thorburn, and J. D. Craggs, *Proc. Phys. Soc. (London)*, **B-67**, 437 (1954). R. Thorburn and J. D. Craggs, **B-69**, 682 (1956). M. A. Fineman and A. W. Petrocelli, *J. Chem. Phys.* **36**, 25 (1962).

66. See, for example, H. D. Hagstrum and J. T. Tate, *Phys. Rev.* **55**, 1136 (1939), **59**, 354 (1941). J. A. Hipple, *J. Phys. Colloid. Chem.* **52**, 456 (1948). R. E. Fox and J. A. Hipple, *Rev. Sci. Instr.* **19**, 462 (1948). C. E. Berry, *Phys. Rev.* **78**, 597 (1950). H. D. Hagstrum, *Rev. Mod. Phys.* **23**, 185 (1951). C. A. McDowell and J. W. Warren, *Trans. Faraday Soc.* **48**, 1084 (1952). R. J. Kandel, *J. Chem. Phys.* **22**, 1496 (1954). H. D. Hagstrum, **23**, 1178 (1955).

67. G. H. Dunn, *Phys. Rev. Letters* **8**, 62 (1962).

68. G. H. Dunn and L. J. Kieffer, *Fifteenth Annual Gaseous Electronics Conference*, Boulder, Colo., October 1962.

69. W.W. Lozier, *Phys. Rev.* **36**, 1285 (1930).

70. G. H. Dunn and L. J. Kieffer, *Phys. Rev.* **132**, 2109 (1963).

71. D. R. Bates and G. W. Griffing, *Proc. Phys. Soc. (London)* **A-66**, 961 (1953), **A-68**, 90 (1955). M. R. C. McDowell and G. Peach, *Phys. Rev.* **121**, 1383 (1961). D. R. Bates, M. R. C. McDowell, and A. Omholt, *J. Atmospheric Terrestr. Phys.* **10**, 51 (1957).

72. W. L. Fite and R. T. Brackmann, *Phys. Rev.* **112**, 1151 (1958). W. L. Fite, R. F. Stebbings, and R. T. Brackmann, **116**, 356 (1959). R. F. Stebbings, W. L. Fite, D. G. Hummer, and R. T. Brackmann, **119**, 1939 (1960). See Fite[5] for corrigenda to these publications.

73. W. Lichten and S. Schultz, *Phys. Rev.* **116**, 1132 (1959).

74. R. T. Brackmann, W. L. Fite, and K. E. Hagen, *Rev. Sci. Instr.* **29**, 125 (1958).

75. W. L. Fite, R. T. Brackmann, D. G. Hummer, and R. F. Stebbings, *Phys. Rev.* **116**, 363 (1959).

76. W. Lichten, *Phys. Rev. Letters* **6**, 12 (1961).

77. R. Dorrestein, *Physica* **9**, 433, 447 (1942).

78. G. J. Schulz and R. E. Fox, *Phys. Rev.* **106**, 1179 (1957).

79. R. F. Stebbings, *Proc. Roy. Soc. (London)* **A-241**, 270 (1957).

80. G. J. Schulz, *Phys. Rev.* **112**, 150 (1958). *Proceedings of Fourth International Conference on Ionization Phenomena in Gases*, Uppsala, 1959, North-Holland, Amsterdam, 1960, Vol. 1, p. 14.

81. G. J. Schulz, *Phys. Rev.* **116**, 1141 (1959).

82. G. J. Schulz, *J. Chem. Phys.* **33**, 1661 (1960).
83. G. J. Schulz, *Phys. Rev.* **125**, 229 (1962).
84. H. Maier-Leibnitz, *Z. Phys.* **95**, 499 (1935). For additional information on the Maier-Leibnitz method see reference 91; G. S. Higginson and L. W. Kerr, *Proc. Phys. Soc. (London)* **77**, 866 (1961); R. J. Fleming and G. S. Higginson, **81**, 974 (1963); R. J. Fleming, **82**, 1006 (1963); and R. J. Fleming and G. S. Higginson, *Sixth International Conference on Ionization Phenomena in Gases*, Paris, 1963.
85. J. P. M. Woudenberg and J. M. W. Milatz, *Physica* **8**, 871 (1941).
86. S. J. B. Corrigan and A. Von Engel, *Proc. Phys. Soc. (London)* **72**, 786 (1958).
87. C. Smit, W. J. Vredenberg, and J. A. Smit, *Physica* **24**, 380 (1958).
88. A. H. Gabriel and D. W. O. Heddle, *Proc. Roy. Soc. (London)* **A-258**, 124 (1960).
89. H. M. Jongerius, W. Van Egmond, and J. A. Smit, *Physica* **22**, 845 (1956). References 2 and 3 of this chapter contain references to some excellent earlier Dutch work on mercury.
90. W. Lichten, *Phys. Rev.* **109**, 1191 (1958). M. N. McDermott and W. L. Lichten, **119**, 134 (1960).
91. R. Haas, *Z. Physik.* **148**, 177 (1957).
92. G. J. Schulz and J. T. Dowell, *Phys. Rev.* **128**, 174 (1962).
93. L. S. Frost and A. V. Phelps, *Phys. Rev.* **127**, 1621 (1962).
94. S. J. B. Corrigan and A. Von Engel, *Proc. Roy. Soc. (London)* **A-245**, 335 (1958).
95. W. Lichten, *Phys. Rev.* **120**, 848 (1960).
96. W. Lichten, *Phys. Rev.* **126**, 1020 (1962).
97. L. Kerwin, P. Marmet, and E. Clarke, *Can. J. Phys.* **39**, 1240 (1961). See also M. Krauss and A. Kropf, *J. Chem. Phys.* **26**, 1776 (1957). P. Marmet and L. Kerwin, *Can. J. Phys.* **38**, 972 (1960). L. Kerwin and P. Marmet, *J. Appl. Phys.* **31**, 2071 (1960).
98. G. J. Schulz, *J. Chem. Phys.* **34**, 1778 (1961).
99. A. V. Phelps and J. P. Molnar, *Phys. Rev.* **89**, 1202 (1953). A. V. Phelps, **99**, 1307 (1955). A. V. Phelps and J. L. Pack, *Rev. Sci. Instr.* **26**, 45 (1955). A. V. Phelps, *Phys. Rev.* **114**, 1011 (1959).
100. A. V. Phelps, *Phys. Rev.* **110**, 1362 (1958).
101. H. G. Dehmelt, *Phys. Rev.* **105**, 1487 (1957), **109**, 381 (1958).
102. K. Rubin, J. Perel, and B. Bederson, *Phys. Rev.* **117**, 151 (1960).
103. W. Lichten, *J. Chem. Phys.* **37**, 2152 (1962).
104. S. N. Foner and R. L. Hudson, *J. Chem. Phys.* **37**, 1662 (1962).

SUPPLEMENTARY BIBLIOGRAPHY ON THERMAL
EXCITATION, IONIZATION AND DISSOCIATION

1. M. N. Saha, *Phil. Mag.* **40**, 472, 809 (1920). *Proc. Roy. Soc. (London)* **A-99**, 135 (1921).
2. L. H. Aller, *Astrophysics: The Atmospheres of the Sun and Stars*, Ronald, New York, 1953.
3. L. H. Aller, *Gaseous Nebulae*, Wiley, New York, 1956.
4. R.v.d.R. Woolley and D. W. N. Stibbs, *The Outer Layers of a Star*, Clarendon, Oxford, 1953.
5. *Astrophysics* (edited by J. A. Hynek), McGraw-Hill, New York, 1951.
6. J. C. Pecker and E. Schatzman, *Astrophysique générale*, Masson, Paris, 1959.
7. A. D. Thackeray, *Astronomical Spectroscopy*, Macmillan, New York, 1961.
8. "Astrophysik I," Vol. L in *Handbuch der Physik*, Springer-Verlag, Berlin, 1958.

9. W. Finkelnburg and H. Maecker, "Elektrische Bögen und thermisches Plasma," in *Handbuch der Physik*, Springer-Verlag, Berlin, 1956, Vol. XXII.

10. A. von Engel and M. Steenbeck, *Elektrische Gasentladungen*, Springer, Berlin, 1932 (reprinted by Edwards Brothers, Ann Arbor, 1944).

11. A. Unsöld, *Physik der Sternatmosphären* Second Edition, Springer, Berlin, 1955.

12. L. D. Landau and E. M. Lifshitz, *Statistical Physics*, Addison-Wesley, Reading, Mass., 1958, Section 103.

13. J. D. Cobine, *Gaseous Conductors*, Dover, New York, 1958.

14. R. H. Fowler, *Statistical Mechanics*, Second Edition, Cambridge University Press, Cambridge, 1936.

15. M. N. Rosenbluth, "The Problems of Thermonuclear Fusion and High-Temperature Plasmas," in *Plasma Dynamics* (edited by F. H. Clauser), Addison-Wesley, Reading, Mass., 1960.

16. W. B. Thompson, *Plasma Physics*, Addison-Wesley, Reading, Mass., 1962.

17. E. Schatzman, "Les Plasmas en astrophysique," in *La Théorie des gaz neutres et ionisés* (edited by C. De Witt and J. F. Detoeuf), Wiley, New York, 1960.

18. *Theoretical Astrophysics* (edited by V. A. Ambartsumyan), Pergamon, New York, 1958.

19. R. N. Thomas and R. G. Athay, *Physics of the Solar Chromosphere*, Interscience, New York, 1961.

20. A. G. Gaydon and H. G. Wolfhard, *Flames, Their Structure, Radiation, and Temperature*, Chapman and Hall, London, 1960.

21. A. G. Gaydon, *The Spectroscopy of Flames*, Wiley, New York, 1957.

22. A. C. Kolb and H. R. Griem, "High-temperature Shock Waves," in *Atomic and Molecular Processes* (edited by D. R. Bates), Academic, New York, 1962.

6

INELASTIC COLLISIONS

BETWEEN HEAVY PARTICLES

Studies of inelastic collisions between atomic systems date back to the earliest work (circa 1900) on the passage of alpha particles through gases and thin metallic foils. The principal concern of the early experimental and theoretical investigations was to examine the range of atomic projectiles in matter and the ionization produced by these projectiles. Interest in these subjects has continued unabated up to the present time, but during the last two decades a great deal of effort has also been expended in studying excitation, dissociation, charge transfer, and ion-molecule reactions. Information on these types of collisions is useful in the design of radiation detectors, in studies of the upper atmosphere, in astrophysics, in radiation damage and radiation chemistry, and more recently in the development of controlled thermonuclear devices and gas masers.

The literature on heavy-particle inelastic collisions is now enormous, and in this chapter we must content ourselves with discussing only a small fraction of what is available. The emphasis here is on experimental studies, which are discussed in Parts $\mathscr{A}$ and $\mathscr{B}$. A brief outline of the theory of inelastic collisions appears in Part $\mathscr{C}$. The experimental discussion is divided according to the energy of relative motion of the collision partners: Part $\mathscr{A}$ deals with energies from thermal up to about 500 ev and Part $\mathscr{B}$, with higher energies. The reasons for this division between low and high energies are that the relative importance of the various types of reactions is generally different in the two energy regimes and also that the experimental techniques employed at low and high energies are somewhat different. Of course, the exact location of the dividing line is arbitrary. Several important aspects of heavy particle inelastic collisions are not treated here at all: ion-ion recombination is covered in Chapter 12, and for a discussion of range and energy loss the reader is referred to the review by Dalgarno.[1]

PART $\mathscr{A}$. COLLISIONS AT LOW ENERGIES (THERMAL TO 500 EV)

6-1. CLASSIFICATION OF INELASTIC COLLISIONS

Even when examining the relatively simple impact of an atomic ion A^+ on a stationary atom B, we are struck by the variety of types of inelastic reactions that can occur. Some of the possibilities are listed in Table 6-1-1. In the first example there is only a transfer of internal excitation energy. On the other hand, electrons may be ejected into the continuum either from the projectile A^+ (*stripping*) or from the target B (*ionization*), or one

TABLE 6-1-1. Enumeration and classification of some of the inelastic reactions that can occur in the impact of an atomic ion A^+ on an atom B. The term *charge exchange* is frequently synonymous with charge transfer. Collisions that result in a change in the charge state of the projectile are generally called *charge-changing collisions*. Charge transfer and stripping, but not simple ionization, fall in this category. According to the numerical classification scheme used in this table and in the text, the cross section for the reaction (ij/kl) is denoted $_{ij}q_{kl}$.

Equation	Numerical Classification	Verbal Designation
(1) $A^{+*} + B \rightarrow A^+ + B^*$	$(1*0/10*)$	Excitation transfer
(2) $A^+ + B \rightarrow A + B^+$	$(10/01)$	Single charge transfer
(3) $A^+ + B \rightarrow A^- + B^{2+}$	$(10/-12)$	Double charge transfer
(4) $A^+ + B \rightarrow A^+ + B^+ + e$	$(10/11e)$	Ionization
(5) $A^+ + B \rightarrow A + B^{2+} + e$	$(10/02e)$	Transfer ionization
(6) $A^+ + B \rightarrow A^{2+} + e + B$	$(10/2e0)$	Stripping
(7-a) $A^+ + B \rightarrow A^* + B^+$	$(10/0*1)$	Charge transfer to an
(7-b) $A^+ + B \rightarrow A + B^{+*}$	$(10/01*)$	excited level

or more electrons may be transferred from one of these structures to a bound state of the other structure (*charge transfer*). Combinations of these types of reactions are also possible, so that the need for some system of classification is apparent. The classification scheme in Table 6-1-1 is one suggested by Hasted;[2,3] here the charge states of the reactants are indicated by the integers on the left side of the solidus within the brackets and the charge states of the products are denoted by the numbers on the right side. An asterisk is used to label an excited state, and the production of a free electron is indicated by the symbol *e*. The inadequacy of a verbal nomenclature and the utility of a numerical classification scheme are made apparent by the following considerations. If both collision partners are in motion in the laboratory frame before the collision occurs, or if the event is viewed from the center-of-mass coordinate system, the distinction between projectile and target is lost. For example, the fourth reaction listed in the table would be considered ionization if the atom B were labeled the target but stripping if B were identified as the projectile. In order to specify unambiguously the structure from which the electron is ejected, it is necessary to use a classification scheme, such as Hasted's, or to write a reaction equation, as in Table 6-1-1.

Still other reactions are possible if either of the colliding structures are molecular. In this case rotational and vibrational excitation or dissociation may result. There is also the possibility of a heavy particle being transferred from one structure to the other or of the two structures combining to form a single stable system. Reactions of the last two types (which are essentially chemical in nature) are known as *ion-molecule reactions*. They are discussed in Sections 6-3, 9-6, and 9-9.

6-2. CHARGE TRANSFER (Charge Exchange)

In discussing charge transfer, it is convenient to distinguish between *symmetrical resonance reactions* such as

$$A^+ + A \rightarrow A + A^+ \qquad (6\text{-}2\text{-}1)$$

and *asymmetric reactions* (reactions between unlike systems) such as

$$A^+ + B \rightarrow A + B^+ \qquad (6\text{-}2\text{-}2)$$

The energy dependence of the cross section for the first of these reactions is generally quite different from that of the second; the reason for this difference may be discussed in terms of Massey's "adiabatic hypothesis."

A. THE ADIABATIC HYPOTHESIS; SYMMETRIC AND ASYMMETRIC CHARGE TRANSFER. Let us consider a charge transfer reaction of the type in (6-2-2) and suppose that the ionization energy of atom A differs from that of atom B by an amount ΔE. The quantity ΔE, which represents the energy change in the electronic transition (6-2-2), is called the *energy defect* of the reaction. Massey[4,5] used a correspondence principle argument to show that in general the cross section for charge transfer at very low relative velocity of approach will be extremely small unless ΔE is small. Under the assumption that the velocity of approach of the two atomic systems is small compared with the velocities of the orbital electrons, the interaction between A^+ and B will change so slowly that the electrons will have time to readjust themselves to the perturbation produced by the interaction without an electronic transition occurring. In this case the collision will be nearly adiabatic. Massey described this situation classically in terms of the vibration produced by applying a disturbing force to an oscillator whose natural frequency is ν. Suppose the disturbance varies with time according to some function $F(t)$ and expand this function in a Fourier integral. Only the components of this expansion with frequencies near ν can have an appreciable effect in producing a forced oscillation. Therefore the duration of the collision τ must not be large compared with one period of the natural vibration of the oscillator. The excitation will be weak if $\tau\nu \gg 1$. If l represents the range of the interaction between A^+ and B and v is their relative velocity of approach, then τ will be of order l/v and the condition for weak excitation becomes $l\nu/v \gg 1$. In the quantum mechanical analogue the frequency is replaced by $\Delta E/h$, where h is Planck's constant. The probability of occurrence of the electronic transition in the charge transfer will be small if

$$l\frac{\Delta E}{hv} \gg 1 \qquad (6\text{-}2\text{-}3)$$

For a given pair of atomic systems l and ΔE are fixed, although the "adiabatic parameter" l is not well defined. The foregoing discussion indicates that the cross section should be small if v corresponds to the adiabatic region of kinetic energy, that is, if $v \ll l\,\Delta E/h$. If v is increased to a value

$$v^* \approx l\frac{\Delta E}{h} \qquad (6\text{-}2\text{-}4)$$

the collision is no longer adiabatic since the collision time has become comparable with the transition time $h/\Delta E$. Then the cross section for charge transfer would no longer be expected to be small. In fact, the cross section might be expected to attain its peak value (which may be large) at an impact energy corresponding to condition (6-2-4). This energy may be expressed as

$$T_{(\max\,q_T)} = T^* = 36(\Delta E)^2 m l^2 \text{ ev} \qquad (6\text{-}2\text{-}5)$$

where the energy defect ΔE is expressed in ev, the mass m of the incident particle in atomic mass units, and the range of the interaction l in units of the Bohr radius ($a_0 = 0.53 \times 10^{-8}$ cm).

Thus, in general, we would predict that the cross section for *non-resonance* charge transfer would be very small at low impact energies, rise to a maximum near the energy given by (6-2-5), and then decrease rapidly at higher energies. Indeed, the cross section must eventually decrease with increasing kinetic energy, since the interaction time ultimately becomes too short for the transition to be likely. In the adiabatic region the cross section varies roughly as

$$_{10}q_{01} = Ke^{-l|\Delta E|/4hv} \tag{6-2-6}$$

where K is a constant which depends on the particular nonresonance reaction considered.[3] Dalgarno[6] has pointed out, however, that it may be misleading to use (6-2-6) to extrapolate experimental data to thermal energies. We should note that not only is the nonresonance process generally inefficient at thermal energies; the cross section will be zero for $T_{CM} < \Delta E$ if the reaction is endothermic. Such would be the case if the ionization energy of the structure A is less than that of structure B in (6-2-2). Here T_{CM} represents the kinetic energy of relative motion, that is, the kinetic energy in the center-of-mass system.

In *symmetrical resonance* we expect the cross section for atomic ion charge transfer to increase monotonically as the impact energy decreases. At thermal energies the cross section for this reaction usually attains a value* considerably greater than gas kinetic values, which are of the order of 5×10^{-16} cm². The low-energy behavior of molecular ions XY^+ undergoing symmetrical resonance charge transfer

$$XY^+ + XY \rightarrow XY + XY^+ \tag{6-2-7}$$

is less certain than that of atomic ions, but the cross sections probably remain finite in the limit of vanishing energy.[6] The usual experimental techniques cannot be applied to measure charge transfer cross sections for ions passing through gases at energies less than a few ev, but it is possible to deduce some information from data on the velocity with which ions drift through gases under the influence of an applied electric field (see Section 9-3). Mobility data can be interpreted to yield collision cross sections of about 10^{-14} cm² for O_2^+ in O_2 and for N_2^+ in N_2 at thermal energies.[7] These cross sections may refer partly to resonance charge transfer.

* Typical values have been listed by A. Dalgarno, *Phil. Trans. Roy. Soc. London* **250**, 426 (1958).

The theory of nonresonance charge transfer has been reviewed by Massey and Burhop,[5] Bates and Dalgarno,[8] and Hasted.[2,3] Some measure of success has been achieved in analyzing experimental data in terms of (6-2-5); the product of the adiabatic parameter l and the number of electrons transferred are found to have a mean value of about 7 Å for many cases.[9] However, for many other pairs of collision partners discrepancies occur in the prediction of the energy corresponding to the maximum cross section. Some of these discrepancies may be attributed to the reactants or products being in undetermined excited states, so that the correct value of ΔE is uncertain. Other discrepancies arise from the fact that the energy defect ΔE is a function of the distance of separation between the colliding particles. Bates and Massey[10] have discussed the problem in terms of the curve-crossing method,* which may be applied when ΔE nearly vanishes at some separation distance during the approach. However, Bates[11] has more recently shown that this method rests on dubious assumptions and that quantitative results based on it are questionable. Nonetheless, as Dalgarno[6] points out, the qualitative picture is useful in demonstrating how certain nonresonance reactions can proceed rapidly at thermal energies.

It is clear that the adiabatic considerations do not really constitute a quantitative theory but rather only provide a useful qualitative guide. We note in particular the adiabatic hypothesis gives no indication of the magnitude of the maximum cross section to be expected as a function of ΔE for fixed v and l or as a function of v for fixed ΔE and l. Refined quantum mechanical calculations on the specific systems involved are usually required for precise results, although Firsov and Fetisov[12] have had considerable success with their approximate quantal theory of symmetrical resonance charge transfer. A useful review of the theoretical work on charge transfer has recently been published by Bates and McCarroll.[13]

Before turning to experimental studies, it is necessary to comment on another class of reactions, in which the colliding structures are not the same atomic or molecular species but in which the energy defect happens by chance to be exactly or nearly zero. This reaction is called *asymmetric* (or *accidental*) *resonance charge transfer*. Examples are

$$O^+(^4S) + H(1s) \rightarrow O(^3P_J) + H^+ \begin{cases} -0.01 \text{ ev } (J = 0) \\ +0.00 \text{ ev } (J = 1) \\ +0.02 \text{ ev } (J = 2) \end{cases} \quad (6\text{-}2\text{-}8)$$

and

$$He^{2+} + H(1s) \rightarrow He^+(2s \text{ or } 2p) + H^+ \quad (6\text{-}2\text{-}9)$$

Controversy has arisen in the theoretical predictions regarding these processes. Gurnee and Magee[14] have maintained that in collisions

---

* See Section 12-4-C for a discussion of the crossing of potential energy curves.

involving a small energy defect the cross sections are of the same order of magnitude as symmetric resonance cross sections with maxima at rather low velocities, whereas when the energy defect is zero the process is essentially indistinguishable from one that has symmetric resonance. On the other hand, Bates and Lynn[15] hold that these two processes should exhibit quite different behavior, accidental resonance resulting in a cross section that is small at low relative velocities and tends rapidly to zero with decreasing velocity. Fite and his colleagues[16] have made measurements on the reactions (6-2-8) and (6-2-9) and also on the symmetric resonance reaction

$$H^+ + H(1s) \rightarrow H(1s) + H^+ \qquad (6\text{-}2\text{-}10)$$

down to low impact energies. Their data are displayed in Fig. 6-2-8 (Section 6-2-C). The similarity of their results for the O^+—H and the H^+—H processes are in accord with the predictions of Rapp and Ortenburger,[17] who applied the theoretical methods of Gurnee and Magee[14] to the process (6-2-8). However, the experimental results are not necessarily in conflict with the predictions of Bates and Lynn, since the cross section for the O^+—H reaction may depart from the true resonance behavior below the lowest experimental energy (25 ev). On the other hand, the nonresonance behavior of the He^{2+}—H reaction seems to be established by the experimental results.

B. EXPERIMENTAL METHODS OF STUDYING CHARGE TRANSFER AT LOW ENERGIES. 1. *Single-beam techniques.* Most measurements of charge transfer cross sections at low energy have been made on beams of positive ions passing through neutral unexcited target gases. Space charge and stray field effects (cf. Section 4-1-A) prevent these experiments from being conducted at beam energies below several ev; for this reason the energies of the target particles are at least two orders of magnitude smaller than those of the ionic projectiles and may be ignored. In the low-energy range considered here the cross sections for ionization, transfer ionization, and stripping are quite small; therefore mostly positive ions, and few free electrons, are formed in the target gas (see Table 6-1-1). Furthermore, these positive ions are produced with negligibly small kinetic energies,*

* There is an exceptional case to consider, however. Although the electron transfer is almost always accomplished with a negligible transfer of momentum from the projectile to the target, the product ion may be formed with a kinetic energy of several ev if it results from a *dissociative* reaction, in which internal energy of the parent molecular structure is converted into kinetic energy during the breakup of that structure (see Section 8-1-B). It is of interest to note that in nondissociative charge transfer the weak impulse given the slow ions is directed very nearly at right angles to the primary beam direction. (In a minute fraction of the collisions between fast heavy projectiles and targets a significant amount of momentum is transferred and the projectile is scattered through a large angle. Studies of these violent collisions are discussed in Section 6-6-A-5.)

and the scattered projectiles pass through the interaction region with negligible changes in direction. These facts make it possible to obtain the cross section for charge transfer by allowing the projectiles to proceed through the collision volume and collecting the slow positive ions produced in the gas. In order to avoid complications that would be produced by multiple collisions of a single projectile, it is necessary that the product of the thickness and pressure of the gas target be small enough to obtain

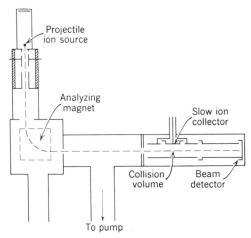

FIG. 6-2-1. Typical apparatus used to measure the cross section for charge transfer between low-energy ions and neutral molecules. The method illustrated here is frequently called the *condenser method* because of the geometry of the slow ion collector electrode system.

"thin-target" conditions (cf. Section 4-1-A). If thin-target conditions do apply, the charge transfer cross section q_T is given by the linear approximation

$$i_s = i_0 N q_T x \qquad (6\text{-}2\text{-}11)$$

where i_s is the collected current of slow positive ions, i_0 is the incident beam current, N is the number density of the gas target, and x is the effective target thickness. Of course, the cross section measured by this technique is the apparent charge transfer cross section (cf. Section 5-2-A), since slow ions in various charge states may be produced and collected. Generally single-charge transfer will predominate, but if the contributions of multiple electron transfer are desired the slow ions can be subjected to e/m analysis.

The apparatus that Cramer used for low-energy charge transfer measurements on beams of positive ions was described in Section 4-8. Another typical instrument is shown schematically in Fig. 6-2-1. The analyzing

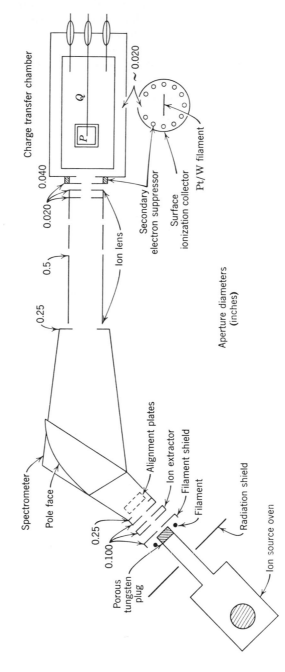

FIG. 6-2-2.   The apparatus used by Marino et al.[18] for studies of charge transfer between positive cesium ions and cesium atoms.

magnet serves to select the desired species of projectile ion from the total beam emerging from the source and to focus these ions on the entrance slit of the collision chamber. Differential pumping is provided to keep the gas pressure low outside the intended collision region. In the apparatus of Fig. 6-2-1 a transverse electric field is applied to sweep the slow positive ions to the collector plate, which is provided with guard plates for precise definition of the effective collision region. The beam detector is a Faraday cup, designed so that secondary electrons ejected by the beam particles cannot reach the slow ion collector. Secondary electrons ejected from the slow ion collector (see Section 13-2-A) may be returned to it by a biased high-transparency grid in front of the collector. Other electric and magnetic field configurations used for collection of the slow ions are described by Hasted,[2,3] who also discusses alternative methods of beam detection. In addition, Hasted's reviews contain valuable surveys of techniques for preparing focused and monoenergetic projectile beams and for extracting the slow collision products into an e/m analyzer.

Figure 6-2-2 illustrates the method that Marino et al.[18] applied to measure the cross section for charge transfer between Cs^+ ions and Cs atoms in the energy range 50 to 4000 ev.* This study was partially motivated by the interest in cesium ion propulsion for space vehicles and in the cesium diode as a thermoelectric device. The projectile ions are obtained by the surface ionization of atoms diffusing through a heated porous tungsten plug (see Section 13-6). These ions are then accelerated, mass analyzed,† and finally focused into the charge transfer chamber. This chamber contains neutral cesium atoms whose number density is measured with a surface ionization detector. The primary beam passes between two parallel electrodes Q, one of which is visible in the figure. The right-hand ends of these plates are turned over so that they overlap but do not touch. Thus the Q plates form an open-ended rectangular box. Small plates P are situated in opposing square holes cut in the plates Q. Equal positive and negative potentials of about 10 volts with respect to the ion beam are applied to the Q plates and to their respective P plates, so that a uniform transverse electric field exists

---

* Additional studies of charge transfer between rubidium ions and cesium atoms were reported by L. L. Marino at the Third International Conference on the Physics of Electronic and Atomic Collisions, London, 1963.
† A nonsymmetrical magnetic spectrometer is employed to analyze the primary ion beam. As shown by E. T. S. Walton, *Proc. Roy. Irish Acad.* **57-A**, 1 (1954), this instrument focuses incident rays to a very high order over large entrance angles. By contrast, the symmetrical analyzer gives only first-order focusing and requires the incident rays to deviate from the normal to the magnetic field boundary by only small angles. The spectrometer in Fig. 6-2-2 focuses an incident ion beam whose maximum divergence is 25° and whose central ray enters the magnetic field boundary at an angle of 65°.

in the vicinity of the P plates. Slow positive ions formed both by charge transfer and by ionization are drawn to the negative electrode system; electrons produced in ionizing events are swept to the positive P and Q electrodes. By measuring only the net current to the pair of P plates, the equal positive and negative currents resulting from ionization can be made to cancel, leaving only the positive contribution from charge transfer. The primary beam is collected at the bottom of the box formed by the Q plates, the net current to which equals the primary ion beam current less the small net current to the P plates.

For additional information on techniques used for making charge transfer measurements on beams of low-energy positive ions, the reader may consult the papers listed in Refs. 19 to 24. Very few charge transfer studies have been made at low energies with beams of negative ions or neutral projectiles. Bailey[25] has studied electron detachment and apparent electron transfer in collisions of O^- and O_2^- ions with O_2 molecules. (Other studies of the detachment of free electrons from negative ions are discussed in Section 8-6-A.) Bukhteev et al.[26] have investigated electron capture by O_2 and Cl_2 molecules bombarded with fast alkali atoms.

2. *Crossed-beam techniques.* Fite and his colleagues[16,27] have used crossed-beam techniques to measure cross sections for charge transfer between ions and both stable and unstable neutral targets. A recent version of their apparatus[16] is given in Fig. 6-2-3. Since most of the techniques they employed have been described in Chapters 4 and 5, we shall discuss only those design features that permitted them to make measurements at energies lower than would normally be possible.

In the apparatus in Fig. 6-2-3 ions are produced in an electron bombardment source located at the extremity of an arm extending out from the wall of the experimental chamber. The ions are extracted from this source and focused before they enter the analyzing magnetic field. In their earlier work Fite et al. made the practice of extracting the ions from the source at the final collision energy and then focusing and resolving the desired ions from those of neighboring mass. This procedure was adequate for ion energies greater than a few hundred ev, but at lower energies the enhanced influence of space charge necessitated a modification. In the apparatus illustrated here, regardless of the desired final energy, the ions are always extracted from the source, focused, and resolved under identical conditions that are selected to give the maximum ion current with adequate resolution. The ions are given their final energy only when they emerge into the experimental chamber. The arm is insulated from the experimental chamber by a Teflon flange, and three electrostatic lens elements are provided to keep the ion beam focused as its energy changes during the passage across the interface. Thus, to produce a beam of 20 ev ions, the anode of the ion source is maintained at a potential of 20 volts above the interaction region, which is held at ground potential. The source arm provides the environment for the ions during their analysis and is maintained about 2000 volts below ground. The voltages for the source and for the focusing electrodes are applied from the arm as a reference ground. To change the

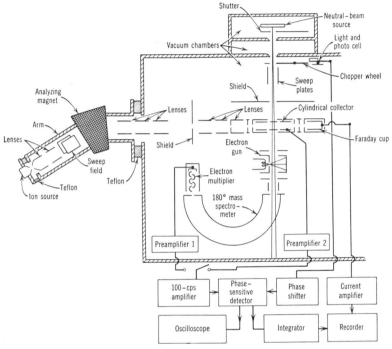

FIG. 6-2-3. The crossed-beam apparatus used by Fite and his co-workers[16] for charge transfer measurements at low energies.

final ion energy, it is therefore necessary only to change the potential applied between the arm and ground. This arrangement permits the reduction of the final ion beam energy to 20 ev with comparatively little intensity loss. After entering the experimental chamber, the ions pass through a narrow collimating slit in a shield, which intercepts unwanted ions of adjacent masses. The final ion beam then travels through three additional cylindrical lens elements and another collimating slit before entering the interaction region.

In their work at ion energies of several hundred ev (described in the earlier papers listed in Ref. 27) Fite and his co-workers used a weak electrostatic field to sweep the slow charge transfer ions to a negative collector plate. At low energies, however, this collection field deflects the primary ions as they pass through the collection region and introduces uncertainty into the collision conditions. To overcome this difficulty, the arrangement shown in Fig. 6-2-3 is used, in which no electric fields transverse to the direction of the primary beam are required. The ion and neutral beams are made to intersect at the center of a cylindrical collector whose axis coincides with the primary ion beam. The potential of this collector is maintained negative with respect to that of the surrounding electrode, and the slow charge transfer ions are collected on the surface of this cylinder, since they are unable to escape from the potential well in which they were formed. The two apertures through which the neutral beam passes are positioned diametrically in the collector and covered with a fine grid of 99% optical transparency to prevent field penetration. Saturation of the ion current is obtained by applying to the collector a negative potential of a few volts. On leaving the interaction region, the primary ions pass through a further defining slit before they are collected in a Faraday cup. The dimensions of the apertures in the collision region are such that all ions that pass through this final defining slit necessarily pass through the neutral beam.

Provision is also made for e/m analysis of the product ions. In order to make this analysis, the cylindrical collector is racked away from the inter-section region of the two beams, and another set of electrodes (not shown in the drawing) is positioned to sweep the slow ions into the entrance slit of a 180° magnetic mass spectrometer. The mass spectrometer is also used with an electron gun to determine the degree of dissociation of the neutral beam by observation of the reduction in the signal of molecular ions as the furnace is heated.

3. *The Aston peak method.* There is a strong body of evidence which indicates that charge transfer and other types of cross sections depend to a significant degree on the states of excitation of the collision partners.[28] However, until recently very little had been done to determine whether the ion beams used in collision studies contain only ground state ions, and less had been done to measure cross sections other than those pertaining to a mixed beam consisting of ions in excited states as well as the ground state. McGowan and Kerwin[29] have recently outlined a method that permits the identification of low-lying metastable ions and the investigation of their effect on dissociation and charge transfer cross sections. This method involves the use of a magnetic mass spectrometer in which the two drift regions bracketing the analyzer contain gas and serve as collision chambers. When the gas pressure in these regions is raised appreciably above the low level used in conventional mass spectrometric studies, broad peaks are observed in the mass spectrum. These peaks are known as *Aston bands*[30] and result from ions formed by collisions which take place in or past the

ion-accelerating region. The presence of Aston banding may be exploited to separate the primary and product ion beams. By comparing the appearance potential curves of the primary ion beam with those of the products, McGowan and his co-workers are able not only to identify metastable species but in some cases to obtain information on the cross sections of metastable ions relative to that of the ground state ion.[31]

C. CHARGE TRANSFER DATA (LOW ENERGY). Experimental data on charge transfer cross sections are presented in Figs. 6-2-4 through 6-2-17, with theoretical predictions included for comparison in some cases.

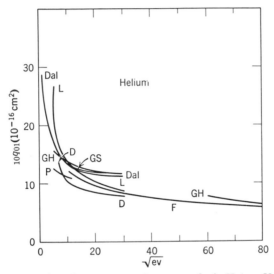

FIG. 6-2-4. Cross sections for resonance charge transfer in He$^+$ on He. Reference key: GH (Gilbody and Hasted, 1956); GS (Ghosh and Sheridan, 1957); D (Dillon et al., 1955); P (Potter, 1954); L (Gustafsson and Lindholm, 1960); Dal (Dalgarno, 1958). The curve marked F gives the results of the Firsov formula[12] with the factor A taken to be unity.

Other collections of data are to be found in Brown[32] and Nawrocki and Papa.[33] Reference 33 contains a great deal of information on reactions of special interest in the physics of the upper atmosphere.

Figures 6-2-4 through 6-2-6 provide data compiled by Hasted[3] on resonance charge transfer in helium, neon, and argon. References to most of the papers in which these cross sections were originally published have already been cited in this chapter. Additional data on He, Ne, and A are displayed in Fig. 4-9-1.

Mention has already been made in Section 6-2-A of the results presented in Figs. 6-2-7 and 6-2-8. We note that in the energy range covered there

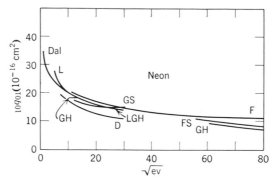

FIG. 6-2-5. Cross sections for resonance charge transfer in Ne$^+$ on Ne. The key is the same as that in Fig. 6-2-4, with FS denoting I. P. Flaks and E. S. Solov'ev, *Sov. Phys. Tech. Phys.* **3**, 564 (1958).

the cross sections for the H$^+$—H and O$^+$—H reactions vary with impact energy T as $q_T^{1/2} = a - b \log T$, where a and b are constants. This energy dependence characterizes symmetric resonance charge transfer. In their work on the He^{2+}—H reaction Fite, Smith, and Stebbings[16] made no attempt to ascertain the state of the resulting helium ions, and their measurements therefore refer to processes leading to capture into all possible states of He$^+$. Their interest centered on those processes that lead to the production of He$^+$ ions in the 2s or 2p levels, since only these reactions are

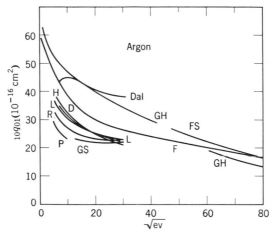

FIG. 6-2-6. Cross sections for resonance charge transfer in A$^+$ on A. The key is the same as that in Fig. 6-2-4, with R denoting A. Rostagni, *Nuovo Cimento* **12**, 134 (1935) and H denoting Hasted (1951).

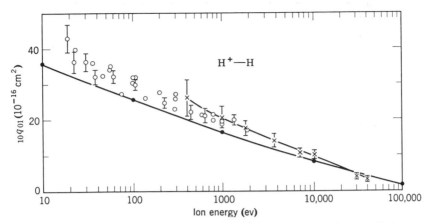

FIG. 6-2-7. Cross sections for charge transfer between H^+ ions and atomic hydrogen. The circles denote the experimental data in Fite, Smith, and Stebbings[16]; the crosses are experimental data in Fite et al. (1960); the dots are the results of a perturbed-stationary-state calculation by A. Dalgarno and H. N. Yadav, *Proc. Phys. Soc. (London)* **A-66,** 173 (1953).

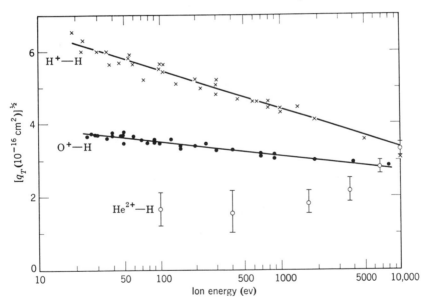

FIG. 6-2-8. Symmetric and asymmetric resonance charge transfer in atomic hydrogen (Fite, Smith, and Stebbings[16]).

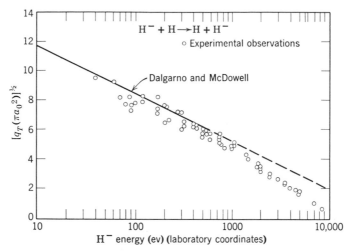

FIG. 6-2-9. Cross section for charge transfer between hydrogen negative ions and hydrogen atoms. The experimental data were obtained by Hummer et al.[27] (1960); the line on the graph refers to a perturbed-stationary-state calculation by A. Dalgarno and M. R. C. McDowell, *Proc. Phys. Soc.* (*London*) **A-69**, 615 (1956).

resonant. Transitions leading to other states make extremely small contributions to the total charge transfer at low energies. The He^{2+}—H curve obviously has a nonresonance energy dependence. It is worth noting that Fite et al. used the mass-3 isotope of helium to avoid any confusion that might result from H_2^+ ions (with the same e/m ratio) formed by traces of hydrogen in the ion source.

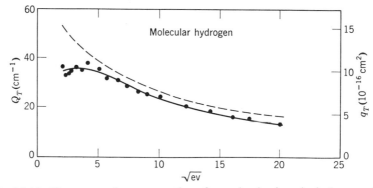

FIG. 6-2-10. Charge transfer cross sections for molecular ions in hydrogen. Solid curve: H_2^+ on H_2—W. H. Cramer, *J. Chem. Phys.* **35**, 836 (1961). Dashed line: D_2^+ on D_2—W. H. Cramer and A. B. Marcus, *J. Chem. Phys.* **32**, 186 (1960). The quantity Q_T is the macroscopic charge transfer cross section.

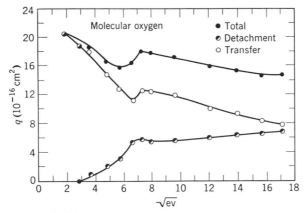

FIG. 6-2-11. Cross sections for O_2^- in O_2 (Bailey[25]).

Special interest attaches to the data presented in Figs. 6-2-13 through 6-2-16 because of their importance in establishing equilibrium in the upper atmosphere. We should also comment on the extremely large cross section for charge transfer between cesium ions and atoms indicated in Fig. 6-2-17.

Amme and Utterback[28] have presented evidence to the effect that some of the ions in the beams used by Stebbings et al.[27] were in excited states when they entered the collision chamber. (Stebbings and his colleagues had previously discussed this possibility.) Indeed, the curve shown in Fig. 6-2-13 for charge transfer between O_2^+ and N_2 has a resonance shape despite the fact that the reaction is endothermic by over 3 ev. The observed energy dependence would be expected only if an excited state were involved with energy appropriate to give an accidental resonance. Stebbings et al.[27] used an ion source in which the electrons producing the

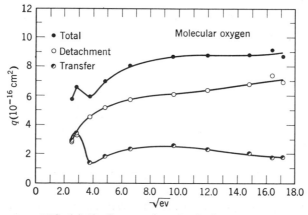

FIG. 6-2-12. Cross sections for O^- in O_2 (Bailey[25]).

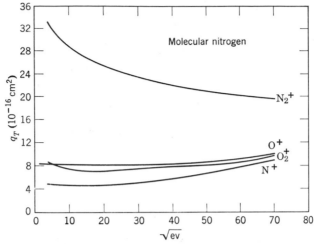

FIG. 6-2-13. Cross sections for charge transfer of various ions in molecular nitrogen. The data are normalized to the results of Stier and Barnett for charge transfer between protons and nitrogen at high energy. At 5000 ev, q_T is taken to be 11.6×10^{-16} cm² for H^+–N_2 (Stebbings, Turner, and Smith[27]). As explained in the text, the curves for O_2^+–N_2 and N_2^+–N_2 in this figure probably pertain to incident ions in excited states.

ions had high energy, about 100 ev. Amme and Utterback,[28] on the other hand, worked with ion source electrons whose energy could be varied between 16 and 24 ev. The latter investigators observed a resonance shape for the O_2^+–N_2 cross section when electron energies above 22 ev were used, but a strongly non-resonance behavior when the electron energy was reduced below 18 ev. The resonant N_2^+–N_2 cross section observed by Amme and Utterback varied as a function of ion energy in the manner generally reported by other investigators, but its value decreased by about 15 per cent when the source electron energy was increased from 17 to 23 ev. The ion impact energy range covered by Amme and Utterback extended from 40 to 1000 ev.

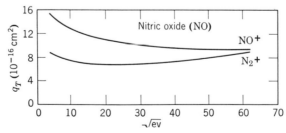

FIG. 6-2-14. Charge transfer cross sections for NO^+ and N_2^+ ions in nitric oxide (Stebbings, Turner, and Smith[27]).

6-3. ION-ATOM INTERCHANGE

We have seen that in general charge transfer cross sections are small at thermal energies. There are other types of inelastic reactions, however, which do not involve the transfer of electrons and which can proceed at very high rates at thermal energies. These processes are known as *ion-molecule reactions*. They are of great importance in the upper atmosphere, and, as shown in Chapters 9 and 12, they can also have decisive effects in laboratory experiments on ionized gases. Here we single out one type of ion-molecule reaction for discussion; others are mentioned in Section 9-9.

The reaction under consideration here is that of ion-atom interchange, in which an atom is transferred from one of the collision partners to the other. Examples of this process which may occur in the ionosphere are[34]

$$O^+ + N_2 \rightarrow NO^+ + N \qquad (6\text{-}3\text{-}1)$$

$$O^+ + O_2 \rightarrow O_2^+ + O \qquad (6\text{-}3\text{-}2)$$

$$O^+ + NO \rightarrow NO^+ + O \qquad (6\text{-}3\text{-}3)$$

$$O^+ + NO \rightarrow O_2^+ + N \qquad (6\text{-}3\text{-}4)$$

$$N^+ + O_2 \rightarrow NO^+ + O \qquad (6\text{-}3\text{-}5)$$

$$N^+ + NO \rightarrow NO^+ + N \qquad (6\text{-}3\text{-}6)$$

$$N^+ + NO \rightarrow N_2^+ + O \qquad (6\text{-}3\text{-}7)$$

$$N_2^+ + N \rightarrow N^+ + N_2 \qquad (6\text{-}3\text{-}8)$$

$$O_2^+ + N \rightarrow NO^+ + O \qquad (6\text{-}3\text{-}9)$$

$$O_2^- + O \rightarrow O_2 + O^- \qquad (6\text{-}3\text{-}10)$$

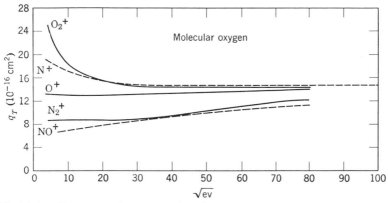

FIG. 6-2-15. Charge transfer cross sections for various ions in molecular oxygen. The data are normalized to the results of Stier and Barnett for charge transfer between protons and oxygen at high energy. At 5000 ev, q_T is taken to be 9.3×10^{-16} cm^2 for H^+–O_2 (Stebbings, Turner, and Smith[27]).

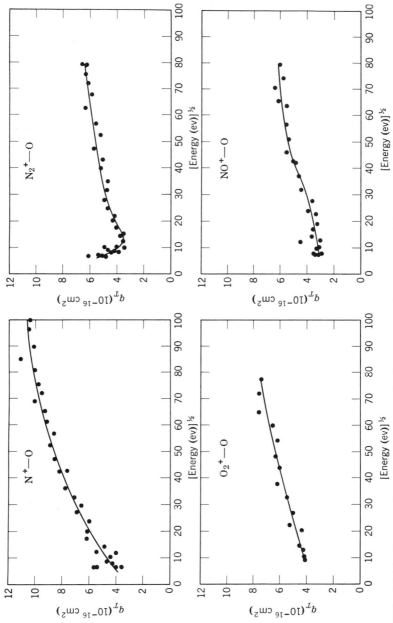

FIG. 6-2-16. Cross sections for charge transfer between atomic oxygen and ions of nitrogen, oxygen, and nitric oxide (Stebbings, Smith, and Gilbody[17]).

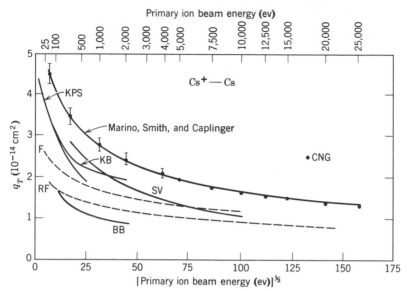

FIG. 6-2-17. Cross sections for charge transfer between Cs^+ ions and Cs atoms, taken from the paper by Marino, Smith, and Caplinger.[18] References to the original data sources are given by Marino et al.

The rate coefficients of ion-atom interchange reactions can be as high as about 10^{-9} cm³/sec if the activation energy is small. One reason for their importance is that they can convert efficiently atomic ions, which typically have very small electron recombination coefficients, into molecular ions, for which the recombination may proceed rapidly (see Sections 12-5 and 12-7).

Ion-atom interchange, which was first suggested by Bates[35] as an important process, is similar to an ordinary chemical reaction. The cross section for ion-atom interchange is generally expressed as the product

$$q_{\text{interchange}} = P q_0 \qquad (6\text{-}3\text{-}11)$$

where q_0 is the cross section for orbiting collisions between the original ions and molecules (see Section 3-6) and P is the probability that the interchange will result if orbiting occurs. The orbiting cross section is equal to

$$q_0(v_0) = \frac{2\pi}{v_0} \left[e^2 \left(\frac{\alpha}{M_r} \right) \right]^{1/2} \qquad (3\text{-}6\text{-}6)$$

where v_0 is the relative velocity of approach, α is the polarizability of the molecule, and M_r is the reduced mass of the ion and molecule; P may usually be taken to be unity, unless an intermediate step is involved in the formation of the final products, in which case the process is not really one of ion-atom interchange and P may be much less than unity.

Experimental studies of ion-atom interchange are carried out either in a mass spectrometer or in a discharge chamber with an attached ion extraction and analysis system. Typical studies are listed in Ref. 36; some of the techniques are discussed in Hasted's review[2] and in Section 9-6. Comparatively few studies of these important reactions have been made to date and much more work remains to be done.

6-4. IONIZATION AND STRIPPING

As we shall see in Part $\mathscr{B}$, an enormous amount of work has been devoted to the study of ionization and stripping in collisions between heavy particles at high energies. By contrast, little has been done at energies below 500 ev. The reason for this can be traced to the fact that the cross sections for free electron production at low energies are much smaller than those for other reactions, so that in most low-energy applications and phenomena, other reactions play the dominant roles. Recently, however, the increased interest in shock waves, plasma physics, and high-temperature chemistry has created a need for data on ionization and stripping at energies of a few tens or hundreds of ev, and an upsurge of activity in this area of experimentation may be expected. Results on a few systems have been reported during the last decade. Moe[37] has studied the ionization of neon, argon, krypton, and xenon by K^+ ions at impact energies up to 300 ev. Utterback and Miller[38] have measured the cross sections for production of electrons by N_2 and O_2 molecules and He atoms colliding with several neutral target structures. The energy range covered in these experiments was 20 to 1000 ev.

In addition to processes in which the kinetic energy of the colliding particles is used to eject electrons into the continuum, there is also the process of *Penning ionization*, in which electron ejection occurs by a transfer of internal excitation energy from one structure to the other. This process can occur at thermal energies when an atom in a metastable state* collides with an atom or molecule whose ionization energy is less than the excitation energy of the metastable. The cross sections at thermal energies are usually somewhat larger than gas kinetic cross sections and the process is generally quite efficient. Some important consequences of

* The lifetimes of ordinary excited states are so short compared with collision mean free times that Penning ionization is unlikely to occur unless the excited state is metastable. Ordinary excited states typically have lifetimes of the order of 10^{-8} sec against the spontaneous emission of radiation, whereas metastable states have radiative lifetimes in the range from 10^{-4} sec to minutes.

Penning ionization are discussed in Section 13-2-A-5. Recent experimental and theoretical studies of this process have been made by Muschlitz and his co-workers[39] and by Benton et al.[40]

6-5. DISSOCIATION

A fair amount of information has been obtained on the dissociation of simple ions and molecules in mass spectrometric studies of their collisions at low energies. For data on such processes, we may consult the papers of Lindholm and his co-workers,[24] Melton and Wells,[30] and McGowan and Kerwin.[30]

PART 𝓑. COLLISIONS AT HIGH ENERGIES (ABOVE 500 EV)

6-6. CHARGE TRANSFER

The transfer of electrons between heavy particles colliding at high energies has been the subject of many experimental investigations since 1922, when the first quantitative measurements were made. The early work has been surveyed by Massey and Burhop,[5] Allison,[41] and Allison and Garcia-Munoz.[42] Here we shall concentrate on experimental studies made since about 1954. These studies were motivated by a need for data to which theoretical predictions could be compared and by the recently intensified interest in the application of these data to natural and laboratory problems.

Certain high-energy charge transfer reactions play an important role in geophysics and the physics of the upper atmosphere. For example, reactions in which a hydrogen atom loses its electron are involved in the trapping of protons in the earth's magnetic field, and the effective life-time of the trapped protons is determined in part by their cross sections for electron capture. In controlled fusion research the primary goal is the establishment of a hot dense hydrogen plasma, and a number of factors make its attainment difficult by providing mechanisms for cooling the hydrogen ions or allowing them to escape from the confining fields. One of the most serious of these processes is charge neutralization of the hydrogen ions in electron-capture collisions with impurities present in the plasma. As another example of the importance of high-energy charge transfer data, we may cite its need in the design of tandem Van de Graaff accelerators, in which energy multiplication is accomplished by reversing the charge of the ions in the accelerated beam.

A. EXPERIMENTAL METHODS OF STUDYING CHARGE TRANSFER AT HIGH ENERGIES. Experimental studies of charge transfer fall into several categories, which require different techniques and provide different types of data. One class of experiment consists of determining the equilibrium charge state composition of a beam of projectiles passed through a gas or solid target thick enough to ensure an equilibrium between the production and loss reactions of each of the possible charge states. The data obtained from this experiment are particularly valuable in connection with the design of tandem accelerators and with the production of beams of fast neutral projectiles and negative ions for use in various types of collision studies. In another class of experiment, one involving a thin gas target, the interest lies in obtaining the microscopic cross sections for single collisions to produce a specified change in the charge state of the projectile, regardless of changes in the target molecule. Generally such experiments do not directly yield individual cross sections, but only algebraic combinations thereof, and additional data (such as equilibrium charge state distributions) are required for extraction of individual cross sections from these combinations. A comparatively small number of investigations have been made of the combined angular and charge state distributions of projectiles experiencing single collisions in a thin gas target, and a few measurements have been made of the energy and angular distributions of the recoiling target particles. Experiments are also being set up to examine simultaneously the projectile and its recoiling target particle after single collisions in thin targets.* These experiments which are obviously quite difficult require coincidence measurements on both collision partners, but they can provide much more detailed information about the reactions than studies in which attention is confined to only one of the particles.

1. *Studies of beam equilibration.* Figure 6-6-1 illustrates schematically an experimental arrangement for determination of the equilibrium distribution among the charge states of a beam passing through a thick gas target. A beam of "monoenergetic" projectiles of a single known type is fired into a cell which contains gas at a pressure high enough to establish an equilibrium among the various competing electron capture and loss processes for the projectile-target combination. (The differential equations that determine the approach to and attainment of equilibrium are derived by Allison and Garcia-Munoz.[41,42]) When the equilibrated beam emerges into the high vacuum through the aperture at the far end of the converter cell, it passes through an electrostatic (or magnetic) field which splits the total beam into its various charge states. The intensity of each of the observable final components is measured by an appropriate type of detector, and the fractional composition of the equilibrated beam is thus

* The results of the first of these experiments were reported by V. V. Afrosimov, Yu. S. Gordeev, M. N. Panov, and N. V. Fedorenko at the Sixth International Conference on Ionization Phenomena in Gases, Paris, 1963.

determined. It is interesting to note that if the gas target in the converter cell is thick enough ("infinitely thick") to produce an equilibrated beam the composition of the final beam will be independent of the charge state of the incident beam.

In the simple case of a two-component system (in which only two charge states are involved to an appreciable degree) data on the equilibrium distribution may be combined with data obtained at gas pressures lower than the minimum equilibration value to obtain the cross sections for transfer between the two charge states.[42]

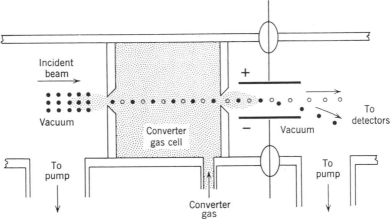

FIG. 6-6-1. Schematic diagram of apparatus used in charge equilibration studies on fast projectile beams. For simplicity it is assumed here that the beam has only two components: neutral atoms and positive ions in a single charge state. The figure is not drawn to scale: in practice, the length of the gas cell is usually greater than the aperture diameters by a factor of about 100.

Faraday cups are frequently used to measure the intensity of charged particle beams in high-energy collision experiments, whereas secondary electron detectors (cf. Section 13-2-A) and calorimetric detectors may be used for either charged or neutral beams. (Calorimetric detectors respond to the amount of energy deposited in the form of heat per unit time by the impinging beam. They contain thermocouples or thermistors which develop an electrical signal in an external circuit.) Electron multipliers (Section 13-2-A), scintillators, proportional counters, or solid-state junction devices may also be employed for detection either of ions or neutral projectiles. If operated as discrete particle counters rather than as a measure of continuous currents, these devices offer unmatched sensitivity and thus are indispensable for use with weak beams. Furthermore, the particle-counting detectors usually provide enough gain and can be operated with sufficiently high pulse-height discrimination that their counting efficiency is almost independent of the charge on a projectile of a given atomic species. (This is not the case with secondary electron detectors, which must be calibrated separately for each type of projectile used.) The major disadvantage associated with the use of particle-counting detectors is that their associated electronic circuitry becomes saturated at counting rates above about 10^5/sec. Also, their lifetimes are limited by radiation damage effects and in some cases by exposure to air.

The reader may turn to papers by Barnett's group[43–46] and by Allison and his colleagues[47] for detailed descriptions of charge equilibration measurements and for discussion of techniques employed in various types of high-energy charge-changing experiments.*

At this point it is appropriate to stress the importance of proper detector design and location in all high-energy beam experiments. Each detector must be large enough to intercept nearly all the particles in the beam directed toward it, and it must be designed so that secondary electrons and photons produced by the impinging beam cannot escape into critical regions outside the detector. However, each detector generally should have an aperture with a diameter no greater than a few times the diameter of the beam; otherwise particles belonging to other beams, or projectiles undergoing scattering outside the intended collision region, may enter it. It is good practice to determine the profile of each beam by scanning it with a narrow slit located in front of its detector or, if the beam is charged, by sweeping the beam across and to each side of the detector by varying an electric or magnetic field.

2. *Measurement of cross sections by beam attenuation in a transverse field.* A large fraction of the determinations of charge transfer cross sections at high energy has involved study of the attenuation of a beam of projectiles in a gas-filled collision chamber across which is applied a transverse electric or magnetic field.

An example of apparatus utilizing an electric sweeping field and suitable for experiments on beams of neutral projectiles is shown in Fig. 6-6-2. This figure is taken from a paper by Stier and Barnett[44] which describes measurements on beams of hydrogen atoms. The same collision chamber was used by Barnett and Stier[46] to measure the cross section for electron loss by neutral helium atoms in hydrogen, helium, nitrogen, oxygen, neon, and argon in the energy range 4 to 200 kev. In these experiments a mass analyzed beam of He^+ ions was sent into the first gas cell, which is designated as the neutralizer. This cell contains a converter gas at a pressure of a

---

* By a *charge-changing collision* we mean one in which the projectile experiences a change in its charge state, regardless of what changes may occur in the target particle. Charge-changing reactions thus include both charge transfer and electron stripping but not simple ionization (cf. Table 6-1-1).

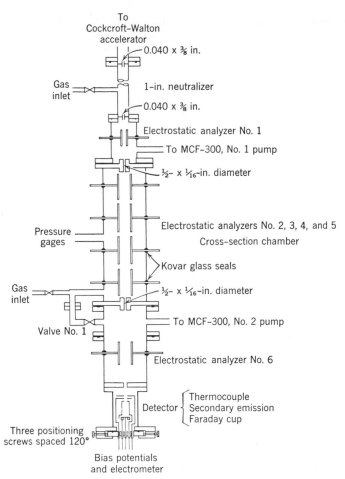

FIG. 6-6-2. Apparatus used by Barnett's group for measurements of charge-changing cross sections by observation of the attenuation of a beam of neutral particles in a transverse electric field.

few microns. The aperture sizes were chosen so that a pressure differential of about 100:1 was obtained across the openings to the gas cell. The deflection plates in the first electrostatic analyzer shown removed all ions remaining in the beam emerging from this cell so that only neutral helium atoms were incident on the second gas cell, which contained the target gas. An electrostatic field in this cell (the "cross section chamber") swept aside the ions produced by charge-changing collisions with the target gas as soon as they were formed. The field electrodes were segmented to permit the elimination of end effects. The cross sections for electron loss were determined by measuring the attenuation of the transmitted neutral beam, whose intensity was registered by a secondary emission detector at the bottom of the figure.

Actually in an experiment such as Barnett and Stier's an individual cross section is not measured (except in a two-component system), since the observed beam attenuation includes contributions of charge-changing collisions leading from the initial neutral state to all possible charged states. If we denote the neutral state by 0 (zero) and any particular final ionic state by the letter f, where f is a positive or negative integer indicating the magnitude and sign of the charge on the ion, then we might represent

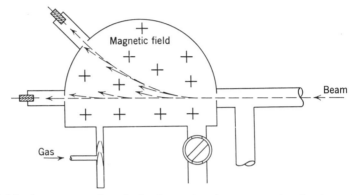

FIG. 6-6-3. Apparatus used to obtain charge-changing cross sections by the method of beam attenuation in a transverse magnetic field.[41]

the measured cross section by the sum $\sum_f {_0q_f}$. Here we are using a modified version of Hasted's notation (cf. Section 6-1); the indices for the target particle are omitted. It is understood that the initial charge on the target is zero, but its final state is unknown. The cross sections for electron capture and for double electron loss by helium atoms are known to be small compared to those for single electron loss in the energy range that Barnett and Stier investigated; the cross sections they measured are approximately those for single electron loss $_0q_1$. Barnett and Stier were also able to evaluate the electron capture cross sections $_1q_0$ for He$^+$ ions by combining their $_0q_1$ data with their measured values of the equilibrium fractions for helium beams.

An apparatus employing a transverse magnetic field is shown in Fig. 6-6-3, which is taken from the review article by Allison.[41] Here the beam incident on the target chamber may be pure or mixed in its charge states. If the incident beam is mixed, it will be split into separate beams by the magnetic field. With no target gas in the collision chamber, values of the deflection field and locations of the detectors are found so that the various beams enter their detectors through apertures larger than, but comparable to, the diameters of the beams themselves. When gas is admitted to the chamber, each beam particle whose charge is changed in a collision is lost to the beam because it can no longer continue in its old orbit, and a beam attenuation due to charge-changing is observed.

3. *The slow ion collection or condenser method.* Cross sections for electron capture by a fast ion may be measured by collecting the slow ions produced in a thin gas target by the fast projectiles passing through it, provided electron loss by the projectiles is negligible in the energy range of interest. The basic techniques used in this method were discussed in Section 6-2-B. Positive ions may also be formed in the target gas by ionization of the target molecules, but equal amounts of positive and negative charge are liberated in such reactions. If all of the positive ions and electrons produced in the target gas are collected on the "condenser plates" and the net positive charge is measured, the contributions of charge transfer alone may be measured. However, a simple interpretation of the excess positive current is possible only if electron capture is the sole charge-changing collision occurring in the collision chamber and if the number of electrons captured in a single collision is known.

4. *The growth curve method.* It is also possible to obtain charge transfer cross sections by studying the rate at which a new component grows into the beam emerging from a collision chamber as the target gas pressure is raised from a low value toward the equilibration pressure. This technique is described by Allison and Garcia-Munoz,[42] who point out that the method is particularly valuable in determining the probability of the capture or loss of two electrons in a single collision.

5. *Measurements of angular and energy distributions.* It was stated in Section 6-2-B that projectiles undergoing charge transfer in a gas almost always suffer extremely small changes in direction and that the ions formed in the gas acquire only a small amount of momentum from the projectile in the collision. Nearly all contributions to the total charge transfer cross section come from collisions in which the projectile is scattered in a very narrow cone about the original direction of motion. A rough classical calculation in the case in which a single electron is stripped off the projectile indicates that the maximum angular deflection is about $2m/M$; m and M are the masses of the electron and the projectile, respectively.[42] However, even though the differential scattering cross section varies with scattering angle about as $\csc^4(\vartheta/2)$, there is still a measurable number of collisions that produce large deflections. These deflections result from violent encounters in which a fast projectile passes very close to a target particle. In general, the scattering angle in such collisions

increases with the number of electrons transferred. Everhart and his students[48] have performed a series of experiments in which they measured the angular and charge state distributions of singly charged noble gas ions experiencing single collisions in the energy range from about 1 to 200 kev. One version of their apparatus used for measurements at scattering angles greater than 1° is illustrated in Fig. 6-6-4. The incident ion beam enters

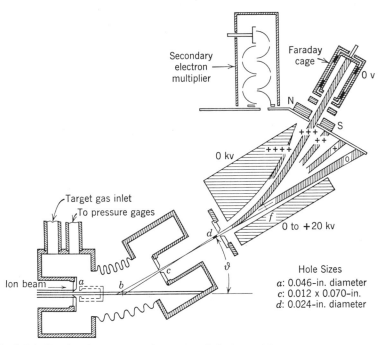

FIG. 6-6-4. Everhart's apparatus for study of single-collision scattering of noble gas ions through angles between 1 and 40° in the laboratory system.[48]

the target chamber through hole a, and a few of the large-angle collisions which happen to occur near b result in scattered projectiles which pass through the resolution holes c and d. (The scattering volume is determined by the slit system and must be calculated.) These projectiles are analyzed into their various charge states and are then detected with the Faraday cup or the electron multiplier. The target gas pressure is about 1 μ of mercury, which is low enough that almost all of the detected particles have undergone only single scattering. A small Faraday cup (drawn with dashed lines) can be put into the path of the beam behind hole a in order to monitor the incident beam.

The apparatus shown in Fig. 6-6-4 has been used for measurements of differential scattering cross sections over angles from 1 to 40° for processes

$(1/f)$, where the final charge number ranges from 0 to $+7$. The angular resolution is about $\pm 0.5°$. These cross sections differ from those calculated from the Rutherford scattering law, and the differences can be interpreted in terms of electron screening, ionization, and charge transfer (cf. Section 4-10). Another collision chamber is used to measure the cross section for scattering into the cone $\vartheta < 1°$ and to determine the charge state distribution of these particles. By integrating the measured differential cross sections, Everhart and his co-workers were also able to evaluate the total scattering cross sections, as a negligible number of particles are scattered through angles above the maximum they can reach.

Measurements similar to those described have been reported by two groups of Russian workers.[49] Everhart and his associates have also used their apparatus to investigate resonance phenomena in large-angle charge transfer collisions.[50]

More recently, Morgan and Everhart[51] have studied the inelastic energy loss in large-angle collisions of A^+ ions with argon atoms as a function of incident energy and recoil angle. They made measurements in the range from 3 to 100 kev incident energy on target particles recoiling at angles between 84 and 52° with respect to the incident beam direction. These recoil angles correspond to collisions in which the projectiles are scattered at angles betweeen about 6 and 38°. The kinetic energies and scattering angles of the recoil particles are accurately measured, and these measurements, together with the requirement of conservation of energy, permit the determination of the inelastic energy loss by the projectiles. The apparatus used in these studies is shown schematically in Fig. 6-6-5.

Some of the data obtained by Everhart's group are displayed later in this section. Other results of theirs appear in Section 6-7, which deals with ionization and stripping.

B. CHARGE TRANSFER DATA (HIGH ENERGY). A substantial amount of data on charge transfer in the low energy region was presented in Section 6-2-C, and many of the curves displayed there extend well beyond the somewhat arbitrarily located upper limit of this region (500 ev). Thus the reader will find a great deal of information on high-energy charge transfer in the figures and references of Section 6-2. Here we emphasize the results obtained on fast hydrogen and helium projectiles, which are of special interest in controlled thermonuclear research. A wealth of additional data on these and other projectiles is presented in the review by Allison and Garcia-Munoz,[42] which contains the best compilation of results on high-energy charge-changing collisions yet published.

Figures 6-6-6 and 6-6-7 display Allison's compilation of data[41] on the equilibrium fractions of the various charge states of a hydrogen beam in

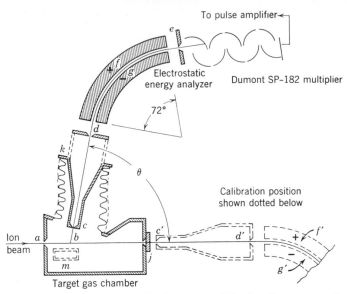

FIG. 6-6-5. The energy analyzer used by Morgan and Everhart[51] to measure the angular and energy distributions of recoiling target particles. These distributions permit the calculation of the energy losses suffered by fast projectiles in inelastic collisions.

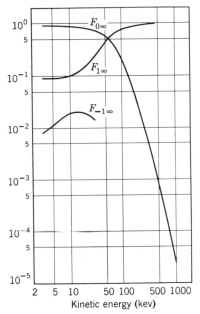

FIG. 6-6-6. Fractions of H⁻, H⁰, and H⁺ in a hydrogen beam equilibrated in hydrogen gas (Allison[41]).

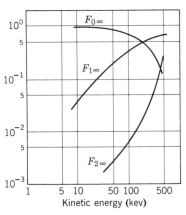

FIG. 6-6-7. Fractions of He⁰, He⁺, and He²⁺ in a helium beam equilibrated in helium gas (Allison[41]).

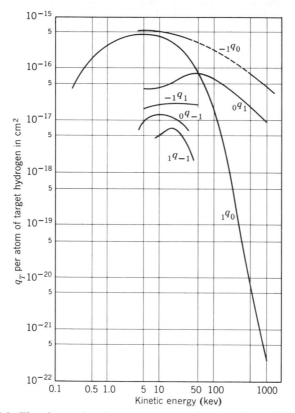

FIG. 6-6-8. The charge-changing cross sections for H^-, H^0, and H^+ ions and atoms moving in hydrogen gas (Allison[41]).

H_2 and a helium beam in He. References to the original sources of these data are tabulated by Allison. In these figures the subscripts ∞ indicate that the charge state fractions F refer to beams traversing "infinitely thick" targets. Charge-changing cross sections for hydrogen and helium atoms and ions are presented in Figs. 6-6-8 and 6-6-9, also taken from Allison's review.[41] We should note that here the measured hydrogen cross sections were divided by two and plotted per atom of target gas. They should be multiplied by two to obtain cross sections for collisions with H_2 molecules.* Figure 6-6-10 shows data on hydrogen atoms and ions in nitrogen gas obtained by Stier and Barnett[44] and Barnett and Reynolds.[45] Results on electron capture by H_2^+ ions in hydrogen gas to form H_2 molecules are

---

* This statement is not meant to imply that the cross section for a molecule is equal to the sum of the cross sections of its constituent atoms.

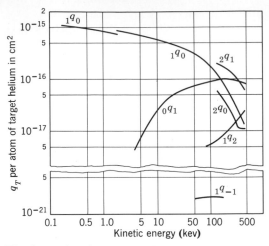

FIG. 6-6-9. The charge-changing cross sections for He⁰, He⁺, and He²⁺ in the target gas helium (Allison[41]).

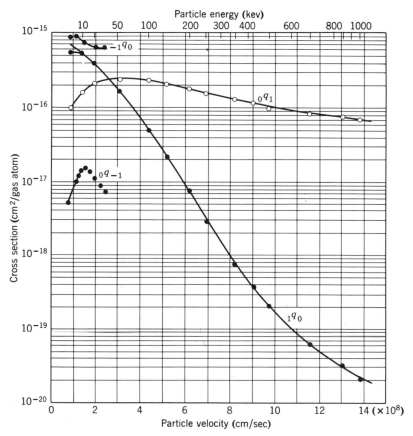

FIG. 6-6-10. Charge transfer cross sections for hydrogen atoms and ions in nitrogen gas (Barnett et al.[44,45]).

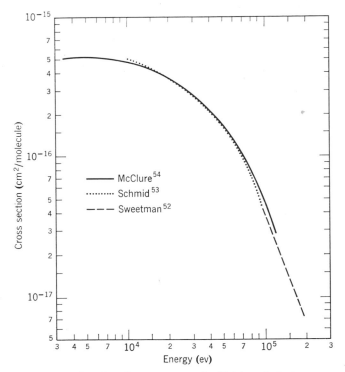

FIG. 6-6-11. Cross sections for electron capture by H_2^+ ions in hydrogen gas to form H_2 molecules.

shown in Fig. 6-6-11. These cross sections were measured by Sweetman,[52] Schmid,[53] and McClure.[54]

Figure 6-6-12, taken from the paper by Jones et al.,[48] presents a sample of the data obtained by Everhart's group on differential cross sections for scattering of noble gas ions in violent collisions. The cross sections plotted there are multiplied by the sine of the laboratory scattering angle ϑ to indicate the differential contributions to the total scattering cross section associated with the designated changes in charge states. The total cross section for scattering the ions between angles ϑ_a and ϑ_b with change in charge numbers 1 to n is given by the equation

$$_1q_n(\vartheta_a \to \vartheta_b) = 2\pi \int_{\vartheta_a}^{\vartheta_b} {}_1q_n(\vartheta) \sin \vartheta \, d\vartheta \tag{6-6-1}$$

Figure 6-6-13 is presented to illustrate the resonance effects which Everhart and his associates[50] discovered in violent charge-changing collisions. Lockwood and Everhart[50] obtained the data on electron capture

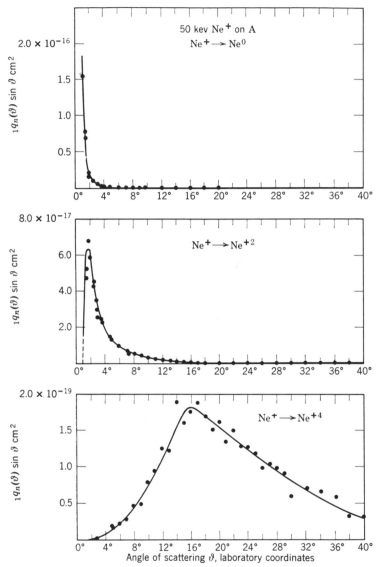

FIG. 6-6-12. Differential cross sections (weighted by sin ϑ) versus laboratory scattering angle for single collisions of Ne$^+$ ions on argon at 50 kev. Empirical lines are drawn through the experimental data points (Jones et al.[48]).

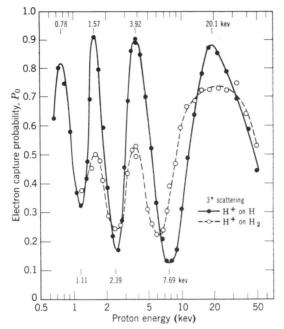

FIG. 6-6-13. The electron capture probability P_0 versus incident proton energy in key for H$^+$ ions on atomic and molecular hydrogen. These data are for violent collisions in which the scattered H$^+$ ions emerge at 3° in the laboratory system (Lockwood and Everhart[50]).

by H$^+$ ions in atomic hydrogen by firing a beam of protons through a furnace containing highly dissociated hydrogen gas. The usual crossed beam technique could not be applied because the density of atomic scattering centers provided would be far too low for these measurements. (Lockwood and Everhart selected for detection only those few projectile-scattered at angles very close to 3°.) Their apparatus was therefore cons structed so that the scattering took place within a furnace in which the density of atoms could be made large enough and in which the temperature was high enough so that the target gas was almost entirely atomic. Ziemba and Russek[55] have given a theoretical treatment of resonance capture in He$^+$ on He (which has been studied by Ziemba et al.[50]), and Lockwood and Everhart[50] have similarly treated protons on atomic hydrogen.

Allison and Garcia-Munoz[42] have compiled an extensive bibliography on high-energy charge-changing collisions in a survey of the literature up to about the end of 1960. Therefore we close this section by citing only a few of the more recent papers by European workers[56–59] and completing our listing of the translated Russian papers[60] on this subject. Some of the

Russian papers listed in Ref. 60 contain valuable information on charge-changing collisions of projectiles of boron, carbon, nitrogen, oxygen, the heavier noble gases, and the alkalis.

6-7. IONIZATION AND STRIPPING

Data on the ionization of atoms and molecules by electron impact were presented in Section 5-3-B. Reference to the figures in that section shows that the cross section for single ionization rises from zero at the ionization energy of the target, rapidly increases to a peak value near 100 ev, and then slowly and monotonically decreases as the electron energy is increased. At 500 ev the cross section generally has fallen to about half its peak value. This behavior is in marked contrast to that observed in heavy particle collisions. With heavy particles the threshold energy for ionization is also low (about a factor of 2 higher than the ionization energy of the heavy particle which loses the electron) and the general shape of the electron yield curve is about the same. However, the energy scale is greatly expanded because of the much larger masses of the colliding particles. The cross section now peaks at an energy in the tens-of-kev region* and remains large up to energies of about 1 Mev. Thus a wide energy range must be covered in mapping heavy particle cross sections.

Another difference develops from the fact that in the energy regions where electron ejection is likely the de Broglie wavelengths of heavy projectiles are small compared to electron wavelengths and to atomic dimensions. Consequently, in heavy particle collisions diffraction effects are negligible except at very small angles, and the trajectories of the colliding particles are nearly those calculated from classical mechanics. As we have seen, heavy particles are generally deflected only slightly even in inelastic collisions, and it is possible to conduct experiments by using well-defined beams of projectiles.

The ionization of gases by fast ions and atoms is a subject of considerable practical and theoretical interest. In the field of controlled thermonuclear research, for example, several fusion machines utilize high-energy injection, and knowledge of the ionization cross sections for light projectiles moving at high velocities through various target gases is of real value. Not only are hydrogen and helium targets of interest in this connection, but heavier gases, such as carbon monoxide, are also important, since they

---

* At impact energies appreciably below the peak energy the relative velocity of the colliding particles is small compared to the velocity of the orbital electrons, and the cross section is small because these electrons have sufficient time to adjust adiabatically to the slowly changing perturbation. At energies far above the peak the interaction is of such short duration that electron ejection is improbable.

are present in fusion devices as contaminants. In addition, the detection of fast ions in gas-filled counters involves the ionization produced by the primary particles, and the detection of neutrons in a number of different types of counting devices depends directly on the production of ion-pairs in the gas following a nuclear reaction in a target material. Ionization and stripping cross sections at high energies also enter into consideration of a number of astrophysical and upper atmospheric phenomena. The density of ions and electrons in the upper atmosphere is determined to some extent by the rates of ionization and stripping reactions for particles from outer space. Some of the electrons thus produced contribute to the excitation of the auroras and to the population of the electronic component of the Van Allen radiation belts.

A. EXPERIMENTAL TECHNIQUES FOR STUDYING HEAVY PARTICLE IONIZA-TION AND STRIPPING. Most experimental studies of ionization and many studies of stripping include the collection of slow ions and/or electrons produced when a primary beam traverses a thin gas target. In some cases it is possible to assess the contribution of charge transfer to the formation of slow ions in the gas. In this event a true ionization cross section may be obtained, but unless the distribution in charge states of the slow ions is determined the data provide only the *apparent ionization cross section* q_i defined by the equation

$$q_i = q^+ + 2q^{2+} + 3q^{3+} + \cdots \tag{6-7-1}$$

where q^{n+} is the sum of the cross sections for all reactions in which n electrons are ejected from a target molecule [Cf. (5-2-2)]. In the usual case in which the contributions of ionization and charge transfer cannot be separated the experimental data yield the cross section for production of slow positive ions. If the electrons produced by ionization and stripping are collected, the cross section for production of slow electrons may be evaluated.* This cross section is equal to the apparent ionization cross section if the projectile has no electrons that can be stripped. Under thin-target conditions an inappreciable number of secondary electrons are usually produced in the gas by electrons ejected from the projectile or target.

In this section we shall discuss techniques for measuring total cross sections, charge state distributions, and energy and angular distributions of the projectile and target particles.

* Electrons produced by ionization and stripping have energies low enough that they can all be collected by applying a transverse field in the collision chamber. This field can be so weak that it will not seriously disturb the fast beam. Because of their small mass, the electrons can be separated from negative ions which might also be produced in the target gas.

1. *Measurement of total cross sections for production of slow ions and electrons.* The early work on measurement of total cross sections is surveyed in Chapter VIII of Massey and Burhop;[5] the more recent work has been reviewed by Fite.[61] Here we shall discuss in detail only the experimental techniques used recently for such measurements at the Georgia Institute of Technology.

The Georgia Tech measurements were on slow ion and electron production in He, Ne, A, H_2, N_2, O_2, and CO by H^{+}[62,63] and He^{+}[64] ions in the energy range 0.15 to 1.0 Mev. The condenser method (cf. Section 6-2-B) was used, with only a transverse electrostatic field for particle collection. The charge-changing cross sections for H^{+} ions in this energy range are quite small, and fairly high target gas pressures and large electrode dimensions could be used without having the incident H^{+} ions capture electrons

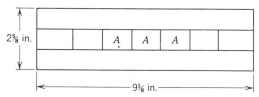

FIG. 6-7-1. Front view of the slow ion collector assembly used by McDaniel et al.[63] for studies of the ionization of gases by H^{+} ions. The secondary electron suppressing grid covering the assembly is not shown. An identical set of electrodes for slow electron collection was used with this set in the collision chamber shown in Fig. 6-7-2.

during their passage through the apparatus. A pair of collector electrodes (See Fig. 6-7-1) was used for slow ion and electron collection in the collision chamber shown in Fig. 6-7-2. The smaller set of electrodes in Fig. 6-7-2 was required for the measurements with He^{+} projectiles, for which the charge-changing cross sections are not negligible in the energy range investigated. In each of the collector assemblies pictured all of the electrodes were held at the same potential, but only currents to the electrodes marked A were measured. The remaining electrodes served only to make the transverse electric field uniform in the vicinity of the active electrodes and to prevent secondary and photoelectrons ejected from slits and the chamber walls from striking the A electrodes.

The two collector assemblies used in each experiment were located parallel to one another, on opposite sides of the beam axis. The ion collector was screened by a biased grid located $\frac{1}{4}$ in. in front of it to suppress secondary electrons ejected from the collector plates. The grid consisted of 0.004-in. diameter stainless steel wires strung 0.100 in. apart and perpendicular to the beam axis. A bias voltage of about 50 volts with respect to the ion collector array was normally used for electron suppression. The

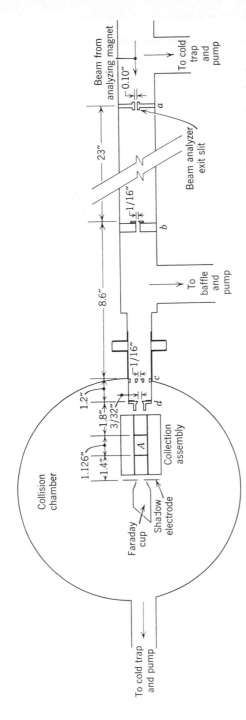

FIG. 6-7-2. Apparatus used by Martin et al.[64] for studies of the ionization of gases by He$^+$ ions. In the collision chamber the beam passes between two identical parallel collector arrays, only one of which is shown. Slow-ion currents collected by only the segment A are measured, with the other segments serving as guards. The suppressor grid covering the entire collector array is not shown. The slit a and the aperture c are designed for small pumping impedance, whereas the apertures b and d are designed for large differential pumping impedance. The incident beam is collimated by b and c.

particle transmission of the grid was assumed to be essentially equal to its geometric transmission, which was 96%. The distance from the grid to the electron collector on the other side of the beam axis was $\frac{1}{2}$ in. Equal and opposite voltages were applied to the grid and the electron assembly, the total potential difference being set between 200 and 2000 volts. Considerable attention must be paid to the design of the collimator system and to the application of proper voltages to the collectors to prevent fast electrons traveling in the beam direction from being swept to the active electrodes.[64] Such electrons can be produced up to their full knock-on energy by fast beam projectiles grazing the slits between the analyzing magnet and collision chamber.[65] Also, care must be taken to provide adequate differential pumping in the beam entrance pipe so that the projectiles will not undergo charge-changing collisions before they enter the chamber.

The source of projectiles in these experiments was a 1-Mev Van de Graaff accelerator, equipped with a beam analyzing and stabilizing system. The incident ion energy was determined by a 90° deflection in a regulated magnetic field, whose value was measured with a precision gaussmeter. The nominal energy spread was ±2 kev at 1 Mev. Target gas pressures in the range 10^{-4} to 10^{-3} mm Hg were used in the H^+ measurements. Because of the large charge-changing cross sections for He^+ ions, the He^+ experiments were performed at gas pressures in the 10^{-5} to 10^{-4} mm Hg range. Beam currents of about 0.5 μa were employed, and slow ion and electron currents of about 10^{-10} to 10^{-11} amp were collected. All currents were measured with vacuum-tube electrometers.

Techniques similar to those described have been used by a number of other investigators (see, for example, Refs. 66 and 67). Other workers have used magnetic fields in addition to a transverse electric field in the condenser method. For instance, Fogel et al.[68] employed a longitudinal magnetic field of about 300 gauss which helps to confine the projectile beam and also eliminates the need for a secondary electron suppressor grid. With this field applied, slow positive ions are swept to their collector, but electrons produced by ionization and stripping are trapped in the axial direction and prevented from reaching their collector. Also, secondary electrons from the ion collector are returned to that collector because their Larmor radius is small compared to the dimensions of the plates and the spacing between the oppositely charged electrodes. When the magnetic field is removed, electrons produced in ionization and stripping reactions and also secondary electrons from the ion collector are able to traverse the gap and are swept to the electron collector. The secondary electron current makes a positive contribution to the apparent slow ion and electron currents, but combination of the field-on and field-off data permits this contribution to be assessed so that the true positive and negative currents can be evaluated.

Gilbody and Hasted[69] have used a magnetic field parallel to the transverse electric field extending between gridded condenser plates. The magnetic field in this arrangement helps to define the gas volume from which electrons are able to pass to their collector and also permits weaker electric fields to be used for particle collection. This field configuration was not used in all the work reported in Ref. 69. Fite, Stebbings, Hummer, and Brackmann[27] have also used a combination of parallel electric and magnetic fields in measurements of the cross section for ionization of hydrogen atoms by protons. Their experiments covered the energy range from 7 to 40 kev. Ireland and Gilbody[70] have recently extended these measurements to 400 kev. Their results are discussed in Section 6-16-B.

2. *Other types of experimental studies of ionization and stripping.* The total cross section measurements described provide no information on the charges or masses of the ions formed in a gas traversed by fast heavy projectiles. However, a substantial body of data of this type has been accumulated during the last few years by Russian investigators, who performed e/m analysis on the ions with mass spectrometers whose entrance probes projected into the collision chamber close to the beam axis.[71] A few measurements have also been made on the energy and angular distributions of the residual ions.[51,72] The apparatus used by Morgan and Everhart[51] for such measurements is shown in Fig. 6-6-5. Some of their data are presented in Section 6-7-B.

A few experimental data are available on the energy distribution of the free electrons produced in heavy particle collisions.[73] Kuyatt and Jorgensen[74] and Rudd and Jorgensen[75] have measured angular as well as energy distributions for ejected electrons. By integrating their data over energy and angle Rudd and Jorgensen obtained total cross sections for ionization of helium by protons with 50-, 100-, and 150-kev energies. Their values are displayed in Fig. 6-7-3. Several theoretical calculations have also been made on the energy distribution of electrons ejected by proton impact.[76] These calculations were discussed in Section 5-7.

B. DATA ON HIGH-ENERGY IONIZATION AND STRIPPING. Experimental data on total cross sections for production of slow ions and free electrons by fast H^+ and He^+ ions are displayed in Figs. 6-7-3 through 6-7-9.* In the energy range (0.15 to 1.0 Mev) covered by McDaniel et al.[63] the charge-changing cross sections for H^+ projectiles are negligibly small, and the cross section for electron production in this range equals that for slow ion

---

* Additional data on the ionization of gases by fast H^+ and He^+ ions have recently become available. See H. B. Gilbody, J. B. Hasted, J. V. Ireland, A. R. Lee, E. W. Thomas, and A. S. Whiteman, *Proc. Roy. Soc. (London)* A-274, 40 (1963); H. B. Gilbody and A. R. Lee, A-274, 365 (1963); and E. S. Solov'ev, R. N. Il'in, V. A. Oparin, and N. V. Fedorenko, Third International Conference on the Physics of Electronic and Atomic Collisions, London, 1963.

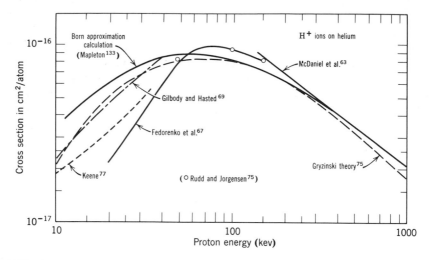

FIG. 6-7-3. Experimental and theoretical cross sections for electron production in helium by fast H^+ ions.

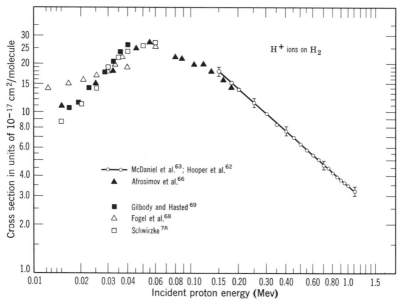

FIG. 6-7-4. Cross sections for production of free electrons by H^+ ions on H_2. See Section 6-16 for discussion of theory.

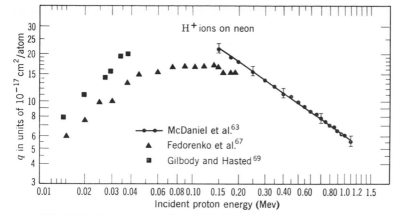

FIG. 6-7-5. Cross sections for production of electrons by H⁺ ions on neon.

production within the accuracy of the experimental data. These cross sections, however, are not equal in general at lower impact energies or for other projectiles. In Fig. 6-7-7 the cross sections for slow ion or electron production may be unambiguously labeled the cross sections for ionization, since not only is charge transfer negligible above 0.15 Mev but also stripping is impossible for H⁺ ions.

Many of the papers already listed in Section 6-6 and earlier in this section contain additional data on slow ion and electron production by fast projectiles. Other sources of information are listed in Refs. 77, 78, and 79. A useful review of the entire subject of ionization by heavy

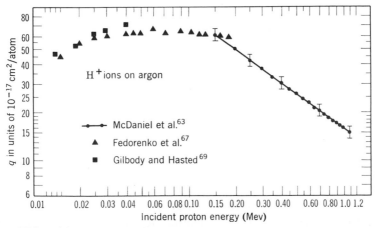

FIG. 6-7-6. Cross sections for production of electrons by H⁺ ions on argon.

particles, covering work up to about the beginning of 1959, has been prepared by Fedorenko.[80]

The peak yields for the production of electrons by protons lie in the energy range extending from about 50 to 100 kev, in accord with predictions by Lee and Hasted[81] based on a classical impenetrable sphere model. The yield maxima lie at higher energies in heavier projectiles.

Everhart's group has obtained data on the probabilities of production of various projectile charge states when fast noble gas ions make violent

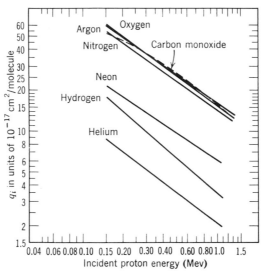

FIG. 6-7-7. Apparent ionization cross sections for H^+ ions on He, Ne, A, H_2, N_2, O_2, and CO (McDaniel et al.[63]).

stripping collisions in noble gases. The results obtained by Fuls et al.[48] for A^+ ions on argon are presented in Fig. 6-7-10. It must be emphasized that scattering of the projectile ions through angles appreciably different from zero is extremely rare, and we must not gain the impression from Fig. 6-7-10 that multiple-stripping and wide-angle scattering events occur with high absolute probability. Russek and his students[82] have developed a phenomenological theory which predicts the shape of curves such as those shown in Fig. 6-7-10 with striking success. In their model the stripping is regarded as a two-step process. In the first step, as the electron distributions of the collision partners sweep through one another, a certain amount of energy is transferred by a frictionlike mechanism from the translational kinetic energy of the atoms to their internal degrees of freedom. In the second step this transferred energy, which is analogous to heat energy,

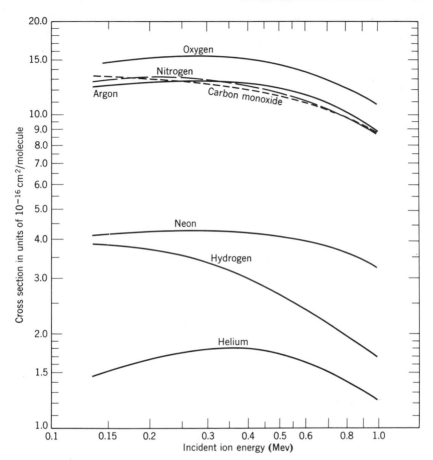

FIG. 6-7-8. Cross sections for the gross production of free electrons by He^+ incident on helium, neon, argon, molecular hydrogen, molecular nitrogen, molecular oxygen, and carbon monoxide (Martin et al.[64]).

is statistically distributed among the electrons. The probability that any given number of electrons will acquire more than the ionization energy is then computed by a straightforward statistical analysis. The probabilities that the collision products will be in the various states of ionization are thereby calculated as functions of the collision parameters. This electron ejection mechanism is analogous to the evaporation of molecules from a heated liquid. This same approach has been used by Hasted[83] in a discussion of the energy transferred in inelastic ion-atom collisions. Data obtained by Morgan and Everhart[51] on the energy losses by A^+ ions experiencing violent collisions with argon atoms are presented in

Fig. 6-7-11. These data pertain only to those rare collisions in which the projectile is scattered through a wide angle. In the great majority of ionizing collisions only a single electron is ejected from a target molecule

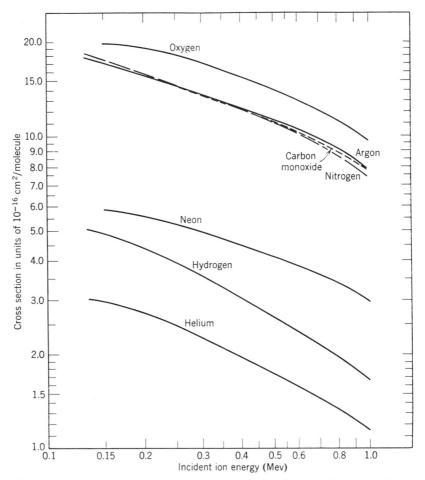

FIG. 6-7-9. Cross sections for the gross production of positive ions by He$^+$ incident on helium, neon, argon, molecular hydrogen, molecular nitrogen, molecular oxygen, and carbon monoxide (Martin et al.[64]).

and the projectile loses only slightly more than the single ionization energy.

Figure 6-7-12 illustrates the results of a calculation by Bates, McDowell, and Omholt[76] on the energy distribution of electrons ejected from neon atoms by fast protons.

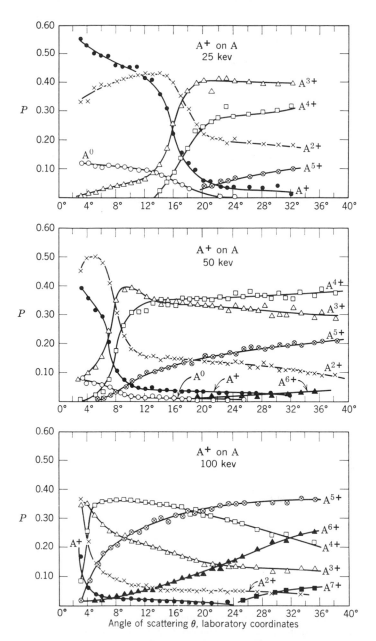

FIG. 6-7-10. Charge analysis of argon ions which have undergone violent collisions with argon atoms. Percentages of the fast ions in their final charge states are plotted versus the projectile scattering angle (Fuls et al.[48]).

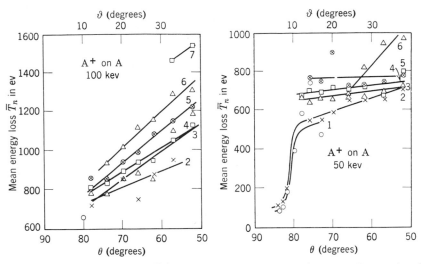

FIG. 6-7-11. Mean energy loss $\bar{T}_n$ versus recoil scattering angle θ at projectile energies of 50 and 100 kev. The projectile scattering angle ϑ is shown at the top of each drawing. The degree of ionization of the recoiling target particle is indicated by the number on each curve; both it and the projectile energy loss increase with increasing impact energy and with decreasing recoil angle (Morgan and Everhart[51]).

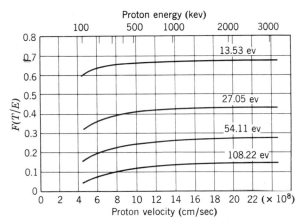

FIG. 6-7-12. The energy distribution of electrons resulting from ionization of neon gas by protons, calculated by Bates, McDowell, and Omholt.[76] $F(T/E)$ is the fraction of electrons with an energy in excess of the amount T ejected from the outer shell by protons of energy E. The value of T in ev is given on each curve.

6-8. DISSOCIATION

One of the most promising approaches to controlled thermonuclear power production involves the establishment of a hot dense plasma by transverse injection of high-energy molecular hydrogen ions into a dc magnetic mirror machine containing hydrogen gas at low pressure.[84] If the fast injected ions are trapped in the mirror field in sufficient numbers and for sufficient time, they may be able to produce enough ionization to build up the required plasma temperature and density, but one of the major problems still to be satisfactorily solved is that of efficiently trapping the incident ions. Particles entering the magnetic field from outside the machine have orbits that are topologically different from those of particles truly trapped

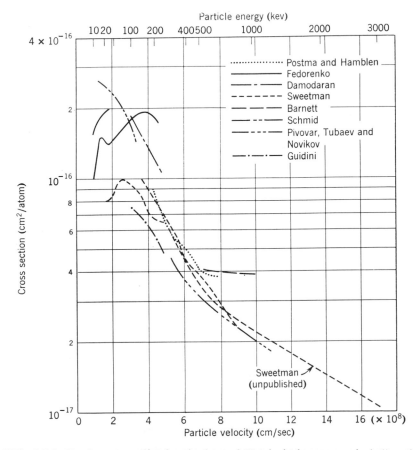

FIG. 6-8-1. Total cross section for the loss of H_2^+ in hydrogen gas, including the reactions $H_2^+ \rightarrow H^0 + H^+$ and $H_2^+ \rightarrow 2H^+ + e$. For data on deuterium ions, see S. E. Kupriyanov, A. A. Perov, and N. N. Tunitskii, *Sov. Phys.–JETP* **16**, 539, 1152(1963).

within the machine, and injected ions will immediately be lost unless their charge-to-mass ratio is altered during their first circulation about the flux lines of the mirror field configuration. Changes in e/m may be effected by dissociating the ions in collisions with other particles inside the machine or by passing the incident ions through a strong electric or magnetic field. This fact has prompted a number of studies of collisional and field dissociation of various species of molecular hydrogen ions during the last decade.

Experiments on collisional dissociation have been conducted with apparatus similar to that used in high-energy charge transfer studies (cf. Section 6-6-A). Data obtained by a number of investigators[85-93] are presented in Figs. 6-8-1 through 6-8-4. The cross sections for collisional

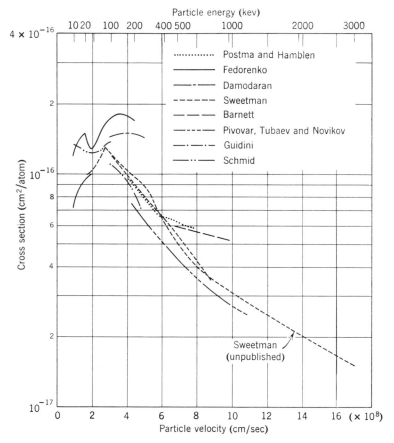

FIG. 6-8-2. Dissociation cross section for proton production by H_2^+ in hydrogen gas, including the reactions $H_2^+ \rightarrow H^+ + H^0$ and $H_2^+ \rightarrow H^+ + H^+ + e$.

dissociation might be expected to depend on the state of vibrational excitation of the molecular projectile, and experimental evidence to this effect has been presented by Riviere and Sweetman[94] and by McClure.[54] The yields of the various dissociation fragments of H_2^+ and H_3^+ primary ions were found by McClure to vary by as much as 20% with changes in ion source conditions. This variation is presumably due to differences in the population of the vibrational energy states of the projectiles.

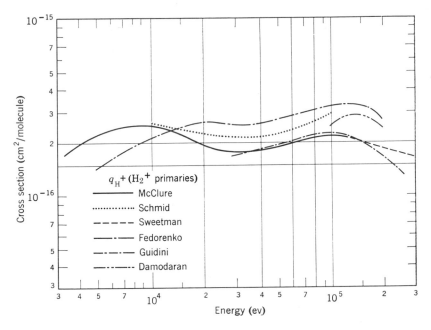

FIG. 6-8-3. Cross sections for production of H^+ ions in dissociation of H_2^+ ions on H_2 molecules.[54]

If a sufficiently strong external electric field $\mathbf{E}$ is applied to a molecular ion, the interatomic potential may be warped in such a way that the higher vibrational states become unstable and dissociation results even in the absence of a collision. The same effect may be produced by the equivalent electric field $\mathbf{E}' = \mathbf{v} \times \mathbf{B}$ caused by motion with velocity $\mathbf{v}$ through a magnetic field of flux density $\mathbf{B}$. The dissociation of molecular hydrogen and deuterium ions by static electric and magnetic fields has been studied experimentally by Riviere and Sweetman[95] and by Kaplan et al.[96] Figure 6-8-5 shows some of the data obtained by Riviere and Sweetman. The

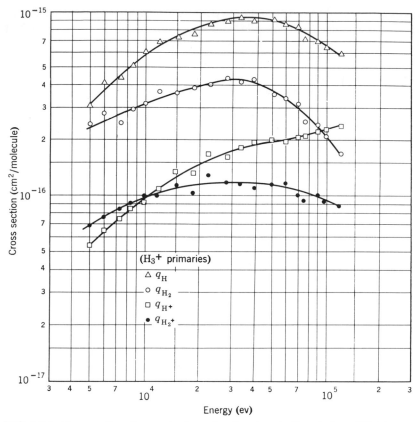

FIG. 6-8-4. Cross sections for production of various ions in dissociation of H_3^+ ions on H_2 molecules.[54]

theory of field dissociation of molecular ions (and also the field ionization of neutral atoms*) has been discussed by Hiskes.[97]

6-9. EXCITATION†

When a fast heavy particle passes through matter, a substantial fraction of its energy is dissipated in the excitation of atomic and molecular states

* Several experimental studies of the field ionization of excited hydrogen atoms have recently been described. See A. C. Riviere and D. R. Sweetman, Sixth International Conference on Ionization Phenomena in Gases, Paris, 1963, and K. H. Berkner, J. R. Hiskes, S. N. Kaplan, G. A. Paulikas, and R. V. Pyle, Third International Conference on the Physics of Electronic and Atomic Collisions, London, 1963.

† This section is based on material prepared by C. Y. Fan for Kaman Nuclear Report KN-62-133(R) by E. W. McDaniel, C. Y. Fan, E. Everhart, and M. R. C. McDowell (edited by J. W. Bond), September 1, 1962.

of the target particles and sometimes of the projectile itself. Measurements of cross sections for excitation of atoms and moelcules by heavy particle impact therefore provide quantitative information about a fundamental process by which fast particles lose energy and by which they affect the medium through which they pass. A particular need for excitation data arises in auroral studies, as any detailed interpretation of auroral

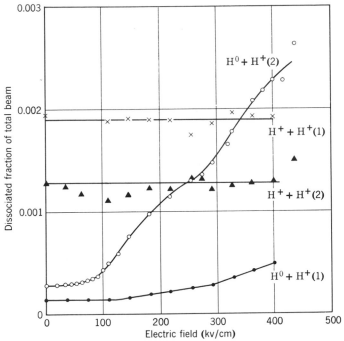

FIG. 6-8-5. The fractional dissociation of H_2^+ ions as a function of electric field intensity.[95] Curves (1): H_2^+ ions direct from source. Curves (2): H_2^+ ions obtained from breakup of H_3^+ ions.

spectra must be based on knowledge of excitation cross sections. Spectral observations have shown that high-energy protons penetrate to auroral heights in the atmosphere during auroral displays, and Doppler-shifted lines of the Balmer series appear in the majority of auroral forms.[98] One interesting feature of excitation collisions is that they can be studied at a remote distance by observations on the electromagnetic radiation which usually accompanies the de-excitation of excited structures. Thus, for example, it is possible to estimate the auroral proton flux from the hydrogen line intensity detected on the ground. Unfortunately, few excitation cross sections have yet been measured with precision. The measurements are difficult because the light produced by excitation processes in a laboratory collision chamber is generally very faint, and calibration of the absolute efficiency of optical apparatus is a tedious procedure.

A. EXPERIMENTAL TECHNIQUES USED IN EXCITATION STUDIES.   In most excitation events one of the colliding particles is left in an ordinary excited state, from which spontaneous radiative transitions to lower energy levels are allowed by dipole selection rules.   The lifetimes of such states are typically of the order of only 10^{-8} sec, and reactions leading to their production may be studied by observing the radiation emitted when spontaneous de-excitation occurs.   Events leading to the excitation of metastable states, from which de-excitation by the emission of electric dipole radiation is forbidden, may be studied by the methods discussed in Sections 5-8 and 5-9.   Here we shall confine our attention to techniques involving the detection of electromagnetic radiation.

1. *The collision chamber.*   When a beam of fast heavy projectiles is fired into a collision chamber, large numbers of secondary electrons may be ejected from the colliding particles and from the chamber walls.   Care must be taken to prevent these electrons from producing measurable excitation.   To guard against the effects of stray radiation produced by electrons ejected from the walls, we may use a large collision chamber and shield the beam impact region from the radiation detectors.   The use of a low-pressure target gas ensures that electrons produced in the gas will have a negligible effect on the measurements, and this point can be checked by determining the dependence of the radiation intensity on the gas pressure. Radiation produced by the primary beam bears a linear relation to the pressure, whereas radiation produced by electrons ejected in gas phase collisions has a quadratic pressure dependence.

It is also desirable to use a low-pressure target gas to avoid collisional de-excitation of the excited particles before they can radiate their excess energy.   This consideration is particularly important in the study of the excitation of the incident particles, for at a given pressure their mean free time is very short because of their high velocity.[99]

2. *Spectrographs and filters.*   A number of spectrographs have been constructed for the study of atomic excitation.   The earlier design of Meinel[100] is particularly well suited for such experiments; it provides high light-collecting power and moderately high dispersion.   A high-quality grating vacuum monochromator for the spectral range 1000 to 6500 Å has been constructed by Sluyters and de Hass and used by Kistemaker's group for several studies.[101]   Kistemaker and his colleagues[102] have also constructed a grazing incidence vacuum monochromator for use in the far ultraviolet region, 200 to 1250 Å.   This instrument is shown in Fig. 6-9-1.

An isolated emission may be detected by means of interference filters or gas-filled absorption cells.   Interference filters were used by Carleton and Lawrence[103] for the study of excitation of N_2 by protons and by Sternberg and Tomas[104] in their investigation of proton and deuteron impact on helium.   Geballe and his colleagues[105] have used an oxygen cell and an iodine-filled Geiger counter to detect Lyman-alpha radiation produced in collisions between hydrogen-hydrogen and hydrogen-helium systems and in impact of protons on noble gas atoms.

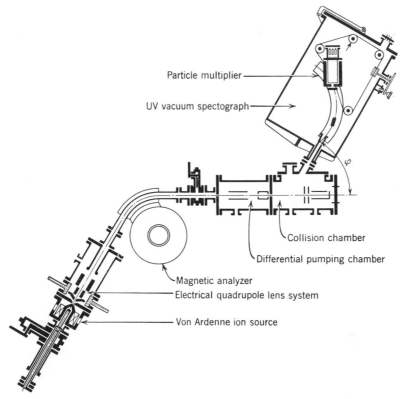

Particle multiplier

UV vacuum spectrograph

Collision chamber

Differential pumping chamber

Magnetic analyzer
Electrical quadrupole lens system

Von Ardenne ion source

FIG. 6-9-1. Apparatus used by Kistemaker's group for studies of excitation by heavy particle impact.[102]

3. *Detectors.*   Photocells, photomultipliers, and photographic plates have been successfully employed for detection of radiation in the wavelength region 3000 to 9000 Å.   Photocells and photomultipliers have an advantage over photographic plates in their linear response to radiation over a wide intensity range.   On the other hand, a photographic plate records an integrated light intensity over a large spectral region.

In the ultraviolet region below 3000 Å photons may be detected by counting the photoelectrons they produce. Alternatively, uv photons may be converted to photons in the visible region by applying a coating of sodium salicylate to the outer surface of a glass-enclosed photomultiplier tube. Johnson et al. and Watanabe et al. found that this photon conversion gives a nearly flat wavelength response down to 540 Å.[106]

The detection of photons of wavelength $\geq 1\mu$ presents a problem of another extreme, for their energy is not high enough to produce photoelectrons in ordinary materials; PbS detectors have been successful in the detection of photons in the range $1\mu < \lambda < 3.5\mu$, and indium antimonide is extremely sensitive for $\lambda \approx 5\mu$. Beyond that wavelength some specially doped Ge detectors have been tried but with less success. In the application of these detectors, cooling at least down to liquid air temperature is an absolute necessity.

4. *Calibration of optical apparatus.* One of the major difficulties in measuring excitation cross sections is in the calibration of the absolute efficiency of the optical apparatus. Common practice places a standard lamp, whose radiation emitted per unit surface area in a unit solid angle per wavelength band is calibrated absolutely with a thermocouple, at the position in which the photon emission from the collision chamber takes place. The relation between the number of photons emitted from the standard lamp and the output signal gives the calibration points.

The difficulty in a calibration of this kind lies in the vast difference in the light intensity of the lamp and the intensity produced in a collision chamber. For example, an ordinary frosted 25w tungsten lamp emits about 10^{12} photons per second per steradian per 1 Å band at $\lambda = 4000$ Å, whereas the number of photons of 3914 Å N_2^+ band emitted per centimeter from a 10 μa proton beam at 200 kev in a collision chamber at a pressure 10^{-2}mm Hg is only 4×10^{10}. This example represents one of the most favorable cases. In general, the light intensity in a collision chamber is only $\frac{1}{100}$ that of the N_2^+ band. Thus a slight nonlinearity in the detecting system will result in large uncertainty in the determination of the number of photons produced per second in the collision chamber.

Because of its extremely nonlinear characteristic and the sensitive dependence of the grain density on developing conditions, a photographic plate is not suitable for absolute cross section measurements. However, with proper control of developing conditions, plates have been successfully used for the comparison of relative intensities of optical radiations in collision chambers.

Greater accuracy can be obtained by photographing an intensity scale on the photographic plate for every single exposure. For a limited wavelength range, a stepwise neutral filter is a convenient scale. For the comparison of intensities of two emission lines with large differences in wavelengths, a rotational sector is essential (since a neutral filter is not truly neutral). A slit whose width varies in steps is more convenient, though not accurate.

5. *Polarization of the radiation.*   Radiation emitted as a result of particle impact often exhibits polarization effects determined by the direction of the particle beam which produces the excitation. Let $I_{||}$ and $I_{\perp}$ be the intensities observed at an angle of $90°$ to the beam with electric vectors parallel and perpendicular to the direction of the beam, respectively. Then the polarization fraction p is defined as

$$p = \frac{I_{||} - I_{\perp}}{I_{||} + I_{\perp}} \qquad (6\text{-}9\text{-}1)$$

In dipole radiation the angular distribution of the radiation intensity is given by the equation

$$I(\theta) = \frac{3I_0}{4\pi(3 - p)}(1 - p\cos^2\theta) \qquad (6\text{-}9\text{-}2)$$

where $I(\theta)$ is the intensity per unit solid angle emitted in the direction between θ and $\theta + d\theta$, with respect to the particle beam, and I_0 is the total intensity. Therefore $I(\theta)$ will be independent of p if the observation is made at an angle of $54.5°$, for which $\cos^2\theta = \frac{1}{3}$.

B. RESULTS.*   Excitation, like most other inelastic processes, can be caused in many different ways. The excitation of negative bands of N_2^+ by proton impact serves as an example; these bands can be excited by the following five reactions:

by primary particles
$$\begin{cases} H^+ + N_2 \rightarrow H + (N_2^+)^* & \text{(electron capture)} \\ H^+ + N_2 \rightarrow H^+ + (N_2^+)^* + e & \text{(ionization)} \\ H^+ + N_2^+ \rightarrow H^+ + (N_2^+)^* & \text{(simple excitation)} \end{cases}$$

by secondary electrons
$$\begin{cases} e + N_2 \rightarrow (N_2^+)^* + 2e & \text{(ionization)} \\ e + N_2^+ \rightarrow (N_2^+)^* + e & \text{(simple excitation)} \end{cases}$$

There are, of course, other but less probable reactions. Unless the detailed process is known, a measurement of the gross effect (which may have practical interest) does not necessarily lead to an understanding of the process. Furthermore, a gross effect depends on the conditions (such as the size of collision chamber, pressure of the gas sample, and beam current) under which the experiment is performed. Unless we are certain about the

---

* For some recent results, see the papers presented by J. van Eck, F. J. de Heer, and J. Kistemaker; N. P. Carleton and S. H. Neff; and E. W. Thomas and H. B. Gilbody at the Third International Conference on the Physics of Electronic and Atomic Collisions, London, 1963.

reliability of extrapolation, it is not safe to apply the results of a laboratory study of a gross effect to other cases in which the conditions may be quite different. Consider, for example, the excitation of 1 PG of N_2, which can be efficiently excited by low-energy electrons. The intensity of this system depends sensitively on the size of the collision chamber, the buffer system to eliminate secondary electrons, and pressure of the gas sample.[107]

1. *Determination of rotational temperatures.** Carleton,[108] Roesler, Fan, and Chamberlain,[100] and Reeves and Nicholls[109] found that the rotational temperature of N_2, derived from the negative bands of N_2^+ excited by protons, agrees well with the gas kinetic temperature. On the other hand, the N_2^+ bands excited by 1 to 5 kev Li^+ ions[109] show a marked departure from the Boltzmann distribution of rotational energies—the energy levels of high and low quantum numbers are enhanced in population. With Li^+ projectiles, the N_2^+ bands are excited by electron capture

TABLE 6-9-1. Excitation of vibrational levels of the negative system of N_2^+

Particles	Relative Intensities		
	4709 (0-2)	4652 (1-3)	4600 (2-4)
Electrons (23 ev)	1	0.51	0.13
Protons (20 kev)	1	0.62	0.34
He^+ ions (150 kev)	1	1.0	0.50
Electrons (120 ev)	1	0.33	0.08
Protons (205 kev)	1	0.33	0.10
He^+ ions (450 kev)	1	0.39	0.21

or ionization. The departure from the Boltzmann distribution is explained as a distortion of the rotational energy distribution by momentum transfer to the target particles from incident ions.

2. *Excitation of vibrational levels.* Momentum transfer can also cause distortion of the energy distribution of the vibrational levels. Table 6-9-1 shows the relative intensities of the $\Delta v' = 2$ sequence of the negative system of N_2^+ excited by electrons, protons, and He^+ ions.[107] The enhancement of higher vibrational levels reflects the increasing probability of large momentum transfer from the incident particles to the target particles towards lower energies.

3. *Excitation cross sections.* (a) H^+ in He. The excitation processes in helium by proton impact have been studied in the energy range 5 to 35 kev

* The concept of rotational temperature is discussed in Chapter 1 of the book by Chamberlain cited in Ref. 98.

TABLE 6-9-2. Excitation cross sections for H^+
on He

Kinetic Energy (kev)	Excitation Cross Sections into the Levels ($\times 10^{20}$ cm^2)		
	4^1S	5^1S	6^1S
10	8.2	3.5	
15	10	4.7	
20	17	7.0	3.3
25	26	11	6.1
30	33	15	8.4
35	37	18	10
200	17.5	7.2	

by van Eck, de Heer and Kistemaker[102] and at 200 kev by Hughes, Waring and Fan.[110] Many He I and He II lines were identified, but only the intensities of the $2p - n^1S$ lines and He II lines are in linear relationship with the pressure of the helium gas, and the radiations are almost isotropic.[102] The nonlinearities are explained by the contribution to the excitation by collisions of the second kind. Tables 6-9-2 and 6-9-3 show the cross sections obtained from these studies. If the ratios of the cross sections of the 4^1S to 5^1S to 6^1S levels are calculated at different energies, a simple approximate dependence on n can be found.

(b) H^+ on N_2. The excitation of N_2 by proton impact has been studied by Carleton and Lawrence[103] and by Hughes, Philpot, and Fan[111] in the energy range 1.5 to 4.5 kev and at 200 kev, respectively. Carleton and Lawrence studied the gross result of a few nitrogen emissions [excitation of

TABLE 6-9-3. Excitation cross sections for H^+ on He

Kinetic Energy (kev)	Excitation Cross Sections into the Levels ($\times 10^{20}$ cm^2)	
	4F	5F
15	1.3	0.39
20	3.5	1.7
25	5.2	2.6
30	6.4	3.2
35	7.0	3.5
200	$n = 4$ He$^+$,	$= 4.3 \times 10^{-20}$ cm^2

the (0–0) band of the first negative system of N_2^+, the (0–2) band of the Meinel system, and a few atomic lines of N by H^+ and H impact]. The determination of the excitation cross sections of $v' = 0$ levels of the $B^2\Sigma$ system of N_2^+ were determined at 200 kev and were found to be 4.3×10^{-17} cm² and 4.3×10^{-18} cm², respectively. The uncertainty was quoted as 50%.[111]

(c) Hydrogen lines excited by charge exchange. With the neglect of the emission of the Hβ line by electron capture into excited states of $n > 4$ for protons in He and N_2, the electron capture cross sections into the $n = 4$ level were estimated as 1.3×10^{-20} cm² and 6.6×10^{-20} cm², respectively, at 200 kev.[110,111] The results are not inconsistent with the total electron capture cross sections, which are 3.6×10^{-18} cm² and 1.5×10^{-17} cm².[2,41] respectively.

TABLE 6-9-4. Excitation of the $^2p^0_{1/2}$ level of A^+

Energy of He atom (kev)	0.5	0.75	1.0	1.25	1.5	1.75	2.0	2.25
Cross section ($\times 10^{19}$ cm²)	4.0	3.8	4.0	4.1	4.0	4.1	4.2	4.5
Energy of Ne atom (kev)	3.75	5.0	6.25	7.5	8.75	10.0	11.15	12.0
Cross section ($\times 10^{19}$ cm²)	0.65	0.95	1.1	1.2	1.5	2.1	2.0	2.0

(d) A^+ in He, Ne, A, Kr, and Xe. The intensities of the 4610 Å, 4658 Å, 4765 Å, and 4806 Å A II lines for A^+ in He, Ne, and A and the 2475 Å Xe II line for A^+ in Xe were measured by Sluyters and Kistemaker.[101] Among these optical emissions only the 4658 Å line in He and Ne is not influenced by other transitions; thus the emission of this line corresponds to the excitation cross section of the $2p^0$ level by the target particles. Table 6-9-4 shows the cross sections in the energy range of the experiment.

PART 𝒞. THE THEORY OF INELASTIC COLLISIONS

The main objective of this discussion is to indicate some of the basic concepts and methods employed in the quantum theory of inelastic collisions. A classical approach to inelastic scattering problems is also briefly outlined. Our treatment here is comparable in depth to the discussion of the quantum theory of elastic scattering presented in Part 𝓑 of Chapter 3. Emphasis is laid on the fundamental aspects of the theory, and some of the discussion, particularly that related to approximation methods, is only qualitative. The reader should consult the standard general references[112–116] for more detailed and comprehensive treatment of this vast and difficult subject. Calculations on specific heavy particle systems are mentioned at various places throughout this chapter, and additional references pertaining to inelastic collisions of electrons and photons with heavy particles appear in Chapters 5, 7, 8, and 12.

6-10. TIME-INDEPENDENT AND TIME-DEPENDENT DESCRIPTIONS OF SCATTERING

Either time-independent or time-dependent theory may be used to discuss atomic collision problems. Here we shall outline the basic approach followed in each of these formulations, although in succeeding sections of this chapter we shall use only the time-independent theory. In Chapter 7 time-dependent theory is applied to the discussion of photoionization.

The starting point in the *time-independent* quantum theory of atomic collisions is the time-independent Schrödinger wave equation for the system of colliding particles. In elastic scattering the scattered amplitude $f(\Theta)$ and differential cross section $I_s(\Theta)\, d\Omega_{CM}$ are obtained in terms of the phase shifts η_l (see Section 3-15-C) or the scattering matrix S.* In the more general inelastic collisions the scattering is described by an integral equation, and the cross section can again be expressed in terms of the S matrix. In either case the total Hamiltonian H of the system is assumed to approach an unperturbed Hamiltonian H_0 when the collision partners are widely separated, and correspondingly the eigenstates of H are assumed to approach the eigenstates of H_0 when the particles are far apart. However, the perturbed eigenfunctions are not unique, and boundary conditions must be applied to obtain solutions for the specific problem at hand. Thus the "stationary-state method" described here involves the solution of a boundary-value problem. The method is not applicable if the Hamiltonian depends explicitly on the time.

In those problems for which the Hamiltonian is *time-dependent* the system is described by the time-dependent wave equation

$$ih \frac{\partial \Psi(\mathbf{r}, t)}{\partial t} = H(\mathbf{r}, t)\, \Psi(\mathbf{r}, t) \tag{6-10-1}$$

where $H(\mathbf{r}, t)$ is the Hamiltonian operator, $\Psi(\mathbf{r}, t)$ is the time-dependent wave function of the system, and $\mathbf{r}$ denotes the coordinates of all the particles composing the system under consideration. (The symbol $\mathbf{r}$ is not meant to represent a vector here.) An example of a problem in which the

---

* The scattering matrix is not covered in any detail in this book, but it is treated in depth by Burhop[114] and by Wu and Ohmura,[116] on whose book the present discussion is based.

Hamiltonian depends explicitly on the time is the calculation of the transition probabilities for an atom in an external, time-varying electric field. Now we have an initial-value problem, since in order to calculate the probability that the system will undergo a transition from one state to another we must solve (6-10-1) subject to the intial condition that Ψ has a specified value at some time $t = t_0$. Approximation methods must be used.[113,116] The most important of these, *Dirac's method of variation of constants*, may be applied if the Hamiltonian operator can be expressed in the form

$$H(\mathbf{r}, t) = H_0(\mathbf{r}) + V(\mathbf{r}, t) \tag{6-10-2}$$

and if V is small enough compared to H_0 to be treated as a small perturbation. A solution may be possible even if V is not small compared with H_0, provided V changes fast enough, in which case the *sudden approximation* may be used, or slow enough, in which case the *adiabatic approximation* is appropriate.* Additional methods are discussed by Wu and Ohmura.[116]

Time-dependent methods may also be used in scattering problems even if the Hamiltonian does not explicitly depend on the time. Let us suppose that the collision partners are infinitely far apart at $t \to -\infty$ and that the system is in an initial state $\Psi_a(-\infty)$, which is an eigenstate of H_0, to which the Hamiltonian H tends as $t \to -\infty$. Then, as the time progresses in the positive direction and the particle separation decreases to some finite value, the interaction V becomes effective, and the wave function of the system evolves with time according to (6-10-1). After the encounter the interaction V again decreases to zero as the collision partners in their final states recede from one another toward infinite separation. At $t \to +\infty$, the system will be in some final state $\Psi_b(+\infty)$, and the problem is to find the relation between Ψ_a and Ψ_b. We see that time-dependent theory may be used in the analysis of scattering problems because even if V does not contain the time explicitly the interaction perturbation is transient in the sense that it starts from zero initially, rises to some finite value, and then falls to zero as the particles pull away from one another.

In order to calculate the transition probability and, subsequently, the collision cross section, it is necessary to introduce some artificial process of switching the interaction on and later switching it off. This switching may be accomplished abruptly by supposing the Hamiltonian to be

$$H = \begin{cases} H_0 & (-\infty < t < 0) \\ H_0 + V & (0 \le t \le \tau) \\ H_0 & (\tau < t < +\infty) \end{cases} \tag{6-10-3}$$

* See Chapter 20 of D. Bohm, Quantum Theory, *Prentice-Hall*, Englewood Cliffs, N.J., 1951. Chapter 21 of Bohm's book is also useful in the comparison of time-dependent and time-independent formulations of scattering problems.

or it may be done continuously, or adiabatically, in a time-independent interaction potential by replacing $V(\mathbf{r})$ by $e^{-\varepsilon|t|}V(\mathbf{r})$, in which $\tau = 1/\varepsilon$ is a time constant that is long compared with the characteristic times of the system. In the second method the Hamiltonian $H = H_0 + e^{-\varepsilon|t|}V$ approaches the unperturbed Hamiltonian H_0 as $t \to -\infty$ and as $t \to +\infty$ but assumes the form $H = H_0 + V$ at $t = 0$. The parameter ε is eventually allowed to approach zero in the calculation so that the switching is done adiabatically. The final state $\Psi'_b(+\infty)$ is, of course, related to the initial state $\Psi'_a(-\infty)$ by (6-10-1) and may be expressed in terms of an operator S according to the equation

$$\Psi'_b(+\infty) = S_{ab}\Psi'_a(-\infty) \tag{6-10-4}$$

6-11. EXCITATION AND IONIZATION OF THE HYDROGEN ATOM BY ELECTRON IMPACT

As stated earlier, there will be no further mention of time-dependent methods in this chapter. We now proceed to discuss some of the elementary features of time-independent inelastic collision theory. From the physical standpoint perhaps the simplest problem we could treat is that of excitation* of the hydrogen atom by proton impact, since here the target has the simplest structure of any atomic system, whereas the projectile is regarded as a structureless point possessing mass and charge. Furthermore, the projectile is dissimilar to the atomic electron, and there are no electron symmetry effects. Only "direct scattering" is possible (i.e., there is no electron exchange). However, the problem of electron impact excitation of the hydrogen atom is simpler in another sense, provided we ignore symmetry and exchange effects, since in this problem there is only a single heavy particle, namely, the nucleus of the target atom. This fact permits us to ignore the motion of the nucleus completely, for we may consider it to be at rest in the laboratory frame initially and further consider it to have infinite mass so that it will not recoil in the collision. If, in addition, we neglect electron spin, we are left with a problem which is truly simple (formally), yet which illustrates the basic method of attack for a large class of inelastic collisions. Having developed the solution for this prototype problem, we may see how to generalize it to account for the finite mass of the collision partners, structural complications, electron exchange and other rearrangement phenomena, symmetry effects, and electron spin. However, we do not wish to leave the impression that it is an easy matter to solve the problems we shall formulate. It is difficult to make detailed

---

* Here we use the term excitation in its broad sense to include ionization, which is, of course, the process of excitation to an unbound state in the continuum.

calculations on even the simplest systems, and the equations to which we are led in the consideration of complex systems are highly intractable, if not completely insoluble. Here we shall follow closely the definitive treatment of Mott and Massey.[112]

A. DEFINITION OF THE EXCITATION CROSS SECTION. Let us consider, then, a beam of monoenergetic electrons moving along the $-Z$ axis toward the origin of the laboratory system of coordinates, at which point the nucleus of a hydrogen atom assumed to be in its ground state is located. The intensity of the incident beam is taken to be one electron per unit cross sectional area per second. The number of electrons scattered per second through an angle ϑ into the solid angle $d\Omega_{\text{Lab}}$ after exciting the target atom into its nth state has the dimensions of area and equals the *differential cross section for excitation*, $I_{\text{on}}(\vartheta)\, d\Omega_{\text{Lab}}$ [cf. (1-4-2) and (1-4-3)]. The total cross section for excitation to state n is then

$$q_{0n} = \int_0^{2\pi} \int_0^{\pi} I_{0n}(\vartheta) \sin \vartheta \, d\vartheta \, d\varphi \qquad (6\text{-}11\text{-}1)$$

B. SEPARATION OF THE TIME AND SPACE DEPENDENCE OF THE WAVE FUNCTION. Since the nucleus of the target atom is so much heavier than the projectile and orbital electrons, the nucleus may be considered to remain at rest throughout the collision, and no term corresponding to nuclear kinetic energy appears in the time-dependent wave equation, which may be written

$$i\hbar \frac{\partial \Psi(\mathbf{r}_b, \mathbf{r}_a, t)}{\partial t} = \left[-\frac{\hbar^2}{2m_e} \nabla_{r_b}^2 - \frac{\hbar^2}{2m_e} \nabla_{r_a}^2 + V(\mathbf{r}_b, \mathbf{r}_a) \right] \Psi(\mathbf{r}_b, \mathbf{r}_a, t)$$

$$(6\text{-}11\text{-}2)$$

Here m_e is the electron mass and V is the interaction potential energy operator, given in terms of the beam electron coordinates $\mathbf{r}_b$, the atomic electron coordinates $\mathbf{r}_a$ and the interelectron distance r_{ba} by the expression

$$V(\mathbf{r}_b, \mathbf{r}_a) = -\frac{e^2}{r_b} - \frac{e^2}{r_a} + \frac{e^2}{r_{ba}} \qquad (6\text{-}11\text{-}3)$$

Since the potential energy does not depend explicitly on the time, we may separate the wave function $\Psi(\mathbf{r}_b, \mathbf{r}_a, t)$ into the product of two functions, one of which depends only on the spatial coordinates and the other only on the time:

$$\Psi(\mathbf{r}_b, \mathbf{r}_a, t) = \psi(\mathbf{r}_b, \mathbf{r}_a)\, \Phi(t) \qquad (6\text{-}11\text{-}4)$$

Equation 6-11-4 is a particular solution, but a general solution can be written as a sum of such separated solutions. If we substitute the right side of (6-11-4) into (6-11-2) and then divide each term of the resulting equation by the product $\psi\Phi$, we obtain

$$\frac{i\hbar}{\Phi}\frac{d\Phi}{dt} = \frac{1}{\psi}\left(-\frac{\hbar^2}{2m_e}\nabla_{r_b}^2\psi - \frac{\hbar^2}{2m_e}\nabla_{r_a}^2\psi + V\psi\right) \tag{6-11-5}$$

Since the left side of (6-11-5) depends only on the time and the right side only on the spatial coordinates, both sides must be equal to the same separation constant, which we denote E. We may readily integrate the resulting time equation to obtain the solution for Φ:

$$\Phi(t) = ce^{-iEt/\hbar} \tag{6-11-6}$$

where c is an arbitrary constant. The equation for ψ is the time-independent wave equation

$$\left[-\frac{\hbar^2}{2m_e}\nabla_{r_b}^2 - \frac{\hbar^2}{2m_e}\nabla_{r_a}^2 + V(\mathbf{r}_b, \mathbf{r}_a)\right]\psi(\mathbf{r}_b, \mathbf{r}_a) = E\psi(\mathbf{r}_b, \mathbf{r}_a) \tag{6-11-7}$$

Since (6-11-7) is homogeneous in ψ, the constant c may be chosen to normalize ψ. Then a particular solution of the time-dependent wave equation is

$$\Psi(\mathbf{r}_b, \mathbf{r}_a, t) = \psi(\mathbf{r}_b, \mathbf{r}_a)e^{-iEt/\hbar} \tag{6-11-8}$$

The quantum mechanical operator for the total energy of the system is $i\hbar(\partial/\partial t)$. If this operator is applied to the total wave function of the system given by (6-11-8), the following equation results:

$$i\hbar\frac{\partial\Psi}{\partial t} = E\Psi \tag{6-11-9}$$

This is an eigenvalue equation; Ψ is an eigenfunction of the operator appearing on the left side, and the constant E on the right is the corresponding eigenvalue. Thus we see that E is equal to the total energy of the system. We may evaluate E by equating it to the sum of the internal energy of the target atom in its ground state and the kinetic energy of the incident electron, $T_{\text{Lab}} = m_e v_0^2/2$, when it is far from the target. An energy eigenfunction like the Ψ of (6-11-8) is said to represent a stationary state of the system, since the probability density $\Psi^*\Psi$ associated with this wave function is independent of time.

C. CALCULATION OF THE EXCITATION CROSS SECTION.   Let us now expand the wave function $\psi(\mathbf{r}_b, \mathbf{r}_a)$ in terms of the complete set of eigenfunctions of the unperturbed hydrogen atom $u_n(\mathbf{r}_a)$ and functions $F_n(\mathbf{r}_b)$ representing the projectile electrons:

$$\psi(\mathbf{r}_b, \mathbf{r}_a) = \left(\sum_n + \int\right)u_n(\mathbf{r}_a) F_n(\mathbf{r}_b) \equiv \underset{n}{S}\, u_n(\mathbf{r}_a) F_n(\mathbf{r}_b) \tag{6-11-10}$$

The functions $u_n(\mathbf{r}_a)$ satisfy the equation

$$-\frac{\hbar^2}{2m_e} \nabla^2_{r_a} u_n - \frac{e^2}{r_a} u_n = E_n u_n \qquad (6\text{-}11\text{-}11)$$

where E_n is the energy of the hydrogen atom in its unperturbed nth state. In (6-11-10) we sum over the states of the discrete spectrum and integrate over the states of the continuous spectrum. Thus the expression for the cross section which we shall obtain will apply for ionization of the target as well as for excitation to a bound state. By substituting (6-11-10) into (6-11-7) and using (6-11-11), we obtain

$$\mathop{S}_{n} u_n(\mathbf{r}_a)\left[\frac{\hbar^2}{2m_e}\nabla^2_{r_b} + (E - E_n)\right]F_n(\mathbf{r}_b) = \left(\frac{e^2}{r_{ba}} - \frac{e^2}{r_b}\right)\psi(\mathbf{r}_b, \mathbf{r}_a) \quad (6\text{-}11\text{-}12)$$

Now we multiply both sides of this equation by $u_n{}^*(\mathbf{r}_a)$ and integrate over the spatial coordinates of the atomic electron. Because of the ortho-normality of the wave functions,

$$\left[\frac{\hbar^2}{2m_e}\nabla^2_{r_b} + (E - E_n)\right]F_n(\mathbf{r}_b) = \int\left(\frac{e^2}{r_{ba}} - \frac{e^2}{r_b}\right)\psi(\mathbf{r}_b, \mathbf{r}_a)u_n{}^*(\mathbf{r}_a)\,d\mathbf{r}_a$$

$$(6\text{-}11\text{-}13)$$

We note that the right side of (6-11-13) vanishes for large r_b, so that the functions $F_n(\mathbf{r}_b)$ become the wave functions for a free electron of energy $(E - E_n)$ at large r_b, where they satisfy the wave equation

$$\left[\nabla^2_{r_b} + \frac{2m_e}{\hbar^2}(E - E_n)\right]F_n(\mathbf{r}_b) = 0 \qquad (6\text{-}11\text{-}14)$$

The wavelength associated with this electron energy is $\lambda = 2\pi/\kappa_n$, where

$$\kappa_n{}^2 = \frac{2m_e(E - E_n)}{\hbar^2} \qquad (6\text{-}11\text{-}15)$$

We see that this wavelength is real only if $E > E_n$; that is, if the electron has enough energy to excite the nth state of the target atom. We shall consider only those values of n for which this condition is satisfied.

Since we have assumed the hydrogen atom to be in its ground state initially, the function $F_0(\mathbf{r}_b)$ must represent the sum of the incident electron wave and an elastically scattered electron wave. The other functions $F_n(\mathbf{r}_b)$ can represent only inelastically scattered waves. Consequently, the asymptotic forms of these wave functions are

$$F_0 \sim e^{i\kappa_0 z} + \frac{1}{r_b} e^{i\kappa_0 r_b} f_0(\vartheta) \qquad (6\text{-}11\text{-}16)$$

and

$$F_n \sim \frac{1}{r_b} e^{i\kappa_n r_b} f_n(\vartheta) \qquad (n = 1, 2, 3, \ldots) \qquad (6\text{-}11\text{-}17)$$

Equations 6-11-16 and 6-11-17 give the boundary conditions on the scattering. It follows from (6-11-17) that $r_b^{-2} |f_n(\vartheta)|^2$ is the number of electrons per unit volume at distance r_b from the target atom which have excited the atom to its nth state. The number of electrons which in one second cross unit area perpendicular to their direction of motion is proportional to $\kappa_n r_b^{-2} |f_n|^2$. Since the number of electrons in the incident beam crossing unit area per second is proportional to its wave number κ_0, the differential cross section for excitation of the atom from its ground state to the nth level is

$$I_{0n}(\vartheta) \, d\Omega_{\mathrm{Lab}} = \frac{\kappa_n}{\kappa_0} |f_n(\vartheta)|^2 \, d\Omega_{\mathrm{Lab}} \qquad (6\text{-}11\text{-}18)$$

(cf. Section 3-14). We see then that we need only the asymptotic form of the functions $F_n(\mathbf{r}_b)$ to obtain the excitation cross sections. However, the functions f_n cannot be calculated exactly, even though the wave functions for the unperturbed hydrogen atom are completely and exactly known. We must resort to approximate methods for their calculation. One of the most important and useful approximations is the *Born approximation*, which is valid at high impact velocities.

Before discussing the Born approximation, we shall rewrite (6-11-13) in a form that will prove more convenient and will also make clear the impossibility of obtaining an exact solution for the cross section. In doing this, we introduce the matrix that describes the interaction of the beam electron with the nucleus and orbital electron of the target atom. This matrix has elements

$$V_{mn} = \int u_n{}^*(\mathbf{r}_a) \left(\frac{e^2}{r_{ba}} - \frac{e^2}{r_b} \right) u_m(\mathbf{r}_a) \, d\mathbf{r}_a \qquad (6\text{-}11\text{-}19)$$

Then if we use (6-11-10) and (6-11-19) in (6-11-13) and introduce the wave number κ_n via (6-11-15), we obtain

$$\left(\nabla_{r_b}^2 + \kappa_n{}^2 - \frac{2m_e}{\hbar^2} V_{nn} \right) F_n(\mathbf{r}_b) = \frac{2m_e}{\hbar^2} \underset{m}{S'} V_{mn} F_m(\mathbf{r}_b) \qquad (6\text{-}11\text{-}20)$$

where the prime indicates that the term $m = n$ is to be omitted in the summation. Thus we see that we have an infinite set of coupled differential equations to solve in order to obtain the asymptotic form of the wave functions $F_n(\mathbf{r}_b)$. Clearly we must use approximate methods, and the approximations consist of selecting only the most important matrix elements and putting all the others equal to zero.

D. THE EXCITATION CROSS SECTION IN THE FIRST BORN APPROXIMATION.[117]

The basic assumption in the Born approximation is that there is little interaction between the projectile and target. Specifically we assume the following:

(1) The incident wave is undistorted by the interaction, so that we may represent the beam electron by an undistorted plane wave moving in the direction defined by the unit vector $\mathbf{n_0}$ (usually taken to have the direction of the polar axis):

$$F_0(\mathbf{r}_b) = \exp i\kappa_0 \mathbf{n}_0 \cdot \mathbf{r}_b$$

(2) Excitation to any final state n comes as the result of a direct transition from the initial state, and intermediate states play no significant role. Since there is then no coupling with intermediate states, we put $V_{mn} = 0$ for $m \neq 0$, where 0 designates the initial state.

(3) The potential energy of interaction between the scattered electron that produced the excitation and the atom in its final (nth) state is small, so that distortion of the scattered wave can be neglected. Since, according to the definition (6-11-19), V_{nn} is a measure of this interaction, we put $V_{nn} = 0$.

Thus we write the wave function for the system as

$$\psi(\mathbf{r}_b, \mathbf{r}_a) = \exp\left(i\kappa_0\mathbf{n}_0 \cdot \mathbf{r}_b\right) u_0(\mathbf{r}_a) \tag{6-11-21}$$

Under these assumptions, the infinite set of equations (6-11-20) reduces to a single equation for excitation to state n:

$$(\nabla_{r_b}^2 + \kappa_n^2)F_n(\mathbf{r}_b) = \frac{2m_e}{\hbar^2} V_{0n} \exp i\kappa_0\mathbf{n}_0 \cdot \mathbf{r}_b \tag{6-11-22}$$

Now only one matrix element $V_{0n} = V_{n0}$ is involved in each calculation. We must solve (6-11-22) subject to the boundary conditions

$$F_n(\mathbf{r}_b) \sim \frac{1}{r_b} f_n(\vartheta) \exp i\kappa_n\mathbf{n}_n \cdot \mathbf{r}_b$$
$$F_n(0) = 0 \tag{6-11-23}$$

As shown by Mott and Massey,[112] the solution of (6-11-22) with the correct asymptotic form is

$$F_n(\mathbf{r}) = \frac{m_e}{2\pi\hbar^2} \int \frac{e^{i\kappa_n|\mathbf{r}-\mathbf{r}_b|}}{|\mathbf{r} - \mathbf{r}_b|} \exp\left(i\kappa_0\mathbf{n}_0 \cdot \mathbf{r}_b\right) V_{0n}\, d\mathbf{r}_b \tag{6-11-24}$$

The asymptotic form of this solution is

$$F_n(\mathbf{r}) \sim \frac{m_e}{2\pi\hbar^2} \frac{1}{r} e^{i\kappa_n r} \int \exp\left[i(\kappa_0\mathbf{n}_0 - \kappa_n\mathbf{n}) \cdot \mathbf{r}_b\right] V_{0n}\, d\mathbf{r}_b \tag{6-11-25}$$

where $\mathbf{n}$ is a unit vector in the direction of the vector $\mathbf{r}$. Thus we finally obtain for the differential excitation cross section

$$I_{0n}(\vartheta)\, d\Omega_{\text{Lab}} = \frac{\kappa_n}{\kappa_0}\, |f_n(\vartheta)|^2\, d\Omega_{\text{Lab}}$$

$$= \frac{\kappa_n}{\kappa_0}\, \frac{m_e^{\;2}}{4\pi^2\hbar^4}\, \left| \int \exp\left[i(\kappa_0\mathbf{n}_0 - \kappa_n\mathbf{n})\cdot\mathbf{r}_b\right]V_{0n}\, d\mathbf{r}_b \right|^2 d\Omega_{\text{Lab}}$$

$$(6\text{-}11\text{-}26)$$

It is possible to extend this method by an iterative process and obtain the *second Born approximation* (cf. Section 3-16). However, this procedure is laborious, and it is better to start with more accurate initial approximations for the wave functions than to extend the Born approximation in order to achieve greater accuracy.

It is interesting to note that the cross section for elastic scattering can also be obtained in the Born approximation from the equations presented here. Let us suppose that the initial state and the final state are the same, and that no intermediate states are concerned. Then the matrix element appearing in (6-11-25) is, say,

$$V_{00} = \int u_0^*(\mathbf{r}_a)\left(\frac{e^2}{r_{ba}} - \frac{e^2}{r_b}\right) u_0(\mathbf{r}_a)\, d\mathbf{r}_a = V(\mathbf{r}') \qquad (6\text{-}11\text{-}27)$$

and we are led directly to (3-16-7), which we have already evaluated in Section 3-16.

6-12. GENERAL TWO-BODY COLLISIONS

Now we wish to generalize the results of the last section by extending our treatment to an arbitrary pair of colliding atomic or molecular structures and by removing the restriction that one of the structures can be considered to remain at rest in the laboratory frame. We shall describe the motion of the system of particles in terms of the motion of the center of mass of the entire system, the relative motion of the centers of mass of the two colliding structures, and the motion of the constituent particles of each structure relative to the center of mass of that structure. Since the motion of the center of mass of the complete system is inconsequential with respect to the calculation of cross sections, we shall ignore this contribution to the total motion.

To see how to generalize our previous discussion, we substitute the expression for the potential energy (6-11-3) into the wave equation (6-11-7) and expand the wave function as in (6-11-10). Then, if we substitute

$E = E_0 + m_e v_0^2/2$, we obtain, using only the $n=0$ term,

$$\left\{ u_0(\mathbf{r}_a)\left[\frac{\hbar^2}{2m_e} \nabla_{r_b}^2 F_0(\mathbf{r}_b) + \frac{m_e v_0^2}{2} F_0(\mathbf{r}_b) \right] + F_0(\mathbf{r}_b)\left[\frac{\hbar^2}{2m_e} \nabla_{r_a}^2 u_0(\mathbf{r}_a) \right. \right.$$

$$\left. + \left(E_0 + \frac{e^2}{r_a} \right) u_0(\mathbf{r}_a) \right] + \left(\frac{e^2}{r_b} - \frac{e^2}{r_{ba}} \right) u_0(\mathbf{r}_a) F_0(\mathbf{r}_b) \right\} = 0 \quad (6\text{-}12\text{-}1)$$

where, as we have said, E_0 is the total energy of the target atom in its ground state. The first term in square brackets in (6-12-1) clearly corresponds to the unperturbed motion of the incident electron, the second term in square brackets, to the internal motion of the unperturbed target, and the final term, to the negative of the energy of interaction between the projectile and target. We must have a term similar to each of these terms in the wave equation for the generalized problem. (Furthermore, in this wave equation there should be a term corresponding to the motion of the center of mass of the entire system, but we have already justified its omission. This term did not appear in the generalization of the prototype problem, since in it the center of mass of the entire system was taken to be stationary in the laboratory frame.)

In the general problem, then, the first term above is to be replaced by one describing the relative motion of the two structures:

$$\left(\frac{\hbar^2}{2M_r} \nabla_r^2 + \frac{M_r v_0^2}{2} \right) F(\mathbf{r}) \quad (6\text{-}12\text{-}2)$$

Here $\mathbf{r}$ denotes the relative coordinates, that is, the spatial coordinates of the center of mass of one structure relative to that of the other; M_r represents the reduced mass of the two structures, and v_0 is their relative speed of approach when they are still widely separated, that is, before they begin to interact.

Next we need to consider the internal motions of the two collision partners. These motions are described by the equations

$$[H_A(\mathbf{r}_A) - E_A] u(\mathbf{r}_A) = 0$$

and $\qquad\qquad\qquad\qquad\qquad\qquad\qquad\qquad\qquad (6\text{-}12\text{-}3)$

$$[H_B(\mathbf{r}_B) - E_B] v(\mathbf{r}_B) = 0$$

where H_A and H_B are the Hamiltonians of the two unperturbed structures. These wave equations are satisfied by the sets of eigenfunctions and eigenvalues $[u_k(\mathbf{r}_A), E_A{}^k]$ and $[v_l(\mathbf{r}_B), E_B{}^l]$. To simplify the notation, we shall not distinguish these two sets of eigenfunctions, but we designate each pair of states of the two structures by a single index n. We may then write the composite wave function of the two structures $\xi_n(\mathbf{r}_A, \mathbf{r}_B)$ as the product of the two functions $u_k(\mathbf{r}_A) v_l(\mathbf{r}_B)$, and the corresponding energy eigenvalue

E_n will be the sum $E_A{}^k + E_B{}^l$. The wave function ξ_n will satisfy the equation

$$[H_A(\mathbf{r}_A) + H_B(\mathbf{r}_B) - E_A - E_B]\xi = 0 \tag{6-12-4}$$

If, finally, we generalize the interaction term by introducing the potential energy $V(\mathbf{r}, \mathbf{r}_A, \mathbf{r}_B)$, we obtain the complete time-independent wave equation for the entire system, except for the trivial motion of its center of mass:

$$\left[\frac{\hbar^2}{2M_r}\nabla_r{}^2 - H_A(\mathbf{r}_A) - H_B(\mathbf{r}_B) + \frac{M_r v_0{}^2}{2} + E_0 - V(\mathbf{r}, \mathbf{r}_A, \mathbf{r}_B)\right]\xi = 0 \tag{6-12-5}$$

Proceeding then by the method of Section 6-11, we may show that the differential cross section in the center-of-mass coordinate frame for excitation from state p to state q of the combined system is, in the first Born approximation,

$$I_{pq}(\Theta)\, d\Omega_{\mathrm{CM}} = \frac{M_r{}^2}{4\pi^2\hbar^4}\frac{\kappa_q}{\kappa_p}$$

$$\times \left| \iiint V(\mathbf{r}, \mathbf{r}_A, \mathbf{r}_B) \exp\left[i(\kappa_p\mathbf{n}_0 - \kappa_q\mathbf{n}) \cdot \mathbf{r}\right]\right.$$

where

$$\left. \times\ \xi_q{}^*(\mathbf{r}_A, \mathbf{r}_B)\, \xi_p(\mathbf{r}_A, \mathbf{r}_B)\, d\mathbf{r}_A\, d\mathbf{r}_B\, d\mathbf{r} \right|^2 d\Omega_{\mathrm{CM}} \tag{6-12-6}$$

$$\kappa_p = \frac{M_r v_0}{\hbar}$$

$$\kappa_q{}^2 = \frac{2M_r}{\hbar^2}\left(\frac{M_r v_0{}^2}{2} + E_p - E_q\right) \tag{6-12-7}$$

and $\mathbf{v}_0$ is the initial velocity of approach of the colliding structures. The cross section in the coordinate system in which one of the structures is at rest initially may be obtained by applying (1-4-16).

6-13. REARRANGEMENT COLLISIONS

Electron exchange scattering, charge transfer and ion-molecule reactions, ion-atom interchange collisions, and other reactions in which there is a transfer of particles between the colliding structures require special consideration. In this section we shall show how the results of Sections 6-11 and 6-12 may be generalized to describe these *rearrangement collisions*.

A. EXCHANGE COLLISIONS BETWEEN ELECTRONS AND HYDROGEN ATOMS. The simplest rearrangement collision is *exchange scattering* of a free electron by a hydrogen atom initially at rest in its ground state. In this case the incident electron is captured into the nth level of the atom, and the orbital electron is ejected into the continuum.

We have already derived the basic equations describing *direct scattering*, in which the incident electron produces excitation to state n but remains in the continuum after the impact. In doing so, we expanded the wave function of the system in the form

$$\psi(\mathbf{r}_b, \mathbf{r}_a) = \underset{n}{S}\, u_n(\mathbf{r}_a)\, F_n(\mathbf{r}_b) \tag{6-11-10}$$

where $\mathbf{r}_b$ and $\mathbf{r}_a$ denote the laboratory coordinates of the beam and atomic electrons, respectively. As shown in (6-11-16), $F_0(\mathbf{r}_b)$ represents the sum of the incident wave and a scattered wave. If the height of the excited state n above the ground state $(E_n - E_0)$ is smaller than the initial kinetic energy of the incident electron (T_0), $F_n(\mathbf{r}_b)$ represents a scattered wave and is described, as in (6-11-17), by an exponential function with an imaginary exponent which corresponds to an undamped wave. If, on the other hand, $E_n - E_0 > T_0$, $F_n(\mathbf{r}_b)$ cannot correspond to an undamped scattered wave, hence must be described by an exponential with a negative real exponent:

$$F_n(\mathbf{r}_b) \sim r_b^{-1} e^{-k_n r_b} f_n(\vartheta) \qquad (E_n - E_0 > T_0) \tag{6-13-1}$$

where $k_n^2 = -\kappa_n^2$, and κ_n^2 is given by (6-11-15). These values of n relate to the possibility of capture of the incident electron and ejection of the atomic electron. To obtain the cross section for exchange collisions, we expand the wave function of the system in the alternate form

$$\psi(\mathbf{r}_b, \mathbf{r}_a) = \underset{n}{S}\, u_n(\mathbf{r}_b) G_n(\mathbf{r}_a) \tag{6-13-2}$$

Then, if we assume that the functions G_n have the asymptotic form

$$G_n(\mathbf{r}_a) \sim r_a^{-1} e^{i\kappa_n r_a}\, g_n(\vartheta) \tag{6-13-3}$$

the differential cross section for capture of the incident electron into the nth state and ejection of the atomic electron into the solid angle $d\Omega_{\text{Lab}}$ is

$$I_{0n}(\vartheta)\, d\Omega_{\text{Lab}} = \frac{\kappa_n}{\kappa_0}\, |g_n(\vartheta)|^2\, d\Omega_{\text{Lab}} \tag{6-13-4}$$

[cf. (6-11-18)]. Here we have treated the beam and atomic electrons as distinguishable, but this is permissible only if their spins are antiparallel. The method for obtaining the cross section for the general case in which the incident beam is unpolarized is discussed later in this section.

To calculate $G_n(\mathbf{r}_a)$, we substitute (6-13-3) into the wave equation (6-11-7), multiply by $u_n^*(\mathbf{r}_b)$, and integrate over the spatial coordinates of the beam electron to obtain

$$\left[\frac{\hbar^2}{2m_e} \nabla_{r_a}^2 + (E - E_n) \right] G_n(\mathbf{r}_a) = \int \left(\frac{e^2}{r_{ba}} - \frac{e^2}{r_a} \right) \psi(\mathbf{r}_b, \mathbf{r}_a)\, u_n^*(\mathbf{r}_b)\, d\mathbf{r}_b \tag{6-13-5}$$

[cf. (6-11-13)]. Equation 6-13-5 is exact, but we can obtain only approximate solutions to it. We assume some appropriate form for ψ on the right side of (6-13-5) and seek a solution of the form (6-13-3) by the methods used in Section 6-11.

To obtain a solution in the *first Born approximation*, we take

$$\psi(\mathbf{r}_b, \mathbf{r}_a) = \exp(i\kappa_0 \mathbf{n}_0 \cdot \mathbf{r}_b) u_0(\mathbf{r}_a) \tag{6-13-6}$$

on the right side of (6-13-5) and find (by the method described by Mott and Massey,[112] Chapter VI)

$$G_n(\mathbf{r}_a) \sim \frac{m_e}{2\pi\hbar^2} \frac{1}{r_a} e^{i\kappa_n r_a}$$
$$\times \iint \left(\frac{e^2}{r_a} - \frac{e^2}{r_{ba}}\right) u_n^*(\mathbf{r}_b) u_0(\mathbf{r}_a) \exp\left[i(\kappa_0 \mathbf{n}_0 \cdot \mathbf{r}_b - \kappa_n \mathbf{n} \cdot \mathbf{r}_a)\right] d\mathbf{r}_b d\mathbf{r}_a \tag{6-13-7}$$

where $\mathbf{n}$ is a unit vector in the direction of the ejected electron. The wave function (6-13-6) does not satisfy the orthogonality conditions

$$\int [\psi(\mathbf{r}_b, \mathbf{r}_a) - F_n(\mathbf{r}_b) u_n(\mathbf{r}_a)] u_n^*(\mathbf{r}_a) d\mathbf{r}_a = 0$$
$$\int [\psi(\mathbf{r}_b, \mathbf{r}_a) - G_n(\mathbf{r}_a) u_n(\mathbf{r}_b)] u_n^*(\mathbf{r}_b) d\mathbf{r}_b = 0 \tag{6-13-8}$$

which are satisfied by the true wave function, but the error is small for high impact velocity.

We must now take note that in (6-13-5) it is not really clear whether we should use the post interaction (e^2/r_a), which is the energy of interaction between the ejected atomic electron and the nucleus, or the prior interaction (e^2/r_b), which is that between the incident beam electron and the nucleus. This uncertainty causes no concern if the wave functions u_0 and u_n are exact solutions of the wave equation, since in this case the two interactions give the same result.[118] (Because of detailed balancing, we should be able to reverse the time in the wave equation and obtain the same cross section by viewing the collision in the reverse direction.) However, if only approximate wave equations are available, the two interaction terms do not give the same result, and it is uncertain whether we should use the prior or post interaction or some mean of the two.

The expression

$$g_n(\vartheta) = \frac{m_e}{2\pi\hbar^2} \iint \left(\frac{e^2}{r_b} - \frac{e^2}{r_{ba}}\right) u_n^*(\mathbf{r}_b) u_0(\mathbf{r}_a) \exp\left[i(\kappa_0 \mathbf{n}_0 \cdot \mathbf{r}_b - \kappa_n \mathbf{n} \cdot \mathbf{r}_a\right] d\mathbf{r}_b d\mathbf{r}_a \tag{6-13-9}$$

for the exchange amplitude was first used by Oppenheimer[119] and the approximation in which it appears is referred to as the *Born-Oppenheimer approximation.** Bates et al.[118] have studied the applicability of this approximation and have shown that generally it yields poor results for electron excitation of bound states. In the treatment of ionization account must be taken of symmetry in the final state.†

B. THE EFFECT OF THE EXCLUSION PRINCIPLE ON EXCHANGE SCATTERING.[120]
Since the incident and atomic electrons are identical particles obeying Fermi-Dirac Statistics, we need to consider the effect of the Pauli principle on the scattering. To do this, we must introduce the electron spin into the wave function for the system and furthermore require that this wave function be antisymmetric (cf. Section 3-18). For scattering of electrons by hydrogen atoms we seek a solution of the form

$$\psi = \underset{n}{S} \{[u_n(\mathbf{r}_b) \, w_n{}^+(\mathbf{r}_a) + u_n(\mathbf{r}_a) \, w_n{}^+(\mathbf{r}_b)]\chi_s$$

$$+ [u_n(\mathbf{r}_b) \, w_n{}^-(\mathbf{r}_a) - u_n(\mathbf{r}_a) \, w_n{}^-(\mathbf{r}_b)]\chi_t\} \qquad (6\text{-}13\text{-}10)$$

where u_n and $w_n{}^\pm$ are the wave functions of the bound and free electrons, respectively, and χ_s and χ_t are the singlet and triplet electron spin functions. The summation is carried out over all possible spatial and spin states. Then, solving the wave equation and putting in the statistical weighting factors described in Section 3-18, we find that the differential cross section for a beam of *unpolarized electrons* has the form[114]

$$I_{0n}(\vartheta) \, d\Omega_{\text{Lab}} = \frac{\kappa_n}{\kappa_0} \left(\tfrac{1}{4} \, |f_n + g_n|^2 + \tfrac{3}{4} \, |f_n - g_n|^2\right) d\Omega_{\text{Lab}} \qquad (6\text{-}13\text{-}11)$$

This expression gives the cross section for scattering *or* ejecting an electron into the element of solid angle $d\Omega_{\text{Lab}}$, with excitation of the hydrogen atom from its ground state to the nth level. The same approach indicated here is followed for electron scattering by other targets, with the form of the linear combination of f and g being determined by the number of electrons and the multiplicities of the states involved.

C. GENERAL REARRANGEMENT COLLISIONS. We now want to obtain the probability that two structures A and B, in states k and l, respectively, will collide, become rearranged, and produce structures C and D in states p and q, respectively. The results will be applicable, for example, to the

---

* This approximation is separate and distinct from the Born-Oppenheimer approximation used in the discussion of molecular energy levels (see Section 8-1-B).
† See R. Peterkop, *Proc. Phys. Soc. (London)* 77, 1220 (1961); S. Geltman, M. R. H. Rudge, and M. J. Seaton, *Proc. Phys. Soc. (London)* 81, 375 (1963); M. R. C. McDowell and J. H. Williamson, *Physics Letters* 4, 159 (1963).

treatment of charge transfer. We express the wave equation for the complete system (neglecting the motion of its center of mass) in the form that is most convenient for discussion of the final structures C and D:

$$\left[-\frac{\hbar^2}{2M_r'}\nabla_\rho'^2 + H_C(\mathbf{r}_C) + H_D(\mathbf{r}_D) + V(\mathbf{r}_C, \mathbf{r}_D, \boldsymbol{\rho}) - E\right]\zeta = 0 \quad (6\text{-}13\text{-}12)$$

Here $\boldsymbol{\rho}$ denotes the relative coordinates of the centers of mass of the *final* structures, whereas $\mathbf{r}_C$ and $\mathbf{r}_D$ refer to the internal coordinates of C and D with respect to their centers of mass; M_r' designates the reduced mass of the final system, $M_C M_D/(M_C + M_D)$. H_C and H_D are the Hamiltonian operators of the internal motion of the structures C and D, and $V(\mathbf{r}_C, \mathbf{r}_D, \boldsymbol{\rho})$ is the energy of interaction between C and D. The similarity of (6-13-12) to (6-12-5) is obvious.

We shall distinguish a pair of stationary states of the initial structures A and B by the index n and write the corresponding composite wave function as $\xi_n(\mathbf{r}_A, \mathbf{r}_B)$ and the energy as E_n. Likewise, a particular pair of stationary states of the final structures C and D will be distinguished by the index s, with composite wave function $\zeta_s(\mathbf{r}_C, \mathbf{r}_D)$ and energy E_s; $\zeta_s(\mathbf{r}_C, \mathbf{r}_D)$ is the product of the two wave functions, $x_i(\mathbf{r}_C)$ and $y_j(\mathbf{r}_D)$, of the separate structures C and D, and E_s is the sum of the corresponding energy values, $E_C{}^i$ and $E_D{}^j$. By generalizing the results of Section 6-13-A, we obtain *in the Born approximation*

$$I_{ns}(\Theta)\, d\Omega_{CM} = \frac{M_r'^2}{4\pi^2\hbar^4}\frac{\kappa_s}{\kappa_n}\left|\iiint V(\mathbf{r}_C, \mathbf{r}_D, \boldsymbol{\rho})\exp\left[i(\kappa_n\mathbf{n}_0\cdot\mathbf{r} - \kappa_s'\mathbf{n}\cdot\boldsymbol{\rho})\right]\right.$$

$$\left.\times\ \xi_n(\mathbf{r}_A, \mathbf{r}_B)\,\zeta_s(\mathbf{r}_C, \mathbf{r}_D)\,d\mathbf{r}_A\,d\mathbf{r}_B\,d\boldsymbol{\rho}\right|^2 d\Omega_{CM} \quad (6\text{-}13\text{-}13)$$

as the differential cross section (in the relative coordinates $\boldsymbol{\rho}$) for the rearrangement reaction in which the sth state of the C–D system is excited from the nth state of the A–B system. Here $\kappa_n = M_r v_0/\hbar$ and $\kappa_s' = M_r' v_s/\hbar$, where $\mathbf{v}_0$ and $\mathbf{v}_s$ are the initial and final relative velocities, respectively. In (6-13-13) $\mathbf{r}$ denotes the relative coordinates of the centers of mass of the initial structures A and B.

6-14. QUANTUM MECHANICAL APPROXIMATIONS

The discussion of the last three sections indicates that it is impossible to obtain exact solutions for atomic collision cross sections. In most instances the requisite wave functions are not known with complete accuracy, and the approximate wave functions on which we must rely are frequently not orthogonal. One serious difficulty is the *post-prior discrepancy*, an example of which has already been given in Section 6-13-A.

Evidently, as the structural complexity of the colliding systems increases, the difficulty of obtaining good wave functions also increases and more complex reactions become possible. Calculations on molecular systems are particularly difficult. To make matters worse, the structure of the equations to be solved is such that approximate methods must be used even if the necessary wave functions are completely and exactly known, as in the case of the hydrogen atom. A few of these approximate methods are discussed in this section.

It should be pointed out that the range of validity of these approximations depends to a considerable degree on the masses of the colliding structures. In particular, collisions of free electrons differ significantly from heavy particle collisions because the masses of atomic systems are so much greater than the mass of an electron. In a collision between heavy particles the energy of relative motion exceeds the threshold energy for inelastic reactions down to much lower relative velocities than in the electron impact case. This fact is important because the relative velocity, rather than the energy, is the parameter that generally determines which of the prospective approximations might be acceptable, and in many instances, the lower the relative velocity, the more refined the approximation must be if it is to be satisfactory.

A. THE BORN APPROXIMATION; THE BORN-OPPENHEIMER (BO) APPROXIMATION.   The Born approximation has already been discussed in Sections 6-11 through 6-13. It is valid in the case of high velocity impacts, but accurate cross sections can be obtained by its use only if accurate wave functions for the stationary states of the colliding structures are available. At low relative velocities the Born approximation generally overestimates the cross section, although it can be used at very low impact energies, provided the interaction energy is too shallow to accommodate a bound state of the interacting system.[121] Mention of the Born-Oppenheimer approximation was made in Section 6-13-A.

B. THE DISTORTED WAVE (DW) APPROXIMATION.   The starting point for discussion of this approximation is the infinite set of coupled differential equations (6-11-20), derived for the excitation of hydrogen atoms by electron impact but capable of being generalized to more complex systems and other collisions. These equations may be solved in the Born approximation by representing the incident beam electron by an undistorted plane wave

$$F_0(\mathbf{r}_b) = \exp i\kappa_0 \mathbf{n}_0 \cdot \mathbf{r}_b$$

and taking the interaction matrix elements V_{nn} and V_{mn} to be zero except for $m = 0$, where 0 designates the initial state and n the final state of the system. As the relative impact velocity decreases, we try to improve on this approximation by considering more terms on the right side of (6-11-20). The *distorted wave*, or *distortion, approximation* ignores transitions through intermediate states (as does the Born) but takes account of the distortion of the incident and scattered waves by the field of the target. The distortion is allowed for by retaining the matrix elements V_{0n}, V_{nn}, and V_{00}; all the other elements are set equal to zero. The infinite set of equations (6-11-20) then reduces to the pair of equations

$$\left(\nabla^2 + \kappa_0^2 - \frac{2m_e}{\hbar^2} V_{00}\right) F_0 = \frac{2m_e}{\hbar^2} V_{0n} F_n \tag{6-14-1}$$

$$\left(\nabla^2 + \kappa_n^2 - \frac{2m_e}{\hbar^2} V_{nn}\right) F_n = \frac{2m_e}{\hbar^2} V_{0n} F_0 \tag{6-14-2}$$

The additional approximation is made in the distorted wave method of neglecting the term on the right side of (6-14-1) on the grounds that F_n will usually be much smaller than F_0 (weak coupling). This approximation may not be justified, however, if the matrix element V_{0n} is not small and there is strong coupling between (6-14-1) and (6-14-2). If weak coupling is assumed, the first equation may be solved to give a function with asymptotic form

$$F_0 \sim e^{i\kappa_0 z} + r^{-1} e^{i\kappa_0 r} f_0(\vartheta) \tag{6-14-3}$$

When this solution is put into the second equation, a solution is found for it with asymptotic form

$$F_n \sim r^{-1} e^{i\kappa_n r} f_n(\vartheta) \tag{6-14-4}$$

The function in (6-14-3) represents the incident particle. It corresponds to a distorted wave with the asymptotic form of a plane wave plus an outgoing spherical wave. The scattered particle is represented by a distorted wave function with the asymptotic form of an outgoing spherical wave.[112,114]

If the coupling constant V_{0n} is so large that the right side of (6-14-1) cannot be set to zero (strong coupling), we may reduce (6-11-20) to a set of simultaneous ordinary differential equations which can be solved numerically.[114]

C. THE PERTURBED STATIONARY STATE (PSS) AND PERTURBED ROTATING ATOM (PRA) APPROXIMATIONS. The number of matrix elements which are important in the description of the interaction between colliding systems generally increases rapidly as the relative impact velocity decreases, so that the use of the distorted wave or second Born approximation does not permit reliable calculations to be made at much lower velocities than does the first Born approximation. It is evident that slow collisions cannot be accurately treated by expanding the wave function of the system in terms of the eigenfunctions of the isolated target, but Mott[122] suggested that it might be legitimate to perform the expansion in terms of the eigenfunctions that would describe the quasi-molecule formed by the colliding structures if their relative position vector were momentarily fixed in space. This assumption is equivalent to what is frequently called the *perturbed stationary state* (PSS) *approximation*. It allows for the gradual nature of the collision in the near-adiabatic region by treating the kinetic energy of relative motion as a perturbation.

The PSS approximation is unfortunately not satisfactory except for symmetric resonance charge transfer.[113,115] For other reactions, at any given impact velocity, collisions at sufficiently small impact parameters generally are not nearly adiabatic, as assumed, because of the rapid rotation of the internuclear axis, and these close impacts normally give the dominant contribution to the calculated cross section at low energies. However, close encounters make only a small contribution to the cross section for symmetric resonance charge transfer at low velocities, for the probability of this reaction is high up to very large values of the impact parameter.[115]

Originally it was mistakenly assumed that transitions are unlikely between states of the quasi-molecule formed by the slowly interacting bodies and that consequently the only matrix element which need be considered is that joining the states of the quasi-molecule tending to the initial and final states of the target in the separated atoms limit. It was also widely believed until recently that this formulation of the PSS approximation tends to the first Born approximation in the limit of weak interactions and high velocities, but this is not true because of the rotation of the internuclear axis during the collision.

As Bates[115] points out, the PSS approximation is best understood by examining its true limit, the *perturbed rotating atom* (*PRA*) *approximation*,[123] in which the eigenfunctions and eigenenergies of the quasi-molecule are replaced by those of the target perturbed by the projectile, the same rotating frame of reference being used as in the PSS approximation. (Actually, the eigenenergies of the isolated target are used in practice, the error thereby introduced being small at high velocities.) At any given relative velocity the assumption that the interaction of the projectile causes the eigenfunctions to follow the rotation of the internuclear axis is invalid if the impact parameter b is less than some value b_1 or greater than some value b_2. For $b < b_1$ the rotation is too rapid, whereas for $b > b_2$ the interaction is too weak. As the impact velocity is increased, b_1 becomes larger and b_2, smaller, and at sufficiently high v_0 the assumption concerning the eigenfunctions is obviously invalid.

In the PRA approximation there is strong coupling between states differing only in magnetic quantum number, this coupling being a manifestation of the reluctance of the eigenfunctions to follow the rotation of the internuclear axis. When this coupling is allowed for, the modified PRA approximation tends to the first Born approximation in the weak interaction and high velocity limits. Account must also be taken of coupling terms in the PSS approximation, particularly those terms that connect the initial and final states to states differing only in magnetic quantum number either in the combined atom limit or in the separated atoms limit. Because the need for retaining these terms was only recently realized, all published PSS calculations of inelastic cross sections are incorrect.[115] (Symmetric resonance charge transfer does not fall in this category.)

D. OTHER APPROXIMATIONS.   Many other approximations of less general applicability than those described have been used in various cross section calculations. These approximations, which are usually designated by the initials of the investigators who first applied them, are too numerous to describe here, and the reader is referred to Bates[115] and Wu and Ohmura[116] for discussions of them. Here we shall mention only the *Oppenheimer-Brinkman-Kramers (OBK) approximation*, which is frequently cited in the literature. The OBK approximation amounts to the neglect of the nuclear-nuclear interaction term in the quantal treatment of charge transfer. Oppenheimer[124] and Brinkman and Kramers[125] used only the electron-nuclear interaction in their early discussion of electron capture by bare nuclei on the grounds that the nuclear-nuclear term arose because of the nonorthogonality of the wave functions. They also argued that the latter term is physically unrealistic in that it should not appreciably influence the probability of charge transfer occurring. More refined treatments of this problem are discussed in the review paper by Bates and McCarroll[13] and in the review by Bates.[115]

6-15. SEMICLASSICAL AND CLASSICAL METHODS

A. THE SEMICLASSICAL IMPACT PARAMETER METHOD.   Most of the calculations[115,116] performed by applying the foregoing approximations to specific heavy particle collisions were made in the *impact parameter formulation*, in which the nuclei of the colliding systems are regarded as classical particles. Because of the great relative mass of the nuclei, their motion may be described by classical trajectories, which may be considered rectilinear if the relative velocity is sufficiently high that momentum and energy transfers may be neglected. Quantum mechanics must be used however, to treat the electronic motions, so that the impact parameter method is semiclassical. The impact parameter plays the role of the angular momentum through the relationship

$$M_r v_0 b = l\hbar \qquad (6\text{-}15\text{-}1)$$

B. THE CLASSICAL METHOD OF GRYZIŃSKI.* Gryziński[126] has developed an approach to atomic collisions based on the assumption that the interaction between a charged projectile and an atom can be described classically by the Coulomb interaction between the projectile and the atomic electrons. His results depend in first approximation on the binding energy and momentum distribution of the atomic electrons treated quantum mechanically. Gryziński used the results of Chandrasekhar and Williamson,[127] who calculated the energy transfer between two colliding particles moving arbitrarily with respect to one another and interacting through an inverse square law force. Their results were obtained classically in terms of general kinematic parameters describing the collision. Gryziński integrated these results over distributions of the collision parameters corresponding to the impact of projectiles on free electrons with velocity distributions appropriate to the quantum mechanical state of the fixed target atom to obtain $q(\Delta E)\, d(\Delta E)$, the classical cross section for scattering an incident particle with change in laboratory energy ΔE. The curvature of the electron paths in the field of the nucleus is approximately accounted for in the integration over the electron angular distribution. He also separately calculated $I(\Delta E, \vartheta)\, d\Omega_{\text{Lab}}$, the cross section for scattering at angle ϑ with energy change ΔE.

The cross section for a collision with energy loss greater than U is

$$q(U) = \int_U^{\Delta E_{\max}} q(\Delta E)\, d(\Delta E) \qquad (6\text{-}15\text{-}2)$$

and similarly the cross section for an encounter with loss of energy in the interval $U_1 \leq \Delta E \leq U_2$ is

$$q(U_2, U_1) = \int_{U_1}^{U_2} q(\Delta E)\, d(\Delta E) \qquad (6\text{-}15\text{-}3)$$

* For the most recent discussions of the classical method, see the papers presented by M. Gryziński and A. Burgess at the Third International Conference on the Physics of Electronic and Atomic Collisions (London, 1963) and the paper which Gryziński delivered at the Sixth International Conference on Ionization Phenomena in Gases (Paris, 1963).

Gryziński assumes that the cross section for ionization of an atom is given simply by the classical cross section for transfer of at least as much as the ionization energy to the electron treated as a free particle but with a speed distribution appropriate to its bound initial state. Thus the ionization cross section for an atom is

$$q^+ = \sum_i \int_0^\infty N^i(v_e) \, q(U_+{}^i) \, dv_e \qquad (6\text{-}15\text{-}4)$$

where $N^i(v_e)$ is the velocity distribution of i-shell electrons in the atom and $U_+{}^i$ their ionization energy. For the simplest case $N^i(v_e)$ is approximated by the single velocity obtained from the expectation value of the kinetic energy appropriate to an electron in the ith shell.

Likewise, the cross section for excitation of an atom to the level n is represented as the classical cross section for transfer of an amount of energy between $U_n{}^i$ and U_{n+1}^i, these quantities being the quantum energies of levels n and $n + 1$, respectively. Thus the cross section for excitation of the level n is

$$q_{0n} = \sum_i \int_0^\infty N^i(v_e) \, q(U_{n+1}^i, U_n{}^i) \, dv_e \qquad (6\text{-}15\text{-}5)$$

Quantal effects are thus considered only indirectly, by restricting the energy transfer to the electron to values compatible with the fact that it is bound in a quantized state and by the use of a speed distribution for the electrons deduced from the quantum mechanical description of the initial state.

Gryziński[126] has calculated the velocity distribution of electrons scattered and ejected from helium atoms under the impact of 100-ev primary electrons. He also computed the ionization cross sections for H_2 and He and the cross section for K-shell ionization of Ag and Ni by electron impact, as well as the electron excitation cross sections for several transitions in He, Hg, and Na. Good agreement with experiment was claimed in each case,* which is surprising in light of some of the assumptions made in the theory. Gryziński's theory, however, gives relatively inaccurate results for the angular distribution of inelastically scattered 200-ev electrons on H_2; the disagreement, according to Gryziński, was the result of influence of the potential field of the entire atom on the motion of the projectile.[126]

---

* R. G. Alsmiller has repeated these calculations and discovered that the Gryziński method actually gives poor agreement with experiment in the case of excitation of He and Hg. In a private communication to Dr. Alsmiller (1961) Gryziński acknowledged this fact and stated that his numerical results for these calculations had been incorrectly plotted in Fig. 9 of his 1959 paper. Alsmiller also found an algebraic error in this paper and corrected it in Ref. 128.

Because of the comparative ease of making calculations in the Gryziński formulation, it is obviously important to ascertain the limits of usefulness of this approximation. Some progress along these lines has already been made. Alsmiller[128] has used the Gryziński approach to calculate the cross sections for dissociation and ionization of the H_2^+ ion by both electrons and protons. His results for dissociation by electrons differed significantly from those obtained in the Born approximation,[129] but only minor differences appeared in the proton case. No other theoretical data were available for comparison with Alsmiller's ionization cross sections for H_2^+. Results that Alsmiller obtained in the Gryziński formulation for ionization of H_2 molecules by proton impact agreed reasonably well with experiment, but were about 20% too low. Recent unpublished calculations by Alsmiller on the ionization of lithium atoms by electrons gave cross sections much larger than provided by the Born approximation. This disagreement may indicate that the Gryziński approach is not suitable for use on systems with loosely bound electrons, since $q(\Delta E)$ becomes large as ΔE becomes small.

Rudd and Jorgensen[75] have used the Gryziński method for calculations on the ionization of H_2 and He by proton impact. Their calculated total cross sections for He are compared with experiment and with the Born approximation predictions in Fig. 6-7-3, and the agreement is seen to be quite good. However, their calculated cross sections for electron ejection integrated over all angles but differential in electron energy agree with the Born predictions only within factors of 2 to 5.

6-16. THE IONIZATION OF ATOMS BY FAST ELECTRONS AND IONS

In closing this chapter we shall discuss in some detail the ionization of atoms by fast electrons and ions, for this problem has received considerable attention both theoretically and experimentally. The first step in this discussion is to develop the expression for the total ionization cross section in the Born approximation.

A. THE TOTAL IONIZATION CROSS SECTION IN THE FIRST BORN APPROXIMATION. We start with (6-11-26) which gives the differential cross section, in the Born approximation, for direct electron impact excitation of a hydrogen atom from its ground state to state n:

$$I_{0n}(\vartheta)\, d\Omega_{\text{Lab}} = \frac{m_e^2}{4\pi^2\hbar^4} \frac{\kappa_n}{\kappa_0} \left| \int \exp\left[i(\kappa_0 \mathbf{n}_0 - \kappa_n \mathbf{n}) \cdot \mathbf{r}_b\right] V_{0n}(\mathbf{r}_b)\, d\mathbf{r}_b \right|^2 d\Omega_{\text{Lab}}$$

$$(6\text{-}16\text{-}1)$$

Here κ_0 and κ_n are the wave numbers of the projectile electron before and after the collision, respectively, and $\mathbf{n}_0$ and $\mathbf{n}$ are unit vectors in the directions of incidence and scattering. This equation is expressed in laboratory coordinates and applies to the case in which the target nucleus is considered to remain at rest at the origin of the laboratory frame. We may generalize it to apply to a target atom with N electrons and nuclear charge $+Ne$ by writing the interaction energy matrix element in the form

$$V_{0n}(\mathbf{r}_b) = \int \sum_{i=1}^{N} u_n^*(\mathbf{r}_1, \ldots, \mathbf{r}_N) \left(\frac{e^2}{r_{bi}} - \frac{Ne^2}{r_b} \right) u_0(\mathbf{r}_1, \ldots, \mathbf{r}_N) \, d\mathbf{r}_1 \cdots d\mathbf{r}_N$$

$$(6\text{-}16\text{-}2)$$

[cf. Equation (6-11-19)]. Here $\mathbf{r}_b$ designates the coordinates of the incident electron, and $\mathbf{r}_1 \cdots \mathbf{r}_N$ those of the atomic electrons. The distance between the incident electron and the ith target electron is denoted by r_{bi}. The eigenfunctions of the ground and nth states of the target atom are labeled u_0 and u_n, respectively. We note that the nuclear contribution to this integral vanishes if the eigenfunctions are orthogonal, as we shall assume to be the case.

It is convenient to transform from angular to momentum variables. Let us take the axis of polar coordinates to be in the direction of the change in momentum experienced by the incident electron on being scattered through angle ϑ. Then, if we define the vector

$$\mathbf{K} = \kappa_n \mathbf{n} - \kappa_0 \mathbf{n}_0 \qquad (6\text{-}16\text{-}3)$$

the magnitude of the electron's momentum change associated with the scattering angle ϑ is

$$K\hbar = (\kappa_n^2 + \kappa_0^2 - 2\kappa_0\kappa_n \cos \vartheta)^{1/2}\hbar \qquad (6\text{-}16\text{-}4)$$

Since

$$K \, dK = \kappa_0\kappa_n \sin \vartheta \, d\vartheta \qquad (6\text{-}16\text{-}5)$$

the cross section for momentum change between $K\hbar$ and $(K + dK)\hbar$ can be written

$$I_{0n}(K) \, dK = \frac{m_e^2}{4\pi^2\hbar^4} \frac{2\pi}{\kappa_0^2} \left| \int e^{iKz} V_{0n}(\mathbf{r}_b) \, d\mathbf{r}_b \right|^2 K \, dK \qquad (6\text{-}16\text{-}6)$$

This expression may be simplified if we integrate over $d\mathbf{r}_b$. Using Bethe's integration formula[130]

$$\int \frac{e^{i\mathbf{K}\mathbf{n}\cdot\mathbf{r}'}}{|\mathbf{r} - \mathbf{r}'|} \, d\mathbf{r}' = \frac{4\pi}{K^2} e^{i\mathbf{K}\mathbf{n}\cdot\mathbf{r}} \qquad (6\text{-}16\text{-}7)$$

we may write

$$\int e^{iKz} V \, d\mathbf{r}_b = \frac{4\pi e^2}{K^2} \sum_{i=1}^{N} e^{iKz_i} \qquad (6\text{-}16\text{-}8)$$

and thus obtain from (6-16-6) the equation

$$I_{0n}(K)\, dK = \frac{8\pi m_e^2 e^4}{\kappa_0^2 \hbar^4} \frac{dK}{K^3} |\varepsilon_{0n}(K)|^2 \qquad (6\text{-}16\text{-}9)$$

where

$$\varepsilon_{0n}(K) = \sum_{i=1}^{N} \int e^{iK z_i} u_n^*(\mathbf{r}_1, \ldots, \mathbf{r}_N)\, u_0(\mathbf{r}_1, \ldots, \mathbf{r}_N)\, d\mathbf{r}_1 \cdots d\mathbf{r}_N \qquad (6\text{-}16\text{-}10)$$

The integrals in (6-16-10) can be calculated for hydrogenic atoms for all final states n (see Chapter XI, Section 2 in Mott and Massey[112]).

The total cross section for excitation of the atom from the ground state to its nth state by electron impact is therefore

$$q_{0n}(\kappa_0) = 2\pi \int_0^\pi I_{0n}(\vartheta) \sin \vartheta\, d\vartheta = \int_{K_{\min}}^{K_{\max}} I_{0n}(K)\, dK \qquad (6\text{-}16\text{-}11)$$

Now

$$\kappa_0^2 = \kappa_n^2 + \frac{2m_e}{\hbar^2}(E_n - E_0) \qquad (6\text{-}16\text{-}12)$$

so

$$\kappa_n \approx \kappa_0 - \frac{m_e}{\hbar^2} \frac{(E_n - E_0)}{\kappa_0} \qquad (6\text{-}16\text{-}13)$$

when the impact velocities are high and the energy transfers small, as is the case here. Therefore the limits of integration for electron impact are

$$K_{\max} = \kappa_0 + \kappa_n \approx 2\kappa_0 \qquad (\vartheta = \pi) \qquad (6\text{-}16\text{-}14)$$

$$K_{\min} = \kappa_0 - \kappa_n \approx \frac{m_e}{\hbar^2} \frac{(E_n - E_0)}{\kappa_0} \qquad (\vartheta = 0) \qquad (6\text{-}16\text{-}15)$$

The method of generalization of the foregoing results to fast ion impact and center-of-mass motion is obvious. The electron mass m_e is replaced by the reduced mass M_r of the projectile-target combination, and e^2 is replaced by $Z'e^2$, where $+Z'e$ is the charge on the projectile. The lower limit of integration over K now becomes

$$K_{\min} = \frac{M_r(E_n - E_0)}{\hbar^2} \qquad (6\text{-}16\text{-}16)$$

and the upper limit, determined by the requirement of conservation of momentum, becomes

$$K_{\max} = \frac{2\kappa_0 m_e}{M_r + m_e} \approx \frac{2\kappa_0 m_e}{M_r} \qquad (6\text{-}16\text{-}17)$$

where κ_0 is now the wave number associated with the relative motion of the colliding structures.

Equations 6-16-9 through 6-16-11 give the Born cross section for excitation of the target atom to its nth bound state. By integrating over final states in the continuum, we could derive instead the cross section for ionization in the first Born approximation. However, the resulting equations have a complicated form and can be solved only by numerical integration. For the present purposes, therefore, it is better to make a further approximation, the Bethe approximation, in order to obtain results that have a simple mathematical form. Cross sections calculated in the Bethe-Born approximation tend to the more precise Born results at very high velocities and thus provide us with insight into the problem we are seeking to solve. As in the preceding discussion, it is convenient first to discuss excitation to bound states by electron impact and then to extend the results to cover ionization by both electrons and ions.

1. *Excitation of discrete optical levels, in the Bethe-Born approximation.*[130] We shall first obtain the Bethe expression for the total electron impact excitation cross section of a ground state atom to its nth bound state. We shall consider only a single outershell electron (designated by the symbol a) to be involved and drop the summation over the atomic electrons. The results we shall obtain will be valid when only a very small fraction of the impact energy is lost by the projectile in the collision.

The function $I_{0n}(K)$ decreases rapidly as the momentum change $K\hbar$ increases. This conclusion follows from examination of the integral

$$\varepsilon_{0n}(K) = \int e^{iKz} u_n{}^* u_0 \, d\mathbf{r}_a \qquad (6\text{-}16\text{-}18)$$

which appears in the expression for $I_{0n}(K)$, (6-16-9). The value of this integral is small if many oscillations of e^{iKz} occur within the spatial range in which the product of the wave functions $u_n{}^*$ and u_0 is appreciable. Now if Z_{eff} is the effective nuclear charge of the target atom in its ground state, the radius of the ground state orbit will be a_0/Z_{eff}, where a_0 is the radius of the first Bohr orbit of the hydrogen atom. Therefore we see that $I_{0n}(K)$ will be small when

$$K \gg \frac{Z_{\text{eff}}}{a_0} = K_0 \qquad (6\text{-}16\text{-}19)$$

This condition may also be expressed in the form

$$K^2 \gg \frac{2m_e |E_0|}{\hbar^2} = K_0{}^2 \qquad (6\text{-}16\text{-}20)$$

since $Z_{\text{eff}}^2 e^2/2a_0$ equals the ionization energy of the normal state, $|E_0|$, and $a_0 = \hbar^2/m_e e^2$. We therefore see that we need to integrate over momentum change only up to the upper limit $K_0 \hbar$ to obtain the total excitation cross section.

For those values of K which do not satisfy condition (6-16-19) we may make the expansion

$$e^{iKz} \approx 1 + iKz + \frac{(iKz)^2}{2!} + \frac{(iKz)^3}{3!} + \cdots$$

in the integrand of (6-16-18) and obtain the approximate relationship

$$I_{0n}(K) \, dK = \frac{8\pi m_e^2 e^4}{\kappa_0^2 \hbar^4} \frac{dK}{K^3} [K^2 |z_{0n}|^2 + \tfrac{1}{4} K^4 |(z^2)_{0n}|^2 + \cdots] \quad (6\text{-}16\text{-}21)$$

Then the total excitation cross section for electron impact is approximately

$$q_{0n} \approx \frac{8\pi m_e^2 e^4}{\kappa_0^2 \hbar^4} \int_{K_{min}}^{K_0} \left[K^{-1} |z_{0n}|^2 + \frac{K}{4} |(z^2)_{0n}|^2 + \cdots \right] dK \quad (6\text{-}16\text{-}22)$$

where z_{0n}, $(z^2)_{0n}$, ... are the matrix elements of z, z^2, ..., given by the equation

$$(z^s)_{0n} = \int z^s u_n{}^* u_0 \, d\mathbf{r}_a \quad (6\text{-}16\text{-}23)$$

For an optically allowed ($\Delta l = 1$) transition the first (electric dipole) term in (6-16-22) does not vanish, and the remaining terms in the expansion may be neglected in comparison to it in the high velocity limit under consideration here. Thus

$$q_{0n}^{\text{dipole}} \approx \frac{4\pi m_e^2 e^4}{\kappa_0^2 \hbar^4} |z_{0n}|^2 \log \frac{2m_e v_0^2}{E_n - E_0} \quad (6\text{-}16\text{-}24)$$

For an optically forbidden transition with $\Delta l = 0$ or 2, the dipole moment vanishes and the transition is associated with the quadrupole moment. The cross section is then obtained from the second term in the expansion and has the form

$$q_{0n}^{\text{quad}} \approx \frac{2\pi m_e^3 e^4}{\kappa_0^2 \hbar^6} |(z^2)_{0n}|^2 |E_0| \quad (6\text{-}16\text{-}25)$$

We notice that at high impact velocity v_0 the cross section for optically allowed transitions falls off with increasing velocity as $v_0^{-2} \log v_0^2$, whereas the cross section for forbidden transitions decreases slightly faster, as v_0^{-2}. The use of a single term in the series expansion of the exponential in (6-16-18) and the termination of the integration at the upper limit K_0 constitute the *Bethe approximation*. This is a further approximation to those already made in the Born approximation, and gives the form of the Born in the limit of very high impact velocities and small interaction. Equation 6-16-24, which is displayed on p. 241 in Mott and Massey,[112] is the *Bethe-Born expression for excitation of optical levels by electron impact.* The cross section corresponding to (6-16-24) for *optical excitation of an atom by a fast ion of charge* $+Z'e$ is

$$q_{0n} \approx \frac{16\pi^4 Z'^2 e^4}{m_e v_0^2} |z_{0n}|^2 \log \frac{2m_e v_0^2}{E_n - E_0} \qquad (6\text{-}16\text{-}26)$$

(cf. Equation 3 on p. 271, Mott and Massey[112]).

2. *Outershell ionization in the Bethe-Born approximation.*[130]   The cross section for ejection of an electron from the outer shell of an atom by fast electron impact may be obtained in the same way as the cross section for excitation to a bound state. (Innershell ionization is treated in Chapter XI, Section 3.2, of Mott and Massey.[112]) We first need the cross section $q_{nl}^+ d\kappa$ for ionization events in which the wave number of the electron ejected from the outer shell (quantum numbers n and l) lies between κ and $\kappa + d\kappa$, corresponding to a kinetic energy in the range $\kappa^2 \hbar^2 / 2m_e$ to $(\kappa^2 + 2\kappa\, d\kappa)\hbar^2/2m_e$:

$$q_{nl}^+ d\kappa \approx \left(\frac{4\pi m_e^2 e^4 Z_{nl}}{\kappa_0^2 \hbar^4} |z_{nl,\kappa}|^2 \log \frac{2m_e v_0^2}{C_{nl}} \right) d\kappa \qquad (6\text{-}16\text{-}27)$$

[cf. (6-16-24)].   Here Z_{nl} is the number of electrons in the n, l shell, and C_{nl} is an energy of the order of the ionization energy of the n, l shell, $|E_{nl}|$. Then the total cross section for removal of a single electron from the outer shell is

$$q_{nl}^+ \approx \int_0^{\kappa_{max}} q_{nl}^+ d\kappa \qquad (6\text{-}16\text{-}28)$$

Using hydrogenlike wave functions with effective nuclear charge Z_{eff}, Bethe[130] showed that (6-16-27) gives for the *electron impact ionization cross section*

$$q_{nl}^+ \approx \frac{2\pi e^4}{m_e v_0^2} \frac{C_{nl}}{|E_{nl}|} Z_{nl} \log \frac{2m_e v_0^2}{C_{nl}} \qquad (6\text{-}16\text{-}29)$$

where

$$C_{nl} = \frac{Z_{eff}^2}{n^2 a_0^2} \int |z_{nl,\kappa}|^2 d\kappa \qquad (6\text{-}16\text{-}30)$$

Explicit calculations have been carried out on the hydrogen atom,[130] for which the cross section has the form

$$q_{00}^+ \approx 0.285 \frac{2\pi e^4}{|E_0| m_e v_0^2} \log \frac{2m_e v_0^2}{0.048 |E_0|} \qquad (6\text{-}16\text{-}31)$$

This result shows that C_{nl} is about one tenth the ionization energy for the ground state of hydrogen.

We see that at high velocity the ionization cross section decreases with increasing impact velocity in the same way that the cross section does for optically allowed excitation. The *cross section for ionization by a fast ion of charge $+Z'e$ is*

$$q_{nl}^+ \approx \frac{2\pi Z'^2 e^4 c_{nl} Z_{nl}}{m_e v_0^2 |E_{nl}|} \log \frac{2m_e v_0^2}{C_{nl}} \qquad (6\text{-}16\text{-}32)$$

in the Bethe-Born approximation (see p. 271 of Mott and Massey[112]). Here v_0 is the relative velocity of approach between the projectile ion and the target atom. Note that the mass appearing explicitly in (6-16-32) is the electron mass.

B. COMPARISON BETWEEN THEORY AND EXPERIMENT.   Experimental data are available on the ionization of many types of atoms and molecules by electrons, protons, and other ions in the energy range over which the Born approximation is valid. However, detailed calculations have been carried out on only a few systems, and the possibilities for comparison are limited. Here we shall compare some experimental ionization cross sections with theoretical cross sections for single electron ejection from the outer shell of the target. These two cross sections are expected to be nearly equal for a given target, since multiple and innershell ionization events are known to occur relatively infrequently.

The first point to which we wish to call attention is the prediction that at high impact velocities the cross section for ionization of a given target by electron impact should be the same as the cross section for ionization by protons traveling with the same impact velocity [cf. (6-16-29) and (6-16-32)]. Experimental verification of this prediction has been presented in Figs. 5-3-4 through 5-3-10 (taken from a paper by Hooper et al.[131]) which compare the high-energy proton cross sections obtained by McDaniel et al.[63] with the electron cross sections obtained by various investigators. The target gases for which both types of data are available at sufficiently high energies to make valid comparisons are helium, neon, argon, hydrogen, nitrogen, oxygen, and carbon monoxide. The electron and proton cross sections for each of these gases appear to be essentially equal at electron energies above about 300 ev; the corresponding proton energy is 552 kev.

Equation 6-16-32 also predicts that the cross section for ionization by He^{2+} ions ($Z' = 2$) should be four times as large as the proton cross sections at the same projectile velocity, provided the velocity is sufficiently high. Martin et al.[64] have measured the cross sections for free electron production in hydrogen, helium, and nitrogen by He^{2+} impact at energies in the range 0.60 to 1.0 Mev and observed this prediction to be obeyed.

Equation 6-16-32 for ionization by heavy ions of charge $Z'e$ applies strictly to point-charge ions, that is, to completely stripped nuclei. Martin et al.[64] have compared their measurements of the ion production in several gases by He^+ ions with the proton ionization results of McDaniel et al.[63] to examine the proposition that (6-16-32) is applicable to an ion carrying bound electrons by using an "effective" charge $+Z'_{eff}e$ lying between the nuclear charge and the actual net charge of the ion. To be a useful concept, the effective charge for a given incident ion must be independent of the target gas and of the incident ion energy. Equation 6-16-32 is expected to describe only "simple" ionization events in which the incident ion does not gain or lose electrons. Therefore the data of Martin et al.[64] on the total ion and electron production by He^+ had to be corrected for the appreciable contributions from charge-changing events encountered at high energies. With presently available information this correction can be made only approximately, even for those cases in which the stripping cross section has been measured (see Pivovar et al.[60]). It was found that the estimated cross section for simple ionization was greater than that for incident protons of the same velocity by a factor that was very nearly independent of energy above 0.6 Mev and varied only from 1.3 to 1.5 for the four gases H_2, He, A, and N_2. Thus the concept of an effective charge of about $1.2e$ for He^+ does seem to have at least a qualitative validity. It is noteworthy that this value is appreciably less than the effective charge $1.69e$ deduced in variational calculations of the ground state wave functions of He. This difference is not unexpected, since the two cases are quite different and may be most sensitive to quite different spatial regions of the wave function.

The experimental proton ionization cross sections of McDaniel et al.[63] in the energy range 0.15 to 1.0 Mev have been fitted to the theoretical expression of Bethe (6-16-32) to obtain empirical values of the parameters appearing in this expression. For molecular hydrogen the empirically derived parameters are in satisfactory agreement with the values obtained by scaling Bethe's values for atomic hydrogen [see (6-16-31)]. Similar comparisons cannot be made for the other target gases investigated (He, Ne, A, N_2, O_2, and CO), since numerical values for these parameters have not yet been calculated from theory. However, Hooper et al.[131] did demonstrate that the proton ionization data for these gases have the $E^{-1} \log E$ dependence predicted by the Born approximation at high energies E and that these data can be fitted to this energy dependence down to lower incident velocities than the corresponding electron data.

Bates and Griffing[132] have made detailed calculations on the excitation and ionization of hydrogen atoms by proton and by neutral hydrogen atom impact. They used the Born approximation, ignoring exchange, but avoided the additional Bethe approximation. Their results are compared with experimental data in Fig. 6-16-1 and are seen to be in good agreement with the laboratory results of Ireland and Gilbody[70] down to the lowest

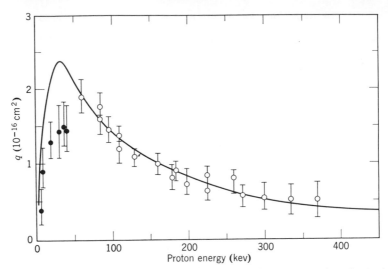

FIG. 6-16-1. Comparison of experimental and theoretical cross sections for ionization of atomic hydrogen by protons. The dots represent the experimental data of Fite, Stebbings, Hummer, and Brackmann[27] and the circles the laboratory results of Ireland and Gilbody.[70] The solid curve displays the results of a Born approximation calculation by Bates and Griffing.[132]

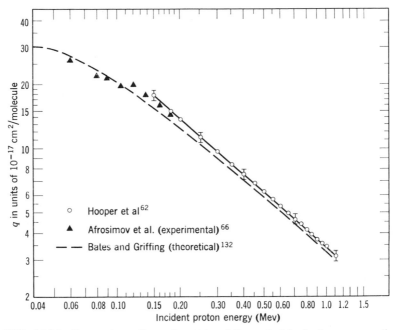

FIG. 6-16-2. Comparison of experimental and theoretical ionization cross sections for protons incident on molecular hydrogen.[62] The theoretical values were obtained by scaling Bates and Griffing's values for atomic hydrogen.

energy (57 kev) reached by these investigators. In addition, the experimental ionization data of Afrosimov et al.[66] and Hooper and his associates[62] for fast protons on molecular hydrogen offer a basis of comparison for some of Bates and Griffing's calculated values. Hooper et al.[62] have scaled Bates and Griffing's theoretical cross sections for ionization of atomic hydrogen by fast protons to H^+ on H_2, using a scaling procedure suggested by Bates and Griffing.[132] The results of this operation are shown in Fig. 6-16-2 and are seen to be in excellent agreement with experiment. It is interesting to note that the Born cross sections for excitation and ionization by neutral H atom impact are about a factor of 10 lower than the corresponding proton impact cross sections at high energies.

Born approximation calculations have also been made by Mapleton[133] for protons on helium. Mapleton's results are compared with experimental cross sections in Fig. 6-7-3. Other calculations and comparisons with experimental results are discussed in the reviews by Bates[115] and Fite[61] and by Seaton,[120] who dealt only with electron impact excitation and ionization.

REFERENCES

1. A. Dalgarno, "Range and Energy Loss," in *Atomic and Molecular Processes* (edited by D. R. Bates), Academic, New York, 1962.
2. J. B. Hasted, "Inelastic Collisions Between Atomic Systems," in *Advan. Electron. Electron Phys.* **13**, 1–81 (1960).
3. J. B. Hasted, "Charge Transfer and Collisional Detachment," in *Atomic and Molecular Processes* (edited by D. R. Bates), Academic, New York, 1962.
4. H. S. W. Massey, *Rept. Prog. Phys.*, **12**, 248 (1949).
5. H. S. W. Massey and E. H. S. Burhop, *Electronic and Ionic Impact Phenomena*, Oxford University Press, Oxford, 1952, Chapters VII and VIII.
6. A. Dalgarno, *Annal. Géophys.* **17**, No. 1, 16–49 (1961).
7. R. N. Varney, *Phys. Rev.* **89**, 708 (1953).
8. D. R. Bates and A. Dalgarno, in *The Airglow and the Aurorae* (edited by E. B. Armstrong and A. Dalgarno), Pergamon, London, 1956.
9. J. B. Hasted and A. R. Lee, *Proc. Phys. Soc. (London)* **79**, 702 (1962). [See also H. B. Gilbody and J. B. Hasted, *Proc. Phys. Soc. (London)* **72**, 293 (1958). J. B. Hasted, *J. Appl. Phys.* **30**, 25 (1959). Ia. M. Fogel, R. V. Mitin, V. F. Kozlov, and N. D. Romashko, *Soviet Phys.-JETP* **35**, 390 (1959)].
10. D. R. Bates and H. S. W. Massey, *Phil. Mag.* **45**, 111 (1954).
11. D. R. Bates, *Proc. Roy. Soc. (London)* **A-257**, 22 (1960).
12. O. Firsov, *Soviet Phys.-JETP* **21**, 1001 (1951); I. K. Fetisov and O. Firsov, **10**, 67 (1960).
13. D. R. Bates and R. McCarroll, *Phil. Mag.* Suppl. **11**, 39 (1962).
14. E. F. Gurnee and J. L. Magee, *J. Chem. Phys.* **26**, 1237 (1957).
15. D R. Bates and N. Lynn, *Proc. Roy. Soc. (London)* **A-253**, 141 (1959). See also M. A. Biondi, "Atomic Collisions Involving Low Energy Electrons and Ions," in *Advan. Electron. Electron Phys. 18*, Academic, New York (1963).

16. W. L. Fite, A. C. H. Smith, and R. F. Stebbings, *Proc. Roy. Soc. (London)* **A-268,** 527 (1962).

17. D. Rapp and I. B. Ortenburger, *J. Chem. Phys.* **33,** 1230 (1960); See also D. Rapp and W. E. Francis, **37,** 2631 (1962).

18. L. L. Marino, A. C. H. Smith, and E. Caplinger, *Phys. Rev.* **128,** 2243 (1962).

19. J. B. Hasted, *Proc. Roy. Soc. (London),* **A-205,** 421 (1951); J. B. Hasted, **A-212,** 235 (1952); J. B. H. Stedeford and J. B. Hasted, **A-227,** 466 (1955); J. B. Hasted and R. A. Smith, **A-235,** 354 (1956); H. B. Gilbody and J. B. Hasted, **A-238,** 334 (1956). J. B. Hasted, J. T. Scott, and A. Y. J. Chong, *Proceedings of the Fourth International Conference on Ionization Phenomena in Gases,* Uppsala, 1959—North-Holland, Amsterdam (1960), Vol. IA, p. 34. J. B. Hasted, *Proceedings of the Fifth International Conference on Ionization Phenomena in Gases,* Munich, 1961, North-Holland, Amsterdam (1962), Vol. I, p. 19. J. B. Hasted and A. Y. J. Chong, *Proc. Phys. Soc. (London)* **80,** 441 (1962).

20. R. F. Potter, *J. Chem. Phys.* **22,** 974 (1954).

21. J. A. Dillon, W. F. Sheridan, H. D. Edwards, and S. N. Ghosh, *J. Chem. Phys.* **23,** 776 (1955); S. N. Ghosh and W. F. Sheridan, **26,** 480 (1957).

22. Yu. F. Bydin and A. M. Bukhteev, *Sov. Phys.-Tech. Phys.* **4,** 10 (1959).

23. V. F. Kozlov and A. M. Rozhkov, *Sov. Phys.-Tech. Phys.* **7,** 524 (1962).

24. E. Lindholm, *Z. Naturforsch.* **9-a,** 535 (1954). E. Lindholm, *Arkiv. Fys.* **8,** 257, 433 (1954); E. Gustafsson and E. Lindholm, **18,** 219 (1960); H. von Koch and E. Lindholm, **19,** 123 (1961); P. Wilmenius and E. Lindholm, **21,** 97 (1962).

25. T. L. Bailey, *Second International Conference on the Physics of Electronic and Atomic Collisions,* Boulder, Colo., 1961. To be published in *J. Chem. Phys.*

26. A. M. Bukhteev, Yu. F. Bydin, and V. M. Dukel'skii, *Sov. Phys.-Tech. Phys.* **6,** 496 (1961).

27. W. L. Fite, R. T. Brackmann, and W. R. Snow, *Phys. Rev.* **112,** 1161 (1958); W. L. Fite, R. F. Stebbings, D. G. Hummer, and R. T. Brackmann, **119,** 663 (1960); D. G. Hummer, R. F. Stebbings, W. L. Fite, and L. M. Branscomb, **119,** 668 (1960). R. F. Stebbings, W. L. Fite, and D. G. Hummer, *J. Chem. Phys.,* **33,** 1226 (1960); R. F. Stebbings, B. R. Turner, and A. C. H. Smith, **38,** 2277 (1963). R. F. Stebbings, A. C. H. Smith, and H. B. Gilbody, **38,** 2280 (1963). R. F. Stebbings, A. C. H. Smith, and H. Ehrhardt, **39,** 968 (1963). W. L. Fite, A. C. H. Smith, R. F. Stebbings, and J. A. Rutherford, *J. Geophys. Res.* **68,** 3225 (1963).

28. See, for example, the paper presented by R. C. Amme and N. G. Utterback at the Third International Conference on the Physics of Electronic and Atomic Collisions, London, 1963, and the paper delivered by W. L. Fite and R. T. Brackmann at the Sixth International Conference on Ionization Phenomena in Gases, Paris, 1963.

29. J. W. McGowan and L. Kerwin, *Can. J. Phys.* **41,** 316 (1963).

30. F. W. Aston, *Proc. Cambridge Phil. Soc.* **19,** 317 (1920). J. Mattauch and H. Lichtblau, *Physik Z.* **40,** 16 (1939). C. E. Melton and G. F. Wells, *J. Chem. Phys.* **27,** 1132 (1957). J. W. McGowan and L. Kerwin, *Can. J. Phys.* **38,** 642 (1960).

31. L. Kerwin and J. W. McGowan, *Proceedings of the Fifth International Conference on Ionization Phenomena in Gases,* Munich, 1961, North-Holland, Amsterdam, 1962, Vol. I, p. 33. J. W. McGowan and L. Kerwin, *Proc. Phys. Soc. (London)* **82,** 357 (1963). J. W. McGowan and L. Kerwin, *Can. J. Phys.* **41,** 1535 (1963). P. Marmet, J. W. McGowan, and L. Kerwin, Third International Conference on the Physics of Electronic and Atomic Collisions, London, 1963.

32. S. C. Brown, *Basic Data of Plasma Physics,* Wiley, New York, 1959.

33. P. J. Nawrocki and R. Papa, *Atmospheric Processes*, Prentice-Hall, Englewood Cliffs, N.J., 1962.

34. D. R. Bates and M. Nicolet, *J. Atmospheric Terrest. Phys.* **18**, 65 (1960).

35. D. R. Bates, *Proc. Phys. Soc. (London)* **A-68**, 344 (1955).

36. P. G. Dickinson and J. Sayers, *Proc. Phys. Soc. (London)* **76**, 137 (1960). V. L. Talrose, M. I. Markin, and I. K. Larin, *Discussions Faraday Soc.*, **33**, 257 (1962); W. L. Fite, J. A. Rutherford, W. R. Snow and V. A. J. Van Lint, **33**, 264 (1962). J. Sayers and D. Smith, Third International Conference on the Physics of Electronic and Atomic Collisions, London, 1963. A. Galli, A. Giardini-Guidoni, and G. G. Volpi, *J. Chem. Phys.* **39**, 518 (1963); C. F. Giese and W. B. Maier, **39**, 739 (1963).

37. D. E. Moe, *Phys. Rev.* **104**, 694 (1956).

38. N. G. Utterback and G. H. Miller, *Rev. Sci. Instr.* **32**, 1101 (1961). N. G. Utterback and G. H. Miller, *Phys. Rev.* **124**, 1477 (1961); N. G. Utterback, **129**, 219 (1963). N. G. Utterback, Third International Conference on the Physics of Electronic and Atomic Collisions, London, 1963.

39. W. P. Sholette and E. E. Muschlitz, *J. Chem. Phys.* **36**, 3368 (1962). E. E. Muschlitz and M. J. Weiss, Third International Conference on the Physics of Electronic and Atomic Collisions, London, 1963.

40. E. E. Benton, E. E. Ferguson, F. A. Matsen, and W. W. Robertson, *Phys. Rev.* **128**, 206 (1962); E. E. Ferguson, **128**, 210 (1962).

41. S. K. Allison, *Rev. Mod. Phys.* **30**, 1137 (1958).

42. S. K. Allison and M. Garcia-Munoz, "Electron Capture and Loss at High Energies," appearing in *Atomic and Molecular Processes* (edited by D. R. Bates), Academic, New York, 1962.

43. P. M. Stier, C. F. Barnett, and G. E. Evans, *Phys. Rev.* **96**, 973 (1954).

44. P. M. Stier and C. F. Barnett, *Phys. Rev.* **103**, 896 (1956).

45. C. F. Barnett and H. K. Reynolds, *Phys. Rev.* **109**, 355 (1958).

46. C. F. Barnett and P. M. Stier, *Phys. Rev.* **109**, 385 (1958).

47. S. K. Allison, *Phys. Rev.*, **109**, 76 (1958); S. K. Allison, **110**, 670 (1958); S. K. Allison, J. Cuevas, and P. G. Murphy, **102**, 1041 (1956); S. K. Allison, J. Cuevas, and M. Garcia-Munoz, **120**, 1266 (1960). W. Meckbach and S. K. Allison, **132**, 294 (1963).

48. E. Everhart, R. J. Carbone, and G. Stone, *Phys. Rev.* **98**, 1045 (1955); E. N. Fuls, P. R. Jones, F. P. Ziemba, and E. Everhart, **107**, 704 (1957); P. R. Jones, F. P. Ziemba, H. A. Moses, and E. Everhart, **113**, 182 (1959).

49. N. V. Fedorenko, L. G. Filippenko, and I. P. Flaks, *Sov. Phys.-Tech. Phys.* **5**, 45 (1960); V. V. Afrosimov, R. N. Il'in, and E. S. Solov'ev, **5**, 661 (1960).

50. F. P. Ziemba and E. Everhart, *Phys. Rev. Letters* **2**, 299 (1959). F. P. Ziemba, G. J. Lockwood, G. H. Morgan, and E. Everhart, *Phys. Rev.* **118**, 1552 (1960); G. J. Lockwood and E. Everhart, **125**, 567 (1962); P. R. Jones, P. Costigan, and G. Van Dyk, **129**, 211 (1963). E. Everhart, and P. R. Jones, G. Van Dyk, and N. Eddy, Third International Conference on the Physics of Electronic and Atomic Collisions, London, 1963. G. J. Lockwood, H. F. Helbig, and E. Everhart, *Phys. Rev.* **132**, 2078 (1963); E. Everhart **132**, 2083 (1963).

51. G. H. Morgan and E. Everhart, *Phys. Rev.* **128**, 667 (1962).

52. D. R. Sweetman, *Proc. Roy. Soc. (London)* **A-256**, 416 (1960).

53. A. Schmid, *Z. Physik* **161**, 550 (1961).

54. G. W. McClure, *Phys. Rev.* **130**, 1852 (1963), **132**, 1636 (1963).

55. F. P. Ziemba and A. Russek, *Phys. Rev.* **115**, 922 (1959). See also W. Lichten, *Phys. Rev.* **131**, 229 (1963).

56. M. Islam, J. B. Hasted, H. B. Gilbody, and J. V. Ireland, *Proc. Phys. Soc.* (*London*) **79**, 1118 (1962).

57. F. J. de Heer, W. Huizenga, and J. Kistemaker, *Appl. Sci. Res.* **B-5**, 337 (1955); F. J. de Heer, W. Huizenga, and J. Kistemaker, *Physica* **23**, 181 (1957); Th. J. M. Sluyters, E. de Haas, and J. Kistemaker, **25**, 1376 (1959); J. Van Eck and J. Kistemaker, **26**, 629 (1960).

58. J. Guidini, *Proceedings of the Fifth International Conference on Ionization Phenomena in Gases*, Munich, 1961, North-Holland, Amsterdam, 1962, Vol. II, 1228.

59. K. Bethge, *Z. Physik* **162**, 34 (1961).

60. Ia. M. Fogel et al., *Soviet Phys.-JETP* **1**, 415 (1955); Ia. M. Fogel and L. I. Krupnik, **2**, 252 (1956); Ia. M. Fogel and R. V. Mitin, **3**, 334 (1956); V. M. Dukel'skii et al., **3**, 764 (1956). N. V. Fedorenko et al., *Soviet Phys.-Tech. Phys.* **1**, 1861 (1956). Ia. M. Fogel et al., *Soviet Phys.-JETP* **4**, 359 (1957). Ia. M. Fogel et al., *Sov. Phys.-Tech. Phys.* **2**, 902 (1957); I. P. Flaks and E. S. Solov'ev, **3**, 564 (1958); I. P. Flaks and E. S. Solov'ev, **3**, 577 (1958); Ia. M. Fogel et al., **3**, 1410 (1958); V. V. Afrosimov et al., **3**, 2080 (1958). V. S. Nikolaev et al., *Soviet Phys.-JETP*, **6**, 239 (1958); V. S. Nikolaev et al., **6**, 1019 (1958); Ia. M. Fogel et al., **7**, 400 (1958); V. V. Afrosimov, et al., **7**, 968 (1958); Ia. M. Fogel et al., **8**, 601 (1959); R. N. Il'in et al., **9**, 29 (1959); Ya. M. Fogel et al., **9**, 963 (1959). I. P. Flaks and L. G. Filippenko, *Sov. Phys.-Tech. Phys.* **4**, 1005 (1959). Ya. M. Fogel et al., *Soviet Phys. JETP* **11**, 18 (1960); Ya. M. Fogel, *Soviet Phys.-Uspekhi* **3**, 390 (1960). N. V. Fedorenko et al., *Sov. Phys.-Tech. Phys.* **5**, 45 (1960); V. V. Afrosimov et al., **5**, 661 (1960); D. V. Chkuaseli et al., **5**, 770 (1960). V. S. Nikolaev et al., *Soviet Phys. JETP* **12**, 627 (1961); Ya. M. Fogel et al., **12**, 826 (1961). I. P. Flaks, *Sov. Phys.-Tech. Phys.* **6**, 263 (1961). Ya. M. Fogel et al., *Soviet Phys.-JETP* **13**, 8 (1961); V. S. Nikolaev et al., **13**, 695 (1961). Yu. M. Khirnyi, *Sov. Phys.-Tech. Phys.* **6**, 427 (1961); R. N. Il'in and E. S. Solov'ev, **6**, 491 (1961); A. M. Bukhteev et al., **6**, 496 (1961). L. I. Pivovar et al., *Soviet Phys. JETP* **14**, 20 (1962); V. S. Nikolaev et al., **14**, 67 (1962); I. P. Flaks et al., **14**, 781 (1962); G. N. Ogurtsov and I. P. Flaks, **15**, 502 (1962); D. V. Pilipenko and Ya. M. Fogel, **15**, 646 (1962); L. I. Pivovar et al., **15**, 1035 (1962). V. F. Kozlov and A. M. Rozhkov, *Sov. Phys.-Tech. Phys.* **7**, 524 (1962). I. S. Dmitriev et al., *Soviet Phys. JETP* **16**, 259 (1963). I. P. Flaks, *Sov. Phys.-Tech. Phys.* **8**, 560 (1963).

61. W. L. Fite, "The Measurement of Collisional Excitation and Ionization Cross Sections," in *Atomic and Molecular Processes* (edited by D. R. Bates), Academic, New York, 1962.

62. J. W. Hooper, E. W. McDaniel, D. W. Martin, and D. S. Harmer, *Phys. Rev.* **121**, 1123 (1961).

63. E. W. McDaniel, J. W. Hooper, D. W. Martin, and D. S. Harmer, *Proceedings of the Fifth International Conference on Ionization Phenomena in Gases*, Munich, 1961, North-Holland, Amsterdam, 1962, Vol. I, 60.

64. D. W. Martin, R. A. Langley, J. W. Hooper, D. S. Harmer and E. W. McDaniel, *Proceedings of the Third International Conference on Electronic and Atomic Collisions*, London, 1963, North-Holland, Amsterdam, 1964.

65. S. Kronenberg, K. Nilson, and M. Basso, *Phys. Rev.* **124**, 1709 (1961).

66. V. V. Afrosimov, R. N. Il'in, and N. V. Fedorenko, *Soviet Phys.-JETP* **7**, 968 (1958).

67. N. V. Fedorenko, V. V. Afrosimov, R. N. Il'in, and E. S. Solov'ev, *Proceedings of the Fourth International Conference on Ionization Phenomena in Gases*, Uppsala, 1959, North-Holland, Amsterdam, 1960, Vol. I, IA-47.

68. Ia. M. Fogel, L. I. Krupnik, and B. G. Safronov, *Soviet Phys. JETP* **1**, 415 (1955).
69. H. B. Gilbody and J. B. Hasted, *Proc. Roy. Soc.* (*London*) **A-240**, 382 (1957).
70. J. V. Ireland and H. B. Gilbody, Third International Conference on the Physics of Electronic and Atomic Collisions, London, 1963.
71. N. V. Fedorenko and V. V. Afrosimov, *Sov. Phys.-Tech. Phys.* **1**, 1872 (1956); V. V. Afrosimov, R. N. Il'in, and N. V. Fedorenko, **3**, 2080 (1958). R. N. Il'in, V. V. Afrosimov, and N. V. Fedorenko, *Soviet Phys.-JETP* **9**, 29 (1959). N. V. Fedorenko, V. V. Afrosimov, R. N. Il'in, and E. S. Solov'ev, Uppsala Conference, Ref. 67. Ya. M. Fogel, A. G. Koval, Yu. Z. Levchenko, and A. F. Khodyachikh, *Soviet Phys.-JETP* **12**, 384 (1961). R. N. Il'in and E. S. Solov'ev, *Sov. Phys.-Tech. Phys.* **6**, 491 (1961). V. V. Afrosimov, R. N. Il'in, V. A. Oparin, E. S. Solov'ev, and N. V. Fedorenko, *Soviet Phys.-JETP* **14**, 747 (1962); I. P. Flaks, G. N. Ogurtsov, and N. V. Fedorenko, **14**, 781 (1962); E. S. Solov'ev, R. N. Il'in, V. A. Oparin, and N. V. Fedorenko, **15**, 459 (1962).
72. V. V. Afrosimov and N. V. Fedorenko, *Sov. Phys.-Tech. Phys.* **2**, 2378 (1957); V. V. Afrosimov and N. V. Fedorenko, **2**, 2391 (1957). V. V. Afrosimov, R. N. Il'in, and N. V. Fedorenko, *Soviet Phys.-JETP* **7**, 968 (1958).
73. E. Blauth, *Z. Physik* **147**, 228 (1957). D. E. Moe and O. H. Petsch, *Phys. Rev.* **110**, 1358 (1958); **115**, 349 (1959); H. W. Berry, **121**, 1714 (1961), **127**, 1634 (1962).
74. C. E. Kuyatt and T. Jorgensen, *Phys. Rev.* **130**, 1444 (1963).
75. M. E. Rudd and T. Jorgensen, *Phys. Rev.* **131**, 666 (1963)
76. D. R. Bates and G. W. Griffing, *Proc. Phys. Soc.* (*London*) **A-66**, 961 (1953); **A-68**, 90 (1955). D. R. Bates, M. R. C. McDowell, and A. Omholt, *J. Atmospheric Terrestr. Phys.* **10**, 51 (1957). M. R. C. McDowell and G. Peach, *Phys. Rev.* **121**, 1383 (1961).
77. J. P. Keene, *Phil. Mag.* **40**, 369 (1949).
78. F. Schwirzke, *Z. Physik* **157**, 510 (1960).
79. Iu. F. Bydin and A. M. Bukhteev, *Soviet Phys. Doklady* **3**, 372 (1958). N. V. Fedorenko, I. P. Flaks, and L. G. Filippenko, *Soviet Phys.-JETP* **11**, 519 (1960); Ya. M. Fogel, A. G. Koval, and Yu. Z. Levchenko, **11**, 760 (1960). Yu. F. Bydin and A. M. Bukhteev, *Sov. Phys.-Tech. Phys.* **5**, 512 (1960). I. P. Flaks, G. N. Ogurtsov, and N. V. Fedorenko, *Soviet Phys.-JETP* **14**, 1027 (1962). N. V. Fedorenko, R. N. Il'in, and E. S. Solovjov, *Proceedings of the Fifth International Conference on Ionization Phenomena in Gases*, Munich, 1961, North-Holland, Amsterdam, 1962, Vol. II, 1300.
80. N. V. Fedorenko, *Soviet Phys.-Uspekhi* **2**, 526 (1959).
81. A. R. Lee and J. B. Hasted, *Proc. Phys. Soc.* (*London*) **79**, 1049 (1962).
82. A. Russek and M. T. Thomas, *Phys. Rev.* **109**, 2015 (1958), **114**, 1538 (1959); J. B. Bulman and A. Russek, **122**, 506 (1961). For an extension of this work, see A. Russek, *Phys. Rev.* **132**, 246 (1963).
83. J. B. Hasted, *Proc. Phys. Soc.* (*London*) **77**, 269 (1961).
84. D. J. Rose and M. Clark, *Plasmas and Controlled Fusion*, Wiley, New York, 1961.
85. H. Postma and D. P. Hamblen, *AEC Report ORNL 2966* (1961).
86. N. V. Fedorenko, V. V. Afrosimov, R. N. Il'in, and D. M. Kaminker, *Soviet Phys.-JETP* **9**, 267 (1959).
87. K. K. Damodaran, *Proc. Roy. Soc.* (*London*) **A-239**, 382 (1957).
88. D. R. Sweetman, *Phys. Rev. Letters* **3**, 425 (1959); *Proc. Roy. Soc.* (*London*) **A-256**, 416 (1960).
89. C. F. Barnett, *Proceedings of the Second U.N. International Conference on Peaceful Uses of Atomic Energy*, United Nations, Geneva, 1958, **32**, 398.

90. A. Schmid, *Z. Physik* **161,** 550 (1961).
91. L. I. Pivovar, V. M. Tubaev, and M. T. Novikov, *Soviet Phys.-JETP* **13,** 23 (1961).
92. J. Guidini, R. Belna, G. Briffod, and C. Manus, *Comptes Rendus* **251,** 2496 (1960). See also J. Guidini, *op. cit.* **253,** 829 (1961). J. Guidini, *Proceedings of the Fifth International Conference on Ionization Phenomena in Gases,* Munich, 1961, North-Holland, Amsterdam, 1962, Vol. II, 1228. J. Guidini, Third International Conference on the Physics of Electronic and Atomic Collisions, London, 1963.
93. C. F. Barnett and J. A. Ray, Third International Conference on the Physics of Electronic and Atomic Collisions, London, 1963.
94. A. C. Riviere and D. R. Sweetman, *Proc. Phys. Soc. (London)* **78,** 1215 (1961).
95. A. C. Riviere and D. R. Sweetman, *Phys. Rev. Letters* **5,** 560 (1960). *Proceedings of the Fifth International Conference on Ionization Phenomena in Gases,* Munich, 1961, North-Holland, Amsterdam, 1962, Vol. II, 1236.
96. S. Kaplan, G. A. Paulikas, and R. V. Pyle, *Phys. Rev. Letters* **7,** 96 (1961); *Phys. Rev.* **131,** 2574 (1963).
97. J. R. Hiskes, *Phys. Rev.* **122,** 1207 (1961); *Nucl. Fusion* **2,** 38 (1962).
98. J. A. Ratcliffe, *Physics of the Upper Atmosphere,* Academic, New York, 1960. J. W. Chamberlain, *Physics of the Aurora and Airglow,* Academic, New York, 1961.
99. C. Y. Fan, *Astrophys. J.* **122,** 350 (1955).
100. F. L. Roesler, C. Y. Fan, and J. W. Chamberlain, *J. Atmospheric Terrestr. Phys.* **12,** 200 (1958).
101. Th. J. M. Sluyters and E. de Haas, *Rev. Sci. Instr.* **29,** 597 (1958). Th. J. M. Sluyters and J. Kistemaker, *Physica* **25,** 182 (1959); Th. J. M. Sluyters and J. Kistemaker, **25,** 1389 (1959); J. van Eck, F. J. de Heer, and J. Kistemaker, **28,** 1184 (1962).
102. J. van Eck, F. J. de Heer, and J. Kistemaker, *Phys. Rev.* **130,** 656 (1963).
103. N. P. Carleton and T. R. Lawrence, *Phys. Rev.* **109,** 1159 (1958).
104. Z. Sternberg and P. Tomas, *Phys. Rev.* **124,** 810 (1961).
105. G. H. Dunn, R. Geballe, and D. Pretzer, *Phys. Rev.* **128,** 2200 (1962). D. Pretzer, B. Van Zyl, and R. Geballe, *Phys. Rev. Letters* **10,** 340 (1963).
106. F. S. Johnson, K. Watanabe, and R. Tousey, *J. Opt. Soc. Am.* **41,** 702 (1951). K. Watanabe, M. Zelikoff, and E. C. Y. Inn, *J. Chem. Phys.* **21,** 1026 (1953).
107. C. Y. Fan, *Phys. Rev.* **103,** 1740 (1956).
108. N. P. Carleton, *Phys. Rev.* **107,** 110 (1957).
109. E. M. Reeves and R. W. Nicholls, *Proc. Phys. Soc. (London)* **78,** 588 (1961).
110. R. H. Hughes, R. C. Waring, and C. Y. Fan, *Phys. Rev.* **122,** 525 (1961).
111. R. H. Hughes, J. L. Philpot, and C. Y. Fan, *Phys. Rev.* **123,** 2084 (1961) [protons on molecular nitrogen]; R. H. Hughes, S. Lin, and L. L. Hatfield, **130,** 2318 (1963) [protons on molecular hydrogen]. See also L. L. Hatfield and R. H. Hughes **131,** 2556 (1963); J. L. Philpot and R. H. Hughes **133,** 107 (1964).
112. N. F. Mott and II. S. W. Massey, *The Theory of Atomic Collisions,* Second Edition, Oxford University Press, Oxford, 1952.
113. D. R. Bates, "Transitions," in *Quantum Theory,* Vol. I (edited by D. R. Bates), Academic, New York, 1961.
114. E. H. S. Burhop, "Theory of Collisions," in *Quantum Theory,* Vol. I (edited by D. R. Bates), Academic, New York, 1961.
115. D. R. Bates, "Theoretical Treatment of Collisions Between Atomic Systems," in *Atomic and Molecular Processes* (edited by D. R. Bates), Academic, New York, 1962.

116. T. Y. Wu and T. Ohmura, *Quantum Theory of Scattering*, Prentice-Hall, Englewood Cliffs, N.J., 1962.

117. M. Born, *Z. Physik* **37,** 863 (1926), **38,** 803 (1926).

118. D. R. Bates, A. Fundaminsky, and H. S. W. Massey, *Phil. Trans. Roy. Soc. (London)* **A-243,** 93 (1950).

119. J. R. Oppenheimer, *Phys. Rev.* **32,** 361 (1928).

120. M. J. Seaton, "The Theory of Excitation and Ionization by Electron Impact," in *Atomic and Molecular Processes* (edited by D. R. Bates), Academic, New York, 1962.

121. L. D. Landau and E. M. Lifshitz, *Quantum Mechanics, Non-relativistic Theory*, Addison-Wesley, Reading, 1958.

122. N. F. Mott, *Proc. Cambridge Phil. Soc.* **27,** 553 (1931).

123. D. R. Bates, *Proc. Roy. Soc. (London)* **A-240,** 437 (1957), **A-243,** 15 (1957). A. M. Arthurs and A. R. Holt, *Proc. Phys. Soc. (London)* **82,** 1073 (1963) have recently shown that the procedure of using rotating coordinates in scattering problems, which can be justified for exact calculations, breaks down in calculations based on the Born approximation.

124. J. R. Oppenheimer, *Phys. Rev.* **31,** 349 (1928).

125. H. C. Brinkman and H. A. Kramers, *Proc. Acad. Sci. Amsterdam* **33,** 973 (1930).

126. M. Gryziński, *Phys. Rev.* **107,** 1471 (1957), **115,** 374 (1959). For a critique of Gryziński's procedure for calculating electron impact ionization cross sections, see S. S. Prasad and K. Prasad, *Proc. Phys. Soc. (London)* **82,** 655 (1963). A useful empirical expression for electron ionization cross sections has been developed by H. W. Drawin, *Z. Phys.* **164,** 513 (1961).

127. S. Chandrasekhar, *Astrophys. J.* **93,** 285 (1941); R. E. Williamson and S. Chandrasekhar, **93,** 305 (1941).

128. R. G. Alsmiller, *Oak Ridge National Laboratory Report ORNL-3232* (January 10, 1962).

129. E. V. Ivash, *Phys. Rev.* **112,** 155 (1958).

130. H. A. Bethe, *Ann. Physik* **5,** 325 (1930).

131. J. W. Hooper, D. S. Harmer, D. W. Martin, and E. W. McDaniel, *Phys. Rev.* **125,** 2000 (1962).

132. D. R. Bates and G. Griffing, *Proc. Phys. Soc. (London)* **A-66,** 961 (1953).

133. R. A. Mapleton, *Phys. Rev.* **109,** 1166 (1958).

7

PHOTOABSORPTION IN GASES

As is well known, photons may be absorbed in passing through a gas. In the absorption process the photons disappear, and the absorbed energy goes into excitation and ionization of the particles with which they interact. Photoabsorption is a phenomenon of considerable laboratory interest in connection with studies of photochemistry and the physics of electrical discharges. Its geophysical and astrophysical significance is even more important,[1] as evidenced by the following considerations. Most of the charged particles in the upper atmosphere are produced by solar ultraviolet and X radiation, and many of the reactions occurring there are photochemical in nature. Thus photoabsorption plays a key role in determining the composition and characteristics of the ionosphere. Photoabsorption is also an important factor in the energy balance of the earth's atmosphere and the outer layers of stars. Photoionization cross sections have a bearing on the ionization equilibrium and consequently the chemical abundances in interstellar space. The cross sections for highly ionized iron and nickel partly determine the physical conditions of the solar corona. In addition, photoabsorption by H^- makes an important contribution to stellar opacity.

In this chapter we are concerned mainly with experimental studies of the absorption of low-energy photons by neutral atoms and molecules.

The energy range to be covered here is about 4 to 60 ev, corresponding to the ultraviolet and soft X-ray regions, which are the regions of greatest general interest in plasma and astrophysical research. This area has been admirably surveyed by Weissler[2] and by Ditchburn and Öpik.[3] The text and review by Evans[4] are suggested as references on scattering and absorption of hard X rays and gamma rays. Photodetachment of electrons from negative ions is treated in Chapter 8. Little is known about photoabsorption by positive ions, and this subject is not covered here.*

7-1. MECHANISMS OF PHOTOABSORPTION

A number of different mechanisms can participate in the absorption of photons by atoms and molecules.[2]

(a) Excitation to upper levels involving resonance transitions without predissociation or preionization.[5],†

(b) Excitation to molecular states adjacent to a dissociation continuum, leading to predissociation.

(c) Excitation to upper states of atoms or molecules adjacent to an ionization continuum, leading to preionization.

(d) Continuous absorption due (1) to direct excitation into an atomic ionization continuum, (2) to dissociation of molecules into two fragments, each of which may be in the ground state or in an excited state, (3) to direct excitation into one of the molecular ionization continua, without dissociation or preionization, (4) to dissociative ionization into an ion and an atom which may be in an excited state, or (5) to dissociative ionization that produces two ions of opposite sign, one of which is in an excited state.

This multiplicity of absorption mechanisms makes the analysis of absorption data difficult. However, information concerning mechanisms can be inferred from the shape of absorption curves and knowledge of the energy levels of the target molecules. It is evident that direct studies of photoionization, particularly those involving mass spectrometric analysis of the ionization products, are of great value, but unfortunately comparatively few studies of this kind have been made.

7-2. EXPERIMENTAL METHODS OF STUDYING PHOTOABSORPTION

Most of the experimental studies of photoabsorption have involved measurement of the attenuation of a beam of photons traversing a

* We should, however, mention the recent measurements on photodissociation of H_2^+ and N_2^+ ions reported by G. H. Dunn at the Third International Conference on the Physics of Electronic and Atomic Collisions, London, 1963.
† Predissociation is discussed in terms of molecular energy levels in Section 8-1-B. Preionization, also known as autoionization, is explained in Section 8-2-A.

gas-filled absorption cell. Figure 7-2-1 shows one of the several experimental arrangements used for these studies. Other apparatus are discussed in the review by Weissler.[2] In Fig. 7-2-1 light from the source D falls on a reflection grating where it is dispersed. The grating can be displaced along the Rowland focusing circle to direct a beam of variable wavelength toward the absorption cell. With no gas in the cell, a certain intensity I_0 is registered by the photomultiplier P. The measured intensity falls to some lower value I when gas is introduced. If x is the length of the cell, these two intensities are related by the equation

$$I = I_0 e^{-\mu x} \tag{7-2-1}$$

where μ is the *absorption coefficient* for the particular wavelength in use; μ, which has units of cm^{-1}, evidently corresponds to a macroscopic cross

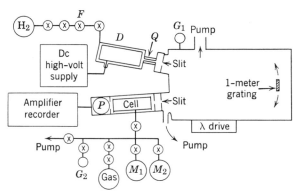

FIG. 7-2-1. Apparatus for the determination of photoabsorption cross sections. K. Watanabe, E. C. Y. Inn, and M. Zelikoff, *J. Chem. Phys.* **21**, 1026 (1953).

section and is related to the *microscopic photoabsorption cross section* q_p by the equation

$$\mu = q_p N \tag{7-2-2}$$

where N is the number density of the gas. The published values of μ usually refer to a gas density corresponding to 0°C and 760 mm Hg. The values of q_p are often expressed in megabarns (1 Mb $= 10^{-18}$ cm²).

There are two conditions on the validity of (7-2-1). First, the radiation must be so nearly monochromatic that there will be no change in effective absorption as the radiation progresses through the gas. Then the measured value of μ will be independent of the value of x chosen, and *Lambert's law* will be obeyed. Second, μ must be independent of the gas pressure and temperature, so that *Beer's law* is obeyed. The second condition will be satisfied if changes in p and T do not significantly change the composition of the gas, by molecular association or dissociation, for example.

The apparatus pictured in Fig. 7-2-2, which is taken from the review by Weissler,[2] permits the direct determination of the cross sections for photoionization. Radiation of known wavelength and intensity passes through a gas cell containing parallel-plate ionization chambers which collect the charged particles of both signs produced in ionization events. Measurements of these currents yield the cross section if the chamber dimensions and gas pressure are known.

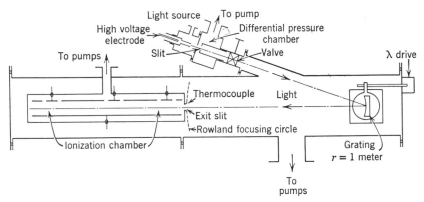

FIG. 7-2-2. Apparatus for the measurement of photoionization cross sections (Weissler[2]).

Recently, vacuum monochromators have been combined with mass spectrometers for the study of photoionization processes.[6] Measurements are made of the ion intensity as a function of photon energy for the parent ions and their fragments. The onset of ionization and the structure of the yield curves can be related to energy levels, to photoionization cross sections, and to photodissociation mechanisms.

Still another approach to the clarification of photoabsorption mechanisms involves the passage of dispersed radiation through a gas and observation of the fluorescence radiation thus induced. Studies of this kind have recently been made on N_2, O_2, and CO by Schoen, Judge, and Weissler,[7] who used the apparatus shown in Fig. 7-2-3. Monoenergetic photons with wavelengths in the range 500 to 1000 Å pass from the exit slit of a Seya-type vacuum monochromator into a target chamber in which fluorescence can be detected with a photomultiplier. The entrance slit to the chamber, which is too near the exit slit of the monochromator to be shown in Fig. 7-2-3, can be covered with a thin film of ethyl cellulose in order to prevent rapid gas flow into the grating housing. The film transparency is 2 to 10% in the spectral region utilized. The light source is a repetitive, condensed, high-voltage discharge through a ceramic capillary in air at a pressure of 0.2 mm Hg. The source delivers photon pulses lasting roughly 2 μsec at a repetition rate of 60 per second. The radiation flux within the monochromator bandwidth of about 8 Å is 10^8 to 10^{10} photons per second at the exit slit for each emission line used. A Dumont 6291 photomultiplier is used to detect the fluorescence.

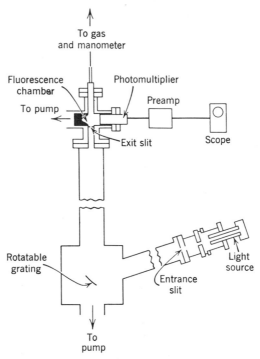

FIG. 7-2-3. Schematic diagram of apparatus used for studies of fluorescence induced by vacuum ultraviolet radiation. R. I. Schoen, D. L. Judge, and G. L. Weissler, *Proceedings of the Fifth International Conference on Ionization Phenomena in Gases*, Munich, 1961, North Holland, Amsterdam, Vol. I, 1962, p. 25.

Finally, it should be pointed out that use of the principle of detailed balancing makes it possible to obtain photoionization cross sections from cross sections, $q_c(v)$, for the inverse process, radiative capture of electrons of velocity v by positive ions. The relationship* between the two cross

---

* This equation is the *Milne formula*, which is discussed further in Section 12-5-A. The principle of detailed balancing may be applied only if the same atomic state is involved in the forward and reverse processes. However, we usually want the cross section for photoionization from the *ground* state, whereas radiative recombination generally occurs to *highly excited* states. The equivalent of (7-2-3) for *plasmas* is Kirchhoff's Law.

sections is

$$\frac{q_c(v)}{q_p(\lambda)} = \frac{\Omega_i e}{2\Omega_f mc^2} \frac{V_p^{\,2}}{300V_e} \qquad (7\text{-}2\text{-}3)$$

where Ω_i and Ω_f are the statistical weights of the initial state and the residual system in the final state, respectively; e and m are the electronic charge and mass, and V_p and V_e are the potentials (in volts) corresponding to the energies of the incident photon and the ejected electron. This relation also follows directly from quantum mechanics. V_p and V_e are related by the equation

$$h\nu = \frac{hc}{\lambda} = \frac{e(V_i + V_e)}{300} = \frac{eV_p}{300} \qquad (7\text{-}2\text{-}4)$$

where ν and λ are the frequency and wavelength of the incident radiation and V_i is the ionization potential of the neutral structure. Approximate values for $q_c(v)$ may be obtained from observations of the recombination radiation emitted by a plasma, if the electron and positive ion number densities and velocity distributions are known.[3]

7-3. EXPERIMENTAL RESULTS*

Photoabsorption data for a large number of gases and vapors are presented in Figs. 7-3-1 through 7-3-27. The papers from which these data were drawn are listed in the legends, and additional references are cited in most of them. The wavelength scale is marked off in angstrom units and in the electron-volt energy equivalents as well. The vertical arrows designated as *IP* denote ionization potentials; other arrows labeled *K*, *L*, and *M* denote X-ray absorption edges. Resonance lines and bands observed in certain instances are omitted from these figures but are included in the original articles and in the figures presented by Weissler.[2] Unless otherwise indicated, the data presented here are experimental. According to Weissler,[2] the uncertainty in most of these data is 10 to 15%.

The photoabsorption cross sections for atomic systems are essentially equal to the cross sections for photoionization. For molecular systems, on the other hand, a multiplicity of absorption mechanisms is available, and interpretation of the absorption data in terms of specific mechanisms

---

* A good compilation of data appears in *Photoionization of Atoms and Molecules* (PB 161 632; National Bureau of Standards, 1962), available from Office of Technical Services, U.S. Department of Commerce, Washington 25, D.C. This document presents quantitative data from experiments on all the alkalis, magnesium, calcium, thallium, the common gases, and all the noble gases except xenon. Absorption of ultraviolet radiation by the atmospheric gases is discussed by R. W. Ditchburn, *Proc. Roy. Soc. (London)* A-236, 216 (1956).

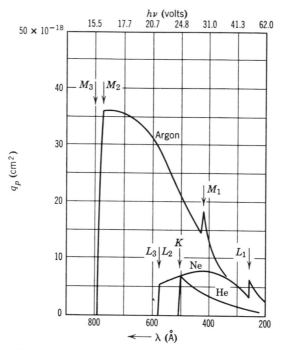

FIG. 7-3-1. Photoabsorption cross sections of A, Ne, and He. Experiment: Po Lee and G. L. Weissler, *Proc. Roy. Soc.* (*London*) **A-220**, 71 (1953); *Phys. Rev.* **99**, 540 (1955); N. Wainfan, W. C. Walker, and G. L. Weissler, *Phys Rev.* **99**, 542 (1955); D. J. Baker, D. E. Bedo, and D. H. Tomboulian, *Phys. Rev.* **124**, 1471 (1961). D. W. Ditchburn, *Proc. Phys. Soc.* (*London*) **75**, 461 (1960). For measurements on krypton and xenon see R. E. Huffman, Y. Tanaka, and J. C. Larrabee, *Appl. Optics* **2**, 947 (1963); *J. Chem. Phys.* **39**, 902 (1963). Theory: A. Dalgarno, *Proc. Phys. Soc.* (*London*) **A-65**, 663 (1952); M. J. Seaton, *Proc. Roy. Soc.* (London) **A-208**, 408 (1951); *Proc. Phys. Soc.*(London) **A-67**, 927 (1954); J. A. Wheeler, *Phys. Rev.* **43**, 258 (1933); J. P. Vinti, *Phys. Rev.* **44**, 524 (1933); A. L. Stewart and T. G. Webb, *Proc. Phys. Soc.* (*London*) **82**, 532 (1963).

is sometimes difficult.* It should be pointed out that an appreciable amount of molecular absorption may occur in vapors (such as those of the alkalis) that are predominantly monatomic. Even though the concentration of molecules may be small, their photoabsorption cross sections are large, and thus their contribution to the total absorption may be significant. Since the molecular absorption coefficient for the alkalis is·obtained by

---

* Also, many of the measurements of absorption spectra for molecular gases have been made with extraneous line sources as background or with continuous sources and instruments of insufficient resolving power to analyse the structure of the bands. These factors make the interpretation of some of the results extremely difficult. Most of the curves shown in this section are smooth curves drawn through wildly scattered points obtained by the use of line sources.

a difference method, the accuracy of the determination is inevitably low, and it is not even certain that it is to be assigned to any particular molecule. The photoabsorption cross section for molecular potassium is shown in Fig. 7-3-5. Molecular absorption in the other alkalis is discussed by Ditchburn, Jutsum, and Marr.[8]

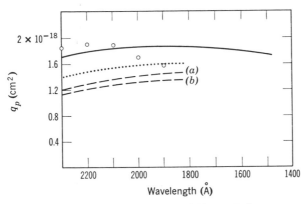

FIG. 7-3-2. Photoionization cross section of lithium. Full curve: experimental results of G. V. Marr, *Proc. Phys. Soc.* (*London*) **81**, 9 (1963). Circles: amended experimental results of J. Tunstead, *Proc. Phys. Soc.* (*London*) **A-66**, 304 (1953). Dotted curves: general formula of A. Burgess and M. J. Seaton, *MNRAS* **120**, 121 (1960). Broken curves: Hartree-Fock calculations by A. L. Stewart, *Proc. Phys. Soc.* (*London*) **A-67**, 917 (1954). (*a*) Dipole length, (*b*) dipole velocity.

Data are presented here for only three hydrocarbons: CH_4, C_2H_2, and C_2H_4. Additional references on photoabsorption by hydrocarbons and other complex structures are listed.[9]

7-4. PHOTOIONIZATION

Of all the mechanisms of photoabsorption, photoionization is the one of greatest practical importance. It is also the best understood from the theoretical point of view, so additional comment on this subject is in order here.

A. GENERAL FEATURES. The alkali vapors can be ionized by ultraviolet photons; the other metallic vapors, the noble gases, and molecular gases require radiation in the short ultraviolet or soft X-ray regions. The threshold frequency v_i and wavelength λ_i for ejection of the least tightly bound electron from an atom or molecule with a first ionization potential V_i is given by the equation

$$h v_i = h \frac{c}{\lambda_i} = e V_i \qquad (7\text{-}4\text{-}1)$$

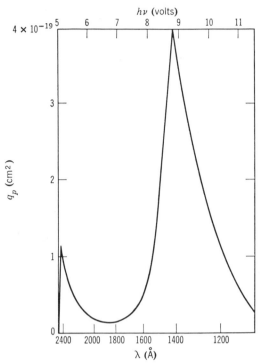

FIG. 7-3-3. Photoabsorption cross section of Na. Experiment: R. W. Ditchburn and P. J. Jutsum, *Nature* **165,** 723 (1950); R. W. Ditchburn, P. J. Jutsum, and G. V. Marr, *Proc. Roy. Soc.* (*London*) **A-219,** 89 (1953); R. D. Hudson, to be published. Theory: B. Trumpy, *Z. Physik.* **71,** 720 (1931); M. Rudkjøbing, *Publ. Kbh. Obs.* **18,** 1 (1940); M. J. Seaton, *Proc. Roy. Soc.* (*London*) **A-208,** 418 (1951).

where h is Planck's constant, c, the velocity of light in a vacuum, and e, the electronic charge. This threshold wavelength expressed in angstroms is related to the ionization potential expressed in volts by the equation

$$\lambda_i = \frac{12{,}398}{V_i} \qquad (7\text{-}4\text{-}2)$$

Ionization at wavelengths longer than this threshold value can occur in a two-step process involving an atom or molecule that has already been excited. Wavelengths shorter than λ_i are required for ejection of electrons other than the one with the smallest binding energy in the atom.

An ultraviolet photon ionizes an atom by ejecting one of the outermost electrons, but X rays act preferentially on the more tightly bound inner electrons. If a photon interacting with an atom has enough energy to ionize the target particle by ejecting an electron from the innermost shell,

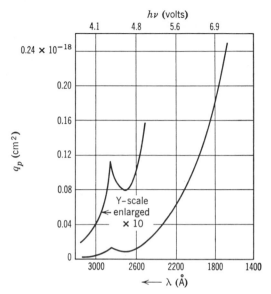

FIG. 7-3-4. Photoabsorption cross section of K. Experiment: R. W. Ditchburn, J. Tunstead, and J. G. Yates, *Proc. Roy. Soc.* (*London*) **A-181**, 386 (1943); F. L. Mohler and C. Boeckner, *J. Res. Nat. Bur. Standards* **3**, 303 (1929); E. O. Lawrence and N. E. Edlefsen, *Phys. Rev.* **34**, 1056 (1929). Theory: D. R. Bates, *Proc. Roy. Soc.* (*London*) **A-188**, 350 (1947); M. J. Seaton, *Proc. Roy. Soc.* (*London*) **A-208**, 418 (1951).

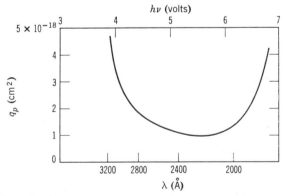

FIG. 7-3-5. Photoabsorption cross section of K_2. Experiment: R. W. Ditchburn, J. Tunstead, and J. G. Yates, *Proc. Roy. Soc.* (*London*) **A-181**, 386 (1943).

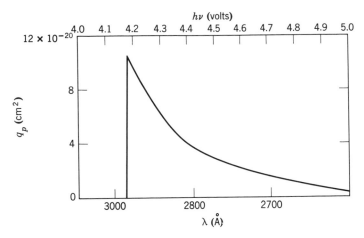

FIG. 7-3-6. Photoabsorption cross section of Rb. Experiment: F. L. Mohler and C. Boeckner, *J. Res. Nat. Bur. Standards* **3**, 303 (1929); E. O. Lawrence and N. E. Edlefsen, *Phys. Rev.* **34**, 233, 1056 (1929). Theory: M. J. Seaton, *Proc. Roy. Soc.* (*London*) **A-208**, 418 (1951).

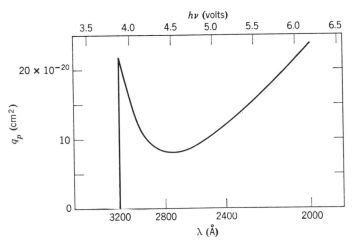

FIG. 7-3-7. Photoabsorption cross section of Cs. Experiment: F. L. Mohler and C. Boeckner, *J. Res. Nat. Bur. Standards* **3**, 303 (1929); H. J. J. Braddick and R. W. Ditchburn, *Proc. Roy. Soc.* (*London*) **A-143**, 472 (1934); E. O. Lawrence and N. E. Edlefsen, *Phys. Rev.* **34**, 233, 1056 (1929). Theory: M. J. Seaton, *Proc. Roy. Soc.* (*London*) **A-208**, 418 (1951).

it is likely that the electron ejected will be from that shell. In plots of the photoionization cross section for atoms peaks occur at the photon energies corresponding to the X-ray absorption edges. The cross section rises abruptly as one of these edges is approached from the low energy side. Generally, q_p then decreases gradually as the photon energy is raised above the threshold for the shell in question. This type of behavior is illustrated by helium, sodium, rubidium, and magnesium (Figs. 7-3-1, 7-3-3, 7-3-6, and 7-3-8). For some atoms, however, the photoionization

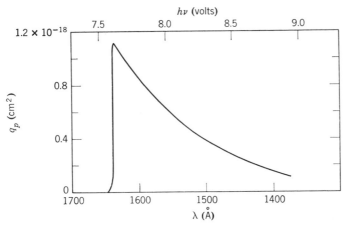

FIG. 7-3-8. Photoabsorption cross section of Mg. Experiment: R. W. Ditchburn and G. V. Marr, *Proc. Phys. Soc.* (*London*) **A-66,** 655 (1953).

cross section continues to rise and then falls as the threshold is passed in the direction of increasing photon energy: Fig. 7-3-1 shows a distinct, broad maximum for neon between the L_1 and L_2 absorption edges, and the cross section for argon has a slight peak close to the M_2 edge on the high energy side.

It should be noted that photoionization differs in several important respects from ionization by particle impact, in which outer electrons are preferentially ejected regardless of the bombarding energy and the cross sections for ionization always peak at energies considerably above the threshold values. Furthermore, in impact ionization frequently more than one electron is ejected. At high projectile energies the energy transferred to the target structure is sometimes viewed as being distributed among many electrons, with an evaporation-type ejection of electrons subsequently taking place (see the discussion of the Russek-Thomas theory in Section 6-7-B). In photoionization, on the other hand, the cross section curve often peaks right at threshold, and, further, only a single electron is ejected by a given photon.

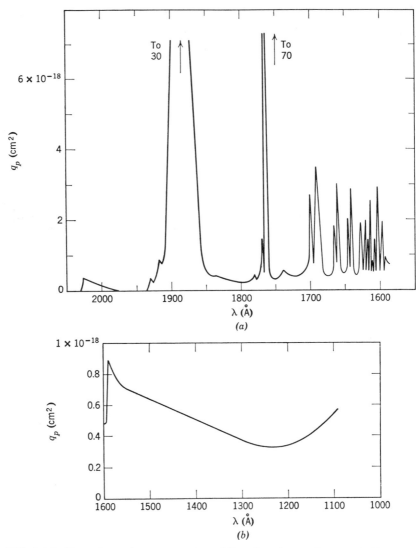

FIG. 7-3-9. Photoabsorption cross section of Ca. Experiment: R. W. Ditchburn and R. D. Hudson, *Proc. Roy. Soc. (London)* **A-256**, 53 (1960); P. J. Jutsum, *Proc. Phys. Soc. (London)* **A-67**, 190 (1954); T. R. Kaiser, *Proc. Phys. Soc. (London)* **75**, 152 (1960). Theory: D. R. Bates and H. S. W. Massey, *Proc. Roy. Soc. (London)* **A-177**, 329 (1941); M. J. Seaton, *Ann. Astrophys.* **18**, 206 (1955).

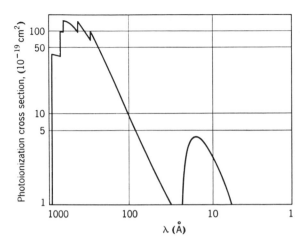

FIG. 7-3-10. Photoionization cross section of atomic oxygen. Theory: A. Dalgarno and D. Parkinson, *J. Atmospheric Terrestr. Phys.* **18**, 335 (1960).

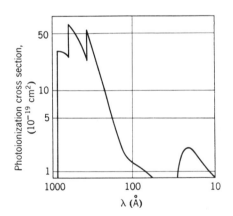

FIG. 7-3-11. Photoionization cross section of atomic nitrogen. Theory: A. Dalgarno and D. Parkinson, *J. Atmospheric Terrestr. Phys.* **18**, 335 (1960).

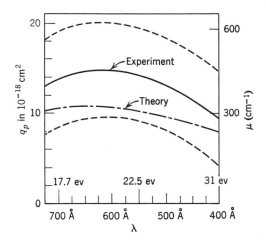

FIG. 7-3-12. Photoabsorption cross section of atomic nitrogen. Experiment: A. W. Ehler and G. L. Weissler, *J. Opt. Soc. Am.* **45**, 1035 (1955). Theory: D. R. Bates and M. J. Seaton, *Mon. Not. Roy. Astron. Soc.* **109**, 698 (1949).

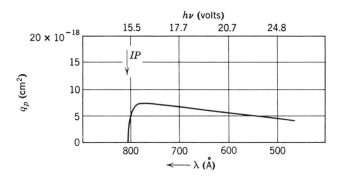

FIG. 7-3-13. Photoabsorption cross section of H_2. Experiment: Po Lee and G. L. Weissler, *Astrophys. J.* **115**, 570 (1952). N. Wainfan, W. C. Walker, and G. L. Weissler, *Phys. Rev.* **99**, 542 (1955); S. M. Bunch, G. R. Cook, M. Ogawa, and A. W. Ehler, *J. Chem. Phys.* **28**, 740 (1958); E. Schönheit, *Z. Naturforsch.* **15-A**, 841 (1960).

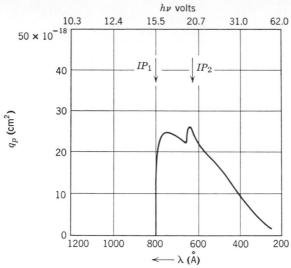

FIG. 7-3-14. Photoabsorption cross section of N_2. Experiment: G. L. Weissler, Po Lee, and E. I. Mohr, *J. Opt. Soc. Am.* **42**, 84 (1952). N. Wainfan, W. C. Walker and G. L. Weissler, *Phys. Rev.* **99**, 542 (1955); *J. Appl. Phys.* **24**, 1318 (1953). K. C. Clark, *Phys. Rev.* **87**, 271 (1952). Po Lee, *J. Opt. Soc. Am.* **45**, 703 (1955). R. E. Huffman, Y. Tanaka, and J. C. Larrabee, *J. Chem. Phys.* **39**, 910 (1963).

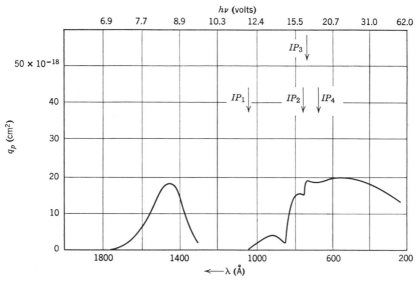

FIG. 7-3-15. Photoabsorption cross section of O_2. Experiment: R. W. Ditchburn and D. W. O. Heddle, *Proc. Roy. Soc.* (*London*) **A-220**, 61 (1953), **A-226**, 509 (1954); G. L. Weissler and Po Lee, *J. Opt. Soc. Am.* **42**, 200 (1952); Po Lee, *J. Opt. Soc. Am.* **45**, 703 (1955); K. Watanabe, E. C. Y. Inn, and M. Zelikoff, *J. Chem. Phys.* **21**, 1026 (1953); N. Wainfan, W. C. Walker, and G. L. Weissler, *J. Appl. Phys.* **24**, 1318 (1953); *Phys. Rev.* **99**, 542 (1955); K. Watanabe and F. F. Marmo, *J. Chem. Phys.*, **25**, 965 (1956); R. W. Ditchburn and P. A. Young, *J. Atmospheric Terrestr. Phys.*, **24**, 127 (1962).

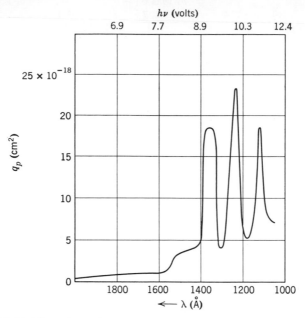

FIG. 7-3-16. Photoabsorption cross section of O_3. Experiment: Y. Tanaka, E. C. Y. Inn, and K. Watanabe, *J. Chem. Phys.* **21,** 1651 (1953); A. G. Hearn, *Proc. Phys. Soc. (London)* **78,** 932 (1961); M. Ogawa and G. R. Cook, *J. Chem. Phys.* **28,** 173 (1958).

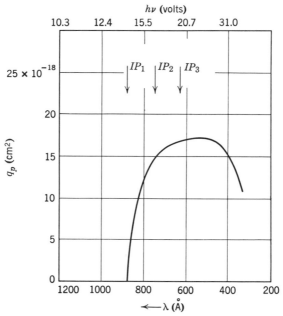

FIG. 7-3-17. Photoabsorption cross section of CO. Experiment: H. Sun and G. L. Weissler, *J. Chem. Phys.* **23,** 1625 (1955).

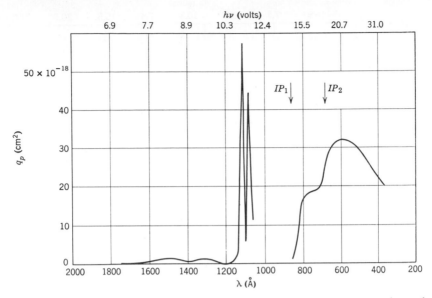

FIG. 7-3-18. Photoabsorption cross section of CO_2. E. C. Y. Inn, K. Watanabe, and M. Zelikoff, *J. Chem. Phys.* **21,** 1648 (1953); H. Sun and G. L. Weissler, *J. Chem. Phys.* **23,** 1625 (1955); P. G. Wilkinson and H. L. Johnston, *J. Chem. Phys.* **18,** 190 (1950); N. Wainfan, W. C. Walker, and G. L. Weissler, *Phys. Rev.* **99,** 542 (1955).

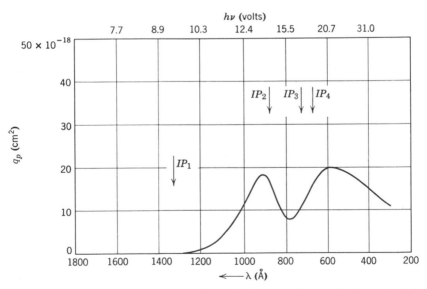

FIG. 7-3-19. Photoabsorption cross section of NO. Experiment: H. Sun and G. L. Weissler, *J. Chem. Phys.* **23,** 1372 (1955); W. C. Walker and G. L. Weissler, *J. Chem. Phys.* **23,** 1962 (1955); F. F. Marmo, *J. Opt. Soc. Am.* **43,** 1186 (1953).

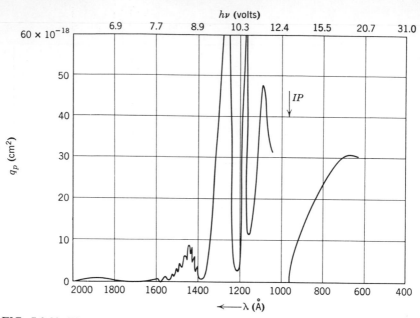

FIG. 7-3-20. Photoabsorption cross section of N_2O. Experiment: M. Zelikoff, K. Watanabe, and E. C. Y. Inn, *J. Chem. Phys.* **21**, 1643 (1953); W. C. Walker and G. L. Weissler, *J. Chem. Phys.* **23**, 1962 (1955).

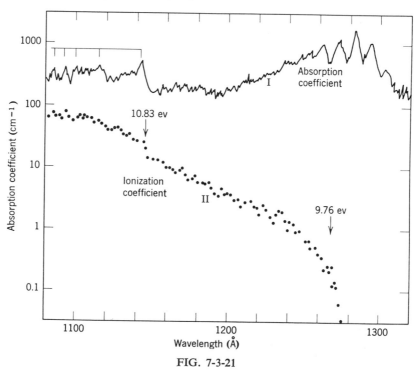

FIG. 7-3-21

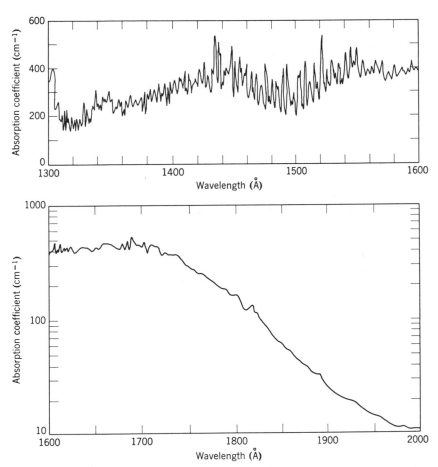

FIG. 7-3-21. Photoabsorption coefficients of nitrogen dioxide, NO_2. Experiment:
T. Nakayama, M. Y. Kitamura, and K. Watanabe, *J. Chem. Phys.* **30,** 1180 (1959).

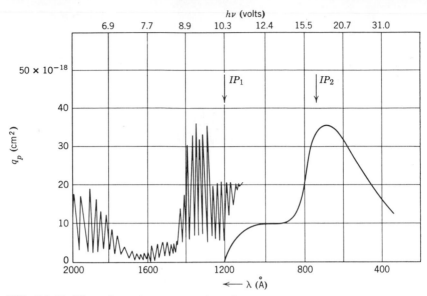

FIG. 7-3-22. Photoabsorption cross section of NH_3. Experiment: K. Watanabe, *J. Chem. Phys.* **22,** 1564 (1954); H. Sun and G. L. Weissler, *J. Chem. Phys.* **23,** 1160 (1955); W. C. Walker and G. L. Weissler, *J. Chem. Phys.* **23,** 1540 (1955).

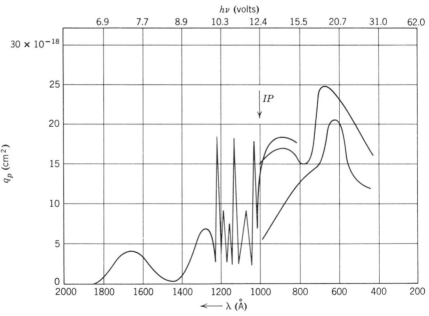

FIG. 7-3-23. Photoabsorption cross section of H_2O. Experiment: P. G. Wilkinson and H. L. Johnston, *J. Chem. Phys.* **18,** 190 (1950); K. Watanabe and M. Zelikoff, *J. Opt. Soc. Am.* **43,** 753 (1953). N. Wainfan, W. C. Walker, and G. L. Weissler, *Phys. Rev.* **99,** 542 (1955).

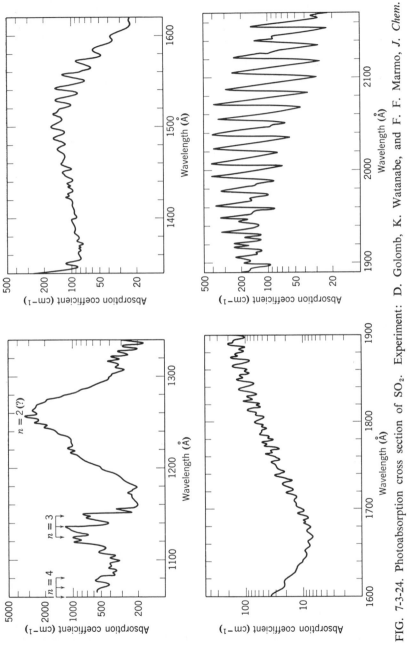

FIG. 7-3-24. Photoabsorption cross section of SO_2. Experiment: D. Golomb, K. Watanabe, and F. F. Marmo, *J. Chem. Phys.* **36**, 958 (1962).

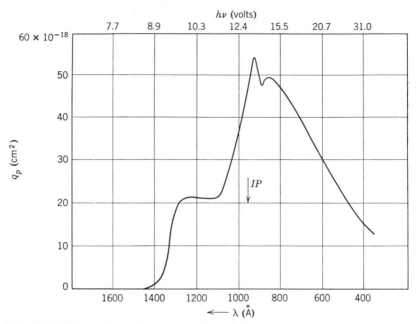

FIG. 7-3-25. Photoabsorption cross section of CH_4. Experiment: P. G. Wilkinson and H. L. Johnston, *J. Chem. Phys.* **18**, 190 (1950); G. Moe and A. B. F. Duncan, *J. Am. Chem. Soc.* **74**, 3140 (1952); R. W. Ditchburn, *Proc. Roy. Soc. (London)* A-229, 44 (1955); H. Sun and G. L. Weissler, *J. Chem. Phys.* **23**, 1160 (1955); N. Wainfan, W. C. Walker, and G. L. Weissler, *Phys. Rev.* **99**, 542 (1955). Theory: A. Dalgarno, *Proc. Phys. Soc. (London)* A-65, 663 (1952).

B. THEORY.* The theory of radiative transitions is developed from time-dependent perturbation theory in most books on quantum mechanics.[10] The transition probability per unit time for an upward transition of an atomic electron from state n to state k is given by the expression

$$\frac{4\pi^2 e^2}{m^2 c \omega_{kn}^2} I(\omega_{kn}) \left| \int \psi_k^*(\exp i\mathbf{k} \cdot \mathbf{r}) \operatorname{grad}_A \psi_n \, d\tau \right|^2 \tag{7-4-3}$$

where $\omega_{kn} = (E_k - E_n)/\hbar$ is the angular frequency associated with the energy change $(E_k - E_n)$; $I(\omega_{kn})$ is the intensity of the incident radiation per unit angular frequency at the frequency ω_{kn}; ψ_k and ψ_n are the final and initial wave functions, respectively; and $\mathbf{k}$ is the propagation vector

* The theory of photoionization is similar to that of photodetachment of electrons from negative ions, which is discussed by L. M. Branscomb in "Photodetachment," in *Atomic and Molecular Processes* (edited by D. R. Bates), Academic, New York, 1962, pp. 100–140.

of the incident radiation.   The magnitude of **k** is ω_{kn}/c, where c is the velocity of light in a vacuum.   The electronic charge and mass are denoted by e and m, respectively.   The symbol grad_A denotes the component of the gradient operator along the polarization vector of the incident wave.

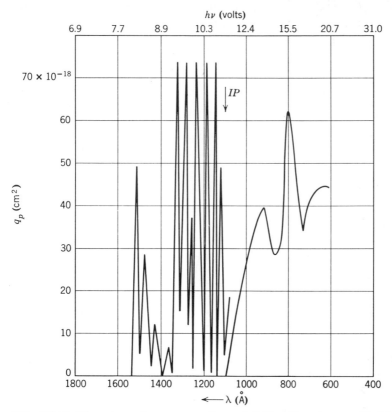

FIG. 7-3-26.   Photoabsorption cross section of C_2H_2.   Experiment: G. Moe and A. B. F. Duncan, *J. Am. Chem. Soc.* **74**, 3136 (1952); W. C. Walker and G. L. Weissler, *J. Chem. Phys.* **23**, 1547 (1955).

If the wavelength of the incident radiation is long compared with the distances over which the wave functions are appreciable, we may make the *dipole approximation*, replacing the exponential factor in (7-4-3) by unity.   Then the integral becomes

$$-\int \psi_k^* \, \text{grad}_A \, \psi_n \, d\tau = -\frac{m}{\hbar} \, \omega_{kn} \int \psi_k^* \, r_A \psi_n \, d\tau \qquad (7\text{-}4\text{-}4)$$

where r_A is the component of the radius vector **r** along the direction of polarization.   The quantity $e\mathbf{r}$ is the electric dipole moment of the electron with respect to an arbitrarily located origin. The addition of a constant vector to $\mathbf{r}$, which would correspond to a shift in the origin, does not affect the matrix element, since ψ_k and ψ_n are orthogonal. Transitions for which the probability can be computed by substitution of (7-4-4) into (7-4-3) are called *electric dipole transitions*, since only the matrix element of the electric dipole moment of the electron is involved.

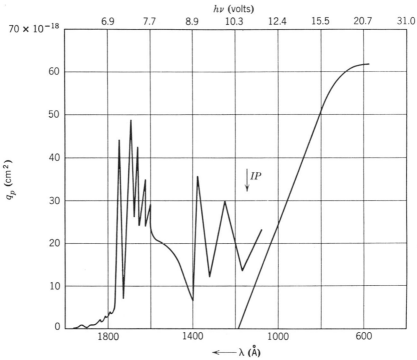

FIG. 7-3-27. Photoabsorption cross section of C_2H_4. Experiment: M. Zelikoff and K. Watanabe, *J. Opt. Soc. Am.* **43**, 756 (1953); W. C. Walker and G. L. Weissler, *J. Chem. Phys.* **23**, 1547 (1955); P. G. Wilkinson and H. L. Johnston, *J. Chem. Phys.* **18**, 190 (1950); J. R. Platt, H. B. Klevens, and W. C. Price, *J. Chem. Phys.* **17**, 466 (1949).

The spectral regions of main interest to us are those corresponding to ultraviolet and soft X-ray radiation, where the wavelength (several thousand to several hundred angstroms) is large compared with atomic dimensions (a few angstroms). Hence the dipole approximation is excellent for our purposes. Using the dipole approximation and assuming only a single electron to be directly involved, Bates[11] writes the formula for the photoionization cross section in the form

$$q_{pv} = \frac{32\pi^4 m^2 e^2}{3h^3 c} \frac{1}{\Omega_i} \sum_i \sum_f vv C_p \left| \int \psi_i^* \left(\sum_j \mathbf{r}_j \right) \psi_f(E) \, d\tau \right|^2 \qquad (7\text{-}4\text{-}5)$$

Here $\mathbf{r}_j$ is the position vector of the jth electron, with the sum $\sum_j \mathbf{r}_j$ charac-terizing the dipole moment, Ω_i is the statistical weight of the initial level, and ν is the frequency of the incident radiation; ψ_i is the normalized wave function for the bound initial state, and $\psi_f(E)$ is the normalized wave function for the ion together with the ejected electron, which has velocity v; C_p is a factor, only slightly less than unity, which allows for the distortion of the wave function of the passive electrons, that is, all electrons in the atom except the one that is ejected. The frequency of the incident radiation is related to the kinetic energy E of the ejected electron by the Einstein relation

$$h\nu = eV_i + E \qquad (7\text{-}4\text{-}6)$$

where V_i is the ionization potential of the atom. The exact application of (7-4-5) would surely yield accurate results. However, such a procedure is not feasible, and resort must be made to approximations.

The integral in (7-4-5) is known as the dipole length matrix element. It may be expressed in terms of the dipole momentum matrix element by use of the identity (for exact wave functions)

$$\int \psi_i^* \left(\sum_j \mathbf{r}_j \right) \psi_f(E) \, d\tau = \left(\frac{-1}{2\pi i \nu m} \right) \int \psi_i^* \left(\sum_j \mathbf{p}_j \right) \psi_f(E) \, d\tau \quad (7\text{-}4\text{-}7)$$

where $\mathbf{p}_j$ is the momentum operator for the jth electron. Still another formulation involves the dipole acceleration matrix element, but wave functions are usually not known with sufficient precision for accurate results to be obtained in this formulation.[12] The main contributions to the foregoing matrix elements come from different regions of space, and generally one of the integrals is more appropriate for use with the available wave functions than the others. There are no general rules to apply in the choice among the various formulations, but certain points are to be considered in making the decision.[13] The wave functions for use in these calculations have usually been obtained from the Hartree-Fock equations (i.e., the self-consistent field with exchange). More recently the quantum defect method* has been utilized for this purpose.

Bates[14] in 1946 gave a summary of the theoretical calculations of cross sections for neutral atoms and positive and negative ions which had been made up to that time. He pointed out that the integrations in the calculations are particularly sensitive to the form of the wave functions employed, since the integrand is positive in some regions of space and negative in others, and the exact value of the integral is strongly dependent on the amount of cancellation.[15] In a companion paper,[11] already referred

* For discussions of the quantum defect method, see *Atomic and Molecular Processes* (edited by D. R. Bates), Academic, New York, 1962, pp. 325–326; T. Y. Wu and T. Ohmura, *The Quantum Theory of Scattering*, Prentice-Hall, Englewood Cliffs, N.J., 1962, pp. 91–92.

to, Bates derived an approximate formula for the continuous radiative absorption cross sections of the lighter atoms and positive and negative ions and applied it specifically to Be, C^+, N^+, O^+, F^+, Ne^+, and Na^+.

In 1951 Seaton[13] summarized the theoretical work that had been done on the elements from boron to neon and described detailed calculations he had made on neon, using both the dipole length and dipole momentum formulations. In Part II of this paper Seaton[16] compared theory and experiment for the alkali metals. Details of a calculation he had made on sodium were described, and it was shown that the essential features of the experimental results could be reproduced. The nonzero minimum that appears experimentally in the data on alkali metals was shown to be attributable to the spin-orbit perturbations of the free electron wave function.

More recently, Burgess and Seaton[17] derived a general formula for the calculation of atomic photoionization cross sections based on the model of a single electron moving in a central field. Approximate bound-state radial wave functions which are accurate at large r may be obtained for use in this formula once the effective quantum numbers $\nu(=n^*)$ are known. Bates and Damgaard[18] have shown that such functions may be used to obtain good estimates for bound-bound transition integrals. For bound-free transitions Burgess and Seaton use approximate free-state radial functions which have the exact asymptotic form. The phases are given by $\delta = \pi\mu$, where μ is the extrapolated quantum defect ($\mu = n - \nu$). Burgess and Seaton summarized the results of extensive numerical calculations in tables that permit the rapid calculation of transition integrals once the energy levels are known. Both bound-free and bound-bound transition integrals may be obtained. The results of Burgess and Seaton were compared with other results from theory and experiment. In nearly all cases their general formula gave results that were at least as accurate as those obtained in the best alternative methods of calculation. However, Moiseiwitsch[19] has recently argued that Seaton's formulation of the quantum defect method gives inexact phase shifts except at threshold, and he offers a more general formulation.

References to many other theoretical papers appear in the legends of the figures in Section 7-3. Ditchburn and Öpik[3] list additional papers and tabulate the results for many structures, including a number of positive ions. Of particular interest are the theoretical results for hydrogen-like structures (H, He^+, Li^{2+}, etc.). No experimental data are available for these systems, but the cross sections may be calculated by the equation

$$q_p(\nu, n) = \frac{g(32\pi^2 e^6 R Z^4)}{(3^{3/2} h^3 \nu^3 n^5)} \tag{7-4-8}$$

which is effectively exact. Here R is the Rydberg constant, n is the principal quantum number of the initial state, and g is a complicated factor to whose evaluation Ditchburn and Öpik give references.

Ditchburn and Öpik also point out that autoionization is important for many elements, among which are Ca, Ba, In, Ga, Cu, and Tl. Auto-ionization must always be considered in the calculation of photoionization cross sections and can seldom be regarded as a mere correction. Pre-ionization may be important in the case of molecules. Little theoretical work has been done on molecules and molecular ions, principally because of the difficulty of obtaining accurate electronic wave functions.

Finally, it should be mentioned that photoionization cross sections can be useful in the estimation of cross sections for ionization by electron impact.[20,21] If $q_p(\lambda)$ is known for two structures at threshold and $q_i(v)$ is also known for one of these systems at threshold and upward, the photoionization cross section for the second structure can be obtained approximately for threshold and higher energies by a comparison procedure.

C. PRODUCTION OF ARTIFICIAL ION CLOUDS IN THE UPPER ATMOSPHERE. The importance of photoionization of species normally present in the upper atmosphere was briefly mentioned in the introduction to this chapter. The production of artificial ion clouds by photoionization of rocket-borne material is also of interest, having proved to be an important means of studying the upper atmosphere. The alkalis and alkaline earths have been especially valuable in this regard because of their low ionization potentials. As pointed out by Hudson,[22] one of the main interests in the absorption coefficients of these metals arises from the desire to know the rate of ionization if one of them is dispersed as a cloud in the upper atmosphere. If we assume that the material is dispersed in a thin layer, the probability per second of photoionization at a given wavelength is equal to the product of the photon flux at this wavelength above the atmosphere and the photoionization cross section. For wavelengths below the series limit this cross section can be taken to be numerically equal to the absorption cross section.

Marmo, Pressman, and Aschenbrand[23] have published a table of photoionization rates to be expected for several metal vapors. They obtained these rates by integrating the product of the photon flux and the measured cross section from the series limit to the lowest wavelength for which values of the cross section were available at the time. Some of their results are given in Table 7-4-1, which also contains values calculated more recently by Hudson,[22] who had more data at his disposal. Hudson's value for sodium is lower by a factor of 2.5 than that given by Marmo et al.[23] This is a large discrepancy in light of the fact that Marmo used data that extended down only to 1600 Å, whereas Hudson's data extended to much lower wavelengths (see Fig. 7-3-3).

The result shown in Table 7-4-1 for calcium is interesting in that the majority of the ionization (2.2×10^{-5} ions/sec) is produced by the auto-ionization lines. According to Hudson,[22] it is likely that a similar result would be obtained for strontium and barium.

TABLE 7-4-1. Calculated photoionization rates in the upper atmosphere for the alkalis and magnesium and calcium

Metal	Probability of Photoionization per Atom per Second	Reference
Lithium	1.38×10^{-4}	23
Sodium	4.0×10^{-6}	22
Potassium	1.85×10^{-5}	23
Rubidium	1.06×10^{-4}	23
Cesium	$\cdot 6.5 \times 10^{-4}$	23
Magnesium	3.6×10^{-6}	23
Calcium	2.5×10^{-5}	22

Additional discussion of photoionization in the upper atmosphere appears in the report by Nawrocki and Papa.[24]

REFERENCES

1. M. J. Seaton, *Proc. Roy. Soc.* (*London*) **A-208**, 408, (1951). K. Watanabe, "Ultra-violet Absorption Process in the Upper Atmosphere," in *Advances in Geophysics*, Vol. 5, Academic, New York, 1958, pp. 153–221. H. S. W. Massey and R. L. F. Boyd, *The Upper Atmosphere*, Hutchinson, London, 1960. *Physics of the Upper Atmosphere* (edited by J. A. Ratcliffe), Academic, New York, 1960. *Papers from the Symposium on Collision Phenomena in Astrophysics, Geophysics, and Masers*, Boulder, Colo., 1961 (Technical Note 124, U.S. National Bureau of Standards, December 1961).
2. G. L. Weissler, "Photoionization in Gases and Photoelectric Emission from Solids," in *Handbuch der Physik*, Vol. XXI, Springer-Verlag, Berlin, 1956, pp. 304–341.
3. R. W. Ditchburn and U. Öpik, "Photoionization Processes," in *Atomic and Molecular Processes* (edited by D. R. Bates), Academic, New York, 1962.
4. R. D. Evans, *The Atomic Nucleus*, McGraw-Hill, New York, 1955, Chapters 23–25. "The Compton Effect," in *Handbuch der Physik*, Vol. XXXIV, Springer-Verlag, Berlin, 1958, pp. 218–298.
5. See G. Herzberg, *Molecular Spectra and Molecular Structure*, Second Edition, Van Nostrand, Princeton, N.J., 1950. R. A. Harris, *J. Chem. Phys.* **39**, 978 (1963).
6. Some of the earlier references to this type of work are H. Hurzeler, M. G. Inghram, and J. D. Morrison, *J. Chem. Phys.* **27**, 313 (1957) and **28**, 76 (1958). E. Schönheit, *Z. Physik* **149**, 153 (1957). R. F. Herzog and F. F. Marmo, *J. Chem. Phys.* **27**, 1202

(1957).   G. L. Weissler, J. A. R. Samson, M. Ogawa, and G. R. Cook, *J. Opt. Soc. Am.* **49,** 338 (1959).

7. R. I. Schoen, D. L. Judge, and G. L. Weissler, *Proceedings of the Fifth International Conference on Ionization Phenomena in Gases,* Munich, 1961, North-Holland, Amsterdam (1962), Vol. I, p. 25. See also R. E. Huffman, Y. Tanaka, and J. C. Larrabee, *J. Chem. Phys.* **38,** 1920 (1963).

8. R. W. Ditchburn, P. J. Jutsum, and G. V. Marr, *Proc. Roy. Soc. (London)* **A-219,** 89 (1953).

9. S. M. Bunch, G. R. Cook, M. Ogawa, and A. W. Ehler, *J. Chem. Phys.* **28,** 740 (1958);   M. Ogawa and G. R. Cook, **28,** 747 (1958);   B. Steiner, C. F. Giese, and M. G. Inghram, **34,** 189 (1961);   J. A. R. Samson, F. F. Marmo, and K. Watanabe, **36,** 783 (1962);   F. A. Elder, C. Giese, B. Steiner, and M. Inghram, **36,** 3292 (1962); R. I. Schoen, **37,** 2032 (1962).

10. See, for example, L. I. Schiff, *Quantum Mechanics,* Second Edition, McGraw-Hill, 1955, Section 35.   D. R. Bates, "Transitions," appearing in *Quantum Theory,* Vol. I (edited by D. R. Bates), Academic, New York, 1961.   The present discussion of transition probabilities is based on the treatment by Schiff.

11. D. R. Bates, *Mon. Not. Roy. Astron. Soc.* **106,** 423 (1946).

12. L. M. Branscomb, "Photodetachment," in *Atomic and Molecular Processes* (edited by D. R. Bates), Academic, New York, 1962.   L. H. Aller, *Gaseous Nebulae,* Wiley, New York, 1956, Chapter IV.

13. M. J. Seaton, *Proc. Roy. Soc. (London)* **A-208,** 408 (1951).

14. D. R. Bates, *Mon. Not. Roy. Astron. Soc.* **106,** 432 (1946).

15. See figures illustrating this point in D. R. Bates, *Proc. Roy. Soc. (London)* **A-188,** 350 (1947).   This difficulty is particularly severe in calculations on sodium and potassium.

16. M. J. Seaton, *Proc. Roy. Soc. (London)* **A-208,** 418 (1951).

17. A. Burgess and M. J. Seaton, *Mon. Not. Roy. Astron. Soc.* **120,** 121 (1960).

18. D. R. Bates and A. Damgaard, *Phil. Trans. Roy. Soc. (London)* **A-242,** 101 (1949).

19. B. L. Moiseiwitsch, *Proc. Phys. Soc. (London)* **79,** 1166 (1962);   **81,** 35 (1963).

20. M. J. Seaton, *Phys. Rev.* **113,** 814 (1959).

21. M. R. C. McDowell and G. Peach, *Phys. Rev.* **121,** 1383 (1961).

22. R. D. Hudson, "The Absorption Coefficients of the Alkali Metals and the Alkali Earths," University of Southern California, Report No. AFCRL-TN-60-680, June 28, 1960.

23. F. F. Marmo, J. Pressman, and L. M. Aschenbrand, *Planetary and Space Science* **1,** 291 (1959).

24. P. J. Nawrocki and R. Papa, *Atmospheric Processes,* Prentice-Hall, Englewood Cliffs, N.J., 1962.

8

NEGATIVE IONS

A negative ion is an atom, molecule, or molecular complex with a net negative charge. Such ions may exist either (a) in liquids or solids or (b) in the gaseous phase, and some species of negative ions are known to exist in all three states of matter. However, since the ions are in intimate contact with neighboring particles in (a) but not in (b), some differences may be expected, and indeed are sometimes observed, in the general characteristics of the negative ions found in the two types of environment. The negative ions occurring in electrolytes and ionic crystals are frequently multiply charged and often are quite complex structures. Free negative ions, on the other hand, can accommodate only a single net negative charge (at least for times long enough to permit observation), and generally, but not always, their structure is less complex than that of the ions in liquids or solids.

In this chapter we shall deal only with gaseous ions and mainly with those ions of particular geophysical and astrophysical importance. We shall be concerned with the structure and stability of negative ions, the methods of their formation, and the detachment of electrons from the ions to form neutral atoms and molecules. Negative ions may be formed directly in the gas phase by the attachment of free electrons, by the dissociation of a neutral molecule or a molecular ion into positive and negative fragments, and by the capture of one or more electrons by one heavy particle in a collision with another. The last mechanism of formation, involving charge transfer, was discussed in Chapter 6 and is not treated here. Negative ions may also be produced in various types of surface phenomena, the discussion of which is deferred to Chapter 13.

A number of comprehensive reviews of negative ion physics exist.[1-10] Since several of these works (especially those of Loeb[3,4]) give exhaustive coverage of the historical development of the field, we shall discuss first some of the basic aspects of the structure of negative ions, and then turn to recent developments in negative ion research. The emphasis here is on work done since the mid-1950's, since few investigations made before that time have not been superseded by more refined studies.

8-1. THE STRUCTURE AND SPECTRA OF NEGATIVE IONS; THE ELECTRON AFFINITY

A. NEGATIVE ATOMIC IONS.   A neutral atom may be regarded as consisting of a point-charge nucleus surrounded by a cloud of atomic electrons. If an additional electron is brought near the atom, it finds itself in an attractive force field which falls off much more rapidly with distance than that acting on one of the atomic electrons in the neutral atom. In the neutral atom, the asymptotic behavior of the field is coulombic, whereas an additional electron in the field of an H atom, for instance, feels something like an inverse-fourth-power attractive potential.* A negative ion may thus be considered in terms of the stationary states of an electron in an attractive field which falls off very rapidly with distance. The number of stationary states is therefore likely to be finite, as contrasted with the infinite number in a Coulomb field. This fact, together with the Pauli exclusion principle, imposes a severe restriction on the number of elements that can form a negative ion.

In the H atom there is a vacancy in the lowest ($n = 1$) level, and the possibility exists for capture of a second electron into the $1s$ subshell, close to the nucleus of the atom. The shielding of the nuclear field by the $1s$ electron already present might then be thought to be weak enough to permit the second electron to be bound by the nuclear field, and the

---

* Massey[1] shows that if polarization effects are ignored the potential energy of an electron at a distance r from a ground-state hydrogen atom is

$$V(r) = -e^2 e^{-2r/a_0} (1/r + 1/a_0),$$

where a_0 is the radius of the first Bohr orbit of the hydrogen atom. However, as pointed out by Massey, polarization effects probably modify the potential to one of inverse-fourth-power form.

existence of the H^- ion, identified experimentally many years ago, is not at all surprising.

In He, however, the $n = 1$ level is fully occupied, and an additional electron can be bound to the atom only in the $n = 2$ state or one of higher quantum number. The nuclear field in the He atom is strongly attenuated by the atomic electrons at distances corresponding to shells with $n > 1$, and until recently it was generally held that the He^- ion could not exist at all.[1] The ion has, however, been observed experimentally,* and indeed variational calculations made in 1955[12] show that the doubly excited $(1s2s2p)^4P_{5/2}$ state of the ion is not subject to autoionization and should be metastable, with a measurably long lifetime, although the extra electron is very weakly bound to the atom. It is still held that He^- cannot exist in the ground configuration $(1s^2 2s)(^2S)$.[10]

In general, those atoms with completely filled outer shells are unlikely to form negative ions. The additional electron would have to be attached in a state of higher total quantum number than that of the outermost atomic electrons, and usually the attractive force is too weak at distances corresponding to these states. Those atoms with single vacancies in their outer shells should be the most likely of all to attach electrons, since in these structures the outer atomic electrons have very little effect in shielding the added electron from the nucleus. Thus it is to be expected that the noble gases should be unable to form stable negative ions but that the halogens should prove to be highly electronegative;† experiment confirms this expectation.

Although the foregoing considerations help us to understand why some atoms form negative ions and others do not, it is necessary to make detailed calculations to obtain quantitative information about an individual atomic species. A necessary condition is supplied by energy considerations, for if a given species of negative ion is to be stable, its binding energy must be greater than that of the corresponding neutral atom. The criterion for stability of a negative ion formed by an atom of Z electrons may therefore

---

* By now many investigators have observed the He^- ion, presumably in the $^4P_{5/2}$ state, and Sweetman[11] has experimentally determined a lower limit of 10^{-5} sec for its lifetime. The He^- ion was first identified as a weak trace in a mass spectrograph by J. W. Hiby, *Ann. Phys.* **34**, 473 (1939), but its existence was not generally acknowledged until the calculation of Holøien and Midtdal was published.[12] It should be pointed out that no contradiction results between the structure arguments presented above and the demonstrated existence of doubly excited, metastable ions such as He^- in the $^4P_{5/2}$ configuration. Quite analogous to this ion is the $N^-(^1D)$ ion. The $N^-(^3P)$ ground state lies in the continuum of $[N(^4S) + e]$, but $N^-(^1D)$ is metastable, because of spin conservation requirements. An interesting contrast between negative and positive ions is that negative ions may exist as unstable species with no infinitely lived bound states at all.
† A gas is said to be *electronegative* if it can pick up electrons and form negative ions.

be expressed as

$$E_1 + \sum_{i=1}^{Z} E_i^- > \sum_{i=1}^{Z} E_i^0$$

or

$$E_1 - \sum_{i=1}^{Z} (E_i^0 - E_i^-) > 0 \tag{8-1-1}$$

where E_i^0 is the binding energy of the ith atomic electron before the attachment takes place, E_i^- is the binding energy of that electron after the attachment, and E_1 is the binding energy of the attached electron. The quantity on the left-hand side of (8-1-1) is called the *electron affinity* of the atom and represents the difference in total energy of the normal states of the atom and ion. This energy, which is denoted by EA, also equals that required to detach the least tightly bound electron from the ion* (the *detachment energy* of the ion). A positive electron affinity indicates stability of the negative ion. It should be emphasized that the binding energies E_i^- are those in the atomic field as modified by the presence of the additional electron. The change in the field resulting from the attachment of the electron can be decisive in determining whether the ion is stable.

The quantities E_i^0 and E_i^- in (8-1-1) are not observables, except in a conceptual experiment in which the atom or ion is built up one electron at a time. This building-up procedure is, however, a common theoretical device. The concept of the electron affinity might be made clearer if we first simply define EA as the difference in the total energies of the normal states of the atom and ion and then state that this energy difference is equal to the minimum photon energy required to eject the valence electron from the negative atomic ion in the photodetachment process $h\nu + X^- \rightarrow X + e$. If we calculate how all the electrons share the total binding energies, we can get the binding energy of the valence electron from the expression

$$E_1 = EA + \sum_{i=1}^{Z} (E_i^0 - E_i^-)$$

Table 8-1-1 displays electron affinities for a number of negative atomic ions obtained by various experimental methods,† by theoretical calculations‡ (for the most part, quantum mechanical calculations on the

---

* This equality does not necessarily hold in the case of a molecular ion, as shown in Section 8-1-B.

† *Negative Ions* by Massey[1] contains a good discussion of several experimental methods for determination of electron affinities. Section (8-6-C) and the works of Branscomb[5,10] should be consulted for description of measurements of EA based on photoabsorption.

‡ See R. J. S. Crossley and C. A. Coulson, *Proc. Phys. Soc. (London)* **81**, 211 (1963).

individual systems), and by empirical extrapolation procedures.[13,14] Additional data are to be found in the works of Branscomb[5,10] and Buchel'nikova.[8] A similar table for molecular ions is presented in Section 8-1-B. According to Branscomb,[10] the experimental and theoretical data listed in Table 8-1-1 are thought to be reliable within about 0.1 ev, except for Na⁻ and P⁻, for which the uncertainties may be much larger. The uncertainties are more difficult to determine in the empirical data, which were obtained by extrapolating along isoelectronic sequences. Other types of extrapolations have been discussed by Branscomb.[5] Since electron affinities are frequently expressed in units other than ev, the following conversion factors may prove useful:

$$1 \text{ ev} = 8066.0 \text{ cm}^{-1} = 23.069 \text{ kcal/mole}$$
$$100 \text{ kcal/mole} = 4.3348 \text{ ev} = 34,965 \text{ cm}^{-1} \qquad (8\text{-}1\text{-}2)$$

We see from Table 8-1-1 that the binding energies of negative atomic ions range from close to zero to about 4 ev. The thresholds for photo-absorption will then lie primarily in the infrared and visible regions of the spectrum. Atomic negative ions generally have only one bound state. Since the binding energy of an electron attached to an atom in the ground state is so low, it is unusual for any discrete state of excited configuration* to exist with an appreciable binding energy, and the states that may be found are likely to be metastable and to lie very near the continuum. A bound metastable excited term of the ground configuration† has been observed for C⁻ (see Section 8-7-C), and it is considered likely that B⁻, Al⁻, Si⁻, and P⁻ also have these states.[10] In addition, there is an unresolved discrepancy in reported values of the electron affinity of atomic oxygen, which has been interpreted by Schulz as evidence of an excited state of O⁻ about 0.5 ev above the ground state (see Sections 8-5-B and 8-7-A).

We see then that the absorption spectrum of a negative atomic ion may be expected to consist of a pure continuum starting from the frequency corresponding to the binding energy of the ion in its ground state and

---

* Here we mean an excited state arising from a bound electronic configuration above the ground state. An example of this excited state is $0^{-}*$ $(1s^2 2s^2 2p^4 3s)$, which lies above the ground state of 0^-, whose configuration is $(1s^2 2s^2 2p^5)$.

† Here we mean an excited state arising from term splitting of the ground electronic configuration. An example of this excited state is the ^2D term of C⁻, which lies about 1 ev above the ^4S term, both of which have the ground electronic configuration $(1s^2 2s^2 2p^3)$. Consideration of the ground configurations shows that it is not unlikely that such terms are also bound in B⁻, Al⁻, Si⁻, and P⁻ and not necessarily close to the continuum. However, all excited terms in these light elements are of different multiplicity from the ground terms, hence are strongly metastable, with lives of milliseconds or longer. As bound states they do not autoionize. They decay slowly through radiation (magnetic dipole or electric quadrupole) if not collisionally deactivated first.

TABLE 8-1-1. Electron affinities of various atoms. The electron affinity EA is equal to the binding energy of the electron attached by the atom to form the indicated negative atomic ion. Most of these data are taken from Table III of Branscomb's review[10]

Ion	EA (ev)	Method	References and Comments
H^- $(1s)^2$	0.75416	Variational calculation	C. L. Pekeris, *Phys. Rev.*, **112**, 1649 (1958)
	0.8 ± 0.1	Surface ionization	V. I. Khvostenko and V. M. Dukel'skii, *Soviet Phys. JETP*, **10**, 465 (1960)
He^- $(1s^2 2s)$	< 0	Variational calculation	T. Y. Wu, *Phil. Mag.*, **22**, 837 (1936)
$(1s 2s 2p)$	> 0.075	Variational calculation	E. Holøien and J. Midtdal, Ref. 12. This ion has been observed in the laboratory. See Sections 8-1-A and 8-6-B
Ne^-, A^-, Kr^-, Xe^-	< 0		Ion never observed
Li^-	0.616	Configuration interaction calculation	A. W. Weiss quoted in Ref. 10
Be^- $(1s^2 2s^2 2p)$	-0.19	Extrapolation	Ref. 14
B^-	0.33	Extrapolation	Ref. 14
	0.82	Extrapolation	Ref. 13
C^-	1.33 ± 0.18	Electron impact	M. A. Fineman and A. Petrocelli, *Bull. Amer. Phys. Soc.*, **3**, 258 (1958)
	1.25 ± 0.03	Photodetachment	M. Seman and L. M. Branscomb, *Phys. Rev.*, **125**, 1602 (1962)
	1.11 ± 0.05	Electron impact	C. R. Lagergren, Thesis, University of Minnesota (1955)
N^- (^4S)	0.05	Extrapolation	Ref. 14
	0.54	Extrapolation	Ref. 13
(^1D)	> 0	Ion observed in high-energy charge transfer experiment*	Ya. M. Fogel, V. F. Kozlov, and A. A. Kalmykov, *Soviet Phys. JETP*, **9**, 963 (1959)

* Negative atomic ions of nitrogen (presumably ^1D) have been produced by high-energy charge transfer of two electrons to N^+ ions in collisions with gas molecules. Formation of N^- ions by other mechanisms has not been reported.

TABLE 8-1-1. (continued)

Ion	EA (ev)	Method	References and Comments
O⁻ (see Section 8-7-A)	1.465 ± 0.005	Photodetachment	L. M. Branscomb, D. S. Burch, S. J. Smith, and S. Geltman, *Phys. Rev*, **111**, 504 (1958)
F⁻	2.0 ± 0.1 ev	Electron impact	G. J. Schulz, *Phys. Rev.*, **128**, 178 (1962)
	3.62 ± 0.09	Surface ionization	T. L. Bailey, *J. Chem. Phys*, **28**, 792 (1958)
	3.48	Lattice energies	D. Cubicciotti, *J. Chem. Phys.*, **31**, 1646 (1959)
	3.47	Surface ionization (assuming EA for Br to be 3.50)	I. N. Bakulina and N. I. Ionov, *Dokl. Akad. Nauk SSSR*, **105**, 680 (1955)
	3.448 ± 0.005	Shock wave heating and photodetachment	R. S. Berry and C. W. Reimann, *J. Chem. Phys.*, **38**, 1540 (1963)
Na⁻	0.84	Statistical theory	R. Gáspár and B. Molnar, *Acta Phys. Hungar.*, **5**, 75 (1955)
	0.47	Extrapolation	Ref. 14
Mg⁻	−0.32	Extrapolation	Ref. 14
Al⁻	0.52	Extrapolation	Ref. 14
	1.19	Extrapolation	Ref. 13
Si⁻	1.46	Extrapolation	Ref. 14
P⁻	1.12	Statistical theory	P. Gombás and K. Ladányi, *Z. Physik*, **158**, 261 (1960)
	0.77	Extrapolation	Ref. 14
	1.33	Extrapolation	Ref. 13
S⁻	2.07 ± 0.07	Photodetachment	L. M. Branscomb and S. J. Smith, *J. Chem. Phys.*, **25**, 598 (1956)
	2.37	Surface ionization	I. N. Bakulina and N. I. Ionov, *Sov. Phys. Doklady*, **2**, 423 (1957)
	2.15	Extrapolation	Ref. 14

Cl⁻	2.79	Extrapolation	Ref. 13
	3.76 ± 0.09	Surface ionization	T. L. Bailey, *J. Chem. Phys.*, **28**, 792 (1958)
	3.69	Lattice energies	D. Cubicciotti, *J. Chem. Phys.*, **31**, 1646 (1959)
	3.613 ± 0.003	Shock wave heating and photodetachment	R. S. Berry and C. W. Reimann, *J. Chem. Phys.*, **38**, 1540 (1963)
	3.71	Surface ionization (assuming EA for Br to be 3.50)	I. N. Bakulina and N. I. Ionov, *Dokl. Akad. Nauk SSSR*, **105**, 680 (1955)
Br⁻	3.51 ± 0.06	Surface ionization	T. L. Bailey, *J. Chem. Phys*, **28**, 792 (1958)
	3.45	Lattice energies	D. Cubicciotti, *J. Chem. Phys.*, **31**, 1646 (1959)
	3.49 ± 0.02	Surface attachment	P. M. Doty and J. E. Mayer, *J. Chem. Phys.*, **12**, 323 (1944)
	3.53 ± 0.12	Photoionization of Br_2	J. D. Morrison, H. Hurzeler, M. G. Inghram, and H. E. Stanton, *J. Chem. Phys.*, **33**, 821 (1960)
	3.363 ± 0.003	Shock wave heating and photodetachment	R. S. Berry and C. W. Reimann, *J. Chem. Phys.*, **38**, 1540 (1963)
I⁻	3.17 ± 0.05	Surface ionization	T. L. Bailey, *J. Chem. Phys.*, **28**, 792 (1958)
	3.14	Lattice energies	D. Cubicciotti, *J. Chem. Phys.*, **31**, 1646 (1959)
	3.13 ± 0.12	Photoionization of I_2	J. D. Morrison, H. Hurzeler, M. G. Inghram, and H. E. Stanton, *J. Chem. Phys.*, **33**, 821 (1960)
	3.23	Surface ionization (assuming EA of Br to be 3.50)	I. N. Bakulina and N. I. Ionov, *Dokl. Akad. Nauk SSSR*, **105**, 680 (1955)
	3.076 ± 0.005	Photodetachment	B. W. Steiner, M. L. Seman, and L. M. Branscomb, *J. Chem. Phys.*, **37**, 1200 (1962)
	3.063 ± 0.003	Shock wave heating and photodetachment	R. S. Berry and C. W. Reimann, *J. Chem. Phys.*, **38**, 1540 (1963)

extending to higher frequencies, plus perhaps one or two forbidden lines in the visible region. The continuum may have structure due to the presence of autoionization transitions involving absorption to unstable doubly excited states. The appearance of allowed lines, arising from very weakly bound higher configurations, just to the long wavelength side of the continuum cannot be ruled out theoretically.[10]

As stated earlier, no doubly charged negative ions have ever been observed in the gaseous phase. Since single electrons are attached to atoms with such a small decrease in energy and since a second electron would suffer strong Coulomb repulsion, it is extremely unlikely that a second electron could also be attached.

B. NEGATIVE MOLECULAR IONS. As a prelude to our treatment of negative molecular ions, we shall review briefly some of the fundamentals of molecular structure. This discussion not only serves our immediate purpose, as related to negative ions, but also covers some topics of more general interest with respect to collisions of molecules.

In a rigorous discussion of the structure of a molecular system, it is necessary to include the effects of interaction among the three different classes of motion in a molecule—electronic, vibrational, and rotational. The frequencies of these motions differ by orders of magnitude, however, and their interaction is relatively weak. Thus in first approximation (the *Born-Oppenheimer approximation**), the nuclei may be regarded as stationary and the energy of a particular electronic state calculated for different relative positions of the nuclei. The vibrational levels corresponding to this electronic state are then calculated by using this potential curve, and the rotational motion is introduced as a splitting of the vibrational levels.

Figure 8-1-1, taken from Rose and Clark,[15] shows a number of potential energy curves for various electronic states of the H_2 molecule and H_2^+ molecular ion. One class of potential curve, corresponding to an attractive state, possesses a minimum. Here there is a discrete set of levels associated with nuclear motion extending up to the top of the potential well and a continuum above. On the other hand, if the potential curve has no minimum, there are no discrete nuclear levels at all, and the state is repulsive. Whenever the nuclear vibration level lies in the continuum, the molecule dissociates. The vertical distance from the lowest vibrational level near the bottom of the well to the horizontal asymptote corresponding to infinite separation of the nuclei is equal to the negative potential energy of the atoms when the molecule is formed adiabatically from atoms initially at

---

* This approximation is unrelated to the Born-Oppenheimer approximation discussed in Section 6-13-A in connection with electron exchange scattering.

rest with infinite separation. (The dissociation limit is the logical zero of potential energy.) If an amount of energy equal to the minimum dissociation energy is supplied internally to the molecule when it is in its lowest vibrational state, it dissociates into two atoms, each of which has zero kinetic energy.

In Fig. 8-1-1 the shaded area indicates the normal vibrational range of the nuclei of the H_2 molecule in the ground electronic state ($^1\Sigma_g$). To dissociate the ground-state molecule into two H atoms without electronic excitation of the molecule requires about 4.4 ev. This separation may be

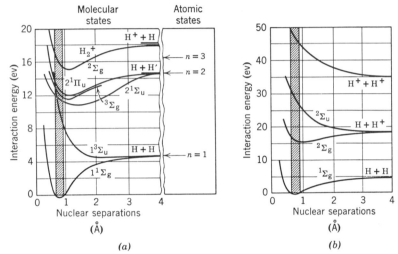

FIG. 8-1-1. Potential energy curves for electronic states of H_2 and H_2^+: (a) shows states within 20 ev of the ground state; (b) shows higher energy states, the uppermost curve representing the Coulomb repulsion of two protons.

effected in thermal dissociation.* However, electron impact dissociation or photodissociation cannot occur by a change only of the vibrational state without a simultaneous electronic excitation.[16] According to the *Franck-Condon principle*, which governs the latter types of dissociation, the nuclei do not have time to change their spacing appreciably during electronic excitation of the molecule, and an electronic transition corresponds to a *vertical* transition between potential curves on the energy

* If a gas is heated, molecules are driven to higher vibrational states by gas kinetic impacts, and some of the molecules may be excited by successive collisions to vibrational levels high enough to produce dissociation. No selection rules apply in the dissociation. There is no difficulty in satisfying the requirements of energy and momentum conservation because at least three particles are involved in the process—the "projectile" molecule and the dissociation fragments of the "target."

diagram. Thus a minimum energy of about 8.9 ev is required to excite the H_2 molecule from its ground electronic and vibrational state to the first excited electronic state $^3\Sigma_u$. This state is repulsive, and a molecule excited to it quickly dissociates into two H atoms, each with about 2.25 ev. If higher electronic states of the H_2 molecule are dissociated, the products include excited and ionized H atoms, as indicated at the right side of the curves of Fig. 8-1-1a. The values of n at the extreme right of this drawing are the principal quantum numbers of the H atoms formed in the dissociation. Excitation to the stable electronic states above $^3\Sigma_u$ will be followed by the emission of ultraviolet light, as radiative transitions occur back to

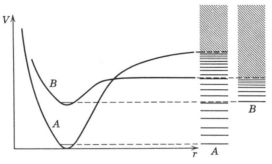

FIG. 8-1-2. Potential energy curves and corresponding vibration term sequences leading to predissociation of a diatomic molecule.

the ground state. Stable H_2^+ ions may be produced by the impact of electrons with energy greater than the vertical ionization energy 15.4 ev. About 18.0 ev is required to produce H^+ ions from H_2, and as we have indicated at least 8.9 ev is required to dissociate the molecule by electron impact.

At this point it is appropriate to discuss the interesting phenomenon of *predissociation*,[16] which has already been encountered in Section 7-1. Let us refer to Fig. 8-1-2, which shows the potential energy curves and vibration level diagrams for two electronically excited molecular states, A and B. We shall suppose that molecules in the ground electronic state, which is not shown in the drawing, are irradiated with light and that transitions up to the state A are possible. If state B were not present, we would observe a sequence of absorption bands corresponding to transitions from the ground state to all vibrational levels of state A and beyond the dissociation limit of A, the dissociation continuum. Now we shall consider the effect of the second electronically excited state B, whose dissociation energy in this example is assumed to be less than that of state A, as shown in Fig. 8-1-2. Suppose that a molecule is in state A but vibrationally excited to the extent that the total internal energy exceeds the dissociation limit of the molecule in state B. Then, if certain selection rules are obeyed, a nonradiative transition may occur into the dissociation continuum of B, with the molecule dissociating before the dissociation limit of state A is reached. According to the Franck-Condon principle, such transitions from A into the continuum of B occur with high probability only in the neighborhood of the intersection of the potential curves of A and B. The possibility of de-excitation by predissociation reduces the lifetime of the discrete states of A and, by the uncertainty principle, thereby increases the width of these energy levels. This fact accounts for the diffuse appearance of the dissociation bands. A phenomenon analogous to predissociation occurs in atoms and involves a radiationless transition into the ionization continuum. Here reference is made to preionization, or autoionization, which is discussed in Section 8-2-A.

Now we return to our discussion of negative ions. The separability of the nuclear and electronic motion in a molecular structure, and the resulting Franck-Condon principle, have two important consequences for molecular negative ions which do not apply to atomic ions.[5] In the first place, molecular negative ions may have a number of excited electronic states in which the ions do not rapidly break up through autoionization. (Molecules, typically, have a larger number of low-lying electronic states than atoms.) Each of the states has the same assembly of vibrational and rotational levels found in the neutral molecules. Second, the electron affinity of a molecule is not simply related to the energy required to detach an electron from the negative molecular ion. If the molecular ion potential curve has a minimum at a larger internuclear separation than the minimum of the neutral molecule potential curve, the energy required to remove an electron by electron impact or by photodetachment may be quite different from the electron affinity of the molecule and may even have the opposite sign. This situation is illustrated by Fig. 8-1-3, which shows the potential curve calculated for the lowest state of H_2^- by Dalgarno and McDowell,[17] together with the ground-state potential curve of H_2. The *electron affinity of a molecule* is defined as the difference in the energies of the neutral molecule and its molecular ion when both structures are in their normal electronic and nuclear states, the affinity being positive when the molecule has the greater energy. This energy difference is equal to the energy of detachment of the electron from the molecule only if transitions between the normal states are involved. The *vertical detachment energy* of the ion is defined as that required to produce a transition from the normal state of the ion to the ground electronic state of the molecule without a change in the nuclear separation. This energy is unequal to the electron affinity except in special cases.

Electron affinities for various molecules and radicals appear in Table 8-1-2. As might be expected, the determination of electron affinities is much more demanding for molecular than for atomic systems, and there are fewer molecules and radicals whose affinities are known with precision. Considerable progress is expected in this direction, however, when photodetachment experiments are performed at higher wavelength resolution.[10,18]

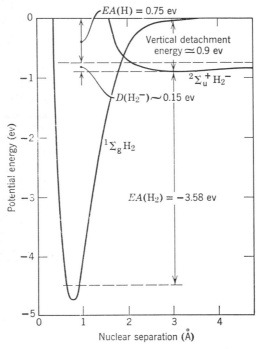

FIG. 8-1-3. One set of calculated potential energy curves for the ground states of the H_2^- ion and H_2 molecule.[17]

The need for higher resolution is dramatized by photodetachment experiments which have been performed on the hydroxyl radical OH^- (see Table 8-1-2). In this case a well-defined photodetachment threshold is observed at 7000 Å (1.78 ev), but there is evidence of a strong structure in the detachment cross section which suggests a peak near the threshold and a minimum about 0.1 ev above the threshold. Until the structure of the spectrum is unequivocally interpreted, it cannot be concluded that the electron affinity of OH is 1.78 ev. The affinity may be higher, probably by one vibrational quantum of OH^-, in which case EA would be about 2.2 ev. Branscomb[18] also points out the necessity of extreme gas purity

TABLE 8-1-2. Electron affinities of molecules and radicals. The electron affinity of H_2 is negative even though there is a bound state of H_2^-; the vertical detachment energy (VDE) of H_2^- is given in the table. The entry for the hydroxyl radical OH is the photodetachment energy (PDE), and its electron affinity may be somewhat higher, as explained in Section 8-1-B

Ion	EA (ev)	Method	References and Comments
H_2^-	0.9 (VDE)	Theory	A. Dalgarno and M. R. C. McDowell, *Proc, Phys. Soc. (London),* **A-69**, 615 (1956)
	—	Ion observed coming from ion source containing H_2O and Sb vapor.	V. I. Khvostenko and V. M. Dukel'skii, *Soviet Phys. JETP,* **7**, 709 (1958)
O_2^- (see Section 8-7-A-2)	0.44 ± 0.02	Swarm experiment	A. V. Phelps and J. L. Pack, *Phys. Rev. Letters,* **6**, 111 (1961); see also L. M. Chanin, A. V. Phelps, and M. A. Biondi, *Phys. Rev.,* **128**, 219 (1962)
OH^- (see Section 8-1-B)	1.78 (PDE)	Photodetachment	S. J. Smith and L. M. Branscomb, *Phys. Rev.,* **99**, 1657 (1955); see also Refs. 5, 10, 18
N_2^-	<0		Ion never observed
NO_2^-	1.6	Lattice energies	K. B. Yatsimirskii, quoted by H. O. Pritchard, *Chem. Rev.,* **52**, 529 (1953)
NO_3^-	3.9	Lattice energies	K. B. Yatsimirskii, quoted by H. O. Pritchard, *Chem. Rev.,* **52**, 529 (1953)
CH^-	~1.6	Electron impact	L. G. Smith, quoted by H. O. Pritchard, *Chem. Rev.* **52**, 529 (1953)
CN^-	3.1 ± 0.1	Surface ionization	I. N. Bakulina and N. I. Ionov, *Dokl. Akad. Nauk, SSSR,* **99**, 1023 (1954)
C_2^-	~3.2	Mass spectra of graphite sublimation	R. E. Honig, *J. Chem. Phys.,* **22**, 126 (1954); see also L. M. Branscomb and B. E. J. Pagel, *Mon. Not. Roy. Astron. Soc.,* **118**, 258 (1958)
C_3^-	2.5	Mass spectra of graphite sublimation	R. E. Honig, *J. Chem. Phys.,* **22**, 126 (1954)
SF_5^-	3.39	Electron impact	R. K. Curran, *J. Chem. Phys.,* **34**, 1069 (1961)

in swarm experiments on negative ions and the desirability of mass analysis to identify the ions that are actually operative in these experiments.

8-2. MECHANISMS FOR FORMATION OF NEGATIVE IONS

Negative ions may be formed by the following processes:

(a) The radiative capture of a free electron by a neutral atom

$$(e + A \rightarrow A^- + h\nu)$$

(b) The capture of a free electron by an atom with a third body taking up the excess energy ($e + A + B \rightarrow A^- + B +$ kinetic energy).

(c) The capture of a free electron by a molecule, with the vibrational excitation of the molecular ion and its subsequent stabilization in a collision with another molecule ($e + XY \rightarrow [XY]^{-*}$; $[XY]^{-*} + A \rightarrow [XY]^- + A +$ kinetic energy + potential energy).

(d) Dissociative attachment: the capture of a free electron by a molecule, the excess energy going into dissociation of the molecule

$$(e + XY \rightarrow [XY]^{-*} \rightarrow X + Y^-)$$

(e) Ion-pair production: the noncapture dissociation of a molecule into positive and negative ions by electron impact ($e + XY \rightarrow e + X^+ + Y^-$).

(f) The transfer of one or more electrons to a neutral structure or a positive ion in a collision with another particle ($A + B \rightarrow A^- + B^+$; or $C^+ + D \rightarrow C^- + D^{2+}$).

Charge-changing collisions, referred to in (f), were discussed in Chapter 6.* Additional mechanisms for negative ion formation which involve surfaces are described in Sections 13-2-B, 13-5-B, and 13-6.

Under ordinary laboratory conditions, and excluding charge-changing collisions, processes (b), (c), and (d) are the most probable. For electrons with energies in excess of about 20 ev (e) will also become important. At very low pressures (a) must be considered, whereas (b) and (c) become unimportant compared with (d).

These processes are discussed here in greater detail; a more complete discussion is given by Massey.[1]

A. THE ATTACHMENT OF FREE ELECTRONS TO NEUTRAL ATOMS.   Assume that an electron with kinetic energy T collides with a neutral atom whose electron affinity is EA. If the electron is to be permanently attached by the atom, an amount of energy equal to $(T + EA)$ must be dissipated.

One of the mechanisms by which the attachment may be accomplished

* For a review of the production of negative ions in heavy particle collisions see also Ya. M. Fogel, *Soviet Phys. Usp.* **3**, 390 (1960).

is that of *radiative capture*, that is, the capture of the electron by the atom with the emission of radiation. It is easy to give an argument to show that the probability of radiative capture of an electron by an atom should be small. From measurements of the lifetimes of excited states of atoms, it is reasonable to assume that a free electron must remain in the field of an atom for times as long as 10^{-8} sec in order that its radiative capture may be probable. However, an electron with an energy as low as 10 ev traverses the field of an atom in about 10^{-15} sec, and the probability of capture to form a negative ion by this process is only of the order of 10^{-7} per collision.*

The other mechanism available for dissipation of the energy released in electron capture is the transfer of this energy to a third body, which may be an electron, ion, atom, or molecule. The effectiveness of these particles in absorbing the energy depends on the mean free path for effective collisions between the capturing atom and the third bodies. The effectiveness of atomic systems in acting as third bodies depends to a great degree on whether they are capable of absorbing internally all of the energy that must be transferred. A resonance process is involved if the transfer of energy may be accomplished wholly by increasing the potential energy of the third body. In this case the cross sections are quite large, and concentrations of third bodies of only $10^{16}/cm^3$ may give attachment comparable with that produced by radiative processes. On the other hand, concentrations of $10^{20}/cm^3$ are necessary if resonance transfer is not possible; the cross sections are very small.[1] It is obvious that molecules, because of their numerous internal degrees of freedom, will be more effective than atoms in promoting electron attachment by acting as third bodies.

Since the probability of electron capture in a three-body collision depends on the availability of third bodies, and thus on the pressure of the gas, it is to be expected that radiative processes will become more and more important in relation to this mode of formation as the pressure is reduced.

A special type of radiative attachment process that should be specifically mentioned here is *dielectronic attachment*,[1] which is the inverse of pre-ionization, or autoionization. Atoms with several electrons have states that correspond to double excitation, that is, to two electrons being in

* The decay of excited atomic states is governed by the usual exponential decay equation $N = N_0 e^{-\lambda t} = N_0 e^{-t/\tau}$, where N_0 is the number of excited atoms at time $t = 0$, N is the number surviving at any time $t > 0$, λ is the probability of decay per atom per unit time, and $\tau = 1/\lambda$ is the average lifetime of the excited state. The probability that a given excited atom will decay during a time interval T which is short compared with τ is λT; in the example above the probability that a given negative ion will be able to dispose of its excess energy by radiation within the allowed period of 10^{-15} sec is only $10^8 \times 10^{-15} = 10^{-7}$.

higher than their normal orbits. If the energy of double excitation exceeds the ionization energy of the ground state atom, the atom may be de-excited in a radiationless transition, wherein one of the excited electrons drops to a lower orbital and the resulting de-excitation energy is expended in ejecting the other excited electron from the atom, without the emission of radiation. This process, known as autoionization, preionization, or the *Auger effect*, occurs very quickly after the atom has been doubly excited. The lifetime of the atom against autoionization is generally much shorter than its radiative lifetime. An example of autoionization is illustrated in Fig. 5-4-11. Now let us consider the inverse process. Suppose an electron collides with an atom and the total energy of the atom plus electron is within the line breadth of a doubly excited state of the negative ion. If certain selection rules are obeyed, the electron may be captured into this state, without the emission of radiation, by the inverse process to that described. Once the capture occurs, the excess energy may be dissipated either by ejection of one of the excited electrons (*autodetachment*) or by the emission of radiation, with the atom returning to the ground state in either case. The probability that de-excitation will be accomplished by radiation so that the negative ion will remain intact is equal to $\tau_a/(\tau_a + \tau_r)$, where τ_r is the lifetime against radiation and τ_a that against autoionization. As a rule, dielectronic attachment is probably much less likely to occur than direct radiative attachment. Calculations by Bates and Massey[19] indicate that this is the case with atomic oxygen.

The radiative capture of electrons with kinetic energy T by neutral atoms gives rise to a continuous emission spectrum which extends in the absence of excited ionic states from a long wavelength limit $\lambda = hc/(T + EA)$ toward indefinitely shorter wavelengths. This spectrum is known as the *affinity spectrum*, or the *radiative attachment continuum*.[10] Wildt[20] in 1939 identified the H^- radiative attachment spectrum as the dominant source in the visible range of the solar continuum, but attempts[1] to observe affinity spectra in the laboratory met with no success until Lochte-Holtgreven's work in 1951 on a water-stabilized hydrogen arc.[21] Weber,[22] in the same laboratory at Kiel, also observed the H^- attachment spectrum from reflected shock waves of hydrogen expanded into low-pressure krypton. In addition, the affinity spectra of O^- and N^- have been studied in emission from high pressure arcs by Boldt[23] at Kiel. Boldt was able to deduce the O^- photodetachment cross section by using Kirchhoff's law and obtained a result that differs by only 30% from the value derived from direct photoabsorption measurements, which are described in Section 8-7. The attachment in nitrogen was explained in terms of the metastable ^1D state of N^-, which had been discussed by Bates and Moiseiwitsch.[24]

The most direct measurements of negative ion spectra in plasmas were made in the shock-wave absorption experiments by Berry and his co-workers. The most precise experimental determinations of affinity spectra are derived from crossed beam measurements of photodetachment cross sections by Branscomb and his colleagues. The work of Berry and Branscomb is discussed in Section 8-6-C.

B. NEGATIVE ION FORMATION IN COLLISIONS OF ELECTRONS WITH MOLE-CULES. As the list of formation mechanisms presented at the beginning of this section shows, negative ions may be produced in impacts of electrons with molecules in reactions of types (c) and (d), which involve the capture of the electron, or in process (e), in which the electron merely causes the molecule to break up into charged fragments.

The transfer of the excess energy in the capture of an electron is greatly facilitated when the electron is attached to a molecule because of the possibility of increasing the kinetic energy of relative motion of the nuclei in the molecule. In fact, the attachment may be thought of as a three-body process in which the third body is bound to the capturing atom. The molecular ion produced in this fashion will be left in a state of vibrational excitation, and the permanence of the structure depends on its "stabilization" in a collision with another body which carries off the excitation energy. Thus the pressure of the gas, as well as the energy of the electron, is important in determining whether process (c) or (d) is operative. If stabilization does not occur quickly, the molecular ion may dissociate or it may revert to the original molecule with the ejection of an electron in a time of the order of 10^{-11} sec.

If the electron is captured and the resulting molecular ion dissociates into a neutral structure and a negative ion, *dissociative attachment* is said to have taken place. The range of electron energy over which processes (c) and (d) occur is quite narrow, usually extending from about 2 to 5 ev.[1] Some molecules, for example, H_2, CO, and CO_2, can form negative ions by free electron attachment only in dissociative processes.

In process (e) the electron simply acts as a source of energy and excites the molecule into an unstable state so that it dissociates into a negative and a positive ion. Of course, there is a certain excitation energy below which this process of *ion-pair production* cannot occur. Above the critical value the probability of its taking place depends on the energy of the electron.

Bloch and Bradbury[25] have worked out the pressure dependence of the attachment probability for process (c). Let τ_s denote the average time taken for the vibrationally excited molecular ion to transfer its excess energy to a gas molecule in a collision, and τ_d, the average lifetime of the ion against spontaneous dissociation. τ_s will be inversely proportional to the gas pressure, and τ_d will be pressure-independent. If we consider an excited ion at $t = 0$, the probability that it will not have dissociated in time t is e^{-t/τ_d}. The probability of transferring its excess energy during the interval t to $(t + dt)$ is $e^{-t/\tau_s} dt/\tau_s$. The total probability that the ion will transfer its excess energy in a collision before it dissociates is

$$\rho = \int_0^\infty \frac{e^{-(t/\tau_d + t/\tau_s)} \, dt}{\tau_s} = \frac{\tau_d}{\tau_d + \tau_s} = \frac{p}{p + p_0} \qquad (8\text{-}2\text{-}1)$$

where p is the gas pressure and p_0, a critical pressure for which $\tau_d = \tau_s$. Thus the attachment probability will be independent of pressure for p much greater than p_0 but proportional to the pressure at low pressures.

8-3. MECHANISMS FOR DESTRUCTION OF NEGATIVE IONS

For each of the modes of electron attachment listed at the beginning of Section 8-2 there is the thermodynamically reverse process of electron detachment. The cross sections of each attachment reaction and its reverse detachment process are related by the *principle of microscopic reversibility*,[1,10] and detailed balancing can be used to obtain information about one type of reaction from its counterpart. It is fortunate that this is so because in many cases a detachment process is even more difficult to investigate experimentally than the reverse attachment process. The main factor in this difference is the difficulty of producing large concentrations of negative ions of known types for detachment studies. By contrast, there is no particular problem in generating large concentrations of electrons for attachment studies.

If reactions involving positive ions and surfaces are not considered, the processes leading to detachment may be listed as follows:[1]

(a) Collisions of negative ions with excited atoms.
(b) Absorption of radiation by the ions (photodetachment).
(c) Collisions with electrons or fast ions or molecules. The detachment cross sections may be larger than gas kinetic cross sections.
(d) Collisions with low-energy ions or molecules.
(e) Collisions with neutral atoms leading to molecule formation (associative detachment).

When positive ions are present, *three-body recombination* (Section 12-4-A) is likely to be the most important process at pressures above a few mm Hg. At lower pressures *mutual neutralization* (see Section 12-4-C) may be more effective. Collisions of negative ions with surfaces provide the most effective means of all of electron detachment if the work function of the surface exceeds the electron affinity.

8-4. DESCRIPTIONS OF THE PROBABILITIES OF NEGATIVE
     ION FORMATION AND DESTRUCTION

The likelihood of electrons producing negative ions in collisions with molecules of a gas depends strongly on the nature of the gas and also on the energy of the electrons. The probability that an electron will undergo capture is usually expressed by giving either the attachment (or capture) cross section or the electron attachment probability* as a function of electron energy. The *capture cross section* has the conventional meaning; the *attachment probability* is defined as the probability that an electron will be attached by a given neutral species of molecule on a single impact. For most electronegative gases the maximum value of the attachment probability is about 10^{-5} to 10^{-3} per collision. The formation of negative ions in dissociative processes not involving electron capture is, strictly speaking, not describable in terms of an attachment probability, and information on the probability of such reactions is expressed in terms of appropriate cross sections. The probability of destruction of negative ions may be described either by a detachment cross section or the probability of electron detachment per collision.

The concept of the attachment probability is most useful in discussions of electron swarms and therefore generally refers to the average behavior of the electrons in a swarm. We denote the attachment probability, as we have defined it, by h. This quantity is related to the average attachment cross section $\bar{q}_a$ by the equation

$$\bar{q}_a = h\bar{q}_t \tag{8-4-1}$$

where $\bar{q}_t$ is the average total cross section for scattering of the electrons. The rate of formation of negative ions is equal to $\bar{v}\bar{q}_a n_e N$, where $\bar{v}$ is the mean velocity of the electrons, and n_e and N are the number densities of electrons and neutrals, respectively.

Now let us consider a swarm of electrons drifting with constant average velocity v_d through a gas under the influence of an electric field. Let λ denote the average mean free path and ν the collision frequency of the electrons. The fractional number of electrons lost by attachment during the drift of the swarm over a distance dx is

$$\frac{dn}{n} = -\frac{h\bar{v}}{\lambda v_d}\,dx = -\frac{h\nu\,dx}{v_d} \tag{8-4-2}$$

---

* The electron attachment probability was used extensively in the older literature, but it is seldom used in the discussion of modern work.

Therefore, if n_0 electrons are present in the swarm at $x = 0$, the number surviving attachment over a drift distance d is

$$n = n_0 \exp - \frac{h\bar{v}}{\lambda v_d} d \qquad (8\text{-}4\text{-}3)$$

This equation, or some alternative form of it, is the basis for the experimental determination of the attachment probability. As we show in Chapter 9, the average energy of charged particles drifting in steady state through a gas in an electric field is determined by E/p, the ratio of the field strength to the gas pressure. The attachment probability is generally measured as a function of E/p, and the variation of h with average electron energy is deduced from the results. The dependence of average electron energy on E/p is discussed in Chapter 11.

8-5. EXPERIMENTAL METHODS FOR STUDY OF NEGATIVE ION FORMATION

Negative ion formation in the gas phase has been studied by swarm and mass spectrometric methods for many years. The first experiments were the swarm type and were conducted at the end of the last century, shortly after the discovery of X rays. Mass spectrographic studies date back to J. J. Thomson's researches around 1910. Both approaches have continued to be very useful up to the present time. Experiments with electron beams and spectroscopic observations of attachment radiation are of more recent vintage. Here we shall enumerate and briefly discuss some of the more important methods involving both electron swarms and beams. The bulk of the most revealing mass spectrometric investigations in recent years has employed beam techniques, hence it is discussed in the beam category. Details of certain of these techniques are presented in Section 8-5-B. More detailed discussions of these and other methods appear in Refs. 1 to 10. The works of Loeb[3,4] and Prasad and Craggs[9] are particularly recommended in this connection. Again, work on charge transfer and surfaces is not included. Measurements of the radiative attachment continuum have already been briefly discussed in Section 8-2-A.

A. SWARM METHODS. The most important methods of investigating attachment in electron swarms may be classified as follows:

1. *The steady-state diffusion method.* The diffusion method of studying electron attachment was introduced by Bailey[26] in 1925 and used by him and his students in several investigations which are described in detail by Healey and Reed.[27] Bailey's original technique has been superseded by a similar but more reliable method developed by Huxley and his co-workers,[28]

who use for their attachment studies the same kind of apparatus that is described in Section 11-2-A in connection with determinations of electron drift velocity and average energy. In their experiments a mixed stream of photoelectrons and negative ions enters a diffusion chamber through a small orifice and drifts a known distance along a known uniform electric field before collection on a circular disk electrode and surrounding annular collectors. Measurement of the currents received by the various segments of the collector and the application of diffusion theory permit the electron attachment probability and average energy to be determined as functions of E/p. Huxley et al.[28] have applied this technique to the study of attachment in oxygen at E/p ranging from 5 to 20 volts/cm-mm Hg. Gas pressures of a few mm Hg and drift distances of 1 to 10 cm were used. (In these particular experiments, the electrons were produced thermionically to guard against the possible production of ozone.)

2. *The steady-state electron filter method.* In 1926 Loeb[3,4] developed a scheme for removing electrons from a mixed swarm of electrons and negative ions drifting through a gas in an electric field. A plane grid is mounted perpendicular to the drift direction, with alternate wires connected to one another, and the two sets of interconnected wires attached to opposite sides of a high-frequency oscillator. When a sufficiently high alternating field is established between alternate wires, electrons are captured on the grid as they attempt to pass through it, but most of the negative ions in the swarm are transmitted, since they respond much more slowly to the rapidly changing field. This device, which is aptly termed an *electron filter*, has been used in negative ion mobility measurements (see Section 9-8-B) and for electron attachment studies.

The best of the early attachment studies based on the electron filter were made by Bradbury[29] on oxygen and oxygen mixtures. He used two filters, G_1 and G_2, which could be inserted one at a time at known positions between a plane photocathode and a plane anode mounted 7 cm away from and parallel to the cathode. Guard rings established a uniform drift field, and the mean potential of each grid was set so that the grid only slightly perturbed the field. The steady-state current of negative carriers to the anode was measured with G_1 in position, both with and without an alternating field applied to the grid. Then G_1 was retracted, G_2 put in place, and the measurements repeated. (The use of two filters permitted the elimination of end effects.) If the dimensions, pressure, and drift field are known, the electron attachment probability may be determined from these current measurements, provided the electron drift velocity is independently assessed.

The electron filter method has recently been used by Kuffel[30] for measurements on oxygen, dry and humid air, and water vapor at E/p from 1 up to about 25 volts/cm-mm Hg. Kuffel's grids, which consists of 0.1-mm wires spaced 1.0 mm apart, are driven at frequencies ranging from 2 to 16 mc. Gas pressures of about 9 mm Hg are employed. Other recent electron filter measurements are discussed by Prasad and Craggs.[9]

3. *The microwave electron-loss method.* Measurements of the electron loss rate in the afterglow of a pulsed microwave discharge have been made to obtain electron momentum transfer cross sections (Section 4-1-C), ambipolar diffusion coefficients (Section 10-10-B), and electron-ion recombination coefficients (Section 12-7-A). If the microwave cavity contains an electronegative gas, electrons will also be lost in negative ion formation, and the attachment contribution to the decay rate may be separated, under suitable experimental conditions, from the contributions due to diffusion and recombination.

Biondi[31] has used microwave techniques to study the dissociative attachment of electrons to iodine molecules in a mixture of iodine vapor and helium. The helium serves as a "buffer" to decrease the ambipolar diffusion loss of the electrons and ensure that the electrons are in thermal equilibrium with the gas during the afterglow. Microwave studies of attachment in oxygen and oxygen mixtures have also been made by Mulcahy et al.[32] and by Chantry and his co-workers.[33]

4. *Pulsed drift tube methods.* A number of pulse techniques have been developed for studying electron attachment in a drift tube following the production of free electrons from a photocathode or directly in the gas.[34–39] These techniques involve measurement of the time dependence of the currents of electrons which survive attachment and currents of negative ions produced by capture of electrons as they drift across the tube. We shall discuss here the method developed by Chanin, Phelps, and Biondi[38] for investigations of the attachment in oxygen of electrons with average energies between a few hundredths and a few ev. The method they used is an extension of that developed by Doehring[35] and permits measurements to be made at very low applied electric fields. Their techniques and results have recently been reported in a comprehensive paper,[39] to which the reader may refer for additional details.

The apparatus used by Chanin et al. for their attachment studies is shown in Fig. 8-5-1. Except for the omission of one grid, this drift tube is identical to that designed by Pack and Phelps for electron drift velocity measurements which are discussed in Section 11-2-B. At the left side of the figure is a photocathode from which electrons are ejected in short periodic bursts by ultraviolet radiation from a pulsed mercury discharge lamp. A series of guard rings is used to maintain a uniform potential gradient between the cathode and control grid (shown as a row of dots in the drawing). The photoelectrons drift through the gas-filled tube under the action of the applied field, and some of them are captured by neutral molecules. The negative ions thus formed drift across the tube much more slowly than the unattached electrons, and the time dependence of the negative ion current arriving at the control grid is used to determine the attachment probability. A time-sampling procedure (to be described) provides a much more accurate determination of the ion current waveform than would be possible by oscillographic observation.

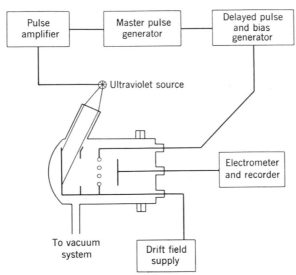

FIG. 8-5-1. Schematic diagram of the apparatus used by Chanin, Phelps, and Biondi for studies of electron attachment in oxygen.[39]

The control grid consists of 0.0025-in. diameter parallel wires with alternate wires connected electrically. The grid is normally kept closed with respect to transmission both of ions and electrons by equal and opposite bias voltages applied to alternate wires. However, during selected evenly spaced time intervals the grid is made transmitting by application of rectangular voltage pulses, which reduce the field between wires to zero and thus allow most of the ions and electrons to pass through to the collector, which is shielded from stray currents. The collector is connected to a vibrating reed electrometer and recorder to measure the ion and electron currents, which vary from 10^{-11} to 10^{-15} amp. The grid is set to open periodically at a certain delay time with respect to the photopulse, and the bursts of current transmitted to the collector during the "open intervals" are integrated over a large number of cycles by the electrometer for this selected delay-time interval. Thus by making runs with various delay times, we may determine accurately the ion current reaching the grid as a function of time without actually measuring the grid current directly. A semilog plot of the current to the grid shows a sharp spike at very early times produced by collection of unattached electrons, followed by a slow linear rise (sometimes over a period of tens of milliseconds), during which negative ions are collected. Chanin et al.[39] show that the ion current during this rise is

$$I(t) = I_0 e^{\alpha w_i t} \qquad (8\text{-}5\text{-}1)$$

where I_0 denotes the initial ion current reaching the control grid, α is the *attachment coefficient per unit drift distance*, and w_i is the ionic drift velocity. The coefficient α, which must not be confused with the first Townsend coefficient to be discussed in the next section, is equal to the electron attachment frequency v_a, divided by the electronic drift velocity v_d. The value of αw_i is determined from the slope of the ln I versus t plot, and w_i is evaluated from the observed transit time of the ions formed adjacent to the photocathode. This transit time is the difference in the time of the maximum electron current and a time intermediate between that of the peak ion current and that at which the ion current has dropped to half its peak value. The exact time to be used depends on the effect of diffusion on the waveform, and this effect can be accurately assessed. Finally, the values of α thus obtained for various field strengths and pressures are converted to the desired two-body and three-body attachment rate coefficients by use of electron drift velocity data obtained by other investigators.

A few additional experimental details of the work by Chanin, Phelps, and Biondi may be of interest. The experimental tube is mounted on a glass and metal ultrahigh vacuum system, and the entire system is baked at 300°C for 16 hours before each set of measurements. Following bakeout, the system pressure is less than 10^{-8} mm Hg, and the background pressure rises at a rate of less than 10^{-9} mm Hg/min. Thus no significant amounts of impurities are added to the gas sample during the course of measurement. Gas pressures between 0.1 and 500 mm Hg are used for the attachment studies. All electrodes in the tube are gold-plated to minimize contact potential differences. The measurements are made with drift distances of 2.54 and 10.16 cm. The duration of the photopulse and the open time of the control grid are less than 5% of the ion transit time. A sufficiently low ultraviolet flux is used to ensure that no appreciable excitation or chemical reactions will take place in the sample gas. The apparatus is cycled at repetition rates between 10 and 200 cps.

The results obtained by Chanin, Phelps, and Biondi on attachment in molecular oxygen are presented in Section 8-7-A, where mention is also made of collisional detachment studies made with this equipment.

5. *Avalanche methods.* Attachment at high values of E/p (up to about 60 volts/cm-mm Hg) has been investigated by various techniques which

involve the production of electron avalanches, or collisional ionization cascades. One technique consists of assessing the modification of the characteristics of a steady-state Townsend avalanche due to electron attachment in the gap between the electrodes. With a strong uniform field applied, and in the absence of secondary effects, a single electron traveling a distance d through a gas in the field direction will produce, on the average, $e^{\alpha d}$ additional electrons, where α is *Townsend's first (or primary) ionization coefficient;* α equals the mean number of ion pairs produced per electron per centimeter of drift in the field direction (α/p is a function of E/p if no pressure-dependent ionization processes are operative). If, in addition, secondary ionization is produced (for example, by positive ion bombardment of the cathode or by photoeffects), but no attachment takes place, the steady-state prebreakdown current flowing between electrodes separated by a distance d is

$$ I = I_0 \frac{e^{\alpha d}}{1 - \gamma(e^{\alpha d} - 1)} \tag{8-5-2} $$

where I_0 is the externally generated current and γ is *Townsend's second (or secondary) coefficient.** This equation holds if diffusion losses are unimportant and if the current density is low, say less than 10^{-10} amp/cm^2, so that space charge effects are negligible; I_0 might be generated, for instance, by the photoelectric effect. Clearly, if electron attachment occurs, the I versus d characteristics of the current flow will be different from that indicated by (8-5-2), and if the gap distance is varied over a sufficiently wide range the attachment probability may be deduced. The accuracy of this method is not great, but it can provide information at higher electron energies than the other swarm methods. The Townsend avalanche method is treated in detail by Prasad and Craggs,[9] who also discuss other pulsed avalanche methods. Of special interest to us are the avalanche measurements that have been made on oxygen,[40-43] carbon monoxide,[44] carbon dioxide,[45] and sulfur hexafluoride.[40,46]

B. BEAM METHODS. Many important studies of negative ion formation have been made by passing a well-collimated beam of electrons of known energy through a low-pressure target gas and collecting negative ions which are formed in collisions with the molecules. Several types of apparatus used for such studies are described here.

1. *The Lozier tube.* Apparatus of the type developed by Lozier in 1930 has been used in many investigations of positive and negative ion formation. Reference was made in Section 5-7 to the work on positive ions.

---

* If the secondary electrons are produced solely by positive ion bombardment of the cathode, γ equals the number of secondaries released per incident positive ion.

Most of the experiments on negative ions during the last decade have been performed by workers at Liverpool. Their apparatus, which differs only slightly from that used by Lozier, is illustrated schematically in Fig. 8-5-2, which is taken from a paper by Tozer.[47] Electrons from a tungsten filament F are accelerated through the $\frac{1}{2}$-mm apertures A, B, and C to the desired energy and passed through the electric-field-free collision chamber D which contains the target gas at a pressure of about 10^{-5} mm Hg. The electrons, which are confined to a narrow beam by an axial magnetic field of about 200 gauss, are collected on E, which is held about 50 volts positive with respect to ground. I represents a set of vanes which is concentric with

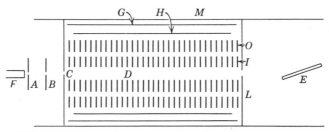

FIG. 8-5-2. Schematic representation of Lozier tube apparatus.[47]

and perpendicular to the chamber axis. These vanes, and C and L as well, are at ground potential. A draw-out potential is applied to the outer set of vanes O. Negative ions whose initial directions of motion lie within about $12°$ of the perpendicular to the axis are collected on the cylindrical electrode H, which is surrounded by the guard electrode G. For measurements of the kinetic energy of the ions a retarding potential is applied to the collector. For cross section measurements, a collecting potential equal to that applied to the outer vanes is used. A reversal of polarities permits the collection and study of positive ions.

By varying the electron beam energy, we can determine the minimum electron energy required to produce ions of a specified kinetic energy and also the relative efficiency of producing ions of a specified minimum kinetic energy as a function of the electron energy. Appearance potentials of negative ions are determined by linear extrapolation of the yields and standardization against known positive ion appearance potentials. Electron affinities may be evaluated by the following technique.* Let us consider, for example, the formation of O^- ions in the dissociative process

$$e + CO_2 \rightarrow CO + O^-$$

* See Ref. 7 (Craggs and Massey) for a full treatment of the energetics of negative ion formation and the technique for determining electron affinities discussed here.

Let $A(O^-)$ be the appearance potential of O^- ions of known kinetic energy, $D(CO_2)$ be the dissociation energy of CO_2 into CO and O, $EA(O)$ be the electron affinity of the oxygen atom, and T be the total kinetic energy of the dissociation fragments. (T is determined from the ion kinetic energy by application of the law of conservation of momentum.) Then it follows that $EA(O)$ is given by the equation

$$EA(O) = D(CO_2) - A(O^-) + T + Q$$

where Q represents any internal energy change produced in the reaction.

Absolute cross sections for the formation of negative ions are obtained by comparison of the yields of negative ions with positive ion yields which are already known. Certain errors which can arise in such determinations are discussed by Tozer.[47] Since ions produced in dissociative processes may have appreciable kinetic energy and ions formed in nondissociative reactions have not, we must determine whether the apparatus discriminates in favor of or against ions with initial kinetic energy. Furthermore, as pointed out by Dunn[48] (cf. Section 5-7), ions resulting from dissociative processes may have angular distributions that are far from isotropic, and angular anisotropies can strongly influence experiments in which ions are collected through a small acceptance angle in a fixed direction. The anisotropies can cause very serious errors, not only in the magnitude of the attachment cross sections but also in their shapes. For these reasons some of the data obtained with Lozier tubes are at variance with those collected on other types of apparatus in which these problems do not occur, or in which they appear in a different way.

The Liverpool group has applied the Lozier tube method to the study of negative-ion formation in oxygen,[49] carbon monoxide,[50] and carbon dioxide.[51] In each of these gases O^- ions are produced in dissociative reactions. Nondissociative free electron capture can occur in O_2, but not in CO and CO_2. The Lozier tube measurements gave values of 1.5 ± 0.2, 1.6 ± 0.2, and 1.2 ± 0.3 ev, respectively, for the electron affinity of atomic oxygen when corrections were made for initial kinetic energy effects. These results are in fair agreement with the value of 1.465 ev obtained by Branscomb in photodetachment studies (see Table 8-1-1), but not with the measurements of Schulz, to be described later.

2. *Total ion collection methods.* Buchel'nikova[52] has made measurements on oxygen, water vapor, and a number of halogen-containing molecules in apparatus somewhat similar to the Lozier type except for the absence of the vanes perpendicular to the electron beam direction. Her results therefore should not reflect all the defects of the Lozier method just mentioned. An RPD electron gun (cf. Section 5-5-A) was used in her measurements.

Schulz has used a tube similar to that shown in Fig. 5-9-2 for studies of dissociative negative ion formation in H_2,[53] H_2O,[54] N_2O,[55] and O_2, CO, and CO_2.[56] His apparatus, which also employs an RPD electron current, was designed specifically to be free of kinetic energy and angular discrimination effects, and nearly all of the ions formed in the tube are collected when cross sections are being measured. The tube is bakeable and background pressures of 10^{-9} mm Hg are achieved. In order to prevent contamination resulting from reactions of the target gas at the hot filament, a differential pumping system is used, and gas is continuously passed through the collision chamber. The cross sections that Schulz measured were independent of the electron beam current, pressure, and intensity of the magnetic field used to confine the beam. (Because of nonlinearities with electron current and pressure, the Liverpool group[49-51] had to extrapolate their data to zero electron current and pressure, in addition to correcting for kinetic energy discrimination. They could not correct for angular discrimination.)

Schulz's collision chamber is formed by a grounded cylindrical grid surrounded by a cylindrical ion collector which is held at a few volts positive to collect negative ions formed by the electron beam along the axis of the chamber. An essential feature of the operation of this tube when cross sections are being measured is the penetration of the collector field through the grid to the axis, in order to ensure collection of all of the ions. This penetrating field is reversed when the kinetic energy of the ions is being measured, for the collector plate is then used as a retarding electrode. The kinetic energy of the ions is determined (a) from ion retarding curves at fixed electron energy and (b) from the shift in onset with a fixed retarding voltage between the grid and collector. The methods described in the discussion of the Lozier tube are used to obtain cross sections for negative ion formation and electron affinities. The cross section versus electron energy curves obtained by Schulz[56] are in satisfactory agreement with those obtained by the Liverpool group on O_2, CO, and CO_2, but the absolute agreement is poor except in the case of CO_2. Also, Schulz obtains a different value for the electron affinity of atomic oxygen, 2.0 ± 0.1 ev, and suggests that the value of 1.465 ev obtained by Branscomb et al. refers to photodetachment from an excited state of O^- about 0.5 ev above the ground state. This discrepancy is discussed further in Section 8-7-A. Schulz's value for the affinity of atomic hydrogen[53,54] is in good agreement with the accepted values listed in Table 8-1-1.

3. *Mass spectrometric analysis.* Since the mid-1950's mass spectrometric studies of negative-ion formation have been made on most of the diatomic and triatomic gases in which negative ions may be produced. A large number of more complex gases have also been studied. The usual

technique is to pass an electron beam of known energy through an ionization chamber containing the sample gas at a pressure of about 10^{-5} mm Hg and to extract the ions thus formed into a mass spectrometer for analysis. Sometimes higher pressures (up to several mm Hg) are used in the collision region to permit the investigation of secondary processes leading to ions that are not produced in single collisions of electrons with molecules. Many of the experiments have made use of RPD electron guns for improved energy resolution. Appearance potentials can be determined mass spectrometrically with high *precision** (within a few hundredths of an ev if RPD techniques are used), and the ions to which the appearance potentials refer can be unambiguously identified in nearly all cases by mass analysis. Cross sections and electron affinities, however, cannot be determined with nearly the same degree of precision, partly because of the angular, energy, and mass discrimination effects that afflict mass spectrometers even more than Lozier tubes.[56] Here we enumerate some of the more recent investigations made with mass spectrometers. Reference may be made to the papers cited for experimental details and for references to earlier work.

Negative ion formation in hydrogen, oxygen, and water vapor has been studied by Muschlitz [57] at pressures up to 4 mm Hg. The only negative ion observed in hydrogen is H^-, formed in dissociative attachment; O^- and O_2^- are produced in oxygen, and bombardment of water vapor at high pressures produces H^-, O^- and OH^- ions. Muschlitz and his co-workers have also investigated negative ion formation in hydrogen peroxide (H_2O_2)[58] and several hydrocarbons.[59] Ion-molecule reactions† may play a role in the formation of some of the ions observed in these studies.

Curran[60] has recently reported the formation of O^-, O_2^-, and O_3^- ions in ozone bombarded by electrons in the ion source of a mass spectrometer. His observation of O_3^- appears to have been the first mass spectrometric detection of this ion. The O_3^- ion can also be formed in ordinary oxygen which is radiated intensely enough that an appreciable amount of ozone is present.

The halogens have not been investigated extensively in mass spectrometers because of their extreme chemical activity, but a careful study of iodine has been made by Fox[31] with modern techniques. The dissociative attachment process $e + I_2 \rightarrow I^- + I$ was found to be the only important one. Several modern studies have been made of the hydrogen halides HCl,

---

* The accuracy of these determinations, however, is not necessarily high because of the difficulty of assessing the effects of surface potentials.

† For discussions of negative ion-molecule reactions, see K. Kraus, W. Müller-Duysing, and H. Neuert, Z. Naturforsch. **16-a**, 1385 (1961); C. E. Melton, "Negative Ion Mass Spectra," in *Mass Spectrometry of Organic Ions* (edited by F. W. McLafferty), Academic, New York, 1963.

HBr, and HI, in which negative atomic halogen ions are formed by dissociative attachment.[61] Complex molecules containing halogen atoms are of particular practical interest because of their high dielectric strengths, which result from their large attachment coefficients. Sulfur hexafluoride (SF_6) has been the subject of several investigations.[62] SF_6^-, SF_5^-, SF_4^-, SF_3^-, F_2^-, and F^- ions are formed in this gas. The cross section for production of SF_6^- from SF_6 peaks at essentially zero energy, and this property has been used in many beam experiments to establish the electron energy scale. Schulz[63] has discussed the precautions that should be observed in the calibration procedure.

Several investigators have studied the formation of negative ions in SO_2.[64] SO_2^-, SO^-, S^-, and O^- ions are observed. The oxides of nitrogen have also received a fair amount of attention. O^- and NO^- ions have been observed in electron impact studies of NO[65] and N_2O,[66] and O^- and NO_2^- are produced in NO_2.[67]

8-6. EXPERIMENTAL METHODS FOR STUDY OF ELECTRON DETACHMENT

A. COLLISIONAL DETACHMENT. The detachment of electrons from negative ions in collisions with molecules has been studied by both beam and swarm techniques. In experiments of the beam type a mass-analyzed, monoenergetic beam of negative ions is passed through a target gas, and free electrons resulting from collisions are collected. In most cases the beam energy is kept sufficiently low enough (10 to 5000 ev) that comparatively few electrons are produced in ionization of the target gas. The techniques employed in these studies are similar to those ulilized in charge transfer experiments (see Chapter 6) and therefore are not discussed here. Branscomb[5] and Hasted[68] have summarized the results obtained in these experiments.

Phelps and Pack[69] and Chanin, Phelps, and Biondi[39] have utilized the drift tube shown in Fig. 8-5-1 for studies of detachment from swarms of negative ions in oxygen. In these experiments the control grid in the drift tube was operated as an electron filter so that the current reaching the collector could be separated into an electron and a negative ion component. These experiments furnished the thermal detachment frequency for O_2^- ions as a function of the gas temperature. When combined with their observed frequency for three-body attachment (the reverse process), these results also yielded a value of 0.44 ± 0.02 ev for the electron affinity of the oxygen molecule (see Section 8-7-A-2). These results are extremely important for studies of electron detachment in air, since they show that, at pressures of a few mm Hg, O_2^- ions are thermodynamically stable only at temperatures below about $1000°K$.

B. DETACHMENT BY ELECTRIC FIELDS.   The apparatus in which Riviere and Sweetman[70] investigated the dissociation of positive molecular ions by strong electric fields (Section 6-8) has also been applied to the study of electron detachment from He$^-$ ions; 1 Mev He$^-$ ions from a Van de Graaff

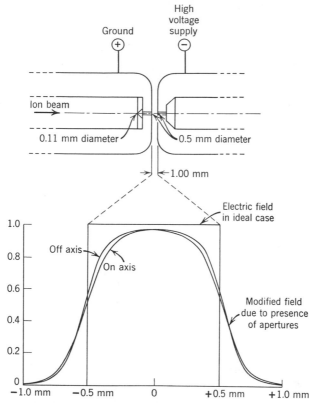

FIG. 8-6-1. The high-field gap in the apparatus used by Riviere and Sweetman for investigation of dissociation of ions in strong electric fields.

accelerator are mass-analyzed and passed through the gap between the two electrodes shown in Fig. 8-6-1. The ions are subjected to a strong electric field while in the gap, and some of them have their outermost electrons detached. Charge-to-mass analysis is performed on the emerging beam, and the intensities of the neutral and negative components are measured with CsI scintillation counters. Figure 8-6-2 shows the fraction of the beam ions which undergoes detachment and indicates that the He$^-$ is completely neutralized when the electric field in the gap is raised to 4.5×10^5 volts/cm. The structure of the detachment curves obtained by Riviere and Sweetman indicates that the He$^-$ ions are in the $^4P_{5/2}$ state. Experiments were also

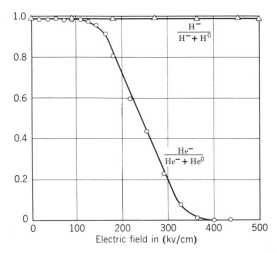

FIG. 8-6-2. The fraction of the ions undergoing detachment in experiments on He⁻ and H⁻, plotted against the intensity of the electric field in the high-field gap.

Principle of Photodetachment Apparatus

$$X^- + h\nu \longrightarrow X + e$$

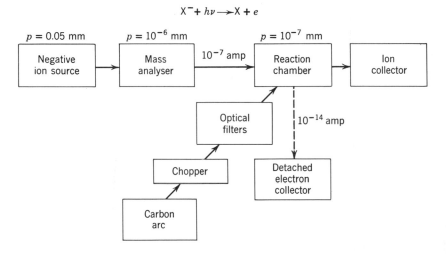

FIG. 8-6-3. Block diagram of a typical photodetachment apparatus.[10]

performed on H⁻ ions, but, as Fig. 8-6-2 shows, no detectable amount of detachment occurred at fields up to the maximum value $(5.4 \times 10^5 \text{ volts/cm})$ used in these experiments.

C. PHOTODETACHMENT.   A number of important experiments have been performed on the detachment of electrons from negative ions by photon absorption. Most of this work has required the use of modulated crossed-beam techniques developed by Branscomb and Smith and their colleagues at the U. S. National Bureau of Standards. A block diagram of one version of their apparatus is shown in Fig. 8-6-3. A beam of mass-analyzed negative ions is intersected at right angles in high vacuum by an intense beam of filtered visible light, and the current of free electrons produced by photon absorption is measured. Glow and hot cathode arc discharges of special design have been used in the ion sources, and a high-intensity carbon arc lamp serves as the light source. An elaborate optical system containing a set of band-pass filters is used to provide about 1 watt of quasi-monochromatic radiation at the beam intersection region. The optical system is illustrated in Fig. 8-6-4. A combination of weak electric and magnetic fields perpendicular to the ion and photon beams permits collection of the photodetached electrons without significantly disturbing the ion beam. The photon beam is mechanically chopped and narrow-band phase-sensitive detection is employed to minimize the contribution of electrons from collisional detachment of the ion beam by the background gas. The use of electron multipliers as detectors (see Fig. 8-6-5) permits experiments to be performed with ion beam currents as low as 5×10^{-10} amp and thereby allows studies to be made on ions (such as C⁻) that are difficult to produce in large quantities. Further experimental details are available in the review by Branscomb[10] and the paper by Smith and Branscomb.[71]

The National Bureau of Standards group has used the foregoing techniques to study the photodetachment spectra of H⁻,[72] O⁻,[73] S⁻,[74] C⁻,[75] I⁻,[76] OH⁻,[77] and O₂⁻.[78] Photodetachment cross sections were measured for H⁻, O⁻, C⁻, and O₂⁻, and accurate electron affinities determined for O, S, C, and I (cf. Table 8-1-1). The interpretation of these experiments is discussed at length in two reviews by Branscomb.[10,18]

A new method of studying photodetachment has been developed by Berry and his co-workers,[79] who made observations of the absorption spectra of atomic halogen negative ions produced in alkali halide vapors which had been heated by shock waves*. In addition to providing the first

---

* R. S. Berry and C. W. David have also reported the observation of *emission* spectra produced by radiative capture of low-energy electrons by the gaseous halogen atoms Cl, Br, and I. These results were presented at the Third International Conference on the Physics of Electronic and Atomic Collisions, London, 1963. Berry and David were apparently the first to observe thresholds for *s*-wave capture of electrons by atoms.

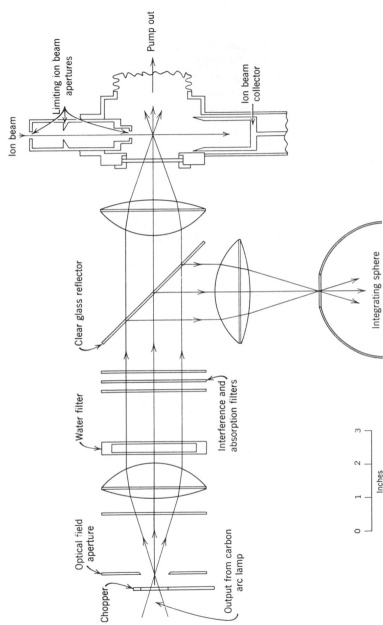

FIG. 8-6-4. The optical system used in certain of the NBS photodetachment studies.[10]   Radiation from a carbon arc is imaged on the field aperture at the left by an elliptical mirror and is monitored in the integrating sphere by a black bolometer inserted into the sphere. A portion of the ion-photon interaction chamber is shown at the right.

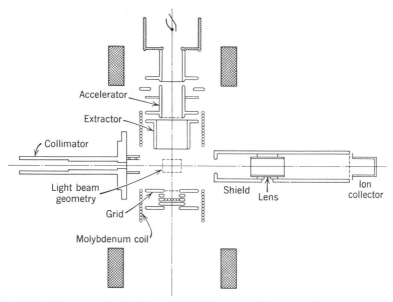

FIG. 8-6-5. The reaction chamber used in Seman and Branscomb's experiments on photodetachment from C⁻.[75] The cross section of the chopped photon beam, whose direction is perpendicular to the plane of the drawing, is indicated by the dashed rectangle. The ion beam passes from left to right from the mass spectrometer, which is not shown. Detached electrons are trapped by the magnetic field produced by the molybdenum coil and the external coil (shown cross hatched) and focused on the cathode of a 10-stage electron multiplier, part of which is shown at the top of the figure.

observations of photodetachment spectra in the ultraviolet, this method has much higher optical resolution than the crossed-beam method, although it does not lend itself as well to absorption cross section measurements. Unfortunately, it is not possible to take full advantage of this high optical resolution because the plasma ion densities required ($n^+ = n^- \approx 10^{15}/\text{cm}^3$) are such that Stark broadening is substantial. Some extremely precise measurements of electron affinities have been made by Berry et al., as indicated by Table 8-1-1.

8-7. DATA ON NEGATIVE ION FORMATION AND ELECTRON DETACHMENT

In the presentation of data on negative ion formation and electron detachment for a number of specific systems heavy emphasis is placed on oxygen because of its importance in upper atmospheric phenomena. Special attention is paid to hydrogen and carbon because of their astrophysical significance.

A. OXYGEN. 1. *Attachment*. The attachment of electrons to oxygen molecules to form negative ions has been the subject of many investigations.* From the earlier studies it was concluded that at pressures of the order of tens of mm Hg the attachment occurred in two-body-processes over the entire energy range.[29,34,35] However, recent work by Hurst and Bortner[37,80] and by Chanin, Phelps, and Biondi[38,39] has shown that the attachment at low energies (<1 ev) involves a three-body process, and this demonstration removes some of the apparent contradictions in previous theoretical explanations of the attachment reactions in oxygen. This section deals mainly with the experimental results of Chanin et al. and with the interpretations of these results in terms of specific mechanisms for the formation of the ions.

The experiments of Chanin, Phelps, and Biondi[38,39] were concerned with the attachment to oxygen molecules of electrons with average energies between a few hundredths and a few electron volts. The pulsed drift tube apparatus shown in Fig. 8-5-1 was utilized in these studies. Pure oxygen and mixtures of oxygen with helium and nitrogen were used in the drift tube at pressures ranging from 0.1 to 500 mm Hg. The admixtures of helium and nitrogen were used to inhibit diffusion effects and thus permit measurements to be made at very low drift fields. The use of the admixtures also allowed the determination of the effectiveness of helium atoms and nitrogen molecules as third bodies in the attachment process.

Electron capture by oxygen molecules at electron energies below about 17 ev may occur either by radiative attachment or by two nonradiative processes. In the nonradiative processes, which were the only significant ones in the experiments of Chanin et al., a negative ion is formed in an intermediate unstable state. This intermediate ion may either eject the captured electron by autodetachment or it may be stabilized by dissociation or by a collision with a third body. The work of Craggs, Thorburn, and Tozer,[49] Buchel'nikova,[52] Schulz,[56] and others has shown dissociative attachment to oxygen molecules to be important at electron energies of several ev. The threshold of this reaction should occur at an electron energy of about 3.6 ev.

In 1935 Bloch and Bradbury[25] suggested that attachment in oxygen at lower (near thermal) energies might be explained in terms of a two-step process involving an electron and two oxygen molecules. According to the *Bloch-Bradbury mechanism*, a low-energy electron collides with an oxygen molecule in its ground ($v = 0$) vibrational state and forms a negative O_2^- ion in the first ($v = 1$) vibrational state of the $^2\Pi_g$ electronic state. The second step in the attachment process concerns the vibrational de-excitation

---

* For bibliographies on attachment in oxygen see Refs. 3, 4, and 39.

of this ion in a collision with a third body. If an oxygen molecule is available nearby to serve as the third body, the vibrational energy of the negative ion may be transferred by a "resonance" process. Chanin, Phelps, and Biondi[39] show, however, that the Bloch-Bradbury mechanism must be modified to place the initially formed O_2^- ion in a higher vibrational state than $v = 1$.* They also show that atoms and molecules other than O_2 may serve to stabilize the excited O_2^- ions formed by electron capture.

Chanin et al.[39] introduce the following rate coefficients to describe the rates of electron loss by the various attachment processes we have discussed. The quantity ν_a is the over all attachment frequency, β is the two-body rate coefficient representing processes of the types

$$e + O_2 \rightarrow O_2^- + h\nu \qquad \text{(unimportant here)}$$

and

$$e + O_2 \rightarrow O_2^{-*} \rightarrow O + O^- + \text{(kinetic energy)}$$

and K is the three-body rate coefficient for reactions of the type

$$e + O_2 + X \rightarrow O_2^- + X + \text{(kinetic energy)}$$

Thus, if n_e, $n(O_2)$, and $n(X)$ are the number densities of electrons, oxygen molecules, and third bodies, respectively, the time rate of electron loss by attachment is given by the equation

$$\left(\frac{dn_e}{dt}\right)_a = -\nu_a n_e = -\beta\, n(O_2)n_e - K(X)\, n(X)\, n(O_2)n_e$$

A two-body process may be characterized by an attachment cross section q_a, which is related to the corresponding β by the equation

$$\beta = \overline{q_a v} = \overline{h q_s v}$$

where v is the velocity of relative motion of the collision partners and the averaging is performed over the energy distribution of the electrons. The techniques used in these experiments do not permit a direct determination of ν_a, β, or K. What is measured instead is the quantity α, the attachment coefficient per unit drift distance of an electron drifting through the gas under the influence of the applied field (see Section 8-5-A-4).

The data obtained by Chanin et al. for the attachment coefficient α in pure oxygen at 300°K are presented in Fig. 8-7-1. The ratio α/p is plotted so that the pressure dependence of the attachment is clearly revealed. The

* The basis for this modification is the high value for the electron affinity, 0.44 ev, for O_2 molecules derived from recent swarm experiments by Pack and Phelps.[69] Support for this value is provided by analyses of attachment in oxygen by D. C. Conway, *J. Chem. Phys.* **36**, 2549 (1962), *Bull. Am. Phys. Soc.* **7**, 131 (1962).

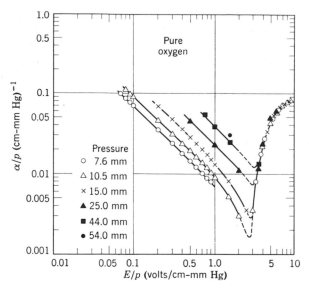

FIG. 8-7-1. Measured values of α/p in pure O_2 at 300°K.[39] The agreement between values of α/p obtained at various pressures for $E/p > 3$ volts/cm-mm Hg shows that α is directly proportional to p. For lower E/p, α/p^2 is independent of pressure.

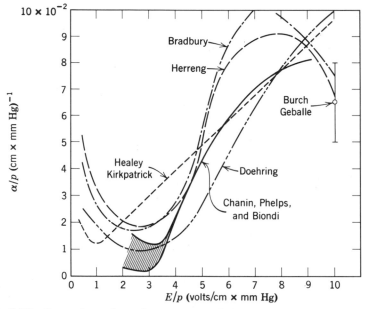

FIG. 8-7-2. Comparison of attachment rate coefficients measured by various investigators.[39] The shaded region for $E/p < 3$ volts/cm-mm Hg corresponds to the region of Fig. 8-7-1 in which α/p varies with pressure.

quantity plotted along the abscissa is E/p, which is a measure of the average energy of the electrons in the swarm.   At low values of E/p ($E/p < 3$ volts/cm-mm Hg, corresponding to average electron energies below about 1 ev) α/p is proportional to the pressure, and three-body attachment is seen to predominate.   At higher E/p, α/p is independent of p, and two-body attachment is indicated.   Figure 8-7-2 shows a comparison of these results with those obtained by other investigators.   Since the other investigators

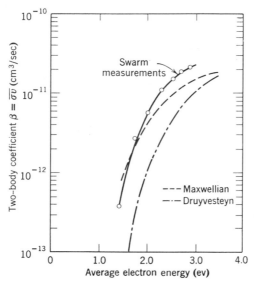

FIG. 8-7-3. Comparison of the two-body attachment coefficient for pure O_2 at 300°K obtained from swarm experiments with values calculated from electron beam experiments by using Maxwellian and Druyvesteyn electron energy distributions.

were unaware of, and did not explore, the three-body nature of the capture process at $E/p < 3$ volts/cm-mm Hg, the lower portions of their curves should be ignored—their results depend on the particular pressure used in each experiment.

The three- and two-body attachment coefficients, K and β, may be determined as functions of the average electron energy by conversion of the E/p values to average energy, using curves that appear in the paper by Chanin, Phelps, and Biondi.[39]   The two-body coefficients of Chanin et al. are compared in Fig. 8-7-3 with values calculated from beam experiment cross sections by Craggs, Thorburn, and Tozer,[49] as corrected by Buchel'nikova[52] and Schulz.[56]   Since the beam data pertain to electrons with a narrow spread in energy, it is necessary to average these data over the electron energy distribution appropriate to the swarm measurements.   The assumption is made that the correct distribution lies somewhere between a

Maxwellian and a Druyvesteyn distribution. The fair agreement between the swarm data and the average beam data leads us to dismiss the mechanism which Bradbury[29] proposed for attachment in this energy range. Bradbury suggested that the attachment at $E/p > 3$ volts/cm-mm Hg is the result of the loss of energy by electrons in inelastic collisions with oxygen molecules and their subsequent capture in the low-energy attachment process.

Figure 8-7-4 shows the values of the three-body rate coefficient obtained by Chanin, Phelps, and Biondi[39] from measurements on oxygen and

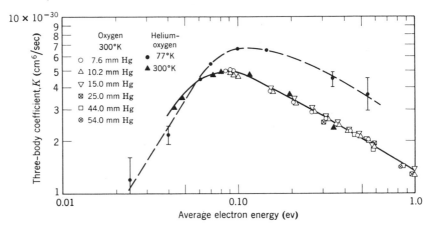

FIG. 8-7-4. The three-body attachment coefficient for oxygen versus average electron energy for gas temperatures of 77 and 300°K.

oxygen-helium mixtures. The relative effectiveness of helium, nitrogen, and oxygen as third bodies in stabilizing the attachment is indicated in Fig. 8-7-5. Helium is roughly one hundred times less effective than oxygen at gas temperatures of 300 and 77°K, nitrogen is intermediate in effectiveness at 300°K.

Important data on negative ion formation in molecular oxygen are also available from beam experiments, to which reference has already been made. The results of studies by Craggs, Thorburn, and Tozer[49] and Schulz[56] on the reaction

$$e + O_2 \rightarrow O + O^-$$

are presented in Fig. 8-7-6. Schulz reports a peak cross section of 1.25×10^{-18} cm² for this reaction at an electron energy of 6.7 ev.

Ion-pair formation is also possible in O_2 at electron energies above about 17 ev.[2,7] The reaction is

$$e + O_2 \rightarrow O^- + O^+ + e$$

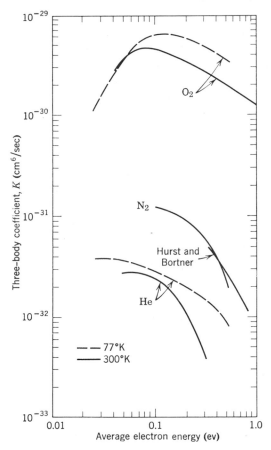

FIG. 8-7-5. Comparison of stabilizing effects of O_2, N_2, and He in three-body electron attachment to O_2 at 77°K (dashed curves) and 300°K (solid curves).

In dissociating the O_2 molecule, 5.1 ev is expended. An additional 13.6 ev is required to ionize one of the O atoms to produce O^+, but 1.5 ev is available from the capture of an electron by the other O atom to form O^- (see Section 8-5-B-2). Thus the threshold of this reaction is (5.1 + 13.6 − 1.5), or 17.2 ev. (The observed onset of O^- production at 17.2 ev tends to support the correctness of the value of EA used.)

2. *Detachment.* As pointed out earlier, collisional detachment of electrons from O_2^- ions drifting through O_2 has been studied by Pack and Phelps,[69] who used the same drift tube apparatus that was employed in the attachment studies previously described. Their data on the detachment frequency are presented as a function of the gas temperature in Fig. 8-7-7.

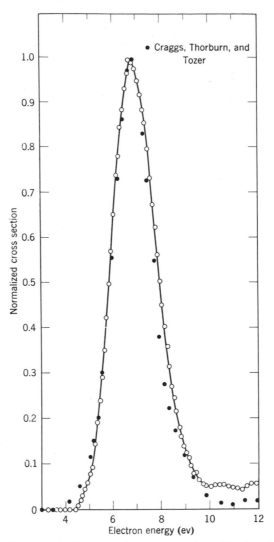

FIG. 8-7-6. The normalized cross section for formation of O ions by electron impact on O_2 molecules. The open circles represent the data of Schulz[56]; the black dots, the results of Craggs, Thorburn, and Tozer.[49] Electron-beam techniques were used in each case. Schulz's cross section has a peak value of 1.25×10^{-18} cm^2 at 6.7 ev. The curve obtained by Craggs et al. has a shape similar to that of Schulz, but its peak value is almost twice as high. Additional data on electron attachment and ionization in oxygen have been recently reported by R. K. Asundi, J. D. Craggs, and M. V. Kurepa, *Proc. Phys. Soc.* (*London*) **82**, 967 (1963)

For plotting, the detachment frequency ν_d is divided by N, the number density of the gas, with which the ions are essentially in thermal equilibrium. Also shown for comparison is the thermal electron three-body attachment frequency ν_a, divided by N^2. The collisional detachment results of Pack and Phelps are of particular interest in connection with ionospheric studies, for they show that the frequency of electron detachment collisions between O_2^- ions and a thermal distribution of oxygen or nitrogen molecules in the lower ionosphere is at least two orders of magnitude smaller

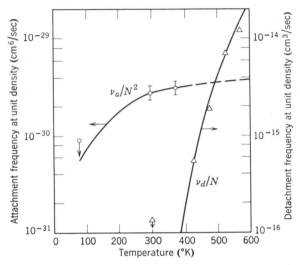

FIG. 8-7-7. Thermal attachment and detachment coefficients in molecular oxygen as a function of the gas temperature. The reactions are $e + 2O_2 \rightleftharpoons O_2^- + O_2$.

than the previously accepted values. (More recent work by Pack and Phelps[81] indicates, however, that the detachment frequencies are really about 30% higher than those plotted in Fig. 8-7-7.) Another important result of this study was the determination of the electron affinity of O_2, which was obtained by equating the rates of attachment and detachment and using the law of mass action. The value thus determined by Pack and Phelps[69] was 0.46 ± 0.02 ev (later revised to 0.44 ev[39]).

We have already mentioned (Section 8-6-C) the work done at the National Bureau of Standards on photodetachment of electrons from atomic and molecular negative ions of oxygen. The photodetachment cross sections for O_2^-, derived from measurements by Burch, Smith, and Branscomb,[78] are displayed in Fig. 8-7-8. Also shown are results for O^- obtained by Branscomb, Burch, Smith, and Geltman,[73] whose measurements are particularly important because they furnish the most accurate value for the electron affinity of atomic oxygen yet obtained, 1.465 ± 0.005 ev. Schulz[56] obtained a higher value, 2.0 ± 0.1 ev, for this quantity in his electron impact experiments described in Section 8-5-B and concluded that the photodetachment value must refer to detachment from an excited state of O^- about 0.5 ev above the ground state. This explanation is hard to accept for the following reasons:

(a) The excited state hypothesis would require that a large fraction of the O^- ions involved in *all* of the photodetachment experiments be in this

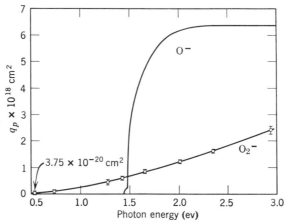

FIG. 8-7-8. The experimental photodetachment cross sections for O_2^- and O^- ions. The O_2^- solid line is a 3-parameter threshold law expansion fitted to the experimental points. No threshold could be found for photodetachment from O_2^-, but the curve extrapolates to zero at a photon energy of 0.15 ev. This intercept occurs far below the last observed point at 0.5 ev. The O^- data yield a value of 1.465 ev for the electron affinity of atomic oxygen.

excited state. Since two different ion sources and two different source gases (O_2 and CO) were utilized in the photodetachment experiments, this requirement appears unrealistic.

(b) The observed threshold dependence of the photodetachment is incorrect for detachment from the metastable $(1s^2 2s^2 2p^4 3s)$ state of O^- but correct for detachment from the ground $(1s^2 2s^2 2p^5)$ state.*

(c) Various calculations show that an electron affinity of about 1.5 ev for atomic oxygen gives a self-consistent photodetachment cross section theoretically but that a value of 2.0 ev with an excited state at about −1 ev requires an impossibly large polarizability for oxygen.†

* The quantum mechanical theory of photodetachment and predictions of threshold laws have been summarized by Branscomb.[5,10] For recent theoretical work on O^-, C^-, Cl^-, and F^- see J. W. Cooper and J. B. Martin, *Phys. Rev.* **126**, 1482 (1962).
† Private communication, L. M. Branscomb (1962).

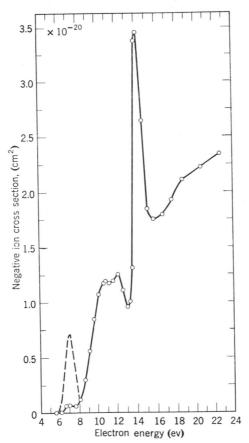

FIG. 8-7-9. The cross section for production of H⁻ ions by dissociative attachment in hydrogen gas.[53] Also see V. I. Khvostenko and V. M. Dukel'skii, *Sov. Phys.* JETP **6,** 657 (1958).

(d) The recent extrapolation calculations[10] of electron affinities of the light elements and analogous estimates of excitation potentials of electronically excited states give excellent agreement with all data on electron affinities if $EA(O) = 1.465$ ev and put the $2p^43s$ state of O⁻ in the continuum. Thus, if Schulz's conclusion is correct, either the theory of photodetachment is in an unbelievably bad plight or there are serious errors in the measured ionization potentials of positive ions in the O⁻ isoelectronic sequence.

B. HYDROGEN.   The formation of H⁻ ions from H_2 molecules has been investigated by Schulz[53] with beam techniques (see Section 8-5-B-2). His results are shown in Fig. 8-7-9. The solid curve in the drawing is associated with the reaction $e + H_2 \rightarrow H^- + H$ below 13.6 ev and the reaction $e + H_2 \rightarrow H^- + H^*$ above 13.6 ev. The simultaneous production of H^- and H^+ ions can occur above 17.2 ev. The dashed curve in Fig. 8-7-9 indicates the formation of additional negative ions when reagent grade hydrogen is introduced into the collision chamber with no liquid air in the trap. These ions are thought to be H^- produced from water vapor. Negative ions cannot be formed by free electron attachment to hydrogen molecules in

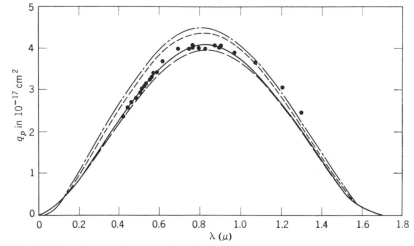

FIG. 8-7-10. The experimental photodetachment cross section for H^- (black dots) compared with the results of four theoretical calculations.[10]

nondissociative processes, although H_2^- ions have been produced in an ion source containing a mixture of water and antimony vapors (see Table 8-1-2).

Figure 8-7-10 shows the photodetachment cross section for H^- measured by Smith and Burch[72] (black dots), compared with the results of four theoretical calculations, which have been discussed by Branscomb.[10] The absolute integrated cross section for detachment from H^- was measured by Branscomb and Smith[72] to an accuracy of about $\pm 10\%$. All four of the theoretical curves are consistent with the experimental cross sections within these limits, and the data at 5280 Å are normalized to the theoretical curve shown as a solid line.

Although radiative attachment to form negative ions has not been observed in a beam experiment in the laboratory, the cross sections and reaction rates may be obtained from the measured photodetachment spectrum by use of the principle of detailed balancing.[10] Radiative attachment rate coefficients thus obtained for atomic hydrogen and oxygen are shown in Fig. 8-7-11. Three illustrative curves are also shown for molecular oxygen for various assumed values of the vertical detachment energy E_0. These curves are correct only if the experimental photodetachment spectrum from which they were calculated refers to single initial and final vibrational states. Curves of the radiative attachment cross sections for H and O are also given in Branscomb's review.[10]

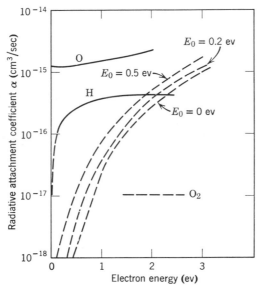

FIG. 8-7-11. Radiative attachment coefficients for atomic hydrogen and oxygen and illustrative curves for molecular oxygen.

C. CARBON. Electron attachment to carbon atoms has never been studied experimentally in the laboratory, but Seman and Branscomb[75] have investigated the structure and photodetachment spectrum of the C^- negative ion. The C^- photodetachment spectrum was measured in the visible region of the spectrum relative to the O^- spectrum, and the O^- data of Smith[73] were used to obtain absolute values for the C^- photodetachment cross section shown in Fig. 8-7-12. The circles (whose diameters indicate the magnitude of the statistical experimental errors) and the circles with error bars represent the experimental cross section data. The solid line represents the best fit to the C^- ground-state threshold data. The lower dashed line indicates absorption by an excited metastable (^2D) state of the C^- ion. Since the relative populations of the metastable ^2D and the ground ^4S states of the C^- in this experiment were unknown, it is impossible to calculate the cross section for photodetachment from the excited state.

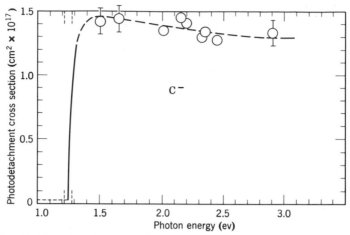

FIG. 8-7-12. The photodetachment cross section for C⁻.[75] The very weak infrared absorption from the C⁻ metastable state is indicated by the lower dashed line, which does not represent a true cross section since the initial state population is not known.

Hence, no significance can be attached to the absolute value of the absorption coefficient from the metastable state. A value of 1.25 ± 0.03 ev for the electron affinity of the carbon atom was derived from these experiments.

D. WATER VAPOR. Two types of negative ions, H⁻ and O⁻, are known from mass spectrometric studies to be formed by single electron impact on H_2O molecules,[57,82] and OH⁻ may be produced in secondary reactions.[57] Under the usual impact conditions the production of H⁻ predominates. Nondissociative attachment does not occur. Figure 8-7-13 shows a reproduction of a recorder trace obtained by Schulz[54] in trapped-electron

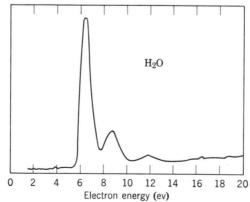

FIG. 8-7-13. A reproduction of a recorder trace obtained by Schulz in trapped-electron studies of negative ion formation in H_2O.[54] The negative ion current is shown as a function of the electron impact energy.

studies of negative ion formation in H_2O. The peaks of H^- production occur at 6.5 and 8.8 ev, with O^- production contributing to some extent to the peak at the higher energy. The peak at 12.0 ev is believed to be due to the O^- ion. Electron swarm experiments of Hurst, O'Kelly, and Bortner[83] provide a value of 7.7×10^{-18} cm²-ev for the capture cross section integrated over the low-energy peak at 6.5 ev. This result is consistent with the value of 6.5×10^{-18} cm²-ev obtained by Buchel'nikova[52] in a beam experiment.

E. CARBON MONOXIDE AND CARBON DIOXIDE.   Dissociative attachment can occur in CO and CO_2 with the formation of O^- ions (see Sections 8-5-B-1 and 8-5-B-2). Schulz[56] has performed beam experiments on negative ion production in both gases; his results are shown in Figs. 8-7-14 and 8-7-15.* The lower portion of the CO curve with an onset around 6 ev is probably due to metastable CO molecules in the $A^3\Pi$ state hitting the grid of his tube and releasing secondary electrons that are collected on the ion collector. The onset at 9.4 ev is interpreted as being due to the arrival of O^- ions at the collector. If the background produced by secondary electrons is subtracted from the total signal, a cross section of 1.6×10^{-19} cm² is obtained for the formation of O^- from CO at the peak of the curve.

F. SULFUR HEXAFLUORIDE. SF_6 is representative of a class of halogen-containing molecules which are of special practical interest because of their large cross section for electron attachment and, consequently, their high dielectric strength. Sulfur hexafluoride, for example, has a higher dielectric strength than nitrogen, even though the dissociation energy of N_2 is 9.76 ev.[7] This property has led to the use of SF_6 in arc-suppressing switches. (If the contacts of a switch carrying a high current are opened in an atmosphere of SF_6, the incipient discharge is extinguished because the free electrons are quickly captured to form negative ions, which themselves cannot help develop the discharge.)

Mass spectrometric studies[62] have indicated that SF_6^-, SF_5^-, SF_4^-, SF_3^-, F_2^-, and F^- ions are produced by electron impact on SF_6 molecules. Hickam and Fox[62] have used their RPD apparatus to study SF_6 at electron energies from 0 to 2 ev; SF_6^- was observed to be formed in a resonance capture process with an extremely high cross section, estimated to be at least 10^{-15} cm². The peak height was a linear function of pressure, and presumably the vibrationally excited SF_6^- ion formed by the electron attachment is not de-excited by collision. The excited vibrational state

* For additional data on attachment and ionization see R. K. Asundi, J. D. Craggs, and M. V. Kurepa, *Proc. Phys. Soc.* (*London*) **82,** 967 (1963); Third International Conference on the Phys cs of Electronic and Atomic Collisions, London, 1963.

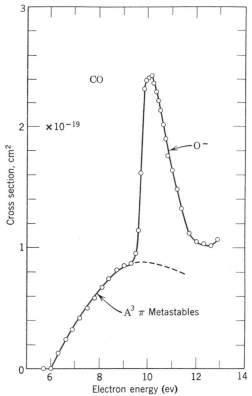

FIG. 8-7-14. The cross section for production of O⁻ ions in electron bombardment of CO molecules.[56] If the background contribution to the collector current due to metastables is subtracted from the true negative ion contribution, a peak cross section of 1.6×10^{-19} cm² is obtained.

must have an unusually long lifetime in order that the ion may accommodate the excess energy, but this is not surprising in light of the many vibrational and rotational modes among which the energy may be distributed. Electron ejection might not be expected to occur until the excess energy becomes concentrated in one of the modes. The capture process leading to SF_6^- developed at less than 0.1 ev and only over an energy range estimated to be less than 0.05 ev wide. Hickam and Fox also observed dissociative attachment leading to SF_5^-. The SF_5^- curve peaked at about 0.1 ev and then decreased to zero at approximately 1.5 ev. Its height was also a linear function of the SF_6 pressure, which was less than 10^{-5} mm Hg. The maximum cross section for the dissociative ion formation process was estimated to be 10^{-17} cm². Plots of the SF_6^- and SF_5^- ion currents obtained by Hickam and Fox are presented in Fig. 8-7-16.

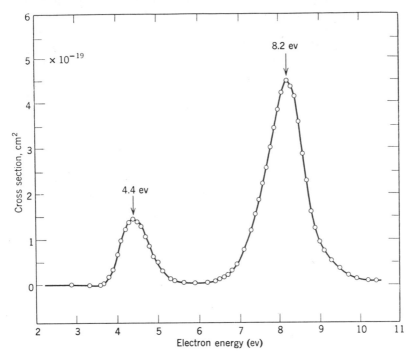

FIG. 8-7-15. The cross section for production of O⁻ ions in electron bombardment of CO_2 molecules.[56] Both peaks are due to formation of O⁻ ions.

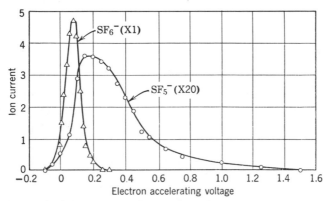

FIG. 8-7-16. The SF_6^- and SF_5^- currents obtained by Hickam and Fox[62] in their mass spectrometric studies of SF_6 using retarding potential difference techniques.

G. OTHER GASES.   In addition to those listed, a number of other gases and vapors can form negative ions and are of interest in gaseous electronics. References are given in Section 8-5-B-3 to studies of negative ion formation in I_2, HCl, HBr, HI, SO_2, NO, N_2O, and NO_2. Additional information on these and other gases such as NH_3 and H_2S may be found in the writings of Loeb[3,4] and Craggs and Massey;[7] H^- and NH_2^- ions are formed in NH_3, and S^- ions, in H_2S.[4] The cross section for dissociative attachment in the halogens is particularly high—in I_2, for example, it has a peak value of 3×10^{-15} cm² at zero electron energy.[31] This cross section corresponds to an attachment probability h (see Section 8-4) of about unity.

8-8. THE ROLE OF NEGATIVE IONS IN NATURE AND IN THE LABORATORY

Negative ions play an important role in astrophysics in determining the spectral distribution of radiation emitted by the sun and certain other types of stars. As pointed out in Section 8-2-A, the radiative formation and destruction of H^- ions provides the dominant source of opacity in the visible range of the solar continuum.[1,84,*] Bound-free transitions associated with photodetachment of electrons from the bound state of H^- furnish the main contribution to the absorption coefficient in the visible region; free-free transitions, in which an electron undergoes a transition between two states of the continuous spectrum of H^-, are the more important in the infrared. (Photon absorption by a completely free electron is impossible because momentum cannot be conserved in such a process.)

Late-type stars show continuous absorption by sources other than H^-. These sources begin to appear in the sun and increase in strength toward later spectral types. Attempts have been made to explain these additional sources by invoking absorption by neutral molecules, but it is possible that negative ions other than H^- may contribute significantly. Branscomb and Pagel[85] have calculated the concentrations of C^-, O^-, OH^-, and CN^- in giants and dwarfs of various compositions under the assumption of local thermodynamic equilibrium† and assessed their possible contributions to the continuous absorption coefficient. They conclude that O^- (and O_2^- as well) is generally unimportant; C^- is likely to be important in stars with very high atomic carbon abundances; OH^- may be significant in the late M and S stars; CN^- may be significant in late N stars; and C_2^- may be important in ultraviolet absorption in carbon stars. Both the electron

---

* Radiative attachment can also make a significant contribution to the emission continuum of arcs and shock-heated gases.

† For a discussion of local thermodynamic equilibrium see S. Chandrasekhar, *Radiative Transfer*, Dover, New York, 1960, and R. N. Thomas and R. G. Athay, *Physics of the Solar Chromosphere*, Interscience, New York, 1961.

affinity and the vertical detachment energy are required for analysis of the effects of the negative molecular ions. The electron affinity is needed for the calculation of the equilibrium concentration of the ions in the stellar atmospheres, the vertical detachment energy, for the determinations of the wavelengths at which the absorption sets in.

Negative atomic ions of hydrogen may also play a part in the formation of stars. McCrea[86] has pointed out that neutral molecular hydrogen appears to be involved in star formation in HI regions. If it is assumed that the hydrogen is initially in atomic form, a mechanism must be found for its conversion to H_2. The normal three-body processes are inadequate at the low densities present, and McCrea and McNally[87] suggested that the conversion could occur in surface reactions on dust grains. McDowell,[88] on the other hand, has suggested that even in the absence of dust grains electrons will act as a catalyst in the formation of H_2 via associative detachment from H^-. The proposed sequence of reactions is

$$e + H \rightarrow H^- + h\nu$$
$$H^- + H \rightarrow H_2^-(^2\Sigma_u) \rightarrow H_2 + e$$

Unfortunately, there is virtually no information, either theoretical or experimental, on the magnitude of the associative detachment cross section.

Turning now from astrophysics to geophysics, we should mention the effect that electron attachment has in determining the density of free electrons in the upper atmosphere and the role that negative ions thereby play in radio communications. Free electrons are produced in the upper atmosphere in photoionization and photodetachment processes involving radiation from the sun. They are also produced by the passage of meteors through the upper atmosphere, by various ionization mechanisms following atmospheric nuclear explosions, by thermal processes in the exhausts of rockets, and by thermal ionization when a space vehicle re-enters the earth's atmosphere. These free electrons act as reflectors of electromagnetic radiation if present at sufficiently high density.[89] This fact makes possible radio communications by reflection from the various layers of the ionosphere and meteor trails and permits radar echo studies of the upper atmosphere. The free electrons are also responsible for the communications "blackouts" which follow nuclear explosions and which are sometimes associated with vehicle re-entry. To discuss the criterion for reflection of an electromagnetic wave by free electrons, let us assume that the ionosphere is horizontally stratified, with the number density of free electrons n_e increasing upward. A plane wave of frequency f incident at an angle i with respect to the vertical will be refracted until it is traveling horizontally at a level at which n_e is great enough to reduce the refractive index of the medium at the wave frequency to the value $\mu = \sin i$. The wave will then return to the ground. If the wave is incident vertically, it will be reflected from a level at which $\mu = 0$ and thus at which

$$n_e = \frac{\varepsilon_0 m}{4\pi e^2} \, \omega^2 = 1.24 \times 10^{-8} f^2 \qquad (8\text{-}8\text{-}1)$$

Here ε_0 is the permittivity of free space, m is the electron mass, and ω is the angular frequency of the wave. The frequency given by (8-8-1) equals the "plasma resonance frequency" of a plasma with electron density n_e, and a vertical wave is reflected from that level in the ionosphere at which the wave frequency equals the plasma frequency.

The electron number density in any region of the upper atmosphere is determined by the rates of the various production and loss mechanisms. Diffusion is always one factor in the diminution of the electron density, and electron attachment and electron-ion recombination (Chapter 12) may also be quite important. In reflection from meteor trails diffusion is thought to be the main factor limiting the duration of radar echoes at heights above about 90 km and, for trails with linear electron densities less than about 10^{14} electrons/cm. At lower heights and greater electron densities the loss of electrons by attachment to neutral oxygen predominates.[90]

The role of negative ions in the laboratory also deserves mention here. Electron attachment to impurities in Geiger tube gas fillings leads to delayed or spurious counts which are particularly troublesome if the tube is used in an anticoincidence array.[91] In proportional counters and pulse ionization chambers delayed counts may be produced and the shape of the pulses badly smeared.[92] The effects of negative ions, however, are not always detrimental. Electronegative gases are used for arc suppression in high-current switches and in Van de Graaff accelerators, and several species of negative ions, including H^-, He^-, and N^-, are utilized in tandem accelerators for beam energy multiplication.

REFERENCES

1. H. S. W. Massey, *Negative Ions*, Second Edition, Cambridge University Press, Cambridge, 1950.
2. H. S. W. Massey and E. H. S. Burhop, *Electronic and Ionic Impact Phenomena*, Oxford University Press, Oxford, 1952, Chapters IV and VI.
3. L. B. Loeb, *Basic Processes of Gaseous Electronics*, University of California Press, Berkeley, 1955, Chapter V.
4. L. B. Loeb, "Formation of Negative Ions," in *Handbuch der Physik*, Vol. XXI, Springer-Verlag, Berlin, 1956, pp. 445-470.
5. L. M. Branscomb, "Negative Ions," in *Advances in Electronics and Electron Physics*, Vol. IX, Academic, New York, 1957, pp. 43-94.

6. F. H. Field and J. L. Franklin, *Electron Impact Phenomena*, Academic, New York, 1957.

7. J. D. Craggs, and H. S. W. Massey, "The Collisions of Electrons with Molecules," in *Handbuch der Physik*, Vol. XXXVII, Springer-Verlag, Berlin, 1959, pp. 314–415.

8. N. S. Buchel'nikova, *Fortschr. Physik* **8**, 626 (1960).

9. A. N. Prasad and J. D. Craggs, "Attachment and Ionization Coefficients," in *Atomic and Molecular Processes* (edited by D. R. Bates), Academic, New York, 1962, pp. 206–244.

10. L. M. Branscomb, "Photodetachment," in *Atomic and Molecular Processes* (edited by D. R. Bates), Academic, New York, 1962, pp. 100–140.

11. D. R. Sweetman, *Proc. Phys. Soc. (London)* **76**, 998 (1960).

12. E. Holøien and J. Midtdal, *Proc. Phys. Soc. (London)* **A-68**, 815 (1955).

13. H. R. Johnson and F. Rohrlich, *J. Chem. Phys.* **30**, 1608 (1959); see also J. W. Edie and F. Rohrlich, **36**, 623 (1962), **37**, 1151 (1962).

14. B. Edlén, *J. Chem. Phys.* **33**, 98 (1960).

15. D. J. Rose and M. Clark, *Plasmas and Controlled Fusion*, Wiley, New York, 1961, p. 37. See also H. S. W. Massey and E. H. S. Burhop, *op. cit.*, pp. 229–232.

16. W. Finkelnburg, *Atomic Physics*, McGraw-Hill, New York, 1950, Chapter 6.

17. A. Dalgarno and M. R. C. McDowell, *Proc. Phys. Soc. (London)* **A-69**, 615 (1956). The potential function of H_2^- has also been calculated by I. Fischer-Hjalmars, who finds considerably stronger binding. See *Ark. Fysik.* **16**, 33 (1959); *J. Chem. Phys.* **36**, 1081 (1962). For recent work see H. S. Taylor and F. E. Harris, **39**, 1012 (1963); H. S. Taylor and J. Gerhauser, **40**, 244 (1964).

18. L. M. Branscomb, *Proceedings of the Fifth International Conference on Ionization Phenomena in Gases*, Munich, 1961, North-Holland, Amsterdam, 1962, Vol. I, p. 1.

19. D. R. Bates and H. S. W. Massey, *Phil. Trans. Roy. Soc. (London)* **A-239**, 269 (1943).

20. R. Wildt, *Astrophys. J.* **89**, 295 (1939).

21. W. Lochte-Holtgreven, *Naturwissenschaften* **38**, 258 (1951).

22. O. Weber, *Z. Physik* **152**, 281 (1958).

23. G. Boldt, *Z. Physik* **154**, 319, 330 (1959).

24. D. R. Bates and B. L. Moiseiwitsch, *Proc. Phys. Soc. (London)* **A-68**, 540 (1955).

25. F. Bloch and N. E. Bradbury, *Phys. Rev.* **48**, 689 (1935).

26. V. A. Bailey, *Phil. Mag.* **50**, 825 (1925).

27. R. H. Healey and J. W. Reed, *The Behavior of Slow Electrons in Gases*, Amalgamated Wireless, Ltd., Sydney, 1941.

28. L. G. H. Huxley, R. W. Crompton, and C. H. Bagot, *Australian J. Phys.* **12**, 303 (1959); L. G. H. Huxley, **12**, 171 (1959); C. A. Hurst and L. G. H. Huxley, **13**, 21 (1960).

29. N. E. Bradbury, *Phys. Rev.* **44**, 883 (1933).

30. E. Kuffel, *Proc. Phys. Soc. (London)* **74**, 297 (1959).

31. M. A. Biondi, *Phys. Rev.* **109**, 2005 (1958); see also R. E. Fox, **109**, 2008, and M. A. Biondi and R. E. Fox, **109**, 2012.

32. M. J. Mulcahy, M. C. Sexton, and J. J. Lennon, *Proceedings of the Fifth International Conference on Ionization Phenomena in Gases*, Munich, 1961, North-Holland, Amsterdam, 1962, Vol. I, 612.

33. P. J. Chantry, J. S. Wharmby, and J. B. Hasted, *Proceedings of the Fifth International Conference on Ionization Phenomena in Gases*, Munich, 1961, North-Holland, Amsterdam, 1962, Vol. I, 630.

34. P. Herreng, *Cahiers Phys.* **38**, 7 (1952).

35. A. Doehring, *Z. Naturforsch.* **7-a**, 253 (1952).

36. K. B. McAfee, *J. Chem. Phys.* **23**, 1435 (1955).
37. T. E. Bortner and G. S. Hurst, *Health Phys.* **1**, 39 (1958). G. S. Hurst and T. E. Bortner, *Phys. Rev.* **114**, 116 (1959); G. S. Hurst, L. B. O'Kelly, and T. E. Bortner, **123**, 1715 (1961).
38. L. M. Chanin, A. V. Phelps, and M. A. Biondi, *Phys. Rev. Letters* **2**, 344 (1959).
39. L. M. Chanin, A. V. Phelps, and M. A. Biondi, *Phys. Rev.* **128**, 219 (1962).
40. M. A. Harrison and R. Geballe, *Phys. Rev.* **91**, 1 (1953).
41. D. S. Burch and R. Geballe, *Phys. Rev.* **106**, 183, 188 (1957).
42. H. Schlumbohm, *Z. angew. Phys.* **11**, 156 (1959). *Proceedings of the Fourth International Conference on Ionization Phenomena in Gases*, Uppsala, 1959, North-Holland, Amsterdam, 1960, Vol. I, p. 127.
43. A. N. Prasad and J. D. Craggs, *Proc. Phys. Soc.* (*London*) **77**, 385 (1961).
44. M. S. Bhalla and J. D. Craggs, *Proc. Phys. Soc.* (*London*) **78**, 438 (1961).
45. M. S. Bhalla and J. D. Craggs, *Proc. Phys. Soc.* (*London*) **76**, 369 (1960).
46. M. S. Bhalla and J. D. Craggs, *Proc. Phys. Soc.* (*London*) **80**, 151 (1962).
47. B. A. Tozer, *J. Electron. Control* **4**, 149 (1958).
48. G. H. Dunn, *Phys. Rev. Letters* **8**, 62 (1962).
49. J. D. Craggs, R. Thorburn, and B. A. Tozer, *Proc. Roy. Soc.* (*London*) **A-240**, 473 (1957); see also J. B. Thompson, *Proc. Phys. Soc.* (*London*) **73**, 821 (1959).
50. J. D. Craggs and B. A. Tozer, *Proc. Roy. Soc.* (*London*) **A-247**, 337 (1958).
51. J. D. Craggs and B. A. Tozer, *Proc. Roy. Soc.* (*London*) **A-254**, 229 (1960).
52. N. S. Buchel'nikova, *Soviet Phys.-JETP* **8**, 783 (1959).
53. G. J. Schulz, *Phys. Rev.* **113**, 816 (1959).
54. G. J. Schulz, *J. Chem. Phys.* **33**, 1661 (1960).
55. G. J. Schulz, *J. Chem. Phys.* **34**, 1778 (1961).
56. G. J. Schulz, *Phys. Rev.* **128**, 178 (1962).
57. E. E. Muschlitz, *J. Appl. Phys.* **28**, 1414 (1957).
58. E. E. Muschlitz and T. L. Bailey, *J. Phys. Chem.* **60**, 681 (1956).
59. T. L. Bailey, J. M. McGuire, and E. E. Muschlitz, *J. Chem. Phys.* **22**, 2088 (1954).
60. R. K. Curran, *J. Chem. Phys.* **35**, 1849 (1961).
61. H. Gutbier and H. Neuert, *Z. Naturforsch.* **9-a**, 335 (1954). R. E. Fox, *J. Chem. Phys.* **26**, 1281 (1957). D. C. Frost and C. A. McDowell, **29**, 503 (1958).
62. R. Geballe and M. L. Reeves, *Phys. Rev.* **92**, 867 (1953). A. J. Ahearn and N. B. Hannay, *J. Chem. Phys.* **21**, 119 (1953); W. M. Hickam and R. E. Fox, **25**, 642 (1956); R. K. Curran, **34**, 1069 (1961); R. E. Fox and R. K. Curran, **34**, 1595 (1961); D. Edelson, J. E. Griffiths, and K. B. McAfee, **37**, 917 (1962).
63. G. J. Schulz, *J. Appl. Phys.* **31**, 1134 (1960).
64. O. Rosenbaum and H. Neuert, *Z. Naturforsch.* **9-a**, 990 (1954). H. Neuert and O. Rosenbaum, *Naturwissenschaften* **41**, 85 (1954). R. M. Reese, V. H. Dibeler, and J. L. Franklin, *J. Chem. Phys.* **29**, 880 (1958).
65. D. C. Frost and C. A. McDowell, *J. Chem. Phys.* **29**, 1424 (1958); P. S. Rudolph, C. E. Melton, and G. M. Begun, **30**, 588 (1959); G. G. Cloutier and H. I. Schiff, **31**, 793 (1959).
66. B. E. Knox and B. P. Burtt, *J. Chem. Phys.* **28**, 1256 (1958); P. S. Rudolph, C. E. Melton, and G. M. Begun, **30**, 588 (1959); R. K. Curran and R. E. Fox, **34**, 1590 (1961).
67. R. E. Fox, *J. Chem. Phys.* **32**, 285 (1960).
68. J. B. Hasted, "Charge Transfer and Collisional Detachment," in *Atomic and Molecular Processes* (edited by D. R. Bates), Academic, New York, 1962, pp. 696–720.
69. A. V. Phelps and J. L. Pack, *Phys. Rev. Letters* **6**, 111 (1961).

70. A. C. Riviere and D. R. Sweetman, *Phys. Rev. Letters* **5**, 560 (1960). *Proceedings of the Fifth International Conference on Ionization Phenomena in Gases*, Munich, 1961, North-Holland, Amsterdam (1962), Vol. II, 1236.
71. S. J. Smith and L. M. Branscomb, *Rev. Sci. Instr.* **31**, 733 (1960).
72. L. M. Branscomb and S. J. Smith, *Phys. Rev.* **98**, 1028 (1955). S. J. Smith and D. S. Burch, *Phys. Rev. Letters* **2**, 165 (1959) and *Phys. Rev.* **116**, 1125 (1959).
73. S. J. Smith and L. M. Branscomb, *J. Research Nat. Bur. Standards* **55**, 165 (1955). L. M. Branscomb and S. J. Smith, *Phys. Rev.* **98**, 1127 (1955); L. M. Branscomb, D. S. Burch, S. J. Smith, and S. Geltman, **111**, 504 (1958). S. J. Smith, *Proceedings of the Fourth International Conference on Ionization Phenomena in Gases*, Uppsala, 1959, North-Holland, Amsterdam (1960), Vol. I, p. 219.
74. L. M. Branscomb and S. J. Smith, *J. Chem. Phys.* **25**, 598 (1956).
75. M. L. Seman and L. M. Branscomb, *Phys. Rev.* **125**, 1602 (1962).
76. B. W. Steiner, M. L. Seman, and L. M. Branscomb, *Bull. Am. Phys. Soc.* **7**, 328 (1962). L. M. Branscomb, M. L. Seman, and B. Steiner, Third International Conference on the Physics of Electronic and Atomic Collisions, London, 1963.
77. S. J. Smith and L. M. Branscomb, *Phys. Rev.* **99**, 1657 (1955).
78. D. S. Burch, S. J. Smith, and L. M. Branscomb, *Phys. Rev.* **112**, 171 (1958); see also erratum, *Phys. Rev.* **114**, 1652 (1959).
79. R. S. Berry, C. W. Reimann, and G. N. Spokes, *J. Chem. Phys.* **35**, 2237 (1961), **37**, 2278 (1962); R. S. Berry and C. W. Reimann, **38**, 1540 (1963).
80. G. S. Hurst and T. E Bortner, Radiation Res. *Suppl.* **1**, 547 (1959).
81 J L. Pack and A. V. Phelps, *Bull. Am. Phys. Soc.* **7**, 131 (1962).
82. W. W. Lozier, *Phys. Rev.* **36**, 1417 (1930); M. M. Mann, A. Hustrulid, and J. T. Tate, **58**, 340 (1940). M. Cottin, *J. Chim. Phys.* **56**, 1024 (1959).
83. G. S. Hurst, L. B. O'Kelly, and T. E. Bortner, *Phys. Rev.* **123**, 1715 (1961).
84. R. v. d. R. Woolley and D. W. N. Stibbs, *The Outer Layers of a Star*, Oxford University Press, London, 1953.
85. L. M. Branscomb and B. E. J. Pagel, *Mon. Not. Roy. Astron. Soc.* **118**, 258 (1958).
86. W. H. McCrea, *Proc. Roy. Soc. (London)* **A-256**, 245 (1960).
87. W. H. McCrea and D. McNally, *Mon. Not. Roy. Astron. Soc.* **121**, 238 (1960).
88. M. R. C. McDowell, *Observatory* **81**, 240 (1961).
89. J. A. Ratcliffe and K. Weekes, "The Ionosphere," in *Physics of the Upper Atmosphere* (edited by J. A. Ratcliffe), Academic, New York, 1960, Section 9.4.
90. J. S. Greenhow and J. E. Hall, *J. Atmospheric Terrestr. Phys.* **21**, 261 (1961).
91. H. R. Crane, *Rev. Sci. Instr.* **32**, 953 (1961).
92. D. H. Wilkinson, *Ionization Chambers and Counters*, Cambridge University Press, Cambridge, 1950.

9

THE MOBILITY

OF GASEOUS IONS

As an ion moves through a gas under the influence of a static uniform electric field, it gains energy from the field between collisions with molecules and loses energy during collisions. It is easy to show that the ratio of the electric field intensity to the gas pressure, E/p, is the parameter that determines the mean energy acquired from the field, above that associated with the thermal motion. The electric force on an ion of charge e is eE, and the resulting acceleration is eE/m. Let us make the crude assumption that when an ion undergoes a collision it loses, on the average, all the energy it acquired from the field during the preceding free path. Then, if τ denotes the collision period, or mean free time, the velocity acquired just before a collision is $eE\tau/m$. Since $\tau \sim 1/p$, the energy obtained between collisions from the field is thus seen to be proportional to $(E/p)^2$. Rigorous calculations also show E/p to be the parameter that determines the "field energy" of the ions.

If E/p is small and constant, the ionic motion consists of a slow uniform drift in the field direction superimposed on the much faster random motion. Knowledge of the drift velocity for various ionic species in various gases is of considerable practical and theoretical importance. It is essential to the quantitative understanding of many types of electrical discharges. In many experiments the sole means of identifying the ions present has been by comparing their measured drift velocity with tabulated experimental data or theoretical predictions. The drift velocity also enters into such basic calculations as that of the rate of dispersion of ions by mutual repulsion (Section 10-11) and the rate of ionic recombination (Section 12-4-A). Finally, comparison of experimental drift velocities and theoretical predictions provides extremely useful information concerning the forces that act between ions and molecules.

9-1. GENERAL CONSIDERATIONS

When the field energy of the ions is small compared with the thermal energy, the *drift velocity* in the field direction, v_d is proportional to the electric field intensity and may be expressed as

$$v_d = \mathscr{K} E \qquad (9\text{-}1\text{-}1)$$

where $\mathscr{K}$, the constant of proportionality, is called the *mobility* of the ions. The field energy is negligible if

$$\left(\frac{M}{m} + \frac{m}{M}\right) eE\lambda \ll kT \qquad (9\text{-}1\text{-}2)$$

where M and m are the molecular and ionic masses, respectively, and $eE\lambda$ is the energy acquired by an ion in moving a distance λ in the field direction. The factor involving the masses accounts for the ability of the ions to store the acquired energy over many collisions if the masses are significantly different. Using the relationships $NkT = p$ and $\lambda = 1/Nq$, where N is the molecular number density and q is the ion-molecule collision cross section, we may express the foregoing inequality as $(M/m + m/M)eE \ll pq$. Taking a singly charged ion moving through the parent gas and making the reasonable assumption that $q = 50 \times 10^{-16}$ cm^2, we find that the field energy is much less than the thermal energy if $E/p \ll 5 \times 10^{-6}$ (statvolt/cm) per (dyne/cm^2) $\approx$ 2 volts/cm-mm Hg. The electric field is said to be "low" when the criterion (9-1-2) is satisfied and "high" when the inequality is reversed. It should be noted that a given field in a gas of given density may change from "low" to "high" if the gas temperature is lowered sufficiently. The velocity distribution of the ions is approximately Maxwellian provided E/p is small. When high-field conditions prevail, the distribution of the ions is complex and usually not known.

At standard conditions of temperature and pressure, the mobility is of the order of several cm^2/v-sec. Positive and negative ions of a given molecular species usually have approximately the same mobility in a given gas. $\mathscr{K}$ varies inversely as the gas density, and as long as the temperature remains constant the mobility is inversely proportional to the pressure. At constant density the mobility is found to be insensitive to small changes in temperature, changes of 100°K or more being necessary to effect a change of about 20% in the mobility.

In our discussion we frequently refer to the *reduced mobility*, $\mathcal{K}_0$, which is the mobility reduced to standard conditions of 273°K and 760 mm Hg at which the gas number density is $2.69 \times 10^{19}/cm^3$. If the mobility is measured to be $\mathcal{K}$ cm²/v-sec, the reduced mobility is

$$\mathcal{K}_0 = \mathcal{K} \frac{p}{760} \frac{273}{T} \tag{9-1-3}$$

where p and T indicate the pressure and temperature (in mm Hg and °K, respectively) at which the measurement was made.

Electrons have drift velocities some thousands of times higher than those of ions under similar conditions. In most cases the drift velocity of electrons is not directly proportional to the applied field, and the mobility concept is of limited applicability to electrons. The subject of electronic drift is treated separately in Chapter 11.

Throughout this chapter the assumption is made that the ionic number density is sufficiently low that all ion-ion interactions may be neglected. This assumption, which is realistic in many situations of interest, greatly simplifies the mathematical treatment of the ionic motion, for the equation for the velocity distribution function is then linear, instead of quadratic. Wannier[1] has shown how criteria for the validity of this assumption may be derived. We must distinguish between two effects that the ions may have on one another.

The first is the space charge effect produced mainly by widely separated ions, and we find that its magnitude depends on the dimensions of the containing vessel. In one dimension Poisson's equation, $\nabla^2 V = -4\pi\rho$, may be written in the form $\partial E/\partial x = 4\pi n e$, where ρ is the charge density and n is the ionic number density. The criterion for negligible space charge distortion of the field is then

$$n \ll \frac{E}{4\pi e L} \tag{9-1-4}$$

where L is the relevant dimension of the apparatus. This inequality predicts space charge distortion of the field at ion concentrations of the order of $10^8/cm^3$. This limit is of real significance only from the experimental point of view, however. Meaningful experiments are difficult to perform if $n \gtrsim 10^8/cm^3$, but the effect of higher assumed number densities on calculations is much less severe, since the space charge does not change the character of the ionic velocity distribution. The interaction producing the space charge field is long-range and causes a smooth modification of the field that can be accounted for in the field assumed given at the outset.

The second effect is produced by random fluctuations of the ionic number density and may alter a velocity distribution derived on the assumption of a low concentration. Neighboring ions are more important than remote ions in this connection, since their relative positions can fluctuate more rapidly. The basis of the disturbance is the randomly fluctuating Coulomb force which produces mutual scattering. This random force may be neglected if it is unable to produce a significant deflection in a single mean free path. Since the magnitude of the force is of order $e^2/\bar{d}^2 = e^2/n^{\frac{2}{3}}$, where $\bar{d}$ is the mean ionic spacing, the effect is small if $e^2 n^{\frac{2}{3}} \lambda \ll$ (mean ion energy). In the low-field region the thermal energy dominates the field energy, and the inequality becomes

$$e^2 n^{\frac{2}{3}} \ll pq \qquad (9\text{-}1\text{-}5)$$

At high field the relative importance of the thermal and field energies is reversed, and the criterion becomes

$$e^2 n^{\frac{2}{3}} \ll eE\left(\frac{M}{m} + \frac{m}{M}\right) \qquad (9\text{-}1\text{-}6)$$

If a pressure of 1 mm Hg and a collision cross section of 50×10^{-16} cm^2 are assumed, (9-1-5) yields $n \ll 10^{11}$ ions/cm^3; (9-1-6) gives similar results.

9-2. CLASSICAL MOBILITY THEORY

In this section we shall discuss what appear to be the most useful and significant classical treatments of the mobility problem. Quantum mechanical theory is presented in the next section.

A. THE THEORIES OF LANGEVIN. 1. *The simple mean free path theory.* In 1903, soon after the first measurements of the mobility of gaseous ions, Langevin[2] published a theory of ionic mobility based on the kinetic theory of gases, which was just becoming widely accepted. He considered the ions and molecules to be solid elastic spheres, the ions differing from the molecules only by possession of an electric charge. Only repulsive forces acting at the instant of impact were taken into account, and E/p was assumed to be small, so that the field energy would be negligible compared with the thermal energy. The ion density was taken to be low in order that ion-ion interactions could be ignored.

The equation obtained by Langevin was

$$\mathcal{K} = \frac{e\lambda}{m\bar{v}} \qquad (9\text{-}2\text{-}1)$$

where λ is the common mean free path for the molecules and ions, m is the common molecular and ionic mass, and $\bar{v}$ is the mean thermal velocity. The assumptions implicit in (9-2-1) are stated in the derivation which follows: let us suppose that all the ions are moving with velocity $\bar{v}$ along zig-zag trajectories, the lengths of whose segments are distributed about the mean free path λ. Each ion will be imagined to lose, in a collision with a molecule, all its velocity in the field direction which it had acquired from the field during the preceding free path. If a denotes the acceleration of the ion by the field, the distance traveled by the ion in the field direction during the period t between two successive collisions is

$$s = \frac{1}{2} a t^2 = \frac{1}{2} \frac{Ee}{m} \frac{x^2}{\bar{v}^2}$$

where x denotes the total distance traveled by the ion between these collisions. The average value of s is obtained by averaging x^2 over the distribution of free paths (cf. Section 1-4). Thus

$$\bar{s} = \frac{Ee}{2m\bar{v}^2} \int_0^\infty x^2 e^{-Qx} Q \, dx \bigg/ \int_0^\infty e^{-Qx} Q \, dx = \frac{Ee}{m\bar{v}^2 Q^2}$$

where $Q = 1/\lambda$ is the macroscopic ion-molecule elastic scattering cross section. Introducing the mean free time, $\tau = \lambda/\bar{v}$, we obtain

$$\bar{s} = \frac{Ee\tau^2}{m}$$

The drift velocity is then

$$v_d = \frac{\bar{s}}{\tau} = \frac{Ee\tau}{m} = \frac{Ee\lambda}{m\bar{v}} \tag{9-2-2}$$

and division by E gives the expression for the mobility in (9-2-1).

If the distribution in free paths is ignored in this derivation, a mobility equal to one half that of (9-2-1) is obtained. On the other hand, if the distributions of both the free paths and velocities about their mean values are considered and the ionic mass m is taken to be different from the molecular mass M, a similar calculation[3] gives for the mobility

$$\mathcal{K} = 0.815 \frac{el}{M v_R} \left(1 + \frac{M}{m}\right)^{1/2} \tag{9-2-3}$$

v_R represents the rms velocity of agitation of the molecules and

$$l \equiv \frac{1}{\pi N D_{12}^2} \tag{9-2-4}$$

where N is the molecular number density and D_{12} is the sum of the ionic and molecular radii. (The discussion of Section 2-3 shows that l is an approximation to the ionic mean free path.)

Comparison with experiment shows (9-2-3) to be deficient in several important respects. First of all, the calculated values are always too high by about a factor of 4. In addition, this equation incorrectly predicts that $\mathcal{K}$ should vary directly with the ionic charge and mean free path and inversely with $\sqrt{T}$. Also, the mobility is not found experimentally to be independent of the dielectric constant of the gas, as (9-2-3) predicts. However, the observed inverse variation of the mobility with density is correctly predicted.

It was obvious to Langevin that one source of error was the assumption that the mean free path of the ion is the same as that of a molecule of the same species. Only by the introduction of a mechanism to shorten substantially the ionic mean free path could the discrepancy between theory and experiment be removed. Furthermore, the crude nature of the mean free path calculations was apparent, and it was evident that more rigorous methods should be applied to the problem.

2. *The rigorous theory.* In 1905 Langevin[4] published an elegant and elaborate theory of ionic mobility based on the momentum transfer method which Maxwell had developed for the investigation of transport problems. The theory applied to the low-field region and took into account the effect of inverse-fifth-power attractive forces between ions and molecules as well as rigid sphere repulsion. An ion attracts neutral molecules by polarization forces in the case of nonpolar gases and, in addition, by direct attraction of the permanent dipoles if the gas is polar. The force of attraction f was shown in Section 1-8 to be

$$f = \frac{(K-1)e^2}{2\pi N r^5} \tag{1-8-3}$$

where K is the dielectric constant of the gas, e is the ionic charge, N is the molecular number density, and r is the distance between the centers of the ion and molecule. This equation holds when r is large compared with the charge separation of the dipole. A decrease in the ionic mean free path results from the increased collision rate, and momentum exchanges take place between the ions and molecules even when they do not actually collide.

Unfortunately the paper in which Langevin's calculation appeared lay unnoticed for about twenty years.* However, during the period from 1905 until 1926, when Hassé[5] published a paper referring to Langevin's work, others became aware of the fact that the attraction of ions for molecules must be considered. Two distinctly different theories[6] involving the concept of polarization attraction were advanced during this interim period. One proposal was that neutral molecules are attracted to and permanently

---

* Perhaps because of its cryptic title, "Une Formule fondamentale de théorie cinétique"!

bound by the ion because of its charge and that the increased size and mass of the ion which result from this attachment are responsible for the low observed value of the mobility. Opposed to this *cluster-ion theory* was the *small-ion theory*, in which the assumption was made that the size of the ion is relatively unimportant, since the ions are retarded in their motion principally by momentum transfers which are due to the action of the attractive forces. In 1926 Hassé[5] discovered Langevin's paper and pointed out that the small-ion equations were approximate forms of a special case of the 1905 Langevin equation.

The concept of the ionic cluster continues to be useful. As we shall see in Section 9-5, there is experimental evidence pointing to the formation of clusters in some gases under certain conditions, particularly at low temperature, although the current view is that clustering in that sense is a rather rare phenomenon. In any event, it is certain that polarization attraction without cluster formation is usually responsible for the lowering of the mobility from the value expected on the basis of the simple mean free path theory.

Langevin's theory provides an equation for the mobility of the form

$$\mathscr{K} = \frac{A}{\sqrt{\rho(K-1)}} \left(1 + \frac{M}{m}\right)^{\frac{1}{2}} \quad \text{(complete Langevin equation)} \quad (9\text{-}2\text{-}5)$$

where ρ is the gas density, K is the dielectric constant, M is the mass of the molecule, and m is the mass of the ion; A is a function of a parameter λ (not the mean free path) which is defined by the equation

$$\lambda^2 = \frac{8\pi p D_{12}^4}{(K-1)e^2} \quad (9\text{-}2\text{-}6)$$

where p is the gas pressure and D_{12} is the sum of the radii of the ion and molecule. Since λ^2 is equal to kT divided by the energy of attraction when the ion and molecule are in contact, λ^2 is a dimensionless temperature. Values of A for different values of λ are given in Table 9-2-1.

Here Langevin's equation is presented in the notation of Hassé,[5] who repeated Langevin's calculations and incorporated some refinements in kinetic theory which had been developed subsequently by Chapman and Enskog.[7] Langevin's results expressed in their original form are given in Appendix II.

The value of λ is also a measure of the relative importance of elastic sphere and polarization scattering; λ increases as D_{12} increases and K decreases. Thus the case of large λ is the one in which the polarization effects are negligible compared with those of elastic sphere scattering. In the limit of

TABLE 9-2-1. Values of Hassé's function A for various values of the parameter λ

λ	A	$A\lambda$	λ	A	$A\lambda$
0.0	0.5105	0.0000	2.1	0.3370	0.7077
0.1	0.5488	0.0549	2.2	0.3236	0.7119
0.2	0.5648	0.1130	2.3	0.3111	0.7155
0.3	0.5756	0.1727	2.4	0.2994	0.7186
0.4	0.5836	0.2334	2.5	0.2886	0.7215
0.5	0.5886	0.2943	2.6	0.2784	0.7238
0.6	0.5904	0.3542	2.7	0.2689	0.7260
0.7	0.5878	0.4115	2.8	0.2599	0.7277
0.8	0.5796	0.4637	2.9	0.2515	0.7293
0.9	0.5662	0.5096	3.0	0.2436	0.7308
1.0	0.5483	0.5483	3.1	0.2362	0.7322
1.1	0.5277	0.5805	3.2	0.2292	0.7334
1.2	0.5057	0.6068	3.3	0.2226	0.7346
1.3	0.4834	0.6284	3.4	0.2163	0.7354
1.4	0.4614	0.6460	3.5	0.2104	0.7364
1.5	0.4402	0.6603	3.6	0.2048	0.7373
1.6	0.4201	0.6722	3.7	0.1994	0.7378
1.7	0.4011	0.6819	3.8	0.1944	0.7387
1.8	0.3834	0.6901	3.9	0.1895	0.7391
1.9	0.3668	0.6969	4.0	0.1849	0.7396
2.0	0.3514	0.7028			

extremely large λ, λA approaches a value of 0.75, and the Langevin expression may be written

$$\mathscr{K}_e = \frac{0.75e}{D_{12}{}^2 \sqrt{8\pi p\rho}} \left(1 + \frac{M}{m}\right)^{\frac{1}{2}} \qquad \text{(elastic sphere limit)} \quad (9\text{-}2\text{-}7)$$

As λ approaches zero, on the other hand, we approach the situation in which the polarization forces completely predominate. For $\lambda = 0$, $A = 0.5105$, and the Langevin equation becomes

$$\mathscr{K}_p = \frac{0.5105}{\sqrt{\rho(K-1)}} \left(1 + \frac{M}{m}\right)^{\frac{1}{2}} \qquad \text{(polarization, or small ion, limit)}$$

$$(9\text{-}2\text{-}8)$$

The fact that the mobility expressed in (9-2-8) contains no dependence on the charge of the ion may be explained as follows. Although the force on the ion due to the electric field is directly proportional to the charge, the momentum loss of the ion due to impacts produced by the inverse-fifth-power electrostatic forces is also proportional to the charge, with the result that the charge dependence cancels out. The temperature independence is also explained on the basis of two effects canceling. An increase in the temperature tends to decrease the mobility by increasing the thermal velocity of the ions, but the momentum loss is also decreased by a factor sufficient to eliminate the temperature dependence. Note that since ρ is directly proportional to M at constant gas number density (9-2-8) predicts that $\mathcal{K}_0\sqrt{M_r}$ should be determined only by the dielectric constant of the gas and therefore be independent of the nature of the ion. (The reduced mass of the ion-molecule system is denoted by M_r.) This prediction, combined with that of temperature independence, is of considerable use in the evaluation of experimental data in terms of the polarization limit of the theory. An inverse-fourth-power potential is the only potential of the form $V \sim r^{-n}$ for which temperature independence is expected, as we shall see in Section 9-2-B.

If the ion is thought to be clustered, the mass of the cluster should be used for m in the equation for $\mathcal{K}$. The evaluation of D_{12} in the complete Langevin equation presents a serious problem, since λ, and thus $\mathcal{K}$, is critically dependent on it, and its value cannot be precisely specified. Difficulties appear because it is particularly hard to estimate the effective ionic radius, and even the value experimentally deduced for the molecular radius depends to some extent on the method used for its determination, the radius in the model having no exact counterpart in the gas. In practice, ionic radii are often calculated from lattice spacings in ionic crystals, whereas molecular radii are obtained from data on viscosity and the constants in the equations of state (cf Section 2-3). The sum of the ionic and molecular radii may also be estimated from high-field mobility data by a method presented in Section 9-2-C.

For reasons that will become apparent the Langevin equation in the polarization limit appears to be the most generally satisfactory mobility equation that does not contain adjustable parameters. It has been more widely used than any other for the calculation of mobilities, and in many cases its predictions agree closely with experimental results. Comparisons of theoretical and experimental data are presented in Section 9-9.

B. THE CHAPMAN-ENSKOG THEORY. During the period between the publication and rediscovery of Langevin's theory Chapman[7,8] and Enskog[9] developed the rigorous kinetic theory for gases composed of spherically symmetric (monatomic) particles. They applied their results to transport problems involving only unionized gases, but their expression for the mutual diffusion coefficient $\mathscr{D}_{12}$ can be evaluated for ion-atom as well as atom-atom interaction potentials and used for the calculation of mobilities. This follows because, as we shall show in Section 10-2, the mobility of an ion at low field is given by the equation

$$\mathcal{K} = \frac{e\mathcal{D}_{12}}{kT} \tag{9-2-9}$$

where $\mathcal{D}_{12}$ is the ion-atom mutual diffusion coefficient. (Equation 9-2-9 is not exactly correct, except for a pure r^{-4} interaction, but it is unlikely to be in error by more than 5% even in the most unfavorable cases.[10])

According to the Chapman-Enskog theory, the ion-atom mutual diffusion coefficient is given to second order by the equation*

$$\mathcal{D}_{12} = \frac{3\sqrt{\pi}}{16} \left(\frac{2kT}{M_r}\right)^{7/2} \frac{1 + \varepsilon_0}{(N_1 + N_2)P_{12}} \tag{9-2-10}$$

where

$$P_{12} = \int_0^\infty v_0^5 q_D(v_0) e^{-M_r v_0^2/2kT} \, dv_0 \tag{9-2-11}$$

and

$$q_D(v_0) = 2\pi \int_0^\infty (1 - \cos \Theta) b \, db \tag{9-2-12}$$

Here M_r is the reduced mass of the ion-atom system, N_1, the gas, and N_2, the ion number density, and ε_0 is a second-order correction which is usually less than experimental errors[7,10] (ε_0 is zero for an inverse-fourth-power potential and has a maximum value of 0.136 for a hard-sphere interaction). The ionic number density N_2 is generally much smaller than N_1 and may be ignored. The second-order correction is also neglected for the present purposes; then (9-2-10) becomes identical with (2-10-3).

P_{12} is an average of the diffusion cross section $q_D(v_0)$ over a Maxwellian velocity distribution. The diffusion cross section depends on the detailed nature of the ion-atom interaction through the impact parameter b and the scattering angle Θ and is thus a function of v_0, the relative velocity of approach at large separation. The use of (3-7-1) shows that (9-2-12) is equivalent to the previously introduced expression for q_D involving the differential scattering cross section:

$$q_D = \int (1 - \cos \Theta) I_s(\Theta) \, d\Omega_{\text{CM}} = 2\pi \int_0^\pi I_s(\Theta)(1 - \cos \Theta) \sin \Theta \, d\Theta \tag{1-6-1}$$

Equation 9-2-10 shows that $\mathcal{D}_{12}$ should be proportional to $(T/M_r)^{1/2}$ if q_D is independent of v_0. This behavior is also predicted by simple mean free path calculations. The variation of $\mathcal{D}_{12}$ with $M_r^{-1/2}$ is predicted by rigorous classical theory for all interactions. Dimensional considerations

* The temperature and reduced mass dependence of $\mathcal{D}_{12}$ suggested by a superficial examination of (9-2-10) is deceptive. See the discussion immediately preceding (9-2-13).

(Section 3-9) show that, for a potential of the form $V(r) \sim r^{-n}$, q_D varies as $v_0^{-4/n}$ and $\mathscr{D}_{12}$ as $T^{2/n}T^{1/2}$ if the gas density is held constant. Since $\mathscr{K} \sim \mathscr{D}_{12}/T$, it follows that

$$\mathscr{K} \sim T^{2/n}T^{-1/2} \qquad (9\text{-}2\text{-}13)$$

It is clear that observations on the temperature variation of mobilities can lead to considerable information on ion-atom interactions. Note that the mobility should be temperature-independent for a pure r^{-4} potential. The scattering of an ion at low temperatures is determined mainly by the long-range attractive polarization potential, which varies as r^{-4}. Thus we should expect all mobilities to become essentially independent of the temperature, provided sufficiently low temperatures can be reached before quantum effects set in. At high temperatures, on the other hand, the scattering is determined principally by the short-range forces. If we represent these forces by a repulsive r^{-12} potential, then we would predict the mobility to vary approximately as $T^{-1/3}$ at high temperatures. At intermediate temperatures there will be some cancellation of the short- and long-range forces, and the mobility should pass through a maximum as the temperature is varied.

In 1931 Hassé and Cook[11] used the Chapman-Enskog theory for a low-field calculation in which the ion-molecule interaction was described in terms of the inverse-fourth-power attractive polarization potential and an inverse-eighth-power repulsive potential. The Hassé-Cook calculation does not seem to represent a general improvement over the Langevin theory. In many instances the mobility is dominated by the polarization forces to the extent that the Langevin polarization limit is essentially exactly correct. When other interactions must be considered, it appears that although the rigid sphere repulsion of the complete Langevin theory is too hard the inverse-eighth-power repulsion of the Hassé-Cook formulation is too soft. A representation of intermediate hardness, say inverse-twelfth-power, would be more accurate. Also, additional attractive terms may be important, particularly the point-charge-induced quadrupole and the London dispersion energy terms, both of which lead to inverse-seventh-power forces. The ion-molecule interaction potential is now usually expressed in the form[12]

$$V(r) = Ae^{-\alpha r} + \sum_{n=4} C_n r^{-n} \qquad (9\text{-}2\text{-}14)$$

The exponential term accounts in an approximate manner for the short-range repulsion due to electron cloud interpenetration and other quantal effects, whereas the series expresses the long-range interactions.

C. THE THEORY OF WANNIER. The theory presented so far is applicable only in the region of low E/p, in which the energy derived from the field is negligible compared with the thermal energy. Wannier[13] has developed a theory based on the Boltzmann transport equation, which is applicable mainly to the high-field region but which also yields results of considerable interest at low E/p. Wannier considered the following types of interaction:

(a) rigid sphere repulsion
(b) symmetry forces
(c) polarization attraction

Symmetry effects[14] are produced when the cores of the ions and the particles of the gas through which the ions are moving are identical. They include resonance attraction and repulsion and resonant charge transfer, in which an electron is considered to shuttle back and forth between the collision partners. Classical theory is unable to cope with these effects— they are purely quantum mechanical.

Wannier used the elastic sphere model for interactions (a) and (b). This model is characterized by isotropic scattering in the center-of-mass system and by a mean free path and collision cross section which are constant, that is, independent of the relative velocity of the collision partners in an ion-molecule collision. Actually, the cross section associated with the symmetry effects is known to vary slowly with the relative velocity. However, combining the effects of (a) and (b) and representing them by a single elastic sphere cross section gives reasonable results and may be viewed as a justifiable procedure.

The cross section for the polarization attraction, on the other hand, varies inversely with the relative velocity, which is determined in the high-field case by the value of E/p. This means that the polarization attraction is characterized by a constant mean free time between collisions rather than by a constant mean free path.

At high field the polarization cross section is small, and thus we have approximately a constant mean free path situation. Wannier shows that it leads to a variation of drift velocity with E/p of the form

$$v_d \sim \sqrt{\frac{\overline{E}}{p}} \quad \left(\text{high } \frac{E}{p}, \text{ constant } \lambda\right) \tag{9-2-15}$$

If, on the other hand, a constant mean free time situation is assumed at high E/p, the drift velocity is predicted to vary linearly with E/p:

$$v_d \sim \frac{E}{p} \quad \left(\text{high } \frac{E}{p}, \text{ constant } \tau\right) \tag{9-2-16}$$

Wannier's theory further predicts that the drift velocity should show no dependence on the temperature in the high-field region.

At low field Wannier's calculations show that the drift velocity should vary directly with E/p regardless of the interaction assumed:

$$v_d \sim \frac{E}{p} \qquad \left(\text{low } \frac{E}{p}\right) \tag{9-2-17}$$

Wannier's predictions concerning the variation of drift velocity with E/p are verified by the results of experiments performed by Hornbeck[15] and Varney[16,17] on the noble gases, oxygen, nitrogen, and carbon monoxide. These experiments are discussed in Section 9-9.

Wannier also shows that the Langevin equation in the polarization limit is exact, not only at low field, but at high E/p as well.* Thus (9-2-8) is of wider applicability than had been previously realized.

Another extremely useful feature of Wannier's theory is that it provides an expression for the total energy of an ion at high E/p if the motion is assumed to be characterized by a constant mean free time. This expression is†

$$\frac{m\overline{v_i^2}}{2} = \frac{mv_d^2}{2} + \frac{Mv_d^2}{2} + \frac{3kT}{2} \tag{9-2-18}$$

where m and M are the ionic and molecular masses, respectively, $\overline{v_i^2}$ is the mean square of the total ionic velocity, and v_d is the drift velocity. The first term on the right side is the field energy associated with the drift motion of the ion, whereas the second term is the random part of the field energy. The last term represents the thermal energy. It is apparent that

$$\frac{\text{random field energy}}{\text{drift energy}} = \frac{M}{m} \tag{9-2-19}$$

Equation 9-2-18 illustrates the capacity that light ions in a heavy gas have for storing energy in the form of random motion. In ions traveling in the parent gas the ordered and random field energies are equal. For heavy ions in a light gas the random field energy is negligible.

In the high-field region the ions do not have a Maxwellian distribution, and, in fact, the distribution has not been calculated except for constant mean free time. At intermediate values of E/p the polarization forces become more important, and neither the mean free path not the mean free time is constant. When the low E/p region is reached, the ions approach a Maxwellian distribution, and the drift velocity depends on the temperature as well as on E/p. At low E/p the polarization forces may not actually

* This result is also demonstrated by Kihara's approach—see Section IVB of ref. 22.
† Unfortunately, no simple relationship such as this has been derived for a more realistic model at high E/p.

predominate in a given gas at room temperature, but they are bound to prevail at a sufficiently low temperature.

The total elastic sphere cross section $q_{ion\text{-}atom}$, which represents the sum of the contributions of gas kinetic repulsion and symmetry effects, may be calculated from mobility data obtained at high E/p. Furthermore, since the gas kinetic repulsion cross section $q_{atom\text{-}atom}$ may be estimated from viscosity data, the relative contributions of the hard-sphere repulsion and symmetry effects may be determined. The cross sections for the gases

TABLE 9-2-2. Elastic sphere cross sections: $q_{ion\text{-}atom}$[19] and $q_{atom\text{-}atom}$[20]

Gas	Ion	$q_{i-a} \times 10^{+16}$ cm^2	$q_{a-a} \times 10^{+16}$ cm^2
He	He$^+$	38	15
Ne	Ne$^+$	45	21
A	A$^+$	93	42
Kr	Kr$^+$	109	55
Xe	Xe$^+$	134	76
O$_2$	O$_2$$^+$	55	41
N$_2$	N$_2$$^+$	85	44
CO	CO$^+$	101	45

studied by Hornbeck and Varney are listed in Table 9-2-2. The values for $q_{atom\text{-}atom}$ were calculated from viscosity data using the equations[18]

$$\eta = 0.499 \frac{M\bar{v}}{\sqrt{2\pi}\,D^2}\ ; \qquad q_{a-a} = \pi D^2 \qquad (9\text{-}2\text{-}20)$$

where η is the coefficient of viscosity of the gas and D is the molecular diameter. The ion-atom cross sections were originally calculated by Wannier[13] who used the equation

$$v_d = 1.147 \left(\frac{a}{Nq_{ion\text{-}atom}}\right)^{1/2} \qquad (9\text{-}2\text{-}21)$$

where a equals the acceleration of the ion due to the electric field and N is the gas number density. In a later paper, however, Wannier[19] showed that the numerical factor in (9-2-21) should be 0.798 instead of 1.147, and that the original values for $q_{ion\text{-}atom}$ were incorrect. The values of q_{i-a} in Table 9-2-2 include Wannier's correction.

D. OTHER CLASSICAL CALCULATIONS. Reference must also be made to several other important calculations based on classical methods. Kihara[21] has extended the methods developed by Chapman and Enskog for the solution of the Boltzmann equation and applied them to the mobility problem. He neglected charge transfer but considered the dependence of the mobility on the temperature and field strength. The mobility was shown to be independent of the field strength as well as the temperature for a pure r^{-4} interaction but to vary with E for other types of interaction. Kihara calculated the mobility in higher approximation than was done in the Langevin treatment, which is now usually referred to as the first approximation. Higher order corrections to the mobility were shown to be small.

Mason and Schamp[22] have used Kihara's extension of the Chapman-Enskog theory to obtain the second- and third-order approximations to the mobility in a weak electric field as a function of the temperature and field strength. They assumed that no clustering would take place and neglected charge transfer and quantum effects. The mobility was expressed as a series in ascending powers of the square of the field strength with coefficients which are complicated functions of the temperature, the ratio of the ionic and molecular masses, and the force law assumed for the ion-molecule interaction. The force law they used takes into account the point charge-induced dipole, the point charge-induced quadrupole, the London dispersion forces, and an inverse-twelfth-power repulsive potential. Three parameters in the potential energy function specify the depth and position of the minimum and the relative contributions of the various terms. Only two of these parameters are disposable, since the polarization force is known if the dielectric constant is. Moreover, of these two, one is disposable only within fairly narrow limits, since the charge-induced quadrupole and the dispersion force can be calculated approximately. The results of Mason and Schamp's calculation were used to analyze experimental data and to evaluate the disposable parameters that determine the force law. Their results are in harmony with experiment except in those cases in which clustering is expected. These detailed calculations verify the type of temperature dependence for the mobility suggested in Section 9-2-B, namely, constancy at very low temperatures, a $T^{-1/3}$ variation at high temperatures, and a maximum at an intermediate temperature. The height of the maximum above the polarization limit depends on the steepness of the short-range repulsive forces, and becomes higher as the repulsion becomes "softer." A new effect also appears when other long-range forces are included (i.e., the dispersion and charge-induced quadrupole terms)—a minimum can now appear at low temperatures. The importance of this minimum is that low-temperature mobility measurements may be extrapolated to the wrong zero-temperature limit if this effect is ignored, hence an apparent disagreement with the polarization limit of the theory may result.

Perel[23] has developed a mobility theory for positive ions in their parent gas in which he considers resonant charge transfer to be the dominant effect. The charge transfer cross section is taken to be independent of the velocity. The mobility was calculated for the atomic noble gas ions, and the results are consistent with experimental data over a wide range of E/p.

9-3. QUANTUM MECHANICAL MOBILITY THEORY

A. QUANTAL CALCULATIONS ON SPECIFIC SYSTEMS.   A number of quantum mechanical mobility calculations take account of the specific interactions between the ion and the particles composing the gas. The first was made in 1934 by Massey and Mohr[24] for He^+ in He at low E/p and room temperature. They showed that symmetry effects were very important. The mobility of He^+ in He has been calculated again, much more recently, by Lynn and Moiseiwitsch[25] over the temperature range $50°–1000°K$ (see Table 9-9-1).

Meyerott[26] in 1944 calculated the interaction energy between the Li^+ ion and He atom and determined the low-field mobility of Li^+ in He as a function of temperature. This computation was repeated, with greater computational accuracy, by Mason, Schamp, and Vanderslice[27] in 1958.

The role of charge transfer in determining the mobility of positive atomic ions in their parent gas has been discussed by Holstein.[28] He calculated quantum mechanically the two possible energies of interaction between the ion and atom and showed how the results can be used in the low-field mobility problem. He showed that the mobility calculation itself can be made on a classical basis once the two energy curves and the charge transfer probability have been given a suitable quantum mechanical treatment. Holstein applied his general method to the specific cases of neon and argon.

Mason and Vanderslice[29] have studied the ions of hydrogen moving in hydrogen. They calculated the force laws for H^+, H_2^+, and H_3^+ in H_2 from the results of scattering of low-velocity ion beams in hydrogen gas, assuming central forces (cf. Part $\mathscr{B}$ of Chapter 4). The results were then used to obtain the low-field mobility of the ions in H_2 as a function of temperature. They predicted that the mobilities of H^+ and H_2^+ should decrease slightly with increasing temperature but that the mobility of H_3^+ should increase strongly. However, their calculation for H_2^+ and H_3^+ did not take account of the conversion process $H_2^+ + H_2 \rightarrow H_3^+ + H$ or of the proton transfer process $H_3^+ + H_2 \rightarrow H_2 + H_3^+$. Since these processes have now been definitely proved to be important, these calculations are probably invalid, although the result for H^+ is probably valid (see also Section 9-9-B).

The low-field mobility of He_2^+ in He has been computed by Geltman.[30] He calculated the forces between the molecular ion and the atom and from the scattering phase shifts evaluated the momentum transfer cross section as a function of energy. The mobility was then obtained as a function of temperature by use of the Chapman-Enskog theory. Geltman suggested that the He_2^+ ion forms a cluster at temperatures below about 170°K.

The H^- ion in atomic hydrogen has been studied by Dalgarno and McDowell.[31] They calculated the interaction energy over a wide range of nuclear separation and used the results to obtain the charge transfer and diffusion cross sections of H^- in H. The latter cross section led to values of the mobility which decrease from 3.5 cm²/v-sec at 100°K to 1.8 cm²/v-sec at 600°K.

Dalgarno and Williams[32] have investigated the second-order correction term in the Chapman-Enskog expression for the mutual diffusion coefficient, paying particular attention to quantal symmetry effects of an ion in its parent gas. They made exact calculations for the general case in which the interaction potential has the form $V \sim \pm r^{-n}$ and obtained approximate solutions for Li^+ and He^+ in He.

Most discussions of the mobility of ions in molecular gases have been based on the assumption that it is permissible to average the interaction over all orientations before computing the appropriate elastic collision cross sections. Arthurs and Dalgarno[33] have developed a theory of scattering which makes it possible to eliminate this assumption, and they have derived a formula for the low-field mobility of an ion in a diatomic molecular gas and obtained quantitative results for mobilities in the limit of vanishing temperature. As an example of the detailed application of the theory, they calculated the ion mobilities in molecular hydrogen and deuterium for which it is necessary to take account of the rotational distributions. It was shown that in contrast to atomic gases, for which the low-temperature mobilities are independent of the temperature, the low-temperature mobilities in molecular gases decrease as the temperature decreases, ultimately passing through a minimum at some very low temperature, because of the interaction between the charge of the ion and the permanent quadrupole of the molecule.

B. GENERAL QUANTUM MECHANICAL THEORY.   The quantum mechanical theory of ionic mobility has been discussed by Dalgarno, McDowell, and Williams. The theory is presented in considerable detail in two papers,[34] the first of which applies to ions in unlike gases, the second to ions in their parent gases. A brief summary of this work follows.

It is evident that the calculation of mobilities by the Chapman-Enskog method is subject to certain limitations if classical theory is used to evaluate the diffusion cross section, although (9-2-10), which is based on classical kinetic theory, is satisfactory. Quantal methods must be employed to obtain q_D if the gas temperature is very low or if the ion and gas atom have identical cores, whatever the temperature (see Section 2-10). However, we can show that the classical and quantum theories otherwise give identical results. The success of the classical theory is the result of the presence in the expression for q_D of the factor $(1 - \cos \Theta)$, which suppresses the contribution of small-angle scattering.

To evaluate q_D quantum mechanically, we substitute the expression for $I_s(\Theta)$ given by (3-15-29) into (1-6-1). After considerable algebraic manipulation,* we may then express q_D in terms of the phase shifts η_l, which were defined in Section 3-15, by the relation

$$q_D(v_0) = \frac{4\pi}{\kappa^2} \sum_{l=0}^{\infty} (l+1) \sin^2 (\eta_l - \eta_{l+1}) \qquad (9\text{-}3\text{-}1)$$

Here $\kappa = M_r v_0 / \hbar$ is the wave number of the relative motion. Equation 9-3-1 applies only if the ion and atom are not of the same species.

If the ion and atom, on the other hand, are of the same species, then the interaction potential may arise from states either symmetric or anti-symmetric in the nuclei, giving rise to phase shifts β_l and γ_l, respectively,

* To derive (9-3-1), we start with $q_D = -2\pi \int_0^\pi I_s(\Theta)(1 - \cos \Theta)\, d(\cos \Theta)$, which is

(1-6-1), make the substitution $\mu = \cos \Theta$, and obtain $I_s(\Theta) = |f(\Theta)|^2$ from (3-15-29). Thus

$$q_D = \frac{\pi}{2\kappa^2} \int_0^\pi \left| \sum_{l=0}^{\infty} (2l+1)(e^{2i\eta_l} - 1) P_l(\cos \Theta) \right|^2 (1 - \cos \Theta)\, d(\cos \Theta)$$

$$= \frac{\pi}{2\kappa^2} \sum_{l=0}^{\infty} \sum_{m=0}^{\infty} (2l+1)(2m+1)(e^{2i\eta_l} - 1)(e^{-2i\eta_m} - 1) \int_{-1}^{+1} (1 - \mu) P_l(\mu) P_m(\mu)\, d\mu$$

$$= \frac{\pi}{\kappa^2} \sum_{l=0}^{\infty} (2l+1) |e^{2i\eta_l} - 1|^2 - \frac{2\pi}{\kappa^2} \sum_{l=0}^{\infty} (l+1)(e^{2i\eta_l} - 1)(e^{-2i\eta_{l+1}} - 1)$$

$$\quad - \frac{2\pi}{\kappa^2} \sum_{l=0}^{\infty} l(e^{-2i\eta_{l-1}} - 1)(e^{2i\eta_l} - 1)$$

$$= \frac{\pi}{\kappa^2} \sum_{l=0}^{\infty} (l+1)(e^{2i\eta_l} - 1)(e^{-2i\eta_l} - e^{-2i\eta_{l+1}})$$

$$\quad + \frac{2\pi}{\kappa^2} \sum_{l=0}^{\infty} l(e^{2i\eta_l} - 1)(e^{-2i\eta_l} - e^{-2i\eta_{l-1}})$$

$$= \frac{\pi}{\kappa^2} \sum_{l=0}^{\infty} (l+1)|e^{2i\eta_l} - e^{2i\eta_{l+1}}|^2 = \frac{4\pi}{\kappa^2} \sum_{l=0}^{\infty} (l+1) \sin^2 (\eta_l - \eta_{l+1})$$

so that q_D becomes

$$q_D(v_0) = \frac{4\pi}{\kappa^2} \sum_{l=0}^{\infty} (l + 1) \sin^2 (\delta_l - \delta_{l+1}) \qquad (9\text{-}3\text{-}2)$$

where $\delta_{2r} = \beta_{2r}$ and $\delta_{2r+1} = \gamma_{2r+1}$. The situation is more complicated if the atom has nonzero nuclear spin, when account must be taken of the statistics.[34]

Quantal predictions of the mobilities rest therefore on the evaluation of summations (9-3-1) and (9-3-2), which through the phase shifts depend on a detailed knowledge of the interaction potentials. Owing to the integral over a Maxwellian distribution in (9-2-11), the only values of $q_D(v_0)$ important in determining the mobility at temperatures within the normal laboratory range are those at energies in the adiabatic region. Therefore, except at very low temperatures, we may employ Jeffreys' approximation to the phase shifts,[35]

$$\eta_l = \int_{r_0}^{\infty} \left[\kappa^2 - \frac{2M_r V(r)}{\hbar^2} - \frac{l(l + 1)}{r^2} \right]^{\frac{1}{2}} dr - \int_{r_0'}^{\infty} \left[\kappa^2 - \frac{l(l + 1)}{r^2} \right]^{\frac{1}{2}} dr \qquad (9\text{-}3\text{-}3)$$

where r_0 and r_0' are the respective outermost zeros of their integrands. Since we are dealing with collisions between heavy particles, a large number of phase shifts contribute to q_D, and it will prove convenient to replace the summations in the expressions for q_D by integrations.

The impact parameter is related to the wave number of the relative motion by the equation

$$b = \frac{\sqrt{l(l + 1)}}{\kappa} \qquad (9\text{-}3\text{-}4)$$

When l is large, η_l can be regarded as a function of a continuous variable, and (9-3-3) can be rewritten as

$$\eta(b) = \kappa \left\{ \int_{r_0}^{\infty} \left[1 - \frac{V(r)}{T_{\text{CM}}} - \frac{b^2}{r^2} \right]^{\frac{1}{2}} dr - \int_{r_0'}^{\infty} \left(1 - \frac{b^2}{r^2} \right) dr \right\} \qquad (9\text{-}3\text{-}5)$$

where T_{CM} is the kinetic energy of relative motion. The difference in the phase shifts can be expressed as

$$\chi(l) = \eta(l) - \eta(l + 1) = -\frac{\partial \eta}{\partial l} \qquad (9\text{-}3\text{-}6)$$

which becomes

$$\chi(b) = -\frac{1}{\kappa} \frac{\partial \eta}{\partial b} \qquad (9\text{-}3\text{-}7)$$

if we make the approximation (called the *Langer modification*)

$$b = \frac{l + \frac{1}{2}}{\kappa} \qquad (9\text{-}3\text{-}8)$$

It can be shown[36] that $\chi = \Phi - \pi/2$, where Φ is related to the scattering angle Θ by the equation

$$\Theta = \pi - 2\Phi \qquad (9\text{-}3\text{-}9)$$

and is given by

$$\Phi(b) = \int_{r_0}^{\infty} \frac{dr}{r\left[\dfrac{r^2}{b^2} - \dfrac{r^2}{b^2}\dfrac{V(r)}{T_{\text{CM}}} - 1\right]^{\frac{1}{2}}} \qquad (9\text{-}3\text{-}10)$$

(cf. Section 3-4). If we now replace in (9-3-1) the summation over l by an integration over b, we obtain

$$q_D = 2\pi \int_0^{\infty} (1 - \cos \Theta)b \, db$$

which is the classical formula (9-2-12). We therefore see that a classical description of the problem is valid, provided the temperature is not extremely low and provided only one interaction potential occurs.*

As we have pointed out, the interaction potential between an ion and an atom, is, to a good approximation, of the form

$$V(r) = Ae^{-\alpha r} - \frac{C}{r^4} - \frac{E}{r^6} + \cdots \qquad (9\text{-}3\text{-}11)$$

in most cases, and for a quantal description we require the phases for potentials of the form $V(r) = Ae^{-\alpha r}$ and $V(r) = C/r^n$. Both types of phases have been calculated[34] by use of the Massey-Mohr approximation to the Jeffreys formula.

The theory of Langevin[4,5] is obtained by choosing the potential

$$V(r) = \begin{cases} \infty & (r < \rho) \\[2mm] -\dfrac{\alpha e^2}{2r^4} & (r > \rho) \end{cases} \qquad (9\text{-}3\text{-}12)$$

where α is the polarizability of the gas and ρ is a cutoff parameter which represents the radius of the hard-sphere repulsive core. If only the attractive part of (9-3-12) is used, Jeffreys' approximation yields[34]

$$q_D = 2.210\pi \left(\frac{\alpha e^2}{2T_{\text{CM}}}\right)^{\frac{1}{2}} \qquad (9\text{-}3\text{-}13)$$

* In practice, semiclassical calculations based on the foregoing approximations have not been so accurate as purely classical calculations, although we have apparently just proved that they are essentially equivalent. The reason is that the simple semiclassical calculation of the phase shifts is invalid in the region of orbiting collisions, which eventually occur in ion-atom collisions at low energies. [K. W. Ford, D. L. Hill, M. Wakano, and J. A. Wheeler, *Ann. Phys.* **7**, 239 (1959); K. W. Ford and J. A. Wheeler, **7**, 259, 287 (1959).]

for the diffusion cross section and

$$\mathscr{K} = \frac{35.9}{\sqrt{\alpha M_r}} \ cm^2/v\text{-sec} \tag{9-3-14}$$

for the mobility, where α is measured in atomic units (a_0^3, a_0 being the radius of the first Bohr orbit), M_r is measured in units of the proton mass, and $\mathscr{K}$ is referred to a constant gas number density of $2.69 \times 10^{19}/cm^3$. This result is identical with (9-2-8), the polarizability limit of the classical Langevin theory. This is to be expected, since both results are based on identical assumptions. We shall demonstrate in Section 9-9-F that (9-3-14) is valid for positive alkali ions in A, Kr, Xe, N_2, and H_2 and also rather unexpectedly for the polar gas CO. The interaction energy between an atomic ion and a heteronuclear polar molecule such as CO presumably includes an r^{-2} term and will be orientation-dependent. The success of (9-3-14) may imply that the r^{-2} term is not significant because it vanishes when averaged over all orientations.* The orientation-dependent terms in the interaction of an ion with a homonuclear molecule such as N_2 or H_2 depend on higher powers of r^{-1}, principally the inverse third power (due to the permanent quadrupole).

It is interesting to note that the value for q_D in (9-3-13) is approximately 10% higher than the cross section for orbiting collisions, q_0, given in (3-6-6). Equation 9-3-13 takes account of trajectories for which $b > b_0$, the critical impact parameter for orbiting collisions, whereas (3-6-6) ignores their contribution.

The effect of charge transfer is important for an ion X^+ diffusing in its parent atomic gas. Dalgarno[34] has shown that in this case the diffusion cross section is approximately equal to twice the cross section q_T for the resonance charge transfer process

$$X^+ + X \rightarrow X + X^+ \tag{9-3-15}$$

except at very low temperatures, at which the contribution of long-range attractive forces is significant; q_T is given by the equation

$$q_T = 2\pi \int_0^\infty \sin^2 (\beta_l - \gamma_l) b \ db \tag{9-3-16}$$

where β_l and γ_l are the lth order phase shifts associated with elastic scattering by the symmetric and antisymmetric potentials, respectively. Since, at low impact energies, resonance charge transfer cross sections decrease

---

* Alternatively, the reason may be that the dipole moment of CO is very small. In fact, for most computational purposes CO may be considered to be nonpolar because of the extreme smallness of the dipole moment.

slowly with increasing energy, the mobility should decrease monotonically with increasing gas temperature. This behavior is to be contrasted with that of ions in unlike gases and is helpful in identifying the ion whose mobility is being measured.

Since the cross section for double charge transfer between an ion X^{2+} and atoms of its parent gas is much smaller than that for single charge transfer, it is likely that doubly charged ions behave more like ions in an unlike gas.[10] The probability of capture of a single electron by X^{2+} to form X^+, however, is so great that the doubly charged ion is unlikely to be observed in many experiments. Ferguson and Moiseiwitsch[37] have made a detailed calculation of the mobility of the He^{2+} ion in helium.

In the papers[34] from which the foregoing discussion was abstracted Dalgarno, McDowell, and Williams made a survey of the available experimental data and a detailed comparison of theoretical and experimental results. The reader is referred to these papers for this discussion and for more details of the theory.

9-4. THE AC MOBILITY AND THE MOBILITY IN MAGNETIC FIELDS

The concept of the mobility of charged particles in an alternating electric field has proved to be quite useful,[38] particularly for electrons, which are better able to follow rapid changes of the field than are ions. To develop this concept, let us consider electrons moving in a gas of uniform pressure under the influence of an electric field which oscillates with a radian frequency ω. If the amplitude of the variation of the field intensity is E_0, we may write $E = E_0 e^{i\omega t}$. Then supposing collisions with the gas molecules to provide a continuous viscous damping force, we may express the drift velocity as

$$v_d = \frac{-e/m}{i\omega + v_m} E \qquad (4\text{-}1\text{-}6)$$

where v_m is the collision frequency for momentum transfer. In deriving (4-1-6), we assumed in Section 4-1 that the damping force is given by $-cv_d$, where c is a constant.

The constant of proportionality between the drift velocity and the electric field intensity is the ac mobility $\mathscr{K}_{ac}$:

$$\mathscr{K}_{ac} = \frac{e/m}{i\omega + v_m} \qquad (9\text{-}4\text{-}1)$$

In the limit of zero applied frequency, or when the gas pressure is high enough that $v_m \gg \omega$, $\mathscr{K}_{ac}$ degenerates into the dc mobility discussed previously:

$$\mathscr{K}_{dc} = \mathscr{K} = \frac{e}{mv_m} \qquad (9\text{-}4\text{-}2)$$

This equation may be compared with the expression (9-2-1) for the mobility deduced from elementary kinetic theory.

It was shown in Chapter 4 that the momentum transfer cross section for electrons in most gases (hydrogen and helium[39] are exceptions) is a rapidly varying function of the electron velocity. Thus (9-4-1) is of quantitative value in only a few cases. Usually, account must be taken of the electron distribution function and the variation of the cross section with velocity.

The addition of a magnetic field greatly complicates the analysis of the motion of charged particles in a gas, in both dc and ac. This problem is considered in Section 10-9. There it is shown that a magnetic field renders an ionized gas anisotropic and that, as a result, the mobility is really a tensor quantity, not a scalar as assumed up to this point. Of course, when the magnetic field approaches zero, the off-diagonal components of the tensor vanish and the mobility assumes a scalar form.

9-5. CLUSTERING

The concept of an ionic cluster was introduced in Section 9-2, in which it was pointed out that an ion might attract and bind to itself one or more molecules due to the inverse-fifth-power force it exerts on the molecules. Langevin[40] apparently was the first to state a quantitative criterion for the stability of a cluster thus formed. His argument was essentially the following: a clustered ion is subjected to repeated collisions with gas molecules, and the kinetic energy available in an impact for transfer to internal potential energy of the cluster is of the order of the thermal energy if E/p is small. If the thermal energy exceeds the binding energy of the cluster, the cluster might be expected to be broken up soon after its formation. Using (1-8-4) for the relative potential energy of an ion and molecule interacting through the polarization force, we may consequently state the criterion for cluster stability as

$$|V(D_{12})| = \frac{(K-1)e^2}{8\pi N D_{12}{}^4} > \frac{3}{2}kT \qquad (9\text{-}5\text{-}1)$$

where r in (1-8-4) has been equated to D_{12}, the sum of the ionic and molecular radii; D_{12} evidently is the distance of closest approach of the molecule to the attracting center. Rewriting (9-5-1), we have

$$\frac{(K-1)e^2}{12\pi p D_{12}{}^4} > 1 \qquad (9\text{-}5\text{-}2)$$

The clustering behavior of an ion drifting at low field through a gas thus depends on a number of factors. Obviously, the nature of both the ion and the molecules composing the gas bear on this point, and the temperature of the gas can also be a decisive factor.

If the value of the diameter of the O_2 molecule is used for D_{12}, the ratio in (9-5-2) is evaluated as 3.1 at standard temperature and pressure. If D_{12} is put equal to twice this diameter, the ratio equals 0.19. Since the largest number of spheres that can be put in a single layer about a sphere of equal size is 12, it appears that a cluster of 12 O_2 molecules about an $O_2^\pm$ ion would be stable. For gases of higher dielectric constant, clusters of up to about 30 molecules might be observed. The fact that clusters of this size are not observed is not surprising, however. The foregoing treatment is admittedly naïve. For example, steric hindrance has been neglected altogether. Also, it is unlikely that the inverse-fifth-power law of attraction will hold accurately at these small distances of separation, and it is obvious that additional attractive and repulsive forces should be considered.

Bloom and Margenau[41] have considered the problem of cluster stability from the viewpoint of classical statistics. Their first model was that of an inverse-fourth-power attractive potential with a hard spherical core of radius D_{12}. On this model appreciable cluster formation was predicted in all the cases considered. However, when the potential crevasse at the radius D_{12} was removed by replacing the hard core with an inverse-twelfth-power repulsive potential, the tendency to cluster was reduced by about a factor of 100. Calculations based on the second model are in general agreement with the results obtained by Munson and Hoselitz[42] in their measurements of the mobility of alkali ions in the noble gases. These investigators found Li^+ to be the only alkali ion that appeared to form clusters in their experiments. [According to (9-5-2), the small radius of Li^+ would favor cluster stability.] As expected, the greater the size, and thus the polarizability, of the noble gas atom, the higher the temperature at which the ion will form a cluster. Xe and Kr appeared to cluster about Li^+ to the extent of two atoms at room temperature, whereas a reduction of temperature was necessary in the case of argon. Unfortunately, Munson and Hoselitz did not specify the pressures at which they worked. In a comparison of their own theoretical predictions with the experimental observations Bloom and Margenau assumed that the pressure was 19 mm Hg in the measurements of Munson and Hoselitz. This is a typical pressure in mobility experiments of the kind performed.

Bloom and Margenau also calculated the tendency of other gases to cluster about Li^+ ions. At room temperature and atmospheric pressure H_2 is not expected to cluster at all, whereas O_2 should cluster to the extent of 2 molecules and CO_2 to the extent of 28 molecules.

The applicability of classical methods to the problem of ion clustering depends on the number of vibrational levels in the potential trough describing the interaction of the ion and molecule. Bloom and Margenau report that calculations based on simplified potentials show this number to be of the order of 50 in most cases, so that quantum effects are usually unimportant.

Even without precise information concerning all the forces acting between ions and molecules, one point appears to be brought out by the calculations discussed here. The formation of stable ion clusters in some gases at normal temperatures is indicated on the basis of reasonable

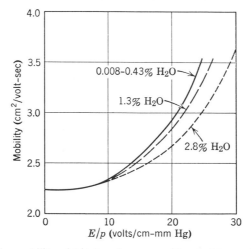

FIG. 9-5-1. The mobility of Li^+ ions in argon with admixtures of water vapor. The rapid rise in mobility with increasing E/p indicates the destruction of clusters. R. J. Munson and A. M. Tyndall, *Proc. Roy. Soc. (London)* **A-172**, 28 (1939).

assumptions, although it appears that there should be other gases in which clustering is not possible, even at low temperatures.

Another type of ion clustering might be expected when

$$\frac{(K - 1)e^2}{12\pi p D_{12}^{\ 4}} \approx 1 \tag{9-5-3}$$

Here it is expected that the size of the ion might change many times as it drifts through the gas as the result of attachments and detachments of molecules. The mobility of these so-called labile clusters[6] would then lie intermediate between the value expected for the monomolecular ion and that for a fixed cluster, and its actual value would be determined by the fraction of the time that it spends in each state.

We now emphasize a feature of cluster formation that is often neglected. Since the clustering reaction is exothermic, the binding energy of a cluster must be dissipated soon after the molecular attachment occurs in order that the reaction may not be reversed. Since de-excitation by photon emission is a very slow process, cluster formation is probably unlikely unless a third body is present to help satisfy the requirements of momentum and energy conservation. For these reasons clustering should be viewed as less probable than the simple considerations indicate. Also, it should be expected that clustered and unclustered ions will exist simultaneously, even when the ratio of the binding energy to the thermal energy is somewhat greater than unity. Cluster formation is not predicted by classical kinetic theory, which deals only with binary collisions and so provides no mechanism for formation. Clustering may, however, be described in terms of reversible chemical kinetics.[43]

Data from a paper by Munson and Tyndall[44] are displayed in Fig. 9-5-1 to illustrate what is apparently the clustering of polar water molecules about Li^+ in argon. It may be noted that as E/p, and thus the ion energy, is increased, the mobility of the ions increases. Evidently ionic clusters which are stable at lower energies are broken up in the more energetic impacts at higher E/p.

The possible astrophysical significance of clustering and other ion-molecule reactions has been discussed recently by various authors.[45]

9-6. ION-MOLECULE REACTIONS OTHER THAN CLUSTERING

Clustering in the sense described above is only one of the many reactions that ions can undergo with molecules. Reactions generally regarded as chemical in nature must also be considered. The collisions in which chemical reactions occur may be induced by forces of polarization attraction (cf. Section 3-6-B), but the forces binding the product ion together are of other kinds.[12] A few specific examples of chemical ion-molecule reactions are cited in Section 9-9. Ion-atom interchange reactions are discussed in Section 6-3.

Many ion-molecule reactions have been studied, and a number of new ions discovered, in mass spectrometric investigations in which the primary ions are allowed to make collisions at low energy in the ion source before they are analyzed. These studies have done a great deal to clarify the results of mobility and other types of experiments in which the identity of the ions present long after the initial ionization had not been definitely established. In many cases the true nature of the ions involved in the experiments had not been suspected by the original investigator. Mass spectrometric ionic reaction studies have also yielded information of great value in chemical and upper atmospheric research.[46] In addition, experimental information concerning ion-molecule reactions can provide certain checks of atomic collision theory and predictions concerning atomic and molecular structure. References to the bulk of the experimental and theoretical work on ion-molecule reactions done before about mid-1961 are listed in the reviews by Melton, Stevenson, and Pahl and Lampe, Franklin, and Field.[47] The authors of these reviews are themselves major contributors to the field. Some of the basic theoretical considerations are discussed in Section 3-6-B of this book and in the review by Polanyi.[48]

In conventional mass spectrometers[49] ions are produced in a low-pressure source having a depth of only a few millimeters, and they are immediately impelled by a weak electric field into the analysis region, which is evacuated continuously by diffusion pumps. The ionization is usually accomplished by bombardment of the sample gas by electrons from a thermionic filament. In such instruments the pressure in the ion source is ordinarily kept so low (10^{-5} to 10^{-6} mm Hg) that a primary ion has almost no chance of undergoing a collision with a gas molecule during its brief lifetime. Thus only the primary mass spectrum of the sample gas is observed, that is, the spectrum corresponding to the various charge states of the parent molecules and to the fragment ions that result from unimolecular breakup of the parent molecular ions. If, however, the source pressure is elevated to a value approaching 1 mm Hg, an appreciable fraction of the primary ions make collisions with molecules during their passage through the ion source, and information about the reactions that occur can be inferred from observations of the secondary (and sometimes tertiary) ions. Most of the present experimental knowledge of ion-molecule reactions was obtained with instruments of this kind.[50] The "transparency" of the gas target in the ion source imposes an obvious limitation on the type and order of reactions that can be studied by this method.

Valuable information on reactions has also been obtained with other apparatus designed to analyze the ion population in gas discharges[51] and in flames.[52] Many of the techniques used in the study of ion-molecule reactions have been applied to investigations of neutral-neutral reactions and free-radical formation as well.[53] Advances in instrumentation continue to be made. For instance, recent work by Giese and Maier[54] has demonstrated the feasibility of low-energy studies of ion-molecule reactions with a mass-analyzed primary ion beam.

McDaniel et al.[55,56] have developed a new type of instrument for the study of ion-molecule reactions occurring under gas-kinetic conditions. Ions are produced by a magnetically confined beam of electrons inside a drift tube 20-in. long containing gas at a pressure of up to about 1 mm Hg (Fig. 9-6-1). The ions diffuse down the drift tube under the influence of an axial electric field, whose strength determines the average ionic energy. A sample of the ion population at the end of the drift tube is extracted through a two-stage, field-free differential pumping section and passed into a 60° magnetic deflection mass spectrometer (Fig. 9-6-2). The number of ion-molecule collisions in the drift tube may be varied over a wide range by changing the source position and/or the gas pressure. Information concerning the nature and probability of the reactions occurring is

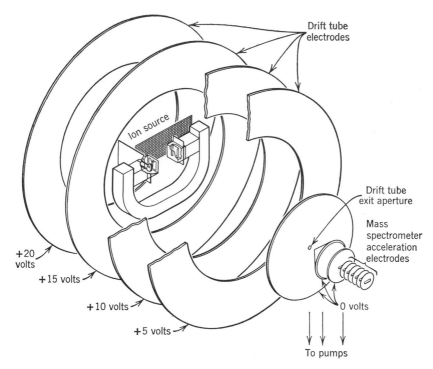

FIG. 9-6-1. Schematic view of the drift tube and differential pumping system used by McDaniel et al.[55] in their studies of ion-molecule reactions and ionic drift velocities. The ion source, described by Martin et al.,[56] can be moved continuously along the drift-tube axis from the outside.

revealed by the resulting changes in the ionic mass spectrum. By the use of very low drift field strengths, reactions may be studied at energies down to essentially thermal values. The ion source may be pulsed periodically rather than operated continuously, so that the ions of any particular charge-to-mass ratio can be sorted electronically according to their time of arrival in the mass spectrometer. In the pulsed mode of operation the locations and shapes of the peaks in the drift time spectrum yield information on both the drift velocities and the diffusion coefficients of the ions.[56]

Techniques for obtaining mobilities of mass-analyzed ions from a pulsed

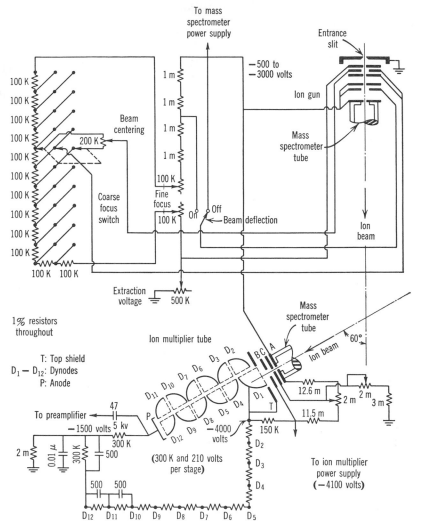

FIG. 9-6-2. The circuitry of the mass spectrometer employed in the drift-tube studies of McDaniel et al.[55,56] The potentials shown are for positive ion operation.

nonself-sustaining discharge have also been reported by McAfee and Edelson.[57] The discharge takes place in a gap about 1 cm wide, at a gas pressure of up to several mm Hg. Mass analysis is performed in a time-of-flight spectrometer on ions that drift out of the gap through a slit in the cathode. The time dependence of the mass spectrometer signal provides the ionic drift velocity.

9-7. THE MOBILITY OF IONS IN MIXTURES OF GASES; BLANC'S LAW

The first measurements of the mobility of ions in binary mixtures of gases as a function of the composition were made by Blanc[58] in 1908. In such measurements, it is frequently observed that the reciprocal of the ionic mobility is a linear function of the fractional concentration of either constituent of the mixture. This relationship is known as *Blanc's law* and is usually derived as follows. Assume that

(a) the ratio of the field strength to pressure is small;
(b) the ionic and molecular number densities are low enough that ion-ion interactions and three-body collisions may be neglected; and
(c) the nature of the ion does not change with the gas composition.

Consider first a single pure gas. Since it is known that the mobility is inversely proportional to the density of the gas, it follows that $\mathscr{K}$ may be expressed as $1/\mathscr{K} = GN$, where $\mathscr{K}$ is the mobility at temperature T and pressure p, G is a constant, and N is the number of molecules per unit volume. Similarly, if $\mathscr{K}_0$ is the mobility at standard conditions, then $1/\mathscr{K}_0 = GN_L$, where N_L is the Loschmidt number.

Now consider a binary mixture composed of N_A molecules per unit volume of a gas A and N_B molecules of a gas B, with constants G_A and G_B. Since $1/\mathscr{K}_{0A} = G_A N_L$ and $1/\mathscr{K}_{0B} = G_B N_L$, $G_A = 1/\mathscr{K}_{0A} N_L$ and $G_B = 1/\mathscr{K}_{0B} N_L$. For an ion of given drift velocity the rate of transfer of momentum to one component of the gas is considered here to be independent of the presence of the other component. Thus, since it is assumed that the nature of the ions does not change when the gases are mixed, the mobility of the ions in the mixture $\mathscr{K}_{AB}$ is given by

$$\frac{1}{\mathscr{K}_{AB}} = G_A N_A + G_B N_B = \frac{N_A}{\mathscr{K}_{0A} N_L} + \frac{N_B}{\mathscr{K}_{0B} N_L}$$

If we now assume a total pressure of 1 atm, so that $N_A + N_B = N_L$, then $\mathscr{K}_{AB}$ becomes $\mathscr{K}_{0AB}$, and the mobility of the ions in the mixture at standard conditions is given by the equation

$$\frac{1}{\mathscr{K}_{0AB}} = \frac{f_A}{\mathscr{K}_{0A}} + \frac{f_B}{\mathscr{K}_{0B}}$$

where f_A and f_B are the fractional concentrations of the A and B molecules, respectively. Since $f_A + f_B = 1$, this equation may be expressed as

$$\frac{1}{\mathscr{K}_{0AB}} = \frac{f_A \mathscr{K}_{0B} + (1 - f_A)\mathscr{K}_{0A}}{\mathscr{K}_{0A}\mathscr{K}_{0B}} \qquad (9\text{-}7\text{-}1)$$

which is Blanc's law.

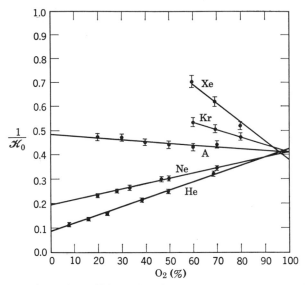

FIG. 9-7-1. Reciprocal mobilities, reduced to 760 mm Hg pressure and 0°C, for the negative ion in mixtures of oxygen and each of the noble gases. E. W. McDaniel and H. R. Crane, *Rev. Sci. Instr.* **28**, 684 (1957).

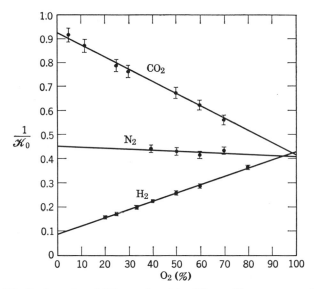

FIG. 9-7-2. Reciprocal mobilities, reduced to 760 mm Hg pressure and 0°C, for the negative ion in mixtures of oxygen and each of the gases CO_2, N_2, and H_2. E. W. McDaniel and H. R. Crane, *Rev. Sci. Instr.* **28**, 684 (1957).

Measurements[59] made by the Bristol group on the positive alkali ions showed Blanc's law to be obeyed in some, but not all, of the gas mixtures studied. In certain cases the plots of reciprocal mobility versus concentration were bowed, with deviations from linearity of a few per cent. In more recent experiments performed by McDaniel and Crane[60] on binary mixtures of oxygen with the noble gases CO_2, N_2, and H_2 a single negative ion was observed, and its mobility varied with the concentration in accordance with Blanc's law, as shown in Figs. 9-7-1 and 9-7-2. (The results on oxygen are discussed in Section 9-9-E.) Studies of helium-neon mixtures at 300, 195, and 77°K have been made by Courville and Biondi,[61] with results that are also consistent with Blanc's law. These observations are in harmony with the predictions[62] of the rigorous Chapman-Enskog theory, according to which only a change in the nature of the ion accompanying a change in the composition of the mixture will produce a deviation from Blanc's law.

9-8. METHODS USED IN THE MEASUREMENT OF MOBILITIES

The first measurements of ionic drift velocities were made by J. J. Thomson and E. Rutherford[6] at the end of the nineteenth century, shortly after the discovery of X rays. The techniques were understandably crude in the early years of experimentation, and a process of continual refinement has extended up to the present time. A score, or more, of methods has by now been used for mobility measurements; five of these methods are described here. The reader is referred to Loeb's book[6] for a discussion of other techniques. Two recently developed methods for obtaining the mobilities of ions whose identities are simultaneously determined in a mass spectrometer are described at the end of Section 9-6.[56,57]

A. THE "FOUR-GAUZE" ELECTRICAL SHUTTER METHODS OF TYNDALL AND HIS CO-WORKERS. An extensive and important series of mobility measurements was made by Tyndall and his collaborators[6,63] at Bristol during the 1930's with the so-called four-gauze, or four-grid, electrical shutter method developed by Tyndall, Starr, and Powell. This method has also been used recently for very precise measurements by Beaty[64] who took advantage of the subsequent advances in electronic and vacuum techniques to improve on the original version of the apparatus. The four-gauze method is discussed in terms of Beaty's apparatus, which is shown in Fig. 9-8-1.

The top drawing is a schematic representation of the electrode geometry. A typical potential distribution applicable for a portion of the measurement cycle is shown in the middle figure; the timing sequence is at the bottom. The two pairs of closely spaced grids form two electrical shutters, a distance of about 1 mm separating the grids composing each shutter. The space between the two shutters is the drift space, and it has guard rings, with 1.0-in. diameter holes, placed 1 cm apart to maintain a uniform electric field. The potential difference across the drift space is labeled V_1. Between the ion source and the first shutter is a space in which the ions

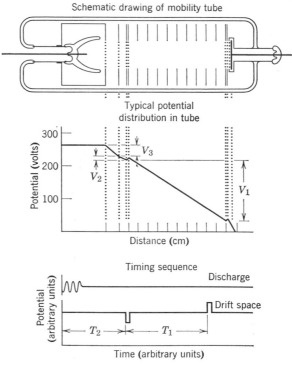

FIG. 9-8-1. Beaty's modification of the four-gauze electrical shutter method of measuring mobilities. E. C. Beaty, *Proceedings of the Fifth International Conference on Ionization Phenomena in Gases*, Munich, 1961, North-Holland, Amsterdam, 1962, Vol. I, p. 183.

from the discharge cool toward the gas temperature before their drift velocity is measured. This thermalizing space is divided into two regions by a grid, and, as indicated, the potentials across these two regions are designated V_2 and V_3; V_1, V_2, and V_3 can be varied independently.

The gas in the discharge can at the left of the top drawing is ionized periodically for intervals of 7 μsec by a gated 20-Mc oscillator. The ions diffuse to the walls under the influence of the space charge fields, with some of the ions going through the holes in the front of the can and into the thermalizing region. After a time T_2 a negative voltage pulse, which is applied to the entire drift space, opens the first shutter and allows ions to enter the drift space. After another delay T_1 a positive pulse opens the second shutter to admit ions to the collector. The advantage of this arrangement of pulsing is that the electric field is not affected by the pulses anywhere except in the shutters. The output of an electrometer attached to the collector is connected to an X-Y recorder. The electrometer current can be plotted as a function of V_1, V_2, V_3, T_1, or T_2, and the drift velocity can be determined as a function of E/p by a straightforward procedure.

The gas-handling system consists of a pyrex vacuum system which can be evacuated to a pressure of 10^{-9} mm Hg, a mercury cutoff to disconnect the pump, a bakeable metal valve to admit gas from a cataphoresis tube,* a mercury manometer, a McLeod gage for reading pressures less than 6 mm Hg, and a liquid nitrogen trap for removing mercury vapor. After sealing the cutoff and with the ionization gage operating at very low emission, it takes several days for the pressure to reach 10^{-6} mm Hg.

Beaty[64] has used this apparatus to measure the mobility of positive ions of argon in the parent gas over an E/p_0 range extending from about 1 to 80 volts/cm-mm Hg. Pressures of 0.4 to 17 mm Hg were used. Beaty and Patterson[65] have also made studies on helium and neon with this apparatus, obtaining mobilities and reaction rates for conversion of atomic to molecular ions. Their data are presented in Section 9-9-A.

B. THE METHOD OF BRADBURY AND NIELSEN.   Another classical method of measuring drift velocities was developed by Bradbury and Nielsen,[66] who applied it to the determination of electron and negative ion drift velocities. Their apparatus, which is shown in Fig. 9-8-2, is described first as applied to electron studies.

Photoelectrons are ejected from the zinc plate P by ultraviolet light and pass upward through the gas under the influence of a uniform electric field. Between alternate wires of the grids G and G' a high frequency alternating potential is applied whose mean value is the value of the uniform field at that point. The frequency and magnitude of the alternating field may be varied between wide limits. Usually, electrons that reach G will be swept out laterally to the grid wires (if the potential between them is high enough), and no current will be transmitted. However, if the amplitude of the alternating voltage is reduced sufficiently, an intermittent electron current will be transmitted. This current will consist of those electrons that reach the grid at a time when the instantaneous value of the alternating voltage is nearly zero. Thus a succession of bursts of

---

* See M. J. Druyvesteyn, *Physica* **2**, 255 (1935); R. Riesz and G. H. Dieke, *J. Appl. Phys.* **25**, 196 (1954); W. Muller and E. F. Tubbs, *J. Appl. Phys.* **34**, 969 (1963).

electrons will pass through G and drift through the uniform field toward the grid G'. To this grid is applied an alternating voltage of the same frequency, amplitude, and phase as is applied to G. If a given burst of electrons reaches G' at any time other than when the voltage is passing through zero, it will be swept out to the grid wires, and no current will be collected by the electrode A. If however, the drift velocity is such that the electrons reach G' in exactly one half-cycle or an integral multiple thereof, the sweeping voltage will be zero and the burst will be transmitted to the collector. Sharp maxima will therefore be observed in the collector

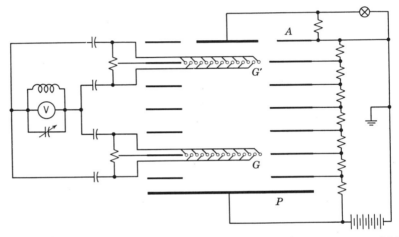

FIG. 9-8-2. The Bradbury-Nielsen electric shutter apparatus for measurement of drift velocities. N. E. Bradbury and R. A. Nielsen, *Phys. Rev.* **49**, 388 (1936).

current corresponding to those frequencies at which the electron transit time through the drift space corresponds to an integral number of half-cycles. Since the drift distance is known, the drift velocity may be obtained at various field strengths and pressures. Recent measurements of electron drift velocities made by Pack and Phelps with a modernized version of the Bradbury-Nielsen technique are discussed in Section 11-2-B.

This method may be used for the measurement of negative ion drift velocities in gases that are electronegative. In this application[67] a steady auxiliary field is applied between P and G which is of appropriate strength to favor electron capture by the gas molecules. Between alternate wires of G a high-frequency alternating voltage of sufficiently high amplitude to sweep all arriving uncaptured electrons to the grid wires but to permit the transmission of the more sluggish negative ions is applied.* A square

* Because of its opacity to electrons, the grid G is referred to as an *electron filter* (cf. Section 8-5-A).

wave alternating voltage is applied between G and the collector A. The frequency of the square wave is variable between 20 and 400 cps. The second grid G' has no function here and is kept at the proper dc potential by connecting all its wires to the adjacent guard electrode. For low frequencies of the square wave the collector current is small and constant. As the frequency is increased, however, the current increases rather abruptly at a critical frequency, the determination of which allows the calculation of the drift velocity.

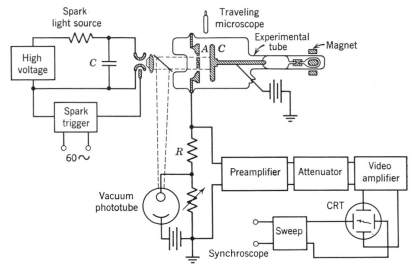

FIG. 9-8-3. Hornbeck's mobility apparatus. J. A. Hornbeck, *Phys. Rev.* **83**, 374 (1951).

The Bradbury-Nielsen technique has been used recently by Crompton and Elford[68] for determinations of the mobility of positive potassium ions in nitrogen and neon. These measurements extended over a range of E/p_0 of about 1 to 50 volts/cm-mm Hg and were accurate to better than 0.5%. The pressure range was 1 to 20 mm Hg, and frequencies of the order of 1000 cps were used. The grids in their apparatus are 4 cm apart, and each grid consists of 0.08-mm diameter nichrome wires with 0.52-mm spacing. Their ions were generated thermionically from an alumino-silicate of potassium (cf. Section 13-5-B).

C. HORNBECK'S METHOD. A number of important mobility measurements have been made with apparatus developed by Hornbeck[69] and shown in Fig. 9-8-3. A 0.1-μsec burst of photoelectrons is released from a cathode C by ultraviolet light from a spark source operated at a repetition rate of 60 cps. These electrons are accelerated through the gas at high field and produce a Townsend avalanche. The primary and avalanche electrons are collected at the anode A in a time of the order of a few tenths of a microsecond, but the exponential distribution of positive ions formed in the avalanche is swept across to the cathode much more slowly. A voltage transient is developed across the resistor R and displayed on an oscilloscope. The transient consists of a sharp spike, attributable to the photoelectrons and their progeny electrons, followed by a smaller component produced by the positive ions. The ionic drift velocity is determined by measuring the arrival time of ions which were formed "at" the

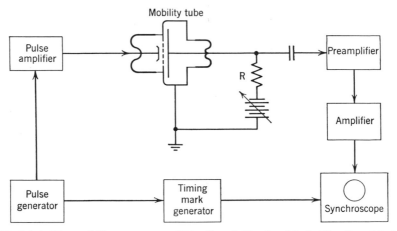

FIG. 9-8-4. The mobility apparatus of Biondi and Chanin. M. A. Biondi and L. M. Chanin, *Phys. Rev.* **94**, 910 (1954).

anode in the discharge, this time being signaled by a break in the voltage trace on the oscilloscope. The separation between the cathode and anode may be varied by means of an external magnet and measured by a traveling microscope. The gap spacing is typically about 1 cm. Pressures in the range 0.1 to 30 mm Hg have been used, and ionic drift times of about 2 to 20 μsec result. The tube current, of the order of 0.1 μamp, is controlled so that negligible space-charge distortion of the applied field occurs. Measurements have been made over a range of E/p_0 extending from about 10 to 1000 volts/cm-mm Hg.

D. THE METHOD OF BIONDI AND CHANIN. Another method that has been successfully used is that of Biondi and Chanin.[70] Their apparatus is shown in Fig. 9-8-4. A discharge is created by the application of a 0.5 μsec, 1000-volt pulse to the electrode at the left in the mobility tube. The spacing between this electrode and the adjacent grid can be varied by means of a magnetic armature to obtain optimum discharge conditions for various gas fillings and pressures. Some of the ions formed in the discharge, which is confined to the space between the first electrode and the grid, move through the grid and into the drift region at the right. A negative dc voltage is applied to the collector electrode at the right, which produces the uniform electric field in which the ions move across the drift space. The spacing between the collector and the grid can be changed by means of a second magnetic armature to permit the elimination of end effects.

The collector electrode is connected to the drift voltage supply through a resistor R. The induced current caused by the motion of the ions in the drift space produces a voltage transient of the order of 10^{-4} volt in amplitude which is amplified and displayed on an oscilloscope. The break in the voltage trace which occurs when the ions arrive at the collector indicates the transit time of the ions. If ions of more than one type are present, the resultant trace is simply the sum of the contributions from each type of ion. Small enough fields may be used in the drift region so that measurements can be made at E/p_0 at which the ions are essentially in thermal equilibrium with the gas. Drift distances of about 1 cm and pressures of several mm Hg are used, and ionic transit times of several tens of microseconds are observed.

E. THE AMBIPOLAR DIFFUSION METHOD. Finally, we should mention the method of mobility determination which is based on measurement of the ambipolar diffusion coefficient of electrons and ions in the afterglow of a pulsed microwave discharge.[71-74] Discussion of this method is deferred until Section 10-10, where the coefficient of ambipolar diffusion is defined. Measurements of this kind are also discussed in Section 12-7.

9-9. EXPERIMENTAL DATA AND THEIR COMPARISON
     WITH THEORETICAL PREDICTIONS

Literally hundreds of experiments have been performed to determine the mobility of gaseous ions, the first measurements having been made as long ago as the end of the last century. Most of the early measurements were vitiated by the poor spatial definition of the groups of ions used and by the presence of impurities. Impurities present even in trace amounts may produce misleading results in several different ways. Charge transfer may occur from the ions under investigation to impurity atoms or molecules. Clustering and other ion-molecule reactions involving the impurities may also take place, particularly if polar impurities are present. Furthermore, in negative ion experiments preferential capture of the primary electrons by impurities is possible and results in the formation of a number

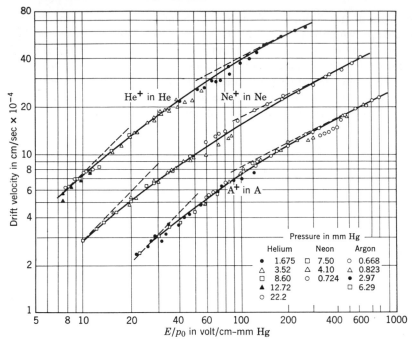

FIG. 9-9-1. The drift velocity of atomic ions in helium, neon, and argon as a function of E/p_0. The broken lines at the left of each experimental curve have slope = 1, whereas the broken lines at the right have slope = $\frac{1}{2}$. J. A. Hornbeck, *Phys. Rev.* **84**, 615 (1951).

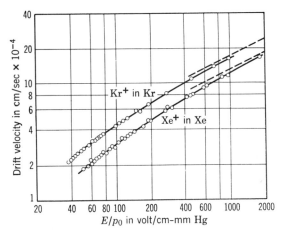

FIG. 9-9-2. The drift velocity of atomic ions in krypton and xenon as a function of E/p_0 on a log-log plot. The broken lines at the right of each curve have a slope of $\frac{1}{2}$. R. N. Varney, *Phys. Rev.* **88**, 362 (1952).

of impurity ions completely out of proportion to the number of impurity molecules present.

For these reasons caution should be used in accepting mobility data obtained before 1930, since it was at about that time that good vacuum and gas purification techniques began to be developed. Another period of rapid improvement in experimental techniques came immediately after World War II when fast pulse and microwave electronics were first applied in the measurement of mobilities. Mention should also be made of the remarkable ultrahigh vacuum techniques which have been developed in the last 15 years, particularly at the Westinghouse Research Laboratories.*

Only a small fraction of the available experimental data is presented here. An effort has been made to select data which are of the greatest general interest and which pertain to ions whose identity has been at least fairly definitely established. Loeb's book[6] gives a much wider coverage of the older experimental results.

A. THE NOBLE GASES.   1. *Ions in their parent gases at room temperature.* Figures 9-9-1 and 9-9-2 show drift velocity data on atomic noble gas ions in their parent gases, obtained by Hornbeck[15] and Varney[16] with Hornbeck's apparatus (Section 9-8-C). As always throughout this book, p_0 denotes the normalized pressure $273\,p/T$, where p is the measured gas pressure and T is the temperature in °K. Hornbeck's and Varney's experiments were performed at room temperature. Both atomic and molecular ions were present at the lowest values of E/p_0 that could be reached by Hornbeck's method, but only atomic ions were in evidence at higher E/p_0. Over the limited range available for comparison, the mobility of each molecular ion was found to be considerably higher than that of its atomic counterpart. The resonant charge transfer experienced by the atomic ions produces a retarding effect which more than offsets the mass effect that would otherwise cause the atomic ions to have the higher mobility. The identification of the slower ions as atomic was based on the observation that the atomic, but not the molecular, ions are easily formed over a wide range of E/p_0. This identification is supported by the agreement between the quantum mechanical predictions for these ions and the low-field results obtained by extrapolation of the experimental data to $E/p_0 = 0$ (see Table 9-9-1).

* See, for example, S. Dushman, *Scientific Foundations of Vacuum Technique*, Second Edition (edited and revised by J. M. Lafferty et al.) Wiley, New York, 1962. A. H. Turnbull, R. S. Barton, and J. C. Riviere, *An Introduction to Vacuum Technique.* Wiley, New York, 1963. R. W. Roberts and T. A. Vanderslice, *Ultrahigh Vacuum and Its Applications*, Prentice-Hall, Englewood Cliffs, N.J. (1963). A. E. Barrington, *High Vacuum Engineering*, Prentice-Hall, Englewood-Cliffs, N.J. (1963). A. Guthrie, *Vacuum Technology*, Wiley, New York (1963).

TABLE 9-9-1. Comparison of experimental and theoretical values of the zero-field mobilities of atomic and molecular ions in the noble gases. The mobilities are expressed in cm^2/v-sec and refer to a temperature of 300°K and a gas number density of 2.69×10^{19}/cm^3. Oskam and Mittelstadt[74] have recently obtained mobilities for ions in helium, neon, and argon from ambipolar diffusion measurements. Their values for the ions in their parent gases are He$^+$: 10.7; Ne$^+$: 4.1; A$^+$: 1.6; He$_2^+$: 16.2; Ne$_2^+$: 6.5; A$_2^+$: 1.9.

Ion/Gas	Experiment			Theory		
	Hornbeck[15] and Varney[16]	Biondi and Chanin[70,75]	Beaty and Patterson	Kerr et al.[73]	Quantum Mechanical Calculations	Langevin
He$^+$ in He	10.8	10.8	10.5[65]	10.6	10.2 (Lynn and Moiseiwitsch[25])	18.3
Ne$^+$ in Ne	4.4	4.2	4.0[65]		4.2 (Holstein[28])	6.68
A$^+$ in A	1.63	1.60	1.535[64]		1.62 (Holstein[28])	2.26
Kr$^+$ in Kr	0.9–0.95	0.90			1.0 (Bernstein[70])	1.34
Xe$^+$ in Xe	0.6–0.65	0.58			0.66 (Bernstein[70])	0.84
? in He	19	20.3	16.7,20[65]	16.2		20(He$_2^+$)
Ne$_2^+$ in Ne	5.85	6.5	6.2[65]			6.0
? in A	1.9	2.65	1.833,2.60[64]			2.1(A$_2^+$)
Kr$_2^+$ in Kr	1.1–1.2	1.21				1.18
Xe$_2^+$ in Xe	0.67–0.77	0.79				0.74

Table 9-9-1 also displays the zero-field atomic and molecular mobilities obtained by Biondi and Chanin[70,75] by extrapolation of their data to $E/p_0 = 0$. Their results are in close agreement with those of Hornbeck and Varney except for the molecular ion in argon, and it is probable that their results refer to a different ion in this case. Using his high resolution apparatus, Beaty[64] observed three separate ions in very pure argon, with zero-field mobilities of 1.535 ± 0.007, 1.833 ± 0.008, and 2.60 ± 0.02 $cm^2/v\text{-sec}$, respectively (see Fig. 9-9-3). The lowest mobility surely refers

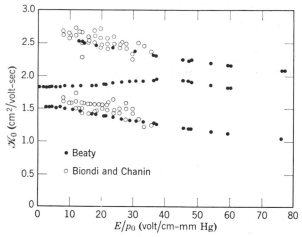

FIG. 9-9-3. The mobilities of ions in argon as functions of E/p_0. The slowest ion is A^+. The ion of intermediate mobility is almost certain to be A_2^+, whereas the fastest ion is likely to be A^{2+}. M. A. Biondi and L. M. Chanin, *Phys. Rev.* **94**, 910 (1954); E. C. Beaty, *Proceedings of the Fifth International Conference on Ionization Phenomena in Gases*, Munich, 1961, North-Holland, Amsterdam, 1962, Vol. I, p. 183.

to A^+. The ion of intermediate mobility is probably A_2^+, and the fastest ion may be A^{2+}.* Beaty's ion of intermediate mobility is observed to be formed by reaction of A^+ ions with the gas and is the chemically stable ion in the pure gas. Beaty did not use cataphoresis in his argon experiments, the use of this technique by Biondi and Chanin having produced no observable effect in their argon measurements. All three ions in Beaty's argon measurements are probably ions of the parent gas, but identification of the molecular ions is not definite at this date.

Beaty and Patterson,[65] Kerr and his colleagues,[73] and Oskam and Mittelstadt[74] have recently measured mobilities in very pure helium with

* K. B. McAfee, D. Edelson, and D. Sipler, *Sixteenth Annual Gaseous Electronics Conference*, Pittsburgh, 1963.

interesting results. They find several ions in helium before final purification by cataphoresis, but following this step only three ions remain in
the experiments of Beaty and Patterson and only two in the experiments of
Kerr et al. and Oskam and Mittelstadt. Their mobilities for the slowest
ion are in good mutual agreement and also agree with the values reported
by Hornbeck and by Biondi and Chanin (see Table 9-9-1). However,
their mobility for the ion of intermediate speed (about 16.5 cm²/v-sec) is
much lower than that derived from the earlier experiments by Hornbeck
and by Biondi and Chanin. This ion is the chemically stable species and is
thought to be He_2^+, notwithstanding the fact that the mobility of 16.5
cm²/v-sec is far below the value of 22.7 predicted for He_2^+ by Geltman.[30]
The fastest ion observed in helium by Beaty and Patterson has a mobility
of 20 cm²/v-sec, which agrees well with the values obtained by the earlier
investigators for the ion they thought to be He_2^+.

Beaty and Patterson[65] report two mobilities for ions in pure neon (see
Table 9-9-1), one for Ne^+ and the other for the chemically stable ion
produced during flight from Ne^+. The latter ion is presumed to be Ne_2^+.

Oskam and Mittelstadt[74] have also obtained mobilities for atomic and
molecular ions of neon and argon from studies of ambipolar diffusion in
these gases. Their values, listed in the legend of Table 9-9-1, are in good
agreement with those reported by Beaty and Patterson.

One should probably regard the mobilities for the other molecular ions
displayed in Table 9-9-1 as tentative until measurements are made with
gases of purity comparable to those used in the experiments of Beaty and
Patterson, Kerr and his co-workers, and Oskam and Mittelstadt.

Diatomic noble gas ions have been observed in many mass spectrometric
studies. There appear to be at least two possible modes of formation for
these ions. Hornbeck and Molnar[76] argue that the molecular ions in
Hornbeck's mobility experiments[15] were diatomic and that they were
created in collisions between neutral atoms X and atoms X* which had
been raised to a high-lying excited state by electron impact during the
photopulse. The reaction for this proposed mode (the *Hornbeck-Molnar
process*) is then

$$X^* + X \rightarrow X_2^+ + e \qquad (9\text{-}9\text{-}1)$$

Hornbeck and Molnar demonstrate that the excited state involved here
cannot be a metastable state. Diatomic ions of the noble gases may also
be formed from atomic ions in three-body collisions represented by the
equation

$$X^+ + 2X \rightarrow X_2^+ + X \qquad (9\text{-}9\text{-}2)$$

Both of these mechanisms have recently been investigated by Dahler et al.[50]
The rates of (9-9-2) have been determined by Beaty and Patterson[65] for

helium and neon. They report values of $10.8 \pm 0.8 \times 10^{-32}$ cm^6/sec and $5.8 \pm 0.8 \times 10^{-32}$ cm^6/sec for helium and neon, respectively.

It is pertinent to point out that Mason and Vanderslice have calculated the binding energy of the He$_2^+$ and Ne$_2^+$ ions from scattering data. They give a maximum binding energy of 2.16 ev for the former ion[77] and a less precise value of 0.3–1.0 ev for the latter.[78] A similar treatment of A$_2^+$ gives a maximum binding energy of 0.056 ev.[79]

The quantum mechanical calculations of Lynn and Moiseiwitsch and Geltman to which reference has been made are discussed in Section 9-3-A. Bernstein's calcuations for Kr$^+$ and Xe$^+$ have not been published but are discussed by Biondi and Chanin.[70] In applying Langevin's theory to obtain the values tabulated in Table 9-9-1, the complete equation (9-2-5) was used for the atomic ions and the polarization limit (9-2-8) for the molecular ions. Polarization forces are dominant for the molecular noble gas ions but play only a minor role in the case of the atomic ions, for which symmetry effects predominate. Wannier's corrected ion-atom cross sections (Table 9-2-2) were utilized in the atomic calculations.* Considerably better agreement with experiment is obtained, however, if the original Wannier cross sections are used in the Langevin equation for the atomic mobilities.[15,16]

2. *The variation of the mobility with the mass of the ion.* Chanin and Biondi[80] measured the low-field mobility of Hg$^+$ ions in He, Ne, and A at $300°$K and obtained values of 19.6, 5.95, and 1.84 cm^2/v-sec, respectively. These values are in agreement with the extrapolation of the mobility versus mass-number curves obtained for the alkali ions in the noble gases by Tyndall and his collaborators.[63] Figure 9-9-4 illustrates how the mobility varies with the ionic mass for atomic ions in the noble gases when symmetry effects are not in evidence.

3. *The variation of the mobility with E/p.* Figure 9-9-5, prepared by Frost,[81] indicates how the mobility of atomic ions of He, Ne, and A varies with E/p over a wide range of E/p. The dots represent data of Biondi and Chanin[70] and the open circles, data of Hornbeck.[15] The curves in Fig. 9-9-5 may be fitted by equations of the form

$$\mathscr{K} = \mathscr{K}^* \left[1 + a\left(\frac{E}{p}\right) \right]^{-\frac{1}{2}} \tag{9-9-3}$$

where $\mathscr{K}^*$ and a are constants which are different for each gas.

4. *The variation of the mobility with temperature.* The temperature variation of the low-field mobility of atomic and molecular ions in He,

---

* These results were furnished to the author by J. A. Rees, private communication (1963).

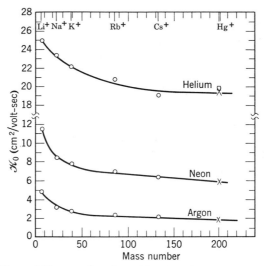

FIG. 9-9-4. The mobility as a function of ion mass in He, Ne, and A. L. M. Chanin and M. A. Biondi, *Phys. Rev.* **107**, 1219 (1957).

Ne, and A has been studied by Chanin and Biondi.[75] The results of their measurements, which covered the range of 77 to 300°K, are compared with predictions of theory in Fig. 9-9-6. If we wished to make a detailed comparison of experimental results with theory by studying the energy dependence of the mobility, it would be preferable to vary the temperature of the gas rather than to increase the drift field to change the ion energy. The reason for this is that ionic drift velocities, unlike those of electrons, are difficult to calculate when ions depart from thermal equilibrium with the gas under the action of an applied field. Comparison with theory is

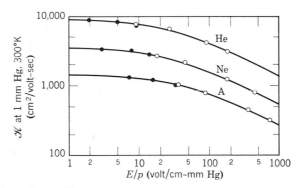

FIG. 9-9-5. The mobility of positive atomic ions of the noble gases in their parent gases. L. S. Frost, *Phys. Rev.* **105**, 354 (1957).

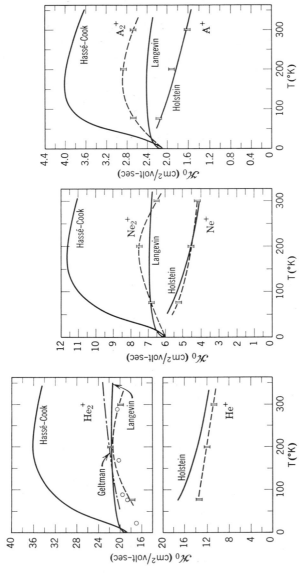

FIG. 9-9-6. Comparison of the measured temperature dependence of the mobilities of ions in helium, neon, and argon with predictions of various theories. The *I* symbols refer to the results of L. M. Chanin and M. A. Biondi, *Phys. Rev.* **106**, 473 (1957); the open circles to measurements of A. M. Tyndall and A. F. Pearce, *Proc. Roy. Soc.* (*London*) A-149, 426 (1935). The identities of the molecular ions are uncertain.

facilitated by taking measurements at low field and varying the ion energy by varying the gas temperature. Measurements of the field variation at low fields could, however, be used·for the purpose.[21,22]

B. HYDROGEN. Figure 9-9-7 shows mobility data for positive ions in hydrogen at room temperature. The most recent measurements are those of Rose,[82] who used the Hornbeck technique, and Chanin,[83] who employed

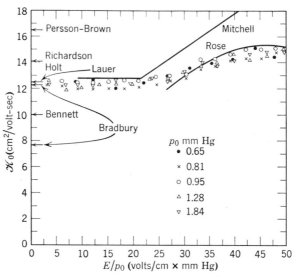

FIG. 9-9-7. The mobility of ions in hydrogen at 300°K. This figure was taken from a paper by L. M. Chanin, *Phys. Rev.* **123**, 526 (1961), whose data are indicated by the symbols. The zero-field value of 12.3 cm²/v-sec which Chanin obtained is believed to be the correct mobility for the only hydrogen ion (H_3^+) usually present in the pure parent gas at large pd.

the Biondi-Chanin method. Their results are in good mutual agreement. The correct zero-field value for hydrogen ions in hydrogen is probably very close to the value of 12.3 cm²/v-sec obtained by Chanin. There is considerable disagreement among the data reported by some of the other investigators.[84] Bradbury's value of 7.6 cm²/v-sec refers to ions about 10^{-2} sec old which probably were not ions of hydrogen. The gas may not have been pure in Bennett's experiment as well. The results reported by Richardson and Holt and by Persson and Brown were derived from microwave measurements of the ambipolar diffusion coefficient in a hydrogen afterglow (see Section 10-10). Rose[82] has pointed out that the presence of higher diffusion modes in the discharge cavity, the effect of gas heating during the discharge pulse and its effect on the afterglow, and the possibility that the diffusion may not have been strictly ambipolar may account for the high mobilities deduced from the microwave experiments.

The ion usually observed in hydrogen mobility experiments has often been labeled H_2^+. Recent mass spectrometric studies[85] indicate, however, that the observed ion is H_3^+ and that the H_2^+ ion is never present at the pd (pressure times drift distance) required for a mobility determination. Both H^+ and H_2^+ are usually produced in the initial ionization process, but both are converted to H_3^+ in collisions with H_2 molecules. The cross section for the H_2^+ conversion reaction

$$H_2^+ + H_2 \rightarrow H_3^+ + H \tag{9-9-4}$$

is enormous, being of the order of 10^{-14} cm^2 at thermal energy.*

As mentioned in Section 9-3-A, Mason and Vanderslice[29] have calculated quantum mechanically the low-field mobility of H^+, H_2^+, and H_3^+ ions in H_2 as a function of the temperature. Their values are 18.3, 13.9, and 22.0 cm^2/v-sec, respectively, for a temperature of 300°K. In the light of the above mentioned mass spectrometric studies, the proximity of Mason and Vanderslice's value of 13.9 cm^2/v-sec for H_2^+ to the experimental value of 12.3 cm^2/v-sec appears to be fortuitous. As pointed out, the experimental value almost certainly refers to H_3^+.

Rose's data[82] for deuterium are compared with his hydrogen results in Fig. 9-9-8.

C. NITROGEN.   The drift velocities of the positive ions of nitrogen in the parent gas have been measured by a number of investigators.[6,17,56,57,86-89] The first measurements over a wide range of E/p_0 were made by Varney,[17] who used the pulsed Townsend discharge method in the pressure range 1 to 35 mm Hg at a gas temperature of 300°K. His results are shown in Fig. 9-9-9a along with the data obtained by Kovar, Beaty, and Varney,[87] using the same technique at temperatures of 77, 300, and 450°K. The data of Varney and his co-workers join smoothly with the results obtained in 1934 at lower E/p_0 by Mitchell and Ridler,[86] whose ions had a zero-field mobility of 2.49 cm^2/v-sec when adjusted to standard conditions.[17] A single positive ion, with mobility of 2.5 $\pm$ 0.1 cm^2/v-sec, has been reported by Davies et al.[88] in low-field measurements on nitrogen. Additional low-field mobility data have recently become available through measurements of ambipolar diffusion coefficients by Zipf.[88] He observed an ion in very pure nitrogen with a mobility of 2.42 $\pm$ 0.12 cm^2/v-sec.

* See C. F. Giese and W. B. Maier, *J. Chem. Phys.* **39,** 739 (1963) for measurements of the cross section for this process. The cross section for the H^+ conversion reaction is probably much smaller, and H^+ may be able to persist in hydrogen under favorable conditions for times long enough to enable its mobility to be measured. Varney and others have recently observed an ion in hydrogen with mobility of about 17 cm^2/v-sec which they believe may be H^+.

The results recently obtained by Martin et al.[56] with their pulsed drift tube-mass spectrometer (see Section 9-6) disclosed the presence of N^+, N_2^+, N_3^+, and N_4^+ ions in nitrogen at low pressures (0.04 to 0.22 mm Hg) and field strengths of from 1 to 4 v/cm. The drift velocities of all four species were found to be linear in E/p_0 for values of E/p_0 less than about

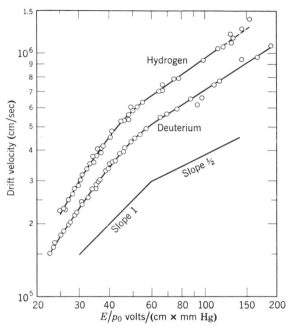

FIG. 9-9-8. Drift velocity of ions in the parent gases H_2 and D_2 versus E/p_0. Lines of logarithmic slope 1 and $\frac{1}{2}$ are shown for reference. D. J. Rose, *J. Appl. Phys.* **31**, 643 (1960).

20 v/cm-mm Hg (see Fig. 9-9-9b). Since the variation in each case had unit slope on a log-log plot, the zero-field reduced mobilities could be calculated accurately. The resulting values, in cm²/v-sec, are N^+: 3.3, N_2^+: 1.8, N_3^+: 3.1, and N_4^+: 2.4, with errors not believed to exceed 5%. These mobilities are the first low-field values to be reported for mass-analyzed ions in a time-of-flight experiment. The N_2^+ data of Martin et al. confirm the conclusion drawn by Varney et al. that the ion they observed at E/p_0 above 100 v/cm-mm Hg was N_2^+. The results obtained by McAfee and Edelson[57] on mass-identified N_2^+ ions at high E/p_0 also support this interpretation. (McAfee and Edelson also meaured drift velocities for mass-analyzed N^+, N_3^+, and N_4^+ ions at E/p_0 above 60 v/cm-mm Hg and obtained a few values for N_4^+ at low field. Because of

the scatter of the low-field data, they did not report a mobility for N_4^+.)*

Varney has attributed the unusual shape of his drift velocity curve between E/p_0 of 38 and 100 v/cm-mm Hg to a reversible reaction scheme by which the ions would spend part of their time as N_2^+ and part as N_4^+. The ions were thought to change their character many times during their

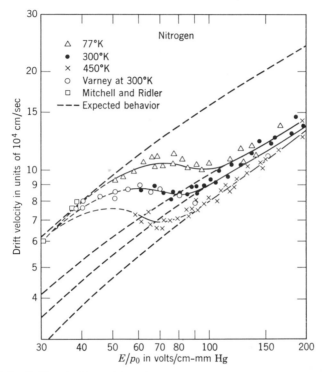

FIG. 9-9-9a. Drift velocities of ions in nitrogen at various temperatures, including extrapolation of velocities to high and low values of E/p_0. F. R. Kovar, E. C. Beaty, and R. N. Varney, *Phys. Rev.* **107**, 1490 (1957).

flight across the drift space, their drift velocity being determined by the relative amounts of time spent as N_2^+ and N_4^+. This interpretation appeared to be supported by the mass spectrometric data of Saporoschenko[90]

---

* The mobility tube used by McAfee and Edelson is the Hornbeck type and in its original form required a high value of E/p_0 throughout the gap for the production of ions. In order to improve the precision of the measurements and to permit measurements to be made at low field, McAfee and Edelson have added a grid parallel to the electrodes which divides the gap into two regions. In the smaller region adjacent to the cathode the field must be high to permit the production of ions, but the field can be low in the other region, which constitutes the main drift space.

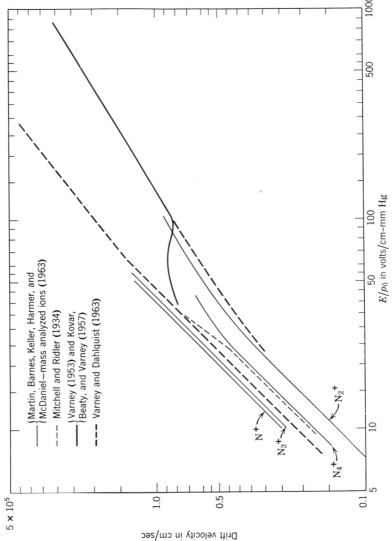

FIG. 9-9-9b. Drift velocities of positive ions of nitrogen in the parent gas at 300°K.

on ion formation in nitrogen. Varney[17] invoked the following reaction scheme to explain the shape of his curve:

$$N_2^+ + N_2 \rightarrow N_4^+; \qquad N_4^+ + N_2 \rightarrow N_2^+ + 2N_2 \qquad (9\text{-}9\text{-}5)$$

According to Varney, at low E/p_0 the reaction proceeds in the direction of the first equation by attachment, and detachment is much slower. At high E/p_0, N_4^+ might not even form by this mechanism, and any N_4^+ ions that are formed are short-lived because of the second reaction, which is now dominant. A single, well-defined drift velocity will be observed if the mean free path for at least one of the above reactions is much less than the drift distance. At relatively high pressures and low E/p_0, the mean free path for the first reaction must be short, whereas at high E/p_0 this condition applies to the second reaction. Both mean free paths must be short in the intermediate region, the position of which depends on the gas pressure. In the low pressure experiments of Martin and his co-workers,[56] the N_4^+ ions appeared to be formed near the source and not to be converted to N_2^+ during their transit through the drift tube, even at the maximum drift distance of 21 cm.

In his analysis of the N_2^+-N_4^+ reaction scheme Varney evaluated the binding energy of the N_4^+ ion against dissociation into N_2^+ and N_2, obtaining a value of 0.5 ev for this quantity.[91] The dissociation equilibrium of the N_4^+ ion (and the H_3^+ and A_2^+ ions as well) has been discussed in terms of chemical and statistical mechanical considerations by Varney.[91]

Although there seems to be little doubt that the ion which Varney observed at very high E/p_0 in his 1953 experiments[17] was N_2^+, it is not possible at this time to identify with certainty his dominant ion at the lowest E/p_0 accessible to him (38 v/cm-mm Hg). As stated earlier, Varney's data at this value of E/p_0 join smoothly with the data of Mitchell and Ridler, whose ion at E/p_0 below 23 v/cm-mm Hg appears to be N_4^+ when comparison is made with Martin's data on N_4^+ (see Fig. 9-9-9b). On the other hand, the most plausible extrapolation of Varney's drift velocities to lower E/p_0 gives a straight line of unit slope almost coinciding with the recent curve of Varney and Dahlquist[89] and the N_3^+ curve of Martin et al.[56] Thus the low-field ion in Varney's 1953 experiments was probably N_3^+. The mobility of N_3^+, according to Martin and his co-workers, is 3.1 cm²/v-sec. The data of Varney and Dahlquist,[89] which presumably refer to N_3^+, correspond to a low-field mobility of about 2.9 cm²/v-sec. The ion observed at low E/p_0 by Mitchell and Ridler, Dutton et al. and Zipf with mobility of about 2.42 cm²/v-sec is probably N_4^+.

The use of the polarization limit of the Langevin theory gives a value of 2.42 cm²/v-sec for the zero-field mobility of the N_4^+ ion in nitrogen.[17] This mobility is in good agreement with the value of 2.4 cm²/v-sec obtained

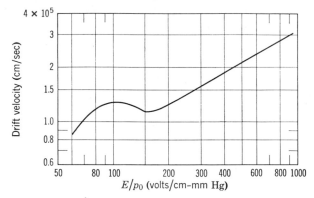

FIG. 9-9-10. The ionic drift velocity in CO. The ion at low and at high E/p_0 is thought to be CO^+. R. N. Varney, *Phys. Rev.* **89**, 708 (1953).

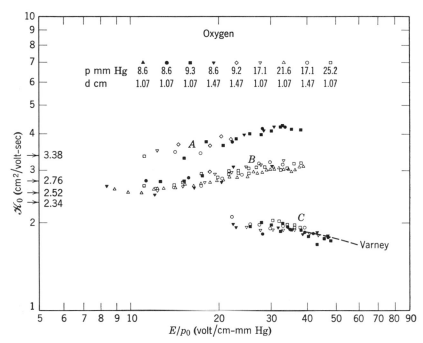

FIG. 9-9-11. Mobilities of oxygen ions in oxygen. The arrows along the ordinate axis refer to Langevin mobilities for O, O_2, O_3, and O_4 ions, respectively, starting from above. The points represent negative ion mobilities observed by D. S. Burch and R. Geballe, *Phys. Rev.* **106**, 183 (1957) and are thought to refer to O^-, O_3^-, and O_2^-, starting from above. The dashed curve denotes the mobility of a positive ion, thought to be O_2^+, observed by R. N. Varney, *Phys. Rev.* **89**, 708 (1953).

by linear extrapolation of the data of Martin et al.[56] to $E/p_0 = 0$. The polarization limit mobilities of N^+, N_2^+, and N_3^+ in N_2 are 3.42, 2.80, and 2.55 cm²/v-sec, respectively.

D. CARBON MONOXIDE. Hornbeck's method has also been used by Varney[17] for measurements of the mobility of positive ions in carbon monoxide (see Fig. 9-9-10). The ion is thought to be CO^+ at high and low E/p_0 and to shuttle back and forth between CO^+ and $(CO)_2^+$ at intermediate E/p_0, according to the attachment-detachment reactions

$$CO^+ + CO \rightarrow (CO)_2^+ \qquad (CO)_2^+ + CO \rightarrow CO^+ + 2CO \qquad (9\text{-}9\text{-}6)$$

The experimental mobility extrapolated to zero field is 1.6 cm²/v-sec. Although Varney's measured drift velocities are probably accurate within a few per cent, the accuracy of this mobility is not likely to be high because of the long extrapolation of the experimental data required to reach $E/p_0 = 0$.

E. OXYGEN. Varney's results[17] for the positive ions of oxygen are shown in Fig. 9-9-11. A single ionic species, thought to be O_2^+, was observed and its mobility, obtained by extrapolation downward from E/p_0 above 40 v/cm-mm Hg, was 2.25 cm²/v-sec.

A number of measurements of the mobility of the negative ions of oxygen in the parent gas have also been made. The most recent are those of Doehring,[92] Burch and Geballe,[93] McDaniel and Crane,[60,94] Chanin et al.,[95] and Eiber.[96] In Doehring's experiment only a single ion with low-field mobility of 2.68 cm²/v-sec was observed. The ion was thought to be O_2^-, but the work of Burch and Geballe indicates that it may have been O_3^-. The O_3^- ion is known to be stable through the mass spectrometric studies of Curran[97] on ozone.

In the experiments of Burch and Geballe,[93] who utilized a pulsed Townsend discharge in apparatus similar to Hornbeck's, there was evidence of three separate species of negative ions. Three distinct and pressure-independent negative ion mobilities consistent with zero-field values of 3.4, 2.6, and 1.95 cm²/v-sec (Fig. 9-9-11) were found. The multiplicity of velocities was ascribed to unidirectional ion-molecule reactions through which initially formed O^- ions were converted into two slower species, O_3^- and O_2^-. Burch and Geballe interpreted the species of intermediate mobility (2.6) as O_3^-, the fastest ion as O^-, and the slowest as O_2^-. Positive ions were also investigated in their experiments. The initially formed positive ion, thought to be O_2^+, retained its identity as it drifted through the gas. No difference was noted between the mobilities of the "O_2^+" and "O_2^-" ions. The experiments of Burch and Geballe covered a range of E/p_0 extending from 9 to 50 volts/cm-mm Hg and a range of pd from 7 to 26 cm-mm Hg; (pd, the product of the pressure in mm Hg and the drift distance in cm, is a frequently used parameter in drift experiments.)

The experiments of McDaniel and Crane[60,94] were performed at very low field on oxygen and binary mixtures of oxygen and other gases (see Section 9-7); pd was varied from about 600 to 2000 cm-mm Hg. The value found for the mobility in oxygen was 2.46 cm²/v-sec and was ascribed to a single ionic species, which McDaniel and McDowell[94] labeled O_3^-. In these experiments a drift velocity spectrum with a sharp leading edge was observed, and the mobility reported was determined from the position of this edge. Other ions with lower mobility contributing to the diffuse trailing edge of the spectrum could not be resolved.

The mobility experiments of Chanin, Phelps, and Biondi[95] were conducted at E/p_0 between 0.15 and 10 volts/cm-mm Hg. At 300°K, a single ion with a mobility of 2.7 cm²/v-sec was observed for E/p_0 below 1.5 volts/cm-mm Hg. The mobility of this ion, which Chanin et al. believed to be O_2^-, decreased fairly rapidly with decreasing temperature and attained a value of 1.8 cm²/v-sec at 77°K. At $E/p_0 > 3$ volts/cm-mm Hg a different ion was observed; its mobility was 3.0 cm²/v-sec at 300°K.

One positive ion and three negative ions were observed by Eiber,[96] whose experiments on oxygen covered the E/p_0 range of 0.1 to 235 volts/cm-mm Hg. The positive ion, which Eiber called O_2^+, had a zero-field mobility of 2.2 cm²/v-sec. The mobilities of the negative ions, extrapolated to $E/p_0 = 0$, were 3.2, 2.5, and 2.25 cm²/v-sec, and the ions were labeled O^-, O_3^-, and O_2^-, respectively. Only the ion thought to be O_3^- was observed at E/p_0 less than about 5 volts/cm-mm Hg. The corresponding ion in the Burch and Geballe experiment was also the only one observed at their lowest E/p_0. In both experiments the scatter of the data and the necessity of wide extrapolation made it impossible to obtain accurate values for the zero-field mobilities of the ions thought to be O^- and O_2^-. However, Eiber's measurements on the ion he labeled O_3^- could be extended to E/p_0 low enough (and they showed sufficiently little scatter) to yield an accurate zero-field mobility (2.5 cm²/v-sec).

In summary, it seems fairly well established that two ions of discrete mobility appear in oxygen at low E/p_0—a positive ion with mobility of about 2.2 cm²/v-sec and a negative ion whose mobility is around 2.5–2.7 cm²/v-sec. At higher E/p_0 (around 5 volts/cm-mm Hg) two additional negative ions appear. The identities of none of these ions has been clearly established, although the positive ion is probably O_2^+ and the negative ion of highest mobility (around 3.3 cm²/v-sec) is very likely O^-.

F. POSITIVE ALKALI IONS IN MONATOMIC AND DIATOMIC GASES.   Positive alkali ions may be conveniently generated thermionically from coated filaments (see Section 13-5-B), and consequently it is easy to produce these ions for mobility measurements in a pure foreign gas. Furthermore, because of the low ionization potentials of the alkali atoms positive alkali ions are energetically incapable of undergoing charge transfer with any impurities likely to be encountered in a mobility experiment. Thus the

TABLE 9-9-2. Comparison of experimental and theoretical zero-field mobility data for positive alkali ions in various gases. The experimental data, which were obtained by Tyndall's group at Bristol,[63] are presented in the form $\mathscr{K}\sqrt{M_r}$, where M_r is the reduced mass of the ion-molecule system expressed in units of the proton mass. These data were obtained at temperatures of about 290°K and refer to gas number densities of $2.69 \times 10^{19}/\mathrm{cm}^3$. According to the Langevin theory in the polarization limit, $\mathscr{K}\sqrt{M_r}$ should equal $35.9/\sqrt{\alpha}$, where α is the polarizability of the gas in units of $a_0{}^3$. The quantity $35.9/\sqrt{\alpha}$ is tabulated for each gas in the row next to the bottom in the table. The value of this quantity for each gas is multiplied by the factor 1.08 to obtain the numbers in the bottom row.

Gas Ion	He	Ne	A	Kr	Xe	H_2	N_2	CO	
Li+	38.6	25.2	11.4	9.4	7.3	15.6	9.3	5.6	Experimental
Na+	41.9	26.8	11.5	9.3	7.5	17.3	10.1	8.1	values
K+	41.0	27.4	11.7	9.6	7.4	17.4	10.2	8.8	of
Rb+	39.3	27.2	11.7	9.5	7.4	17.5	10.3	8.9	$\mathscr{K}\sqrt{M_r}$
Cs+	36.3	25.5	11.5	9.5	7.4	17.6	10.3	8.9	
$35.9/\sqrt{\alpha}$	30.5	21.9	10.8	8.9	6.9	15.6	10.4	9.9	Theoretical
$38.8/\sqrt{\alpha}$	32.9	23.6	11.7	9.6	7.4	16.9	11.2	10.7	predictions

matter of ion identification is simple in these cases. These facts are responsible for the large number of mobility experiments that have been performed with alkali ions to provide tests of mobility theory.

Experimental data on the mobilities of positive ions of the alkalis in various monatomic and diatomic gases, taken from the paper by Dalgarno, McDowell, and Williams,[34] are presented in Table 9-9-2. The experimental mobilities are multiplied by the square root of the reduced mass of the ion-molecule system (expressed in units of the proton mass) in order to facilitate comparison with the predictions of the Langevin theory in the polarization limit (9-3-14). According to this equation, $\mathscr{K}\sqrt{M_r}$ should be independent of the nature of the ion and should equal $35.9/\sqrt{\alpha}$, where α is the polarizability of the gas expressed in atomic units.

We note that the experimental values of $\mathscr{K}\sqrt{M_r}$ in helium and neon are not independent of the ionic type. This is not surprising, since these gases have low polarizabilities. However, $\mathscr{K}\sqrt{M_r}$ is approximately constant for the alkali ions in argon, krypton, and xenon and in the molecular gases hydrogen, nitrogen, and carbon monoxide as well if the Li^+ ion is discounted. Comments concerning the interaction potentials between ions and diatomic molecules appear in Section 9-3.

It has been suggested[34] that the numerical discrepancies between the observed values of $\mathscr{K}\sqrt{M_r}$ and the theoretical predictions of $35.9/\sqrt{\alpha}$ may be caused in part by systematic errors in the experimental data. Indeed multiplication of the theoretical value by the factor 1.08 gives better agreement with experiment for argon, krypton, xenon, and hydrogen. However, the detailed calculations of Mason and Schamp[22] show that at the experimental temperatures the polarization limit has not yet been reached, and the apparent height of the measurements is really due to the influence of the shorter-range forces and not to experimental error. This theoretical conclusion is reinforced by some recent measurements[68] which yield no evidence of an 8% systematic error in the older measurements. In their paper[22] Mason and Schamp compare their theoretical results with experimental data on a number of alkali ion-noble gas combinations. The agreement is indeed impressive. It will be recalled that Mason and Schamp included shorter-range interactions as well as the inverse-fourth-power polarization attraction.

Chen and Raether[98] have applied microwave interferometry techniques to measure the mobility of Cs^+ ions in helium and in cesium. The low-field mobility for Cs^+ in He was determined to be 18.5 ± 0.5 cm²/v-sec, whereas the value for Cs^+ in Cs was 0.4 ± 0.05 cm²/v-sec.*

G. NEGATIVE IONS OF SULFUR HEXAFLUORIDE. Sulfur hexafluoride is a gas of considerable practical and theoretical interest because of its unusually large cross section for the capture of slow electrons (Section 8-7-F). Two accurate measurements have been made of the mobility of negative ions in SF_6. Using the same type of apparatus developed for the oxygen measurements described in Section 9-9-E, McDaniel[94] obtained a low-field mobility of 0.57 ± 0.01 cm²/v-sec. A single narrow and symmetrical peak was observed in the drift time spectrum, consistent with the arrival of a

---

* L. M. Chanin and R. D. Steen (*Phys. Rev.*, **132**, 2554, 1963) have measured mobilities of cesium ions in cesium by a pulsed discharge technique. Their dominant ion, tentatively identified as Cs_2^+, has a mobility of 0.21 cm²/v-sec. They also observed a less abundant ion, thought to be Cs^+, with a mobility of 0.075 cm²/v-sec. These mobilities refer to a gas number density of 2.69×10^{19} atoms/cm³ at temperatures in the range 579 to 679°K.

single ionic species at the detector located at the end of the ionic flight path. Morrison, Edelson, and McAfee[99] more recently reported an ion in SF_6 with a mobility of 0.570 ± 0.005 cm^2/v-sec. Subsequent mass spectrometric work done by their group at the Bell Telephone Laboratories has shown that this ion is SF_6^{-}[100]. The measured mobility has the low indicated value because of the strong retarding effect of electron transfer between the SF_6 ions and molecules.

H. WATER VAPOR.   The Bradbury-Nielsen technique has recently been used by Lowke and Rees[101] for measurements of the drift velocities of negative charge carriers in water vapor. One ionic species was observed at pressures between 1 and 14 mm Hg and 293°K. Its mobility was constant below $E/p_0 = 40$ volts/cm-mm Hg and had a reduced zero-field value of 0.67 ($\pm 1\%$) cm^2/v-sec, in excellent agreement with the result obtained by Eiber.[96]

I. MERCURY VAPOR.   Kovar and Varney[102] have used the Hornbeck method to measure the drift velocity of mercury ions in mercury vapor. Their measurements extended over a range of values of E/p_0 from 40 to 1500 v/cm-mm Hg. At the lower values of E/p_0 two ions were observed. One of these ions (presumably Hg_2^+) disappears at high E/p_0, whereas the other one (believed to be Hg^+) persists at high field conditions. Plotting the mobilities against E/p_0 and extrapolating to zero field, Kovar and Varney obtain 0.24 ± 0.03 and 0.45 ± 0.05 cm^2/v-sec for the atomic and molecular ions, respectively.

REFERENCES

1. G. H. Wannier, *Bell System Tech. J.* **32**, 170 (1953).
2. P. Langevin, *Ann. Chim. Phys.* **28**, 289 (1903).
3. L. B. Loeb, *Kinetic Theory of Gases*, Third Edition, Dover, New York, 1961, pp. 547–552.
4. P. Langevin, *Ann. Chim. Phys.* **5**, 245 (1905). The bulk of this paper is presented in translated and modernized form in Appendix II at the end of this book.
5. H. R. Hassé, *Phil. Mag.* **1**, 139 (1926).
6. L. B. Loeb, *Basic Processes of Gaseous Electronics*, Second Edition, University of California Press, Berkeley, 1960, Chapter I.
7. For a comprehensive treatment of the Chapman-Enskog theory, see S. Chapman and T. G. Cowling, *The Mathematical Theory of Non-uniform Gases*, Second Edition, Cambridge University Press, London, 1952.
8. S. Chapman, *Phil. Trans. Roy. Soc. (London)* A-216, 279 (1916), A-217, 115 (1917).
9. D. Enskog, Dissertation, Uppsala, 1917.
10. A. Dalgarno, "Diffusion and Mobilities," in *Atomic and Molecular Processes* (edited by D. R. Bates), Academic, New York, 1962.
11. H. R. Hassé and W. R. Cook, *Phil. Mag.* **12**, 554 (1931).
12. J. O. Hirschfelder, C. F. Curtiss, and R. B. Bird, *Molecular Theory of Gases and Liquids*, Wiley, New York, 1954, Chapters 1, 12–14.

13. G. H. Wannier, *Bell System Tech. J.* **32**, 170–254 (1953). Abbreviated versions of parts of this paper appear in *Phys. Rev.* **83**, 281 (1951), **87**, 795 (1952).

14. H. S. W. Massey and C. B. O. Mohr, *Proc. Roy. Soc. (London)* **A-144**, 188 (1934). T. Holstein, *J. Phys. Chem.*, **56**, 832 (1952). D. Bohm, *Quantum Theory*, Prentice-Hall, Englewood Cliffs, N.J., 1951, Chapter 19. R. L. Sproull, *Modern Physics*, Second Edition, Wiley, New York, 1963, pp. 236–243.

15. J. A. Hornbeck, *Phys. Rev.* **84**, 615 (1951).

16. R. N. Varney, *Phys. Rev.* **88**, 362 (1952).

17. R. N. Varney, *Phys. Rev.* **89**, 708 (1953).

18. J. H. Jeans, *The Dynamical Theory of Gases*, Dover, New York, 1954, p. 276.

19. G. H. Wannier, *Phys. Rev.* **96**, 831 (1954).

20. H. Landolt and R. Börnstein, *Atom- und Molekularphysik*, Part. I, Springer-Verlag, Berlin, 1950, p. 325.

21. T. Kihara, *Rev. Mod. Phys.* **24**, 45 (1952), **25**, 844 (1953).

22. E. A. Mason and H. W. Schamp, *Ann. Phys. (New York)* **4**, 233 (1958).

23. V. I. Perel, *Soviet Phys.-JETP* **5**, 440 (1957).

24. H. S. W. Massey and C. B. O. Mohr, *Proc. Roy. Soc. (London)* **A-144**, 188 (1934).

25. N. Lynn and B. L. Moiseiwitsch, *Proc. Phys. Soc. (London)* **A-70**, 474 (1957).

26. R. Meyerott, *Phys. Rev.* **66**, 242 (1944).

27. E. A. Mason, H. W. Schamp, and J. T. Vanderslice, *Phys. Rev.* **112**, 445 (1958).

28. T. Holstein, *J. Phys. Chem.* **56**, 832 (1952).

29. E. A. Mason and J. T. Vanderslice, *Phys. Rev.* **114**, 497 (1959).

30. S. Geltman, *Phys. Rev.* **90**, 808 (1953).

31. A. Dalgarno and M. R. C. McDowell, *Proc. Phys. Soc. (London)* **A-69**, 615 (1956).

32. A. Dalgarno and A. Williams, *Proc. Phys. Soc. (London)* **A-72**, 274 (1958).

33. A. M. Arthurs and A. Dalgarno, *Proc. Roy. Soc. (London)* **A-256**, 540, 552 (1960).

34. A. Dalgarno, M. R. C. McDowell, and A. Williams, *Phil. Trans. Roy. Soc. (London)* **A-250**, 411 (1958); A. Dalgarno, Ibid, 426.

35. E. H. S. Burhop, "Theory of Collisions," appearing in *Quantum Theory, Vol. I, Elements* (edited by D. R. Bates), Academic, New York, 1961.

36. N. F. Mott and H. S. W. Massey, *The Theory of Atomic Collisions*, Oxford University Press, Oxford, 1952, Chapter VII. J. de Boer and R. B. Bird, *Physica* **20**, 185 (1954).

37. A. F. Ferguson and B. L. Moiseiwitsch, *Proc. Phys. Soc. (London)* **74**, 457 (1959).

38. S. C. Brown, *Basic Data of Plasma Physics*, Wiley, New York, 1959. W. P. Allis, "Motions of Ions and Electrons," in *Handbuch der Physik*, Vol. XXI, Springer-Verlag, Berlin, 1956, pp. 383–444.

39. J. L. Pack and A. V. Phelps, *Phys. Rev.* **121**, 798 (1961).

40. P. Langevin, *Ann. Chim. Phys.* **28**, 316–321 (1903).

41. S. Bloom and H. Margenau, *Phys. Rev.* **85**, 670 (1952).

42. R. J. Munson and K. Hoselitz, *Proc. Roy. Soc. (London)* **A-172**, 43 (1939).

43. H. Eyring, J. O. Hirschfelder, and H. S. Taylor, *J. Chem. Phys.*, **4**, 479 (1936); J. O. Hirschfelder, C. F. Curtiss and R. B. Bird, *Molecular Theory of Gases and Liquids*, Wiley, New York, 1954, pp. 1097–1098; J. L. Magee and K. Funabashi, *Radiation Research*, **10**, 622 (1959).

44. R. J. Munson and A. M. Tyndall, *Proc. Roy. Soc. (London)*, **A-172**, 28 (1939).

45. See, for example, B. Donn, *Astrophys. J.*, **132**, 507 (1960); D. W. Martin, E. W. McDaniel, and M. L. Meeks, *Astrophys. J.*, **134**, 1012 (1961).

46. W. F. Libby, *J. Chem. Phys.* **35**, 1714 (1961); *The Airglow and the Aurorae* (edited by E. B. Armstrong and A. Dalgarno), Pergamon, New York (1955); *Physics of*

the Upper Atmosphere (edited by J. A. Ratcliffe), Academic, New York, 1960; M. Hertzberg, *J. Atmospheric Terrest. Phys.* **20,** 177 (1961).

47. C. E. Melton, "Ion-Molecule Reactions," in *Mass Spectrometry of Organic Ions* (edited by F. W. McLafferty), Academic, New York, 1963; F. W. Lampe, J. L. Franklin, and F. H. Field, "Kinetics of the Reactions of Ions with Molecules," in *Progress in Reaction Kinetics*, Pergamon, New York, 1961. M. Pahl, *Ergeb. Exakt. Naturwiss.* **34,** 182 (1962). D. P. Stevenson, "Ion-molecule Reactions," in *Mass Spectrometry* (edited by C. A. McDowell) McGraw-Hill, New York, 1963.

48. J. C. Polanyi, "Chemical Processes," in *Atomic and Molecular Processes* (edited by D. R. Bates), Academic, New York, 1962. See D. R. Bates, C. J. Cook, and F. J. Smith, *Proc. Phys. Soc.* (*London*) **83,** 49 (1964) for a classical theory of rearrangement impacts at high impact energies.

49. F. H. Field and J. L. Franklin, *Electron Impact Phenomena*, Academic, New York, 1957. R. M. Elliott, "Ion Sources," in *Mass Spectrometry* (edited by C. A. McDowell), McGraw-Hill, New York, 1963.

50. See for example, D. P. Stevenson and D. O. Schissler, *J. Chem. Phys.* **29,** 282 (1958). M. Saporoschenko, *Phys. Rev.* **111,** 1550 (1958); C. E. Melton, Ref. 47, Fig. 1. J. S. Dahler, J. L. Franklin, M. S. B. Munson, and F. H. Field, *J. Chem. Phys.* **36,** 3332 (1962); M. S. B. Munson, F. H. Field, and J. L. Franklin, **37,** 1790 (1962). R. K. Curran, *J. Chem. Phys.* **38,** 2974 (1963). T. F. Moran and L. Friedman, **39,** 2491 (1963).

51. A. V. Phelps and S. C. Brown, *Phys. Rev.* **86,** 102 (1952). R. L. F. Boyd and D. Morris, *Proc. Phys. Soc.* (*London*) **A-68,** 1 (1955). P. F. Knewstubb and A. W. Tickner, *J. Chem. Phys.* **36,** 674, 684 (1962), **37,** 2941 (1962), **38,** 464 (1963); P. F. Knewstubb, P. H. Dawson, and A. W. Tickner, **38,** 1031 (1963). W. L. Fite, J. A. Rutherford, W. R. Snow, and V. A. J. van Lint, *Discussions Faraday Soc.* **33,** 264 (1962).

52. P. F. Knewstubb and T. M. Sugden, *Proc. Roy. Soc.* (*London*) **A-255,** 520 (1960). P. F. Knewstubb, "Mass Spectrometry of Ions from Electric Discharges, Flames, and Other Sources," in *Mass Spectrometry of Organic Ions* (edited by F. W. McLafferty), Academic, New York, 1963.

53. See, for example, L. F. Phillips and H. I. Schiff, *J. Chem. Phys.* **36,** 1509, 3283 (1962), **37,** 1233 (1962); S. N. Foner and R. L. Hudson, **36,** 2681 (1962).

54. C. F. Giese and W. B. Maier, *J. Chem. Phys.* **35,** 1913 (1961); **39,** 197, 739 (1963).

55. E. W. McDaniel, D. W. Martin, and W. S. Barnes, *Rev. Sci. Instr.* **33,** 2 (1962).

56. E. W. McDaniel et al., *International Symposium on Space Phenomena and Measurement*, Detroit (October 1962), Proceedings published in IEEE Transactions on Nuclear Science, **NS-10,** 111 (1963). D. W. Martin, W. S. Barnes, G. E. Keller, D. S. Harmer, and E. W. McDaniel, *Proceedings of the Sixth International Conference on Ionization Phenomena in Gases*, Paris, 1963.

57. K. B. McAfee and D. Edelson, *Sixth International Conference on Ionization Phenomena in Gases*, Paris, 1963. D. Edelson and K. B. McAfee, *Rev. Sci. Instr.* (1964). D. Edelson, J. A. Morrison, and K. B. McAfee, *J. Chem. Phys.* (1964).

58. A. Blanc, *J. Phys.* (*Paris*) **7,** 825 (1908).

59. H. G. David and R. J. Munson, *Proc. Roy. Soc.* (*London*) **A-177,** 192 (1941).

60. E. W. McDaniel and H. R. Crane, *Rev. Sci. Instr.* **28,** 684 (1957).

61. G. E. Courville and M. A. Biondi, *J. Chem. Phys.* **37,** 616 (1962).

62. A. W. Overhauser, *Phys. Rev.* **76,** 250 (1949).

63. A. M. Tyndall, *The Mobility of Positive Ions in Gases*, Cambridge University Press, Cambridge, 1938.

64. E. C. Beaty, *Proceedings of the Fifth International Conference on Ionization Phenomena in Gases*, Munich, 1961, North-Holland Amsterdam (1962), Vol. I, p. 183.
65. E. C. Beaty and P. Patterson, *Sixth International Conference on Ionization Phenomena in Gases*, Paris, 1963.
66. N. E. Bradbury and R. A. Nielsen, *Phys. Rev.* **49**, 388 (1936).
67. R. A. Nielsen and N. E. Bradbury, *Phys. Rev.* **51**, 69 (1937).
68. R. W. Crompton and M. T. Elford, *Proc. Phys. Soc. (London)* **74**, 497 (1959).
69. J. A. Hornbeck, *Phys. Rev.* **83**, 374 (1951).
70. M. A. Biondi and L. M. Chanin, *Phys. Rev.* **94**, 910 (1954).
71. J. M. Richardson and R. B. Holt, *Phys. Rev.* **81**, 153 (1951).
72. K. B. Persson and S. C. Brown, *Phys. Rev.* **100**, 729 (1955).
73. D. E. Kerr, E. F. Tubbs, C. S. Leffel, and M. N. Hirsch, to be published. See also C. L. Chen, *Phys. Rev.* **131**, 2550 (1963).
74. H. J. Oskam, *Philips Res. Rept.* **13**, 335 (1958). H. J. Oskam and V. R. Mittelstadt, *Phys. Rev.* **132**, 1435 (1963).
75. L. M. Chanin and M. A. Biondi, *Phys. Rev.* **106**, 473 (1957).
76. J. A. Hornbeck and J. P. Molnar, *Phys. Rev.* **84**, 621 (1951).
77. E. A. Mason and J. T. Vanderslice, *J. Chem. Phys.* **29**, 361 (1958).
78. E. A. Mason and J. T. Vanderslice, *J. Chem. Phys.* **30**, 599 (1959).
79. R. D. Cloney, E. A. Mason, and J. T. Vanderslice, *J. Chem. Phys.* **36**, 1103 (1962).
80. L. M. Chanin and M. A. Biondi, *Phys. Rev.* **107**, 1219 (1957).
81. L. S. Frost, *Phys. Rev.* **105**, 354 (1957).
82. D. J. Rose, *J. Appl. Phys.* **31**, 643 (1960).
83. L. M. Chanin, *Phys. Rev.* **123**, 526 (1961).
84. N. E. Bradbury, *Phys. Rev.* **40**, 508 (1932). J. H. Mitchell, quoted in Ref. 63. W. H. Bennett, *Phys. Rev.* **58**, 992 (1940); J. M. Richardson and R. B. Holt, **81**, 153 (1951). E. J. Lauer, *J. Appl. Phys.*, **23**, 300 (1952). K. B. Persson and S. C. Brown, *Phys. Rev.* **100**, 729 (1955).
85. W. S. Barnes, D. W. Martin, and E. W. McDaniel, *Phys. Rev. Letters* **6**, 110 (1961). See also R. N. Varney, *Phys. Rev. Letters* **5**, 559 (1960). D. P. Stevenson and D. O. Schissler, *J. Chem. Phys.* **29**, 282 (1958); I. B. Ortenburger, M. Hertzberg, and R. A. Ogg, **33**, 579 (1960); B. G. Reuben and L. Friedman, **37**, 1636 (1962); P. H. Dawson and A. W. Tickner, **37**, 672 (1962). R. E. Christoffersen, S. Hagstrom, and F. Prosser, **40**, 236 (1964).
86. J. H. Mitchell and K. E. W. Ridler, *Proc. Roy. Soc. (London)* **A-146**, 911 (1934).
87. F. R. Kovar, E. C. Beaty, and R. N. Varney, *Phys. Rev.* **107**, 1490 (1957).
88. P. G. Davies, J. Dutton, and F. Llewellyn-Jones, *Proceedings of the Fifth International Conference on Ionization Phenomena in Gases*, Munich, 1961, North-Holland, Amsterdam (1962), Vol. II, 1326. *Third International Conference on the Physics of Electronic and Atomic Collisions*, London, 1963. J. K. Vogel, *Z. Phys.* **148**, 355 (1957). L. Frommhold, *Z. Phys.* **160**, 554 (1960). E. C. Zipf, to be published in *Phys. Rev.*
89. J. A. Dahlquist, *J. Chem. Phys.* **39**, 1203 (1963). R. N. Varney and J. A. Dahlquist, *Sixth International Conference on Ionization Phenomena in Gases*, Paris, 1963.
90. M. Saporoschenko, *Phys. Rev.* **111**, 1550 (1958).
91. R. N. Varney, *J. Chem. Phys.* **31**, 1314 (1959), **33**, 1709 (1960). *Proceedings of the Fifth International Conference on Ionization Phenomena in Gases*, Munich, 1961, North-Holland, Amsterdam (1962), Vol. I, 42.
92. A. Doehring, *Z. Naturforsch.* **7-a**, 253 (1952).
93. D. S. Burch and R. Geballe, *Phys. Rev.* **106**, 183, 188 (1957).

94. E. W. McDaniel and M. R. C. McDowell, *Phys. Rev.* **114,** 1028 (1959).

95. L. M. Chanin, A. V. Phelps, and M. A. Biondi, *Phys. Rev.* **128,** 219 (1962).

96. H. Eiber, *Proceedings of the Fifth International Conference on Ionization Phenomena in Gases*, Munich, 1961, North-Holland, Amsterdam (1962), Vol. II, p. 1334; *Z. angew. Phys.* **15,** 103, 461 (1963); *Proceedings of the Sixth International Conference on Ionization Phenomena in Gases*, Paris, 1963.

97. R. K. Curran, *J. Chem. Phys.* **35,** 1849 (1961).

98. C. L. Chen and M. Raether, *Phys. Rev.* **128,** 2679 (1962).

99. J. A. Morrison, D. Edelson, and K. B. McAfee, *Fourteenth Annual Gaseous Electronics Conference*, Schenectady, N.Y., October 13, 1961.

100. D. Edelson, J. E. Griffiths, and K. B. McAfee, *J. Chem. Phys.* **37,** 917 (1962). K. B. McAfee and D. Edelson, *Proc. Phys. Soc. (London)*, **81,** 382 (1963).

101. J. J. Lowke and J. A. Rees, *Australian J. Phys.* **16,** 447 (1963).

102. F. R. Kovar and R. N. Varney, *Sixth International Conference on Ionization Phenomena in Gases*, Paris, 1963; *Phys. Rev.* **133,** 681 (1964).

10

DIFFUSION OF ELECTRONS

AND IONS

The diffusion of electrons and ions through a gas is an important example of mutual diffusion, which was defined in Section 2-8 as the process of mass transport in a mixture of substances due to a gradient in the composition. If the density of ionization is low, each species of charged particle may be considered as a separate gas, and charged particles of each type diffuse through the neutral gas without interacting appreciably with one another or with members of the other charged species. The diffusive motion is impeded by random collisions with the gas molecules. It proceeds from regions of higher toward regions of lower concentration. This diffusive flow is superimposed on other types of flow which might be produced by external fields or by gradients in the total pressure. More complicated examples of diffusion occur when a magnetic field is present or when the gas is highly ionized. These cases require special attention and are treated separately.

Diffusion often plays an important role in practice, and its effects should be assessed in any experimental arrangement or natural phenomenon involving electrons and ions in gases. For example, diffusion prevents the maintenance of well-defined boundaries between ionized and un-ionized regions in a gas and in this way complicates the analysis of many experiments. The back-diffusion of electrons to the cathode in certain devices seriously lowers the secondary electron emission coefficient[1] and has a marked effect on the breakdown threshold. Radial diffusion of electrons and ions affects the behavior of all electrical discharges. In the upper atmosphere the effective lifetime of a meteor trail as a reflector of electromagnetic radiation is determined to a large degree by the rate of diffusion of the free electrons away from the positions in which they were produced in the initial ionization process.[2] The phenomenon of diffusion also has some interesting applications in basic studies of ionized gases. For instance, as we shall see in Section 11-2-A, experiments on electron diffusion have led to the evaluation of the average electron energy in various gases as a function of E/p.

10-1. FICK'S LAW OF DIFFUSION AND THE DIFFUSION COEFFICIENT

Fick's law of diffusion, which is the basic equation of diffusion theory, was derived in Section 2-9. It states that the particle current density $\mathbf{J}$, the diffusion coefficient $\mathscr{D}$, and the gradient of the number density of the diffusing particles ∇N, are related by the equation

$$\mathbf{J} = -\mathscr{D}\nabla N \qquad (10\text{-}1\text{-}1)$$

This equation holds only for binary mixtures at uniform temperature and total pressure.* The magnitude of $\mathbf{J}$ equals the number of particles flowing in unit time through unit area normal to the direction of flow. The minus sign indicates that the flow occurs in the direction of decreasing concentration. $\mathscr{D}$ is a joint property of the particles and the medium through which they are diffusing, and (10-1-1) shows it to be a measure of the transparency of the medium to the diffusing particles. Making use of the fact that the velocity of the diffusive flow $\mathbf{v}$ is given by

$$\mathbf{J} = N\mathbf{v} \qquad (10\text{-}1\text{-}2)$$

we may also write Fick's law in the form

$$\mathbf{v} = -\frac{\mathscr{D}}{N}\nabla N \qquad (10\text{-}1\text{-}3)$$

Theoretical expressions for the diffusion coefficient, derived from kinetic theory, are presented in Sections 2-9, 2-10, and 9-2. As might be expected, the simple mean free path expression in (2-9-6) is rather crude and gives only order-of-magnitude agreement with experiment. More detailed mean free path calculations, however, have provided reliable data.[3] The rigorous expressions in (2-10-3) and (9-2-10) are of wide applicability and give good

---

* C. Truesdell, *J. Chem. Phys.* **37**, 2336 (1962).

results. Here the interaction between the diffusing particles and the particles of the scattering medium is explicitly taken into account in the diffusion cross section which appears in the collision integral Ω_D or P_{12}.

Experimentally, the most reliable diffusion data on ions are obtained from the results of mobility measurements, a number of which are discussed in Sections 9-8 and 9-9. The evaluation of the diffusion coefficient from the mobility is made possible because $\mathscr{D}$ is directly proportional to $\mathscr{K}$, a result that is not surprising in light of the fact that the defining equation for the mobility coefficient (9-1-1) shows that $\mathscr{K}$ is also a measure of the transparency of the medium to the motion of the ions. It is found that the diffusion coefficient for ions is of the same order of magnitude as that for molecules of the same species in a given gas but lower by about a factor of 3 to 5 because of polarization effects. Ions of the atmospheric gases have diffusion coefficients of the order of 50 cm²/sec at 1 mm Hg pressure. As expected, $\mathscr{D}$ is found to vary inversely with the density of the gas. Diffusion coefficients for electrons are of the order of 10^3 larger. They may be obtained from electron drift velocity data (Section 11-3) when the mobility concept is applicable.

10-2. THE RELATIONSHIP BETWEEN THE COEFFICIENTS
OF DIFFUSION AND MOBILITY

We shall now derive the relationship between $\mathscr{D}$ and $\mathscr{K}$ by using a method of complete generality. The result to be obtained has a sound theoretical basis and has been verified experimentally.

Consider a cloud of singly charged positive ions diffusing through a uniform gas and apply an electric field in the $-Z$ direction of a strength to balance the tendency of the ions to diffuse in the $+Z$ direction. Denoting the number density of the ions by N_i, we then have

$$v = -\frac{\mathscr{D}}{N_i}\frac{dN_i}{dz} = -\mathscr{K}E \tag{10-2-1}$$

This equality holds because the resistance of the gas to the motion of the ions with a given velocity v is independent of the nature of the force acting to produce the motion. Then, using the fact that the partial pressure of the ions p_i is directly proportional to the ionic number density N_i, we have

$$\frac{\mathscr{K}}{\mathscr{D}} = \frac{1}{EN_i}\frac{dN_i}{dz} = \frac{1}{Ep_i}\frac{dp_i}{dz} \tag{10-2-2}$$

Now consider a right circular cylinder of unit cross-sectional area and length dz with its axis along the Z axis. The ionic partial pressure is p_i at one end of the cylinder and $p_i + dp_i$ at the other. This pressure differential produces a force across the length of the cylinder equal to dp_i. Since the number of ions contained within the cylinder is $N_i\,dz$, the ionic pressure gradient produces a force in the Z direction on each ion equal to $dp_i/N_i\,dz$. In order that there may be no net flow in the $+Z$ direction, this force must be balanced by an oppositely directed electric force, eE, of equal magnitude. Thus

$$\frac{1}{N_i}\frac{dp_i}{dz} = eE \tag{10-2-3}$$

and from (10-2-2) we obtain

$$\frac{\mathscr{K}}{\mathscr{D}} = \frac{eN_i}{p_i} \tag{10-2-4}$$

which is the desired result. This relationship holds only in those situations in which the drift velocity is directly proportional to the electric field intensity and the mobility concept applies. Equation 10-2-4 is thus not generally valid for electrons or for ions at high E/p.

If the ions are close to being in thermal equilibrium with the gas at some temperature T, we may write $p_i = N_i kT$, and (10-2-4) becomes

$$\frac{\mathscr{K}}{\mathscr{D}} = \frac{e}{kT} \tag{10-2-5}$$

Then if $\mathscr{K}$ is expressed in cm²/v-sec, $\mathscr{D}$ in cm²/sec, and T in °K, we have

$$\frac{\mathscr{K}}{\mathscr{D}} = 1.16 \times 10^4/T \tag{10-2-6}$$

(A factor of 300 comes into play here because the electrostatic unit of mobility is cm²/statvolt-sec, and 1 statvolt = 300 volts.) We pointed out in Section 9-2 that (10-2-5) is exactly correct only for a r^{-4} interaction potential. For other potentials this equation is inexact by a small numerical factor. Equation 10-2-5 is known as the *Einstein relation*.

10-3. THE STEADY-STATE SPATIAL DISTRIBUTION
OF IONS IN AN ELECTROSTATIC FIELD

It is of interest to calculate the steady-state spatial distribution of the ions in the situation just described, in which an electric field opposes the tendency of the ions to diffuse along the $+Z$ axis. Let us rewrite (10-2-2) and use the fact that the electric field intensity equals the negative gradient of the potential V. In the steady-state condition of zero net velocity along the $+Z$ axis we find

$$\frac{dN_i}{N_i} = \frac{\mathscr{K}E}{\mathscr{D}}\,dz = -\frac{\mathscr{K}}{\mathscr{D}}\,dV$$

If we now integrate and put $N_i = N_{i0}$ and $V = 0$ at $z = 0$, we obtain

$$N_i = N_{i0}e^{-\mathscr{X}V/\mathscr{D}} \tag{10-3-1}$$

or

$$N_i = N_{i0}e^{-eV/kT} \tag{10-3-2}$$

if we assume the ions to be in thermal equilibrium with the gas. Thus we see that the ionic number density at each point is determined by the local ratio of the electrostatic potential energy to the thermal kinetic energy. The exponential term in (10-3-2) is recognized as the *Boltzmann factor*, and (10-3-2) is seen to be a special case of (2-2-26).

10-4. THE SPREADING OF A CLOUD OF PARTICLES BY DIFFUSION THROUGH AN UNBOUNDED GAS

Imagine a large number of particles, n_0, located at the origin of a one-dimensional coordinate system. If the particles are released at $t = 0$ and allowed to diffuse through a gas filling all space at uniform pressure, the one-dimensional number density at distance x from the origin at time t is

$$N = \frac{n_0}{\sqrt{4\pi\mathscr{D}t}} e^{-x^2/4\mathscr{D}t} \tag{10-4-1}$$

where $\mathscr{D}$ is the coefficient characterizing the diffusive motion of the particles through the gas. This equation, as well as (10-2-5), is known as the *Einstein relation*.[4] At any instant of time a plot of N as a function of x has the shape of a Gaussian error curve. The curve becomes progressively flatter as time elapses. The mean and root-mean-square displacements of the particles from the origin may be calculated from the distribution function in (10-4-1). The results are

$$|\bar{x}| = \frac{1}{n_0} \int_{-\infty}^{\infty} |x|N \, dx = \frac{2}{n_0} \int_0^{\infty} xN \, dx = \left(\frac{4\mathscr{D}t}{\pi}\right)^{\frac{1}{2}} \tag{10-4-2}$$

and

$$\sqrt{\overline{x^2}} = \left(\frac{1}{n_0} \int_{-\infty}^{\infty} x^2 N \, dx\right)^{\frac{1}{2}} = \sqrt{2\mathscr{D}t} \tag{10-4-3}$$

In three dimensions the number density at radius r and time t is

$$N = \frac{n_0}{(4\pi\mathscr{D}t)^{\frac{3}{2}}} e^{-r^2/4\mathscr{D}t} \tag{10-4-4}$$

The mean and root-mean-square displacements in this case are

$$\bar{r} = \left(\frac{12\mathscr{D}t}{\pi}\right)^{\frac{1}{2}} \tag{10-4-5}$$

and

$$\sqrt{\overline{r^2}} = \sqrt{6\mathscr{D}t} \qquad (10\text{-}4\text{-}6)$$

respectively. In two dimensions,

$$\sqrt{\overline{r^2}} = \sqrt{4\mathscr{D}t} \qquad (10\text{-}4\text{-}7)$$

The similarity of the problem considered here to the problem of the random walk is obvious. This matter has been discussed thoroughly by many authors.[5]

The equations derived above are very useful in the estimation of the average lifetime, τ, of particles against collision with the walls of a containing vessel. The expressions for the mean displacement indicate that

$$\tau \approx \frac{d^2}{\mathscr{D}} \qquad (10\text{-}4\text{-}8)$$

where d is the relevant dimension of the container. The discussion in Section 10-8 permits the calculation of more accurate values of τ for various geometries. These results are

(a) for an infinitely long rectangular tube of width a and depth b

$$\tau = \left[\mathscr{D}\pi^2 \left(\frac{1}{a^2} + \frac{1}{b^2} \right) \right]^{-1} \qquad (10\text{-}4\text{-}9)$$

(b) for an infinitely long cylinder of radius r_0

$$\tau = \frac{1}{\mathscr{D}} \left(\frac{r_0}{2.405} \right)^2 \qquad (10\text{-}4\text{-}10)$$

(c) for a sphere of radius r_0

$$\tau = \frac{1}{\mathscr{D}} \left(\frac{r_0}{\pi} \right)^2 \qquad (10\text{-}4\text{-}11)$$

To illustrate the use of this concept, we may use (10-4-10) to calculate the lifetime of an ion originating on the axis of a tube of 1-cm radius containing nitrogen at 1-mm Hg pressure and room temperature. Taking the diffusion coefficient to be 50 cm²/sec, we find τ to be about 3×10^{-3} sec. The total distance traveled during this time is equal to $\bar{v}\tau \approx 160$ cm.

10-5. THE SPREADING OF AN ION CLOUD DURING ITS DRIFT IN AN ELECTRIC FIELD

It is also of interest to determine the extent of the diffusive spreading of a cloud of ions as it drifts through a gas under the influence of an electric field. Let L be the distance of drift during time t, v the drift velocity, E the electric field intensity, and V the potential difference between the extremities of the drift path. The mean displacement of the ions from the center of mass of the moving ion cloud is given by (10-4-2), whereas L is, of course, related to the drift time by the equation $L = vt$. Thus

$$\frac{|\bar{x}|}{L} = \left(\frac{4\mathscr{D}}{\pi vL}\right)^{\frac{1}{2}} \tag{10-5-1}$$

If we assume a temperature of 0°C, (10-2-6) shows that $\mathscr{D} = \mathscr{K}/42.7$. Then, using the relationships $\mathscr{K} = v/E$ and $E = V/L$, we find that

$$\frac{|\bar{x}|}{L} = \frac{0.172}{\sqrt{V}} \tag{10-5-2}$$

The ratio of the spread of the ion cloud to the drift distance is thus independent of the diffusion coefficient and mobility and depends only on the total voltage drop experienced by the ions. It should be emphasized that only diffusion effects were considered in the foregoing development. Dispersion due to mutual Coulomb repulsion of the ions was neglected.

The equations in this section do not generally apply to electrons because the mobility concept is not generally applicable to them. The drift velocity, average energy, and mean free path of electrons are as a rule complicated functions of E/p.

10-6. THE DIFFUSION EQUATION

Let us now consider an ensemble of particles diffusing through an infinite medium which contains no sources or sinks. By definition of the particle current density $\mathbf{J}$ the net leakage outward through an arbitrarily shaped, imaginary closed surface within the medium is $\int \mathbf{J} \cdot d\mathbf{A}$. Gauss's law shows that this leakage may also be expressed by the integral $\int \nabla \cdot \mathbf{J}\, dv$, where the integration is performed over the volume bounded by the surface A. Then if N denotes the number density of the particles, it follows that

$$\int \frac{\partial N}{\partial t}\, dv = -\int \nabla \cdot \mathbf{J}\, dv$$

or

$$\int \left(\frac{\partial N}{\partial t} + \nabla \cdot \mathbf{J}\right) dv = 0$$

Since the choice of A was arbitrary, the integrand must itself vanish. Thus

$$\frac{\partial N}{\partial t} + \nabla \cdot \mathbf{J} = 0 \tag{10-6-1}$$

which is known as the *equation of continuity*.

According to Fick's law of diffusion,

$$\mathbf{J} = -\mathscr{D}\nabla N \tag{10-1-1}$$

Therefore

$$\nabla \cdot \mathbf{J} = -\nabla \cdot (\mathscr{D}\nabla N) \tag{10-6-2}$$

and the equation of continuity gives

$$\frac{\partial N}{\partial t} = \nabla \cdot (\mathscr{D}\nabla N) \tag{10-6-3}$$

which is known as the *time-dependent diffusion equation*, or *Fick's second law*. Note that (10-6-3) allows for the dependence of $\mathscr{D}$ on position (by its dependence on composition).

We are now in position to verify the form of the distribution functions given in (10-4-1) and (10-4-4). Direct substitution into (10-6-3) shows that both functions satisfy the diffusion equation.

Let us now suppose that some steady-state distribution of particles, $N_0(x, y, z)$, has been established within a gas-filled container. In order to maintain steady-state conditions, particles must be continuously supplied within the gas to replenish losses to the walls by diffusion.* If the particles under consideration are electrons or ions, this can be accomplished by continuously ionizing the gas with X rays or microwaves. Now imagine the particle source to be abruptly turned off at $t = 0$. Making the reasonable assumption that the number density at each point will decrease exponentially with time, we write

$$N(x, y, z, t) = N_0(x, y, z)e^{-t/\tau} \tag{10-6-4}$$

where τ is a time constant describing the decay. The diffusion equation then becomes

$$\nabla \cdot (\mathscr{D}\nabla N_0) = \frac{-N_0}{\tau} \tag{10-6-5}$$

and if $\mathscr{D}$ is taken to be independent of position we obtain the *time-independent diffusion equation*

$$\nabla^2 N_0 + \frac{N_0}{\mathscr{D}\tau} = 0 \tag{10-6-6}$$

---

* Conditions are assumed here to be such that losses from recombination, ion-molecule reactions, and electron attachment are negligible. Situations in which this assumption does not hold are treated by S. C. Brown, *Basic Data of Plasma Physics*, Wiley, New York, 1959, Chapters 6 and 8. See also E. P. Gray and D. E. Kerr, *Ann. Phys.* **17**, 276 (1962), for numerical solutions of the diffusion equation with a quadratic loss term applied to account for electron-ion recombination. This paper is discussed in Section 12-8.

The solution of (10-6-6) for $N_0(x, y, z)$ is an eigenvalue problem whose solution depends on the geometry of the container and the appropriate boundary conditions.

10-7. BOUNDARY CONDITIONS

Since the diffusion equation is a second-order differential equation, its general solution will contain two arbitrary constants of integration. In the solution of a specific problem the values of these constants are determined by boundary conditions and other physical considerations.

For charged particles diffusing in a gas-filled container the conditions usually imposed are that the particle number density be finite everywhere within the gas and vanish "at" the walls of the container. If this statement is interpreted as meaning that the inward particle current density must be zero at the walls, so that no particles are reflected back into the gas on impact, diffusion theory actually requires that the number density vary near the wall in such a way that linear extrapolation would cause the number density to vanish at a definite distance *beyond* the wall. This statement will now be proved.

Let us consider the one-dimensional diffusion of charged particles in the Z direction through a gas filling all space to the left of a wall located at the X-Y plane. We assume that the particles will become neutralized at the wall on impact if the wall is conducting or stick to the wall if it is an insulator. This physical consideration requires J_-, the particle current density in the direction of decreasing z, to vanish at $z = 0$. The discussions of Sections 2-6 and 2-9 show that J_- has the form

$$J_- = \frac{N_0}{4} \bar{v} + \frac{\bar{v}\lambda}{6} \frac{dN_0}{dz} \tag{10-7-1}$$

The current density in the direction of increasing z is given by

$$J_+ = \frac{N_0}{4} \bar{v} - \frac{\bar{v}\lambda}{6} \frac{dN_0}{dz} \tag{10-7-2}$$

In each equation the first term on the right is the random contribution, which was calculated in Section 2-6; the second term is the contribution due to the gradient in the concentration of the diffusing particles. The latter is given by half the current density expressed in (2-9-4). Note that the net current density in the $-Z$ direction, $J = J_- - J_+$, has the proper value, $(\bar{v}\lambda/3)(dN_0/dz)$, indicated in (2-9-4).

If we now require that J_- go to zero at $z = 0$, (10-7-1) gives

$$\frac{\bar{v}}{4}(N_0)_{z=0} = -\frac{\bar{v}\lambda}{6}\left(\frac{dN_0}{dz}\right)_{z=0} \tag{10-7-3}$$

Since the left side of (10-7-3) is positive, the derivative dN_0/dz must be negative at $z = 0$, and a plot of N_0 versus z has a negative slope at the origin, as shown in Fig. 10-7-1. If we extrapolate linearly past the physical boundary, using the slope at the origin, we find that

$$\frac{(N_0)_{z=0}}{d} = -\left(\frac{dN_0}{dz}\right)_{z=0} = \frac{3}{2\lambda}(N_0)_{z=0} \qquad (10\text{-}7\text{-}4)$$

or

$$d = \tfrac{2}{3}\lambda \qquad (10\text{-}7\text{-}5)$$

where d is usually called the linear extrapolation distance and is a measure of the extent by which the dimensions of the container are considered to

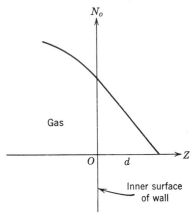

FIG. 10-7-1. Linear extrapolation of the particle number density N_o past the physical boundary to obtain the extrapolation distance d.

be augmented for the mathematical treatment of the diffusion problem. Use of the Boltzmann transport theory instead of the simple diffusion theory provides a slightly different value for the extrapolation distance than the one indicated in (10-7-5). The more nearly correct value[6] is

$$d = 0.71\lambda_m \qquad (10\text{-}7\text{-}5)$$

where λ_m is the momentum transfer mean free path, or transport mean free path, defined in (1-6-2). These extrapolation distances apply only on a plane boundary. Slightly different values of d are appropriate for different geometries.[7]

In the study of ionized gases the extrapolation distance is usually negligible compared with the container dimensions and ignored in calculations. In neutron physics, on the other hand, d is frequently of significant size.

10-8. SOLUTION OF THE TIME-INDEPENDENT DIFFUSION
EQUATION FOR VARIOUS GEOMETRIES

In this section we shall consider the steady-state diffusion of particles of a single species through a gas of uniform temperature and pressure filling containers of various shapes. In each case the particle number density is taken to be negligible in comparison with the number density of molecules, and the average energy of the particles is assumed to be

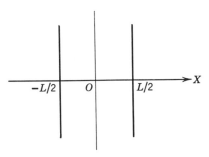

FIG. 10-8-1. A one-dimensional cavity with plane parallel walls.

independent of position in order that $\mathscr{D}$ may be constant. The extrapolation distance is neglected, and N_0 is required to vanish at the geometrical boundaries of the containers.

A. INFINITE PARALLEL PLATES. As the first example of the solution of the time-independent diffusion equation, consider the case of a one-dimensional cavity whose walls are the infinite plane parallel plates shown in Fig. 10-8-1. In this simple case the diffusion equation (10-6-6) becomes

$$\frac{d^2 N_0(x)}{dx^2} + \frac{N_0(x)}{\mathscr{D}\tau} = 0 \tag{10-8-1}$$

Since $\mathscr{D}\tau$ is positive, the solution of (10-8-1) is

$$N_0(x) = A \cos \frac{x}{\sqrt{\mathscr{D}\tau}} + B \sin \frac{x}{\sqrt{\mathscr{D}\tau}} \tag{10-8-2}$$

where A and B are constants of integration which must be determined from the boundary conditions and from the requirement that we shall impose for symmetry about the midplane. If the width of the cavity is L and the origin of the coordinate system is located at the midplane, the boundary conditions are $N_0(x) = 0$ when $x = \pm L/2$.

The symmetry requirement makes $B = 0$, and the boundary conditions force τ to assume one of the infinite number of values τ_k $(k = 1, 2, 3, \ldots)$

which satisfy the equation

$$\cos \frac{L}{2\sqrt{\mathscr{D}\tau_k}} = 0 \quad \text{or} \quad \frac{L}{2\sqrt{\mathscr{D}\tau_k}} = (2k - 1)\frac{\pi}{2} \qquad (10\text{-}8\text{-}3)$$

Now define a quantity Λ_k which represents the *characteristic diffusion length for the kth mode of diffusion*:

$$\Lambda_k{}^2 = \mathscr{D}\tau_k = \left(\frac{1}{2k-1}\frac{L}{\pi}\right)^2 \qquad (10\text{-}8\text{-}4)$$

The diffusion length is useful in describing the shape of a cavity in the diffusion process. The solution for the kth mode can then be written

$$N_0(x)_k = A_k \cos \frac{x}{\Lambda_k} \qquad (10\text{-}8\text{-}5)$$

The function $\cos x/\Lambda_k$ assumes negative values in certain regions within the cavity for all modes of diffusion except the lowest, or fundamental, mode corresponding to $k = 1$. Therefore, if we consider each solution singly, we must discard all but the fundamental mode on physical grounds, since the particle number density can never be negative. However, since the diffusion equation is linear, the total solution of the diffusion problem consists of an infinite number of modes, many of which may be excited simultaneously. Any sum of these modes is then a possible solution, provided the constants A_k have values which prevent the number density from becoming negative. The use of an ionization source that provides uniform ionization throughout the cavity will ensure that the fundamental mode predominates.

After the ionization source is abruptly turned off at $t = 0$ each diffusion mode decays out with its own characteristic time constant τ_k. The total solution of the time-dependent diffusion problem is thus given by

$$N(x, t) = \sum_{k=1}^{\infty} A_k \cos \frac{x}{\Lambda_k} e^{-t/\tau_k} \qquad (10\text{-}8\text{-}6)$$

Equation 10-8-3 shows that

$$\frac{\tau_1}{\tau_k} = (2k - 1)^2 \qquad (10\text{-}8\text{-}7)$$

and $\tau_1/\tau_2 = 9$, $\tau_1/\tau_3 = 25$, $\tau_1/\tau_4 = 49$, etc. Consequently, if higher modes are initially present, they will decay out much faster than the fundamental mode, and only this mode will be observable after a time comparable with τ_1. This fact obviously simplifies the analysis of experiments.

B. RECTANGULAR PARALLELEPIPED. The next case to be treated is that of a cavity in the form of a rectangular parallelepiped (Fig. 10-8-2). Take the origin of rectangular Cartesian coordinates at the center of the cavity, whose x, y, and z dimensions are a, b, and c, respectively. The time-independent diffusion equation is now

$$\frac{\partial^2 N_0}{\partial x^2} + \frac{\partial^2 N_0}{\partial y^2} + \frac{\partial^2 N_0}{\partial z^2} + \frac{N_0}{\mathscr{D}\tau} = 0 \qquad (10\text{-}8\text{-}8)$$

with the boundary conditions that $N_0 = 0$ when $x = \pm a/2$, $y = \pm b/2$,

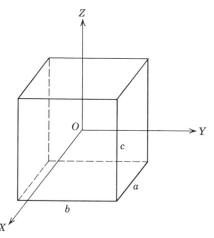

FIG. 10-8-2. A cavity with the shape of a rectangular parallelepiped.

and $z = \pm c/2$. Expressing $N_0(x, y, z)$ as the product of three functions, each of which is a function of only one coordinate,

$$N_0(x, y, z) = X(x)\ Y(y)\ Z(z) \qquad (10\text{-}8\text{-}9)$$

we may separate the variables in the diffusion equation and obtain

$$\frac{1}{X}\frac{d^2 X}{dx^2} + \frac{1}{Y}\frac{d^2 Y}{dy^2} + \frac{1}{Z}\frac{d^2 Z}{dz^2} + \frac{1}{\mathscr{D}\tau} = 0 \qquad (10\text{-}8\text{-}10)$$

Since $\mathscr{D}\tau$ is a constant and each of the first three terms is a function of only one variable, we may equate each of these terms to a separate constant:

$$\frac{1}{X}\frac{d^2 X}{dx^2} = -\alpha^2, \qquad \frac{1}{Y}\frac{d^2 Y}{dy^2} = -\beta^2, \qquad \frac{1}{Z}\frac{d^2 Z}{dz^2} = -\gamma^2 \qquad (10\text{-}8\text{-}11)$$

Equation 10-8-10 shows that

$$\alpha^2 + \beta^2 + \gamma^2 = \frac{1}{\mathscr{D}\tau} \qquad (10\text{-}8\text{-}12)$$

Since there is no essential difference between the x, y, and z directions in this problem and since $\alpha^2 + \beta^2 + \gamma^2$ equals a positive quantity, it follows that α^2, β^2, and γ^2 must separately be positive. Using the boundary conditions and symmetry requirements, we see that the solutions of (10-8-11) are

$$X_i = A_i \cos \frac{(2i-1)\pi x}{a}, \qquad Y_j = B_j \cos \frac{(2j-1)\pi y}{b},$$

$$Z_k = C_k \frac{(2k-1)\pi z}{c} \tag{10-8-13}$$

where i, j, and k may each assume any positive integral values. The total solution to the time-dependent problem then has the form

$$N(x, y, z, t) = \sum_{i=1}^{\infty} \sum_{j=1}^{\infty} \sum_{k=1}^{\infty} G_{ijk} \cos \frac{(2i-1)\pi x}{a} \cos \frac{(2j-1)\pi y}{b}$$

$$\times \cos \frac{(2k-1)\pi z}{c} e^{-t/\tau_{ijk}} \tag{10-8-14}$$

where the three arbitrary constants have been lumped into G_{ijk}. Specification of the mode of diffusion now requires three indices, and corresponding to this triad of indices and this mode of diffusion there is a time constant τ_{ijk} given by

$$\frac{1}{\tau_{ijk}} = \mathscr{D}\pi^2 \left[\left(\frac{2i-1}{a} \right)^2 + \left(\frac{2j-1}{b} \right)^2 + \left(\frac{2k-1}{c} \right)^2 \right] \tag{10-8-15}$$

The diffusion length is now given by

$$\Lambda_{ijk}^2 = \mathscr{D}\tau_{ijk} \tag{10-8-16}$$

When the cavity is cubical, $a = b = c$, and

$$\frac{\tau_{111}}{\tau_{211}} = 3.67, \qquad \frac{\tau_{111}}{\tau_{311}} = 9, \qquad \frac{\tau_{111}}{\tau_{411}} = 17$$

In this case the higher modes persist longer in relation to the fundamental mode than in the one-dimensional case, and their effect thus is enhanced.

C. SPHERICAL CAVITY. Now consider a spherical cavity of radius r_0 (Fig. 10-8-3). For spherical geometry the diffusion equation is

$$\frac{\partial^2 N_0}{\partial r^2} + \frac{2}{r} \frac{\partial N_0}{\partial r} + \frac{1}{r^2 \sin \theta} \frac{\partial}{\partial \theta} \left(\sin \theta \frac{\partial N_0}{\partial \theta} \right) + \frac{1}{r^2 \sin^2 \theta} \frac{\partial^2 N_0}{\partial \varphi^2} + \frac{N_0}{\mathscr{D}\tau} = 0 \tag{10-8-17}$$

but since there is no preferred direction here we shall reduce (10-8-17) to

$$\frac{d^2 N_0}{dr^2} + \frac{2}{r} \frac{dN_0}{dr} + \frac{N_0}{\mathscr{D}\tau} = 0 \tag{10-8-18}$$

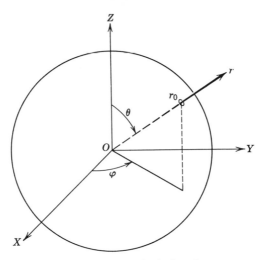

FIG. 10-8-3. A spherical cavity.

discarding, in the process, all but the fundamental angular mode. In order to solve this equation easily, we put $N_0 = u/r$. We then obtain

$$\frac{d^2u}{dr^2} + \frac{u}{\mathscr{D}\tau} = 0 \qquad (10\text{-}8\text{-}19)$$

whose solution is

$$u = A \cos \frac{r}{\sqrt{\mathscr{D}\tau}} + B \sin \frac{r}{\sqrt{\mathscr{D}\tau}} \qquad (10\text{-}8\text{-}20)$$

since $\mathscr{D}\tau$ is positive. Thus the solution for N_0 has the form

$$N_0 = \frac{A}{r} \cos \frac{r}{\sqrt{\mathscr{D}\tau}} + \frac{B}{r} \sin \frac{r}{\sqrt{\mathscr{D}\tau}} \qquad (10\text{-}8\text{-}21)$$

where evidently A must be zero in order that N_0 may remain finite at the origin. The final time-dependent solution is then

$$N(r, t) = \sum_{k=0}^{\infty} \frac{B_k}{r} \sin \frac{r}{\sqrt{\mathscr{D}\tau_k}} e^{-t/\tau_k} \qquad (10\text{-}8\text{-}22)$$

where

$$\frac{r_0}{\sqrt{\mathscr{D}\tau_k}} = k\pi \qquad (k = 0, 1, 2, 3, \ldots) \qquad (10\text{-}8\text{-}23)$$

The diffusion length Λ_k is given by the equation

$$\Lambda_k{}^2 = \mathscr{D}\tau_k = \left(\frac{r_0}{\pi k}\right)^2 \qquad (10\text{-}8\text{-}24)$$

D. CYLINDRICAL CAVITY. As a final example, let us treat the case of a cavity in the form of a right circular cylinder of radius r_0 and height H (Fig. 10-8-4). If we assume symmetry about the axis, there is no dependence on the azimuth angle θ, and the diffusion equation

$$\frac{\partial^2 N_0}{\partial r^2} + \frac{1}{r}\frac{\partial N_0}{\partial r} + \frac{1}{r^2}\frac{\partial^2 N_0}{\partial \theta^2} + \frac{\partial^2 N_0}{\partial z^2} + \frac{N_0}{\mathscr{D}\tau} = 0 \qquad (10\text{-}8\text{-}25)$$

reduces to

$$\frac{d^2 N_0}{dr^2} + \frac{1}{r}\frac{\partial N_0}{\partial r} + \frac{\partial^2 N_0}{\partial z^2} + \frac{N_0}{\mathscr{D}\tau} = 0 \qquad (10\text{-}8\text{-}26)$$

(for the fundamental angular mode). We separate variables by writing

$$N_0(r, z) = R(r)\, Z(z) \qquad (10\text{-}8\text{-}27)$$

and obtain

$$\frac{1}{R}\left(\frac{d^2 R}{dr^2} + \frac{1}{r}\frac{dR}{dr}\right) + \frac{1}{Z}\frac{d^2 Z}{dz^2} + \frac{1}{\mathscr{D}\tau} = 0 \qquad (10\text{-}8\text{-}28)$$

The first term depends only on r and the second only on z, and since $\mathscr{D}\tau$ is a constant each of these terms must be equal to a constant. Set

$$\frac{1}{R}\left(\frac{d^2 R}{dr^2} + \frac{1}{r}\frac{dR}{dr}\right) = -\alpha^2 \qquad (10\text{-}8\text{-}29)$$

and

$$\frac{1}{Z}\frac{d^2 Z}{dz^2} = -\beta^2 \qquad (10\text{-}8\text{-}30)$$

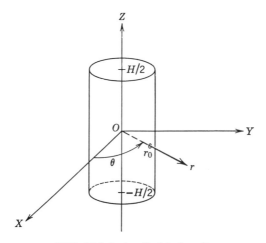

FIG. 10-8-4. A cylindrical cavity.

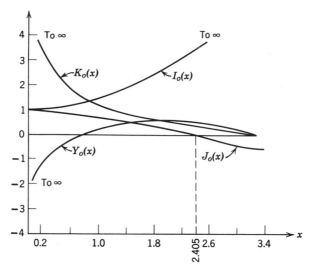

FIG. 10-8-5. Zero-order Bessel functions.

so that

$$\alpha^2 + \beta^2 = \frac{1}{\mathscr{D}\tau} \tag{10-8-31}$$

We must now determine whether α^2 and β^2 are positive or negative.

In solving the r equation (10-8-29), it is convenient to make the substitution $r = u/\alpha$. Then we obtain the equation

$$u^2 \frac{d^2R}{du^2} + u \frac{dR}{du} + u^2 R = 0 \tag{10-8-32}$$

Now the general Bessel equation of order n is

$$x^2 \frac{d^2y}{dx^2} + x \frac{dy}{dx} + (x^2 - n^2)y = 0 \tag{10-8-33}$$

where $(x^2 - n^2)$ is a positive quantity, whereas the modified Bessel equation of order n is

$$x^2 \frac{d^2y}{dx^2} + x \frac{dy}{dx} - (x^2 - n^2)y = 0 \tag{10-8-34}$$

We see that (10-8-32) is a Bessel equation of order zero, unmodified if α^2 is positive, modified if α^2 is negative. In the first instance the general solution is

$$R = A J_0(u) + B Y_0(u) \tag{10-8-35}$$

where J_0 and Y_0 are the Bessel functions of the first and second kinds, respectively, of order zero.[8] In the second instance the solution is

$$R = A' I_0(u) + B' K_0(u) \tag{10-8-36}$$

where I_0 and K_0 are the modified Bessel functions of the first and second kinds, respectively, of order zero. By reference to Fig. 10-8-5 we see that the only satisfactory solution is J_0, and the only possible solution for the r part of our diffusion problem is

$$R(r) = A J_0(u) = A J_0(\alpha r) \tag{10-8-37}$$

α^2 is thus required to be positive.

Applying the boundary condition that N_0 must vanish at $r = r_0$, we see that $R(r_0) = A J_0(\alpha r_0) = 0$. The first zero of J_0 occurs at $\alpha r = 2.405$, so, for the fundamental mode, $\alpha_1 = 2.405/r_0$, and $R(r)$ is given by

$$R(r) = A J_0\left(\frac{2.405r}{r_0}\right) \tag{10-8-38}$$

Turning now to the z equation,

$$\frac{d^2Z}{dz^2} + \beta^2 Z = 0 \tag{10-8-39}$$

we observe that if β^2 is positive the solutions will be $\cos \beta z$ and $\sin \beta z$, whereas if β^2 is negative the solutions are $\cosh \beta z$ and $\sinh \beta z$. Figure 10-8-6 shows that the hyperbolic functions are unacceptable because they would provide a greater number density at the top than at the center of the cavity. The $\sin \beta z$ solution must be discarded because it is an odd function of z. The only remaining possiblity is the cosine solution, and β^2 must be

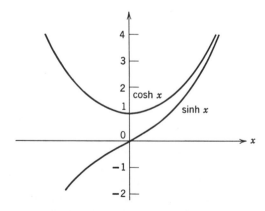

FIG. 10-8-6. The hyperbolic sine and cosine.

positive. The solution of the z equation is then

$$Z(z) = C \cos \beta z \tag{10-8-40}$$

The boundary conditions that N_0 must vanish at $z = \pm H/2$ require that $\beta_1 = \pi/H$ for the fundamental mode.

The time-dependent solution for the lowest mode of diffusion can now be written

$$N(r, z, t) = G_{11} J_0\left(\frac{2.405r}{r_0}\right) \cos \frac{\pi z}{H} e^{-t/\tau_{11}} \tag{10-8-41}$$

where

$$\frac{1}{\Lambda_{11}^2} = \frac{1}{\mathscr{D}\tau_{11}} = \left(\frac{2.405}{r_0}\right)^2 + \left(\frac{\pi}{H}\right)^2 \tag{10-8-42}$$

The total solution, containing the radial higher modes as well as the fundamental, is

$$N(r, z, t) = \sum_{i=1}^{\infty} \sum_{j=1}^{\infty} G_{ij} J_0(\alpha_i r) \cos \frac{(2j-1)\pi z}{H} e^{-t/\tau_{ij}} \tag{10-8-43}$$

The diffusion length is given by

$$\frac{1}{\Lambda_{ij}^2} = \frac{1}{\mathscr{D}\tau_{ij}} = \alpha_i^2 + \left[\frac{(2j-1)\pi}{H}\right]^2 \tag{10-8-44}$$

where $\alpha_i r_0$ is the ith root of J_0.

10-9. THE DIFFUSION AND MOBILITY OF CHARGED PARTICLES IN A MAGNETIC FIELD

In nature and in the laboratory there are many important examples of diffusion of charged particles through a gas in the presence of a magnetic field. This phenomenon occurs in stellar atmospheres, the Van Allen radiation belts, the ionosphere, controlled thermonuclear experiments, and in many types of apparatus used for basic studies of ionized gases. The presence of the magnetic field complicates the motion of the charged particles by causing a curvature of their trajectories. The motion along the lines of force is unaffected, but the movement perpendicular to the field direction is impeded by the action of the field. A magnetic field in this way renders an ionized gas anisotropic by making some of its properties direction-dependent. For example, we shall show that diffusion occurs at a slower rate normal to the field lines than along them, as if the "transverse pressure" of the gas were increased above the "longitudinal pressure." The diffusion coefficient is thus really a tensor quantity, not a scalar as implied up to this point. Of course, in the limit of zero field strength the tensor degenerates to a scalar, as will be shown. Since the diffusion coefficient is directly proportional to the mobility, it follows that $\mathscr{K}$ is also a tensor quantity.

We shall now derive expressions for the components of the diffusion coefficient and the mobility in a magnetic field by using the mean free path method. The results to be obtained are only approximate numerically but do correctly show the effects of the magnetic field. Our treatment is one presented by Chapman and Cowling.[9] Rigorous treatments based on the

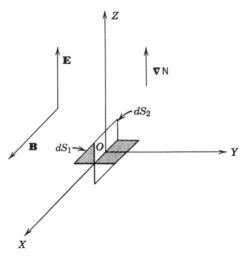

FIG. 10-9-1. The coordinate system used in discussion of the transport of charged particles in a magnetic field.

Boltzmann equation are also given by Chapman and Cowling and by Allis.[10] A necessary first step in our development is to investigate the free motion of a single charged particle in crossed electric and magnetic fields.

A. THE FREE MOTION OF A CHARGED PARTICLE IN CROSSED ELECTRIC AND MAGNETIC FIELDS.   Consider a particle of charge q and mass m moving between collisions in the electric- and magnetic-field combination shown in Fig. 10-9-1. The fields are specified as constant in time and uniform in space. The electric field is in the Z direction and its intensity is E. The magnetic field is in the X direction, and the magnetic flux density is denoted by B. The equations of motion of the particle are

$$0 = m\ddot{x}, \qquad qB\dot{z} = m\ddot{y}, \qquad qE - qB\dot{y} = m\ddot{z}$$

Defining the "cyclotron frequency" ω_b as

$$\omega_b = \frac{qB}{m} \qquad (10\text{-}9\text{-}1)$$

we may write the equations of motion as

$$\ddot{x} = 0, \qquad \ddot{y} = \omega_b \dot{z}, \qquad \ddot{z} = \frac{q}{m} E - \omega_b \dot{y} \qquad (10\text{-}9\text{-}2)$$

Now integrate to obtain the position **r** and velocity **v** at time t in terms of the position **r**′ and velocity **v**′ at $t = 0$. The velocity components are

$$v_x = v_x{}'$$

$$v_y = \left(v_y{}' - \frac{qE}{m\omega_b} \right) \cos \omega_b t + v_z{}' \sin \omega_b t + \frac{qE}{m\omega_b} \qquad (10\text{-}9\text{-}3)$$

$$v_z = v_z{}' \cos \omega_b t - \left(v_y{}' - \frac{qE}{m\omega_b} \right) \sin \omega_b t$$

The coordinates are given by

$$x = x' + v_x{}' t$$

$$y = y' + \frac{1}{\omega_b} \left[\left(v_y{}' - \frac{qE}{m\omega_b} \right) \sin \omega_b t + v_z{}'(1 - \cos \omega_b t) + \frac{qEt}{m} \right] \qquad (10\text{-}9\text{-}4)$$

$$z = z' + \frac{1}{\omega_b} \left[v_z{}' \sin \omega_b t - \left(v_y{}' - \frac{qE}{m\omega_b} \right)(1 - \cos \omega_b t) \right]$$

It is evident that the motion along the X axis is not affected by the fields. In the special case in which E is zero the component of the motion parallel to the Y-Z plane is circular, with angular frequency ω_b; ω_b is called the cyclotron frequency because it is the angular frequency at which ions gyrate in a cyclotron. The total motion in this special case is seen to be a spiral about the magnetic lines of force. If an electric field is present in the Z direction, there is a steady drift in the Y direction as well as the circular motion parallel to the Y-Z plane and the constant motion along X. In vector notation the "cross drift" velocity in the Y direction is given by **E** × **B**/B^2. The net motion parallel to the Y-Z plane is trochoidal. Since the motion along X is unaffected by the magnetic field, we shall not consider particle flow along the X axis in what follows.

B. EVALUATION OF THE DIFFUSION AND MOBILITY COEFFICIENTS IN A MAGNETIC FIELD. Assuming electric and magnetic fields to be applied as in Fig. 10-9-1, let us investigate the transport of ions through a gas of uniform temperature and pressure by the combined action of the applied electric field and a gradient in the ionic number density. The ionic number density N_i is assumed to vary only in the Z direction. The ionic mean free time* τ is taken to be independent of the velocity of the ions.

* τ is standard notation for the mean free time and also for the decay constant appearing in the solution of the time-dependent diffusion equation (Section 10-8). No confusion should exist because of its dual usage.

The number of collisions occurring per unit time within a volume element $d\mathbf{r}$ centered at $\mathbf{r}$ is $N_i \, d\mathbf{r}/\tau$. Let $f(v, z) \, dv \, d\mathbf{r}/\tau$ be the number of collisions which result in an ion entering the velocity element $d\mathbf{v}$ centered at $\mathbf{v}$. The form of f will be close to Maxwellian if E/p is not high. Now consider the ions which, between times t' and $t' + dt'$, cross an area dS_1 located at the origin in the X-Y plane and which have velocities in the range $d\mathbf{v}$ at $\mathbf{v}$. At the time t' these ions lie within a cylinder with dS_1 as its base and a volume $v_z \, dt' \, dS_1$. In the absence of collisions, at some earlier time $t' - t$ the ions occupied a volume element $d\mathbf{r}'$ at $\mathbf{r}'$ and had velocities within the range $d\mathbf{v}'$ at $\mathbf{v}'$. We have

$$d\mathbf{r}' = v_z \, dt' \, dS_1$$

and

$$d\mathbf{v}' = d\mathbf{v}$$

This relationship, proved by Chapman and Cowling,[9] states that ions in the element $d\mathbf{v}$ at $\mathbf{v}$ at the beginning of a time interval dt will occupy a velocity element of equal size at the end of this interval. Since $\mathbf{r}'$ and $\mathbf{v}'$ specify the initial position and velocity of an ion which after an interval t is at the origin with velocity $\mathbf{v}$, the vectors $\mathbf{r}'$ and $\mathbf{v}'$ satisfy (10-9-3) and (10-9-4) with $x = y = z = 0$. Let us refer to the ions that lie in $d\mathbf{r}'$ at $\mathbf{r}'$ with velocities in $d\mathbf{v}'$ at $\mathbf{v}'$ at time $t' - t$ as belonging to the set A. Ions move by collisions into and out of this set as time progresses. The number entering A in the interval $dt = t' - t$ is

$$f(v', z') \, d\mathbf{v}' \, d\mathbf{r}' \, \frac{dt}{\tau} = f(v', z') \, d\mathbf{v} v_z \, dS_1 \, dt' \, \frac{dt}{\tau}$$

Of these ions, a fraction $e^{-t/\tau}$ remain in the set until it reaches dS_1 at time t'. The total number of ions crossing dS_1 during dt' with velocities in the range $d\mathbf{v}$ is then

$$v_z \, d\mathbf{v} \, dS_1 \, dt' \int_0^\infty f(v', z') e^{-t/\tau} \frac{dt}{\tau}$$

and the net number passing upward through dS_1 with all velocities is

$$dS_1 \, dt' \int_0^\infty \left[\int f(v', z') v_z \, d\mathbf{v} \right] \frac{e^{-t/\tau}}{\tau} \, dt \tag{10-9-5}$$

Now let us replace the integration over $\mathbf{v}$ with an integration over $\mathbf{v}'$, covering all values of $\mathbf{v}'$, since there is a one-to-one correspondence between any value $\mathbf{v}$ and the value $\mathbf{v}'$ at a time earlier by the amount t. The integral in (10-9-5) then becomes

$$dS_1 \, dt' \int_0^\infty \left[\int f(v', z') v_z \, d\mathbf{v}' \right] \frac{e^{-t/\tau}}{\tau} \, dt = N_i \bar{v}_z \, dS_1 \, dt'$$

where $\bar{v}_z$ is the average flow velocity in the z direction. Thus we may write

$$N_i \bar{v}_z = \int_0^\infty \left[\int f(v', z') v_z \, dv' \right] \frac{e^{-t/\tau}}{\tau} \, dt \qquad (10\text{-}9\text{-}6)$$

As in Section 2-9, perform an expansion in a Taylor series about the origin and express the distribution function as

$$f(v', z') = f(v', 0) + z' \frac{\partial f(v', 0)}{\partial z}$$

Now substitute for z' and v_z in terms of $\mathbf{v'}$ from (10-9-3) and (10-9-4) with $x = y = z = 0$. Dropping terms of second order in E and omitting integrals of odd functions of v_y and v_z, we find

$$N_i \bar{v}_z = \int_0^\infty \left\{ \frac{q}{m} E \int f(v', 0) \, dv' \right.$$
$$\left. - \frac{\partial}{\partial z} \int f(v', 0)[v_z'^2 \cos \omega_b t + v_y'^2(1 - \cos \omega_b t)] \, dv' \right\} \frac{\sin \omega_b t}{\omega_b \tau} e^{-t/\tau} \, dt$$

Since the distribution function $f(v', 0)$ is nearly Maxwellian, we may write

$$N_i = \int f(v', 0) \, dv'$$

and

$$p_i = \int f(v', 0) m v_y'^2 \, dv' = \int f(v', 0) m v_z'^2 \, dv'$$

where here N_i is the ionic number density and p_i, the ionic partial pressure evaluated at the origin. Thus, finally,

$$\bar{v}_z = \left(\frac{qE}{m} - \frac{1}{mN_i} \frac{\partial p_i}{\partial z} \right) \int_0^\infty \frac{\sin \omega_b t}{\omega_b \tau} e^{-t/\tau} \, dt$$

or

$$\bar{v}_z = \left(\frac{qE}{m} - \frac{1}{mN_i} \frac{\partial p_i}{\partial z} \right) \frac{\tau}{1 + \omega_b^2 \tau^2} \qquad (10\text{-}9\text{-}7)$$

If we remove the magnetic field, ω_b goes to zero, and the flow velocity in (10-9-7) becomes

$$\bar{v}_z = \left(\frac{qE}{m} - \frac{1}{mN_i} \frac{\partial p_i}{\partial z} \right) \tau \qquad (10\text{-}9\text{-}8)$$

The effect of the magnetic field is evidently to reduce the velocity of diffusive flow in the Z direction by the factor $1/(1 + \omega_b^2 \tau^2)$. The flow rate due to the electric field is also reduced by this same factor. Thus the electrical conductivity in the Z direction is lowered by the presence of the magnetic field.

We can also show that the magnetic field in the X direction produces a flow in the Y direction. If we apply a similar argument to the flow of ions through a surface element dS_2 located at the origin in the X-Z plane, we find that the component of the flow velocity in the Y direction, $\bar{v}_y$, is given by

$$N_i \bar{v}_y = \int_0^\infty \left\{ \int \int \left[f(v', 0) + z' \frac{\partial f(v', 0)}{\partial z} \right] v_y \, dv' \right\} \frac{e^{-t/\tau}}{\tau} \, dt$$

Using (10-9-3) and (10-9-4), we obtain

$$\bar{v}_y = \left(\frac{qE}{m} - \frac{1}{mN_i} \frac{\partial p_i}{\partial z} \right) \int_0^\infty (1 - \cos \omega_b t) \frac{e^{-t/\tau}}{\omega_b \tau} \, dt$$

or

$$\bar{v}_y = \left(\frac{qE}{m} - \frac{1}{mN_i} \frac{\partial p_i}{\partial z} \right) \frac{\omega_b \tau^2}{1 + \omega_b^2 \tau^2} \tag{10-9-9}$$

This flow in the Y direction produced by a magnetic field in the X direction is called the *Hall current*.

Having calculated the effects of a magnetic field on the diffusive and mobility flows, we may write down the tensors representing the diffusion and mobility coefficients. Let us take the magnetic field to be in the Z direction, as is conventional, and allow $\mathbf{E}$ to have an arbitrary orientation. We shall express our results in terms of the collision frequency ν, instead of the mean free time τ. Equation 2-9-6* gives for the zero-field scalar diffusion coefficient $\mathscr{D} = \bar{v}\lambda/3 = (\bar{v}^2/3)(1/\nu)$, and (10-9-8) gives for the corresponding mobility $\mathscr{K} = q\tau/m = (q/m)(1/\nu)$. The tensor quantities evidently have the form[10]

$$\mathscr{D} = \frac{\bar{v}^2}{3}
\begin{vmatrix}
\dfrac{\nu}{\nu^2 + \omega_b^2} & \dfrac{\omega_b}{\nu^2 + \omega_b^2} & 0 \\[2mm]
\dfrac{-\omega_b}{\nu^2 + \omega_b^2} & \dfrac{\nu}{\nu^2 + \omega_b^2} & 0 \\[2mm]
0 & 0 & \dfrac{1}{\nu}
\end{vmatrix}
=
\begin{vmatrix}
\mathscr{D}_T & \mathscr{D}_H & 0 \\[2mm]
-\mathscr{D}_H & \mathscr{D}_T & 0 \\[2mm]
0 & 0 & \mathscr{D}_\|
\end{vmatrix}
\tag{10-9-10}$$

and

$$\mathscr{K} = \frac{q}{m}
\begin{vmatrix}
\dfrac{\nu}{\nu^2 + \omega_b^2} & \dfrac{\omega_b}{\nu^2 + \omega_b^2} & 0 \\[2mm]
\dfrac{-\omega_b}{\nu^2 + \omega_b^2} & \dfrac{\nu}{\nu^2 + \omega_b^2} & 0 \\[2mm]
0 & 0 & \dfrac{1}{\nu}
\end{vmatrix}
=
\begin{vmatrix}
\mathscr{K}_T & \mathscr{K}_H & 0 \\[2mm]
-\mathscr{K}_H & \mathscr{K}_T & 0 \\[2mm]
0 & 0 & \mathscr{K}_\|
\end{vmatrix}
\tag{10-9-11}$$

* Equation (10-9-8) gives a result that differs only by a small numerical factor produced by differences in averaging procedures.

where the symbols T, H, and $\parallel$ stand for "transverse," "Hall," and "parallel," respectively. The ith components of the flow velocities are given in terms of the components of these tensors by the equations

$$(v_i)_{\text{diffusion}} = -\frac{1}{N}\mathcal{D}_{ij}\frac{\partial N}{\partial r_j} \tag{10-9-12}$$

and

$$(v_i)_{\text{mobility}} = \mathcal{K}_{ij}E_j \tag{10-9-13}$$

Summation over the dummy index j is implied in the last two equations. For example,

$$(v_x)_{\text{diffusion}} = -\frac{1}{N}\left(\mathcal{D}_{xx}\frac{\partial N}{\partial x} + \mathcal{D}_{xy}\frac{\partial N}{\partial y} + \mathcal{D}_{xz}\frac{\partial N}{\partial z}\right)$$

C. DEPENDENCE OF THE DIFFUSION COEFFICIENT ON THE MAGNETIC FLUX DENSITY AND THE MASS OF THE PARTICLES. In many cases of interest the cyclotron frequency ω_b is much greater than the collision frequency ν, and according to (10-9-10) the transverse component of the diffusion coefficient will then vary as $1/\omega_b^2$ or $1/B^2$. This would be a fortunate circumstance in regard to controlled thermonuclear experiments, for it would mean that strong axial magnetic fields would be quite effective in reducing diffusion losses to the walls of plasma devices. (Actually, diffusion in a strong magnetic field is much more complicated than our analysis indicates, and there has been great controversy about whether the diffusion coefficient is proportional to $1/B$ or to $1/B^2$ for large fields.)

Another interesting observation is that when $\omega_b \gg \nu$, $\mathcal{D}_T$ varies as $\bar{v}^2/\omega_b^2 \sim \bar{v}^2 m^2$ for constant q and B. Thus for any energy distribution likely to be encountered the transverse component of the diffusion coefficient is much larger for ions than for electrons. Consequently, ions diffuse more rapidly than electrons across the magnetic field lines but more slowly in the direction of the field. The rapid diffusion of ions across the field lines may be understood by realizing that diffusion across the field occurs by means of random shifts of the centers of gyration of the particles on each collision. The shift is of the order of the cyclotron radius, $r_b = mv/qB$, and for equal energies and collision frequencies heavier particles diffuse faster across the field lines than lighter particles.

Discussions of these topics and others related to diffusion of plasmas in magnetic fields appear in books on plasma dynamics.[11-14]

10-10. AMBIPOLAR DIFFUSION

Up to this point we have dealt only with weakly ionized gases and neglected the interaction among charged particles during diffusion. This approximation is legitimate below ionization densities of about 10^7–10^8/cm^3

but above this level space charge effects produced by the interaction between the electrons and positive ions become important and must be taken into account.

In books dealing with the collective aspects of plasmas it is shown that the number density of electrons in a highly ionized gas must approximately equal the number density of positive ions at each point, provided we are not within about 1 debye length of a boundary (cf. Appendix I). Any deviation from charge equality produces electric forces which oppose the charge separation and tend to restore the balance. Because their diffusion coefficient is much higher than that of the ions, the electrons attempt to diffuse more rapidly than the ions toward regions of lower concentration, but their motion is impeded by the restraining space charge field thereby created. This same field has the opposite effect on the ions and causes them to diffuse at a faster rate than they would in the absence of the electrons. Both species of charged particles consequently diffuse with the same velocity, and since there is now no difference in the flow of the particles of opposite sign the diffusion is called *ambipolar*. The concept of ambipolar diffusion was introduced by Schottky[15] in 1924 in an analysis of the positive column of the glow discharge.

A. THE COEFFICIENT OF AMBIPOLAR DIFFUSION. Let N represent the common number density of the electrons and positive ions and v_a, the velocity of ambipolar diffusion. We shall assume that the gas pressure is high enough that the particles will make frequent collisions. The mobility concept will then be assumed to apply, not only for the ions but for the electrons as well. Let E denote the intensity of the electric field established by the charge separation. Since the velocity of diffusion is the same for both species, we have,

$$v_a = -\frac{\mathscr{D}^+}{N}\frac{dN}{dx} + \mathscr{K}^+ E \qquad (10\text{-}10\text{-}1)$$

and

$$v_a = -\frac{\mathscr{D}^-}{N}\frac{dN}{dx} - \mathscr{K}^- E \qquad (10\text{-}10\text{-}2)$$

where $\mathscr{K}^+$ and $\mathscr{K}^-$ are the mobilities of the ions and electrons, respectively. $\mathscr{K}^+$ and $\mathscr{K}^-$ are both positive numbers. By eliminating E, we obtain

$$v_a = -\mathscr{D}_a \frac{1}{N}\frac{dN}{dx} \qquad (10\text{-}10\text{-}3)$$

where $\mathscr{D}_a$ is the *coefficient of ambipolar diffusion* defined by the equation

$$\mathscr{D}_a = \frac{\mathscr{D}^+ \mathscr{K}^- + \mathscr{D}^- \mathscr{K}^+}{\mathscr{K}^+ + \mathscr{K}^-} \qquad (10\text{-}10\text{-}4)$$

$\mathscr{D}_a$ characterizes the diffusive motion of both species.

If we assume that $\mathcal{K}^- \gg \mathcal{K}^+$ and $T^- \gg T^+$ and use the relationship

$$\frac{\mathcal{D}}{\mathcal{K}} = \frac{kT}{e} \tag{10-3-2}$$

we find that

$$\mathcal{D}_a \approx \mathcal{D}^- \frac{\mathcal{K}^+}{\mathcal{K}^-} = \frac{kT^-}{e} \mathcal{K}^+ \tag{10-10-5}$$

When $T^+ = T^- = T$, on the other hand,

$$\mathcal{D}_a \approx 2\mathcal{D}^+ = \frac{2kT}{e} \mathcal{K}^+ \tag{10-10-6}$$

B. EXPERIMENTAL RESULTS.   The time-dependent diffusion equation for the ambipolar case is

$$\frac{\partial N}{\partial t} = \nabla \cdot (\mathcal{D}_a \nabla N) \tag{10-10-7}$$

If $\mathcal{D}_a$ is taken to be constant and the particle number density is assumed to decay as $e^{-t/\tau}$, the time-independent ambipolar diffusion equation is obtained:

$$\nabla^2 N_0 + \frac{N_0}{\mathcal{D}_a \tau} = 0 \tag{10-10-8}$$

This equation is solved for specific problems by the methods of Section 10-8. $\mathcal{D}_a$ is given in terms of the decay constant τ, and the appropriate diffusion length Λ, by the equation

$$\mathcal{D}_a = \frac{\Lambda^2}{\tau} \tag{10-10-9}$$

Hence $\mathcal{D}_a$ may be evaluated from a determination of the rate of decay of the charged particle density in a cavity after the ionization source has been turned off.

Gas in a cavity may be broken down to form a plasma by the application of microwaves, and the electron density may be determined by measuring the shift in the frequency of resonance[16] (see also Section 12-7). The experimental values of N are then plotted as a function of t on a semilogarithmic scale. If the plot is linear, indicating that the decay is exponential as assumed, the diffusion coefficient may be obtained from the slope. Since the sensitivity of the microwave method is not great enough to allow determination of electron densities below about $10^7/cm^3$, the diffusion coefficient measured is $\mathcal{D}_a$. Here we assumed that the effects of electron attachment and recombination are negligible, as is frequently the case in practice. The techniques of analyzing diffusion data when attachment and recombination must be considered are discussed by Brown in Chapters 6 and 8 of his book and in Section 12-8 of this book.

Sometimes the plots are not linear on a semilogarithmic scale even though diffusion is the controlling mechanism. Nonlinearity, in this case, indicates the simultaneous presence of more than one mode of diffusion. (The higher modes may be excited by breaking down the gas in an asymmetric discharge.) The discussion in Section 10-8 shows that the higher modes decay faster than the fundamental mode, and regardless of its initial complexity

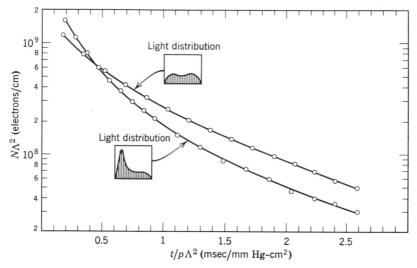

FIG. 10-10-1. The influence of the initial spatial distribution on the decay of electron density. K. B. Persson and S. C. Brown, *Phys. Rev.* **100**, 729 (1955).

the plot will approach linearity for large values of t. Two plots corresponding to different discharge conditions and different combinations of modes are shown in Fig. 10-10-1.[17] Note that the curves become straight and parallel to one another at large t, each having the slope corresponding to the lowest mode of diffusion. The "light distributions" shown in the figure are qualitative measures of the initial spatial electron density at the start of the decay period. They were obtained by scanning the discharge with a photomultiplier and slit system and displaying the signal on an oscilloscope.

Theory predicts that $\mathscr{D}_a$ will vary inversely with the pressure if the electrons and ions are in thermal equilibrium with the gas at a temperature that is held constant as the gas pressure is varied. A verification of this prediction taken from a paper on ambipolar diffusion in helium by Biondi and Brown,[18] is presented in Fig. 10-10-2. (The identity of the ions to which these data refer is uncertain. The $\mathscr{D}_a p$ products for He^+ and He_2^+ ions in helium are given in Table 10-10-1.) Figure 10-10-3, taken from the same

TABLE 10-10-1. Values of the pressure-ambipolar diffusion coefficient product for various ion-gas combinations. Values of the reduced mobility $\mathcal{K}_0$, calculated from the diffusion data, are also displayed for those few cases in which the identity of the ion is almost certain and in which the measured diffusion coefficient is consistent with the measured mobility cited in Section 9-9. Additional measurements on He, Ne, and A have been reported by M. J. Mulcahy and J. J. Lennon, *Proc. Phys. Soc.* (*London*), **80**, 626 (1962). H. J. Oskam and V. R. Mittelstadt, *Phys. Rev.* **132**, 1435 (1963), have also measured ambipolar diffusion coefficients for He, Ne, and A and report mobilities for these gases which are in excellent agreement with the values obtained in recent time-of-flight measurements (see Table 9-9-1).

Gas	Ion	$\mathcal{D}_a p$ (cm²-mm Hg/sec)	$\mathcal{K}_0$ (cm²/v-sec)	Reference
He	He⁺	460	10.6	C. S. Leffel, M. N. Hirsh,
	He₂⁺	697 ± 9	16.2	and D. E. Kerr, to be published.
N₂	N₄⁺	105 ± 5	2.42	E. C. Zipf, to be published in *Phys. Rev.*
He	?	540		M. A. Biondi and S. C. Brown, *Phys. Rev.* **75**, 1700 (1949)
He	?	560		A. V. Phelps and S. C. Brown, *Phys. Rev.* **86**, 102 (1952)
He	A⁺	900		M. A. Biondi, *Phys. Rev.* **83**, 1078 (1951)
He	N₂⁺	900		W. H. Kasner, W. A. Rogers, and M. A. Biondi, *Phys. Rev. Letters* **7**, 321 (1961)
Ne	?	180		M. A. Biondi, *Phys. Rev.* **93**, 1136 (1954)
Ne	N₂⁺	450		W. H. Kasner, W. A. Rogers, and M. A. Biondi, *Phys. Rev. Letters* **7**, 321 (1961)
	O₂⁺	450		
A	?	69		M. A. Biondi, *Phys. Rev.* **93**, 1136 (1954)
H₂	?	700		K. B. Persson and S. C. Brown, *Phys. Rev.* **100**, 729 (1955)
N₂	?	150		A. C. Faire and K. S. W. Champion, *Phys. Rev.* **113**, 1 (1959)

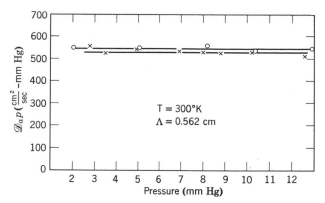

FIG. 10-10-2. Variation with pressure of the ambipolar diffusion coefficient for helium (see Table 10-10-1). M. A. Biondi and S. C. Brown, *Phys. Rev.* **75,** 1700 (1949).

paper, shows that the diffusion length Λ is a proper variable for analysis of diffusion. Figure 10-10-2 verifies that $\mathscr{D}_a p$ at constant energy is independent of the pressure, whereas Fig. 10-10-3 indicates that $\mathscr{D}_a p$ is independent of $p\Lambda$. From this we conclude that the measured values of $\mathscr{D}_a$ do not depend on the choice of Λ.

Table 10-10-1 presents experimental data on the ambipolar diffusion coefficients of various ions in several gases, multiplied by p to remove the dependence on the pressure. The data refer to room temperature; the range of accuracy of most of the measurements is about ± 8 to 20%. The identity of the ions in most cases has not been definitely established.

Biondi's values for neon and argon in Table 10-10-1 were obtained with small admixtures of helium to eliminate the effects of "diffusion cooling."

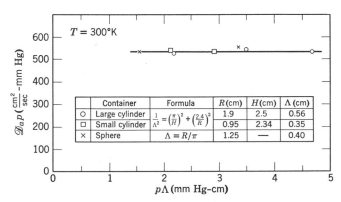

FIG. 10-10-3. Effect of the variation of the diffusion container size and shape on the measured values of $\mathscr{D}_a$. M. A. Biondi and S. C. Brown, *Phys. Rev.* **75,** 1700 (1949).

This term describes the situation in which the average energy of an electron swarm is reduced by the diffusion of the faster electrons to the container walls. In low-pressure neon and argon afterglows the "thermal contact" between the electrons and gas atoms is poor and the rapid diffusion loss of the faster component of the electrons causes a large reduction of the electron temperature with respect to the gas temperature. The thermal contact is greatly improved by the addition of a small fraction of 1 mm Hg of helium, and the electrons are restored to thermal equilibrium with the gas.

Several other important papers dealing with ambipolar diffusion should also be mentioned here. Allis and Rose[19] have analyzed the transition from ambipolar to free diffusion which occurs when the charged particle number density falls below the value characterizing ambipolar diffusion. Since the number density must decrease monotonically as we near the walls of a discharge vessel, such a transition will invariably occur. In certain situations the transition and free diffusion regions are thick enough to make consideration of this effect mandatory. Allis and Rose defined an effective diffusion coefficient $\mathscr{D}_s$ which takes into account the combined effects of diffusion and space charge fields:

$$\mathscr{D}_s = \mathscr{D}_a\left(1 + \mathscr{K}^- \frac{\rho}{\sigma}\right)$$

Here ρ is the space charge density and σ the plasma conductivity. Eckert[20] has incorporated this effective transition diffusion coefficient into the characteristic equations for a steady-state radiofrequency discharge. Frost[21] has treated the problem of ambipolar diffusion in cylindrical geometry for the case in which the ionic mobility undergoes a transition from constancy to a dependence on the energy of the ions. The form of the variation of the mobility he used was given in Section 9-9.

10-11. MUTUAL REPULSION OF CHARGED PARTICLES IN A GAS

Before leaving the subject of diffusion, it is appropriate to discuss another phenomenon that produces similar effects even though it has a fundamentally different origin. We have seen that diffusion of charged particles through a gas smooths out inequalities in the concentration and causes particles to be lost to the walls of the containing vessel. Mutual electrostatic repulsion among particles of like charge has a similar action, if particles of the opposite charge are not present in approximately equal concentrations. Therefore, in any experiment, spreading of a cloud of charged particles by mutual repulsion should be considered with the spreading by diffusion. Indeed, the effect of mutual repulsion can be the larger of the two. Sometimes mutual repulsion can lead to such serious losses that particles of the opposite sign must be injected to provide "space charge neutralization." (Obviously this stratagem is not feasible in all types of experiment.)

The accurate treatment of mutual repulsion in a gas is quite difficult, and here we shall be content with a simple approximate treatment. Our discussion is based on that of Von Engel.[22] The related problem of space-charge-produced dispersion of a beam of charged particles moving through a vacuum is discussed by Pierce.[23]

A. MUTUAL REPULSION, DIFFUSION EFFECTS BEING IGNORED. We shall now examine the one-dimensional expansion of a sheath of ions through a gas by the agency of mutual repulsion. The effects of diffusion are ignored here. Imagine the sheath to be established parallel to the Y-Z plane with its midplane at the origin of coordinates. The initial charge density is taken to be uniform throughout the sheath, and the ions are assumed to be in thermal equilibrium with the gas molecules. The gas is assumed to have a uniform temperature and pressure. Our point of departure is the *equation of continuity* which in one dimension gives

$$-\frac{\partial \rho}{\partial t} = \nabla \cdot (\rho \mathbf{v}) = \frac{\partial(\rho v)}{\partial x} = \rho \frac{\partial v}{\partial x} + v \frac{\partial \rho}{\partial x} \tag{10-11-1}$$

We shall drop the last term in this equation, since the space charge repulsion in which we are interested will prevent the charge density ρ from varying rapidly with x. The velocity in (10-11-1) is the drift velocity of the ions in the space charge field E. Thus $v = \mathcal{K} E$. Poisson's law states that

$$\nabla^2 V = \frac{\partial^2 V}{\partial x^2} = -4\pi \rho \tag{10-11-2}$$

where V is the electric potential, but V and E are related in one dimension by the equation

$$E = -\frac{\partial V}{\partial x} \tag{10-11-3}$$

Therefore

$$\frac{\partial E}{\partial x} = 4\pi \rho$$

and

$$-\frac{\partial \rho}{\partial t} = \mathcal{K} \rho \frac{\partial E}{\partial x} = 4\pi \mathcal{K} \rho^2 \tag{10-11-4}$$

We thus have the differential equation

$$\frac{d\rho}{\rho^2} = -4\pi \mathcal{K} \, dt$$

whose solution is

$$\frac{1}{\rho} - \frac{1}{\rho_0} = 4\pi \mathscr{K} t \qquad (10\text{-}11\text{-}5)$$

if the charge density is taken to be ρ_0 at $t = 0$. It is apparent that the time rate of decrease of charge density is greater for larger initial charge densities and higher mobilities, as expected. For large t the charge density at a given point varies as $1/t$ and has little dependence on the initial value ρ_0.

A numerical estimate of the importance of mutual repulsion in a common situation is provided by the following example. If the pressure is 1 mm Hg and the ionic number density is $10^8/cm^3$, only 0.4×10^{-3} sec is required for the charge density to decrease by a factor of 100 if we assume a value for the mobility of 2.0 cm^2/v-sec at atmospheric pressure.

B. COMPARISON OF THE EFFECTS OF MUTUAL REPULSION AND DIFFUSION. Let us again consider a sheath of ions centered about the Y-Z plane and assess the effects of mutual repulsion and diffusion in reducing its charge density. The two factors are viewed independently here; otherwise the analysis would be very complicated.

Mutual repulsion is treated first. Let the initial width of the ion sheath be $2x_0$. Viewed from along the X axis, the sheath is seen to contain a charge of $\sigma = 2x_0\rho_0$ esu/cm^2. By Gauss's theorem the field intensity outside the sheath is then $E = 2\pi\sigma$. Ions at the surface of the sheath move under the influence of this field with a drift velocity $v = \mathscr{K} E = 2\pi\sigma\mathscr{K}$. Thus in time t an ion on the right-hand edge of the sheath moves along the X axis a distance approximately equal to

$$x - x_0 = vt = 2\pi\sigma\mathscr{K} t \equiv X_{MR} \qquad (10\text{-}11\text{-}6)$$

Now consider the effect of diffusion. In the absence of mutual repulsion the root-mean-square displacement of an ion due to diffusion alone during this time t is

$$\sqrt{2\mathscr{D} t} \equiv X_D \qquad (10\text{-}11\text{-}7)$$

We may now let $X_{MR} = X_D$ and obtain the time T for which the two effects assume equal importance; T is given by

$$T = \frac{\mathscr{D}}{2\pi^2\sigma^2\mathscr{K}^2} \qquad (10\text{-}11\text{-}8)$$

It will be noted that X_{MR} increases linearly with time, whereas X_D increases only as the square root of t. If we assume that the plots of X_{MR} and X_D cross at time T, we will see that diffusion is the dominant factor for $t < T$, whereas mutual repulsion predominates for $t > T$.

Also X_{MR} varies as $1/p$, but X_D varies as $1/\sqrt{p}$. Thus mutual repulsion becomes of less relative importance as the pressure is increased.

REFERENCES

1. J. K. Theobald, *J. Appl. Phys.* **24**, 123 (1953). J. A. Dahlquist, *Phys. Rev.* **128**, 1988 (1962).
2. T. R. Kaiser, "Radio Echo Studies of Meteor Ionization," *Advances in Physics* **2**, 495 (1953). E. J. Öpik, *Physics of Meteor Flight in the Atmosphere*, Interscience, New York, 1958, Chapter 7.
3. L. G. H. Huxley, *Australian J. Phys.* **10**, 118 (1957).
4. A. Einstein, *Investigations on the Theory of the Brownian Movement* (edited by R. Fürth), Dover, New York, 1956.
5. See for example, R. D. Present, *Kinetic Theory of Gases*, McGraw-Hill, New York, 1958, Chapter 4. E. H. Kennard, *Kinetic Theory of Gases*, McGraw-Hill, New York, 1938, Chapter VII. *Selected Papers on Noise and Stochastic Processes* (edited by N. Wax), Dover, New York, 1954.
6. A. M. Weinberg and E. P. Wigner, *The Physical Theory of Neutron Chain Reactors*, University of Chicago Press, Chicago, 1958, p. 199.
7. S. Glasstone and M. C. Edlund, *The Elements of Nuclear Reactor Theory*, Van Nostrand, Princeton, N.J., 1952, p. 403.
8. N. W. McLachlan, *Bessel Functions for Engineers*, Clarendon Press, Oxford, 1934.
9. S. Chapman and T. G. Cowling, *The Mathematical Theory of Non-uniform Gases*, Second Edition, Cambridge University Press, London, 1952, Chapter 18.
10. W. P. Allis, "Motions of Ions and Electrons," in *Handbuch der Physik*, Vol. XXI, Springer-Verlag, Berlin, 1956.
11. A. Simon, *An Introduction to Thermonuclear Research*, Pergamon, New York, 1959, Chapter 9. S. Glasstone and R. H. Lovberg, *Controlled Thermonuclear Reactions*, Van Nostrand, Princeton, N.J., 1960, Chapter 12.
12. D. J. Rose and M. Clark, *Plasmas and Controlled Fusion*, Wiley, New York, 1961.
13. L. Spitzer, *Physics of Fully Ionized Gases*, Second Edition, Wiley, New York, 1962.
14. C. L. Longmire, *Elementary Plasma Physics*, Wiley, New York, 1963.
15. W. Schottky, *Phys. Z.* **25**, 635 (1924). For a refinement of Schottky's analysis, see R. G. Fowler, *Proc. Phys. Soc. (London)* **80**, 620 (1962).
16. M. A. Biondi and S. C. Brown, *Phys. Rev.* **75**, 1700 (1949). M. A. Biondi, *Rev. Sci. Instr.* **22**, 500 (1951). S. J. Buchsbaum and S. C. Brown, *Phys. Rev.* **106**, 196 (1957). C. B. Wharton, "Microwave Diagnostics for Controlled Fusion Research," in *Plasma Physics* (edited by J. E. Drummond), McGraw-Hill, New York, 1961. S. Glasstone and R. H. Lovberg, *op. cit.*, Chapter VI.
17. K. B. Persson and S. C. Brown, *Phys. Rev.* **100**, 729 (1955).
18. M. A. Biondi and S. C. Brown, *Phys. Rev.* **75**, 1700 (1949).
19. W. P. Allis and D. J. Rose, *Phys. Rev.* **93**, 84 (1954).
20. H. U. Eckert, *Proceedings of the Fifth International Conference on Ionization Phenomena in Gases*, Munich, 1961, North-Holland, Amsterdam (1962), Vol. I, p. 537.
21. L. S. Frost, *Phys. Rev.* **105**, 354 (1957).
22. A. Von Engel, *Ionized Gases*, Oxford University Press, London, 1955, Chapter 5.
23. J. R. Pierce, *Theory and Design of Electron Beams*, Second Edition, Van Nostrand, Princeton, N.J., 1954, Chapter IX.

11

ELECTRONIC ENERGY
DISTRIBUTIONS AND
DRIFT VELOCITIES

In this chapter our interest is centered on the energy distributions and drift velocities of slow electrons in gases in the presence of externally applied electric fields. By slow electrons here we mean electrons with energies below a few tens of ev.

There are certain obvious similarities between the motions of electrons and ions in gases, but for reasons to be discussed there are also differences that are important enough to warrant separate treatment of the two classes of particles. Since much of the present knowledge concerning the behavior of electrons was derived from studies of their diffusive motion, it was decided to postpone the treatment of electrons until the material on diffusion in Chapter 10 had been presented and not deal with electronic motion immediately after the discussion of ionic motion in Chapter 9.

11-1. DIFFERENCES BETWEEN ELECTRONIC AND IONIC BEHAVIOR IN GASES

Because of their small mass electrons are accelerated rapidly by an electric field, and they lose little energy in elastic collisions with molecules. Therefore electrons can acquire kinetic energy from an electric field faster than ions, and they can store this energy between collisions to a much greater degree until they reach energies at which inelastic collisions become important. Even with only a weak field imposed on the gas through which the electrons are moving, the average electronic energy may be far in excess of the thermal value associated with the gas molecules. Furthermore, the electronic energy distribution is not Maxwellian except at extremely low values of E/p.

Other differences between electrons and ions arise in connection with their collision cross sections. The cross sections for elastic scattering of electrons in most gases are strong functions of the electronic energy, whereas the corresponding cross sections for ions are smooth well-behaved functions of energy (cf. Chapter 4). The differences concerning inelastic collisions are equally pronounced. Electronic excitation is frequently an important factor in electron impacts even for energies of less than 10 ev, and in molecular gases the onset of vibrational and rotational excitation occurs at energies far below 1 ev. These energies are often attained by electrons in situations of common interest. The laboratory-frame thresholds for the corresponding modes of excitation by ions are higher than for electrons, and the excitation cross section curves peak at energies considerably above these thresholds (cf. Chapter 6). Therefore ions have insufficient energy to produce much excitation under the usual gas kinetic conditions. These considerations make the analysis of electronic motion in gases more difficult than the analysis of ionic motion.

In Section 9-2-A-1 we displayed several simple equations for the mobility of charged particles. These equations are frequently used for rough calculations of electronic drift velocities, but if we examine the assumptions on which these equations were derived in the light of the foregoing comments it becomes evident that they can be expected to give only crude results. In fact, the very concept of mobility is of limited value for electrons because, for a given pressure, the electronic drift velocity is usually not a linear function of the applied electric field intensity. In order to obtain meaningful results, it is necessary to use considerably more sophisticated theory and to calculate the drift velocity as a function of the applied field strength. These calculations yield the energy distribution function as well as the drift velocity—in fact, the drift velocity is determined from the calculated distribution function, as we shall see in Section 11-4. Before discussing the theory, however, we shall investigate some of the experimental methods used to study slow electrons in gases and present some of the data which have been obtained.

11-2. EXPERIMENTAL METHODS OF STUDYING SLOW ELECTRONS IN GASES

Most of our information concerning the behavior of slow electrons in gases was deduced from investigations of *electron swarms*, that is, clouds of electrons undergoing diffusive motion in a gas. By means of the techniques subsequently discussed, it is possible to obtain data on the agitation energies of the electrons and to measure their drift velocities. From these data the application of kinetic theory permits the calculation of the electronic mean free paths, collision frequencies, and cross sections for momentum transfer and also the mean energy lost by electrons in collisions with gas molecules. The general methods for making these calculations are covered by Huxley and Crompton[1] and by Loeb,[2] who provide references to the original investigations, and a vast amount of data is presented by Loeb[2] and Healey and Reed.[3] Information of this kind has many applications in plasma physics, gaseous electronics, and upper atmospheric studies.

A. THE TOWNSEND DIFFUSION METHOD.   One of the most important and effective methods of investigating the behavior of slow electrons in gases was introduced by Townsend at about the turn of the century. Its use continues to the present day. This method is suitable for determining both the average energy and the drift velocity, from which collision frequencies, mean energy losses, etc., may be calculated.

1. *Determinations of the average energy.*   In Section 10-2 the following equation is shown to hold for charged particles moving through a gas with which they are essentially in thermal equilibrium:

$$\frac{\mathscr{K}}{\mathscr{D}} = \frac{eN_i}{p_i} \qquad (10\text{-}2\text{-}4)$$

Here $\mathscr{K}$ is the mobility, $\mathscr{D}$, the diffusion coefficient, e, the charge on each particle, N_i, the number density of the charged particles, and p_i, the charged particle partial pressure. The mobility is related to the drift velocity v_d and the electric field intensity E by the equation $\mathscr{K} = v_d/E$, and because of the assumption of thermal equilibrium $N_i/p_i = 1/kT$, where k is the Boltzmann constant and T the gas temperature. Therefore we may write for the equilibrium situation

$$\frac{v_d}{\mathscr{D}} = \frac{Ee}{kT} \qquad (11\text{-}2\text{-}1)$$

If the charged particles are electrons, this equation must be modified to account for the fact that the particles are not generally in thermal equilibrium with the gas. Since the quantity kT in the denominator of (11-2-1) is directly proportional to the mean agitation energy of the charged particles if they are in equilibrium with the gas, it is reasonable to assume that in nonequilibrium this equation should read

$$\frac{v_d}{\mathscr{D}} = \frac{Ee}{\eta kT} \qquad (11\text{-}2\text{-}2)$$

where the quantity η equals the ratio of the mean agitation energy of the electrons to the mean molecular energy; η is known as the *Townsend energy factor*. We see from (11-2-2) that measurement of the ratio of v_d to $\mathscr{D}$ will permit the determination of the mean electronic agitation energy. Further, if v_d is separately determined, the diffusion coefficient of the electrons may be obtained. We may also write (11-2-2) in the form

$$\frac{\mathscr{D}}{\mathscr{K}} = \frac{\eta kT}{e} \tag{11-2-3}$$

The quantity $\mathscr{D}/\mathscr{K}$ is seen to have the dimensions of energy and is sometimes referred to as the *characteristic energy* of the electrons (see Section 11-5).

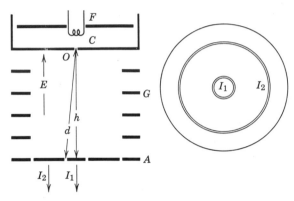

FIG. 11-2-1. The modified Townsend apparatus for the determination of the ratio of the electronic drift velocity to the diffusion coefficient.

A modern version of the Townsend apparatus used for the determination of the ratio $v_d/\mathscr{D}$ is illustrated in Fig. 11-2-1. The drawing on the left shows a diffusion chamber containing a filament F, cathode C, guard rings G, and segmented anode A. A plan view of the anode is given in the drawing on the right. The hole in the cathode is about 1 mm in diameter, and the chamber is several centimeters high. The chamber contains gas at a pressure of a few mm Hg, and a uniform electric field is maintained along the axis of the chamber. Both the cathode and anode are gold-plated to prevent the establishment of spurious electric fields.

Electrons are emitted continuously from the filament and stream toward the cathode. Those electrons that pass through the hole at 0 drift slowly toward the anode, undergoing diffusion during this drift. The divergence of the electron stream crossing the chamber is determined by measuring the ratio $R = I_1/(I_1 + I_2)$, where I_1 and I_2 are the currents collected by the two interior segments of the anode. (These currents are kept below about 10^{-11} amp to avoid space charge effects.) Huxley, who developed the apparatus geometry shown, has solved the appropriate diffusion problem and shown[1] that

$$R = 1 - \frac{h}{d} e^{-\lambda(d-h)}$$

where h and d are the distances shown in Fig. 11-2-1 and $\lambda = v_d/2\mathscr{D}$. Thus $v_d/\mathscr{D}$ can be determined from the measured value of R, and η may then be obtained by use of (11-2-2).

An apparatus similar to that shown in Fig. 11-2-1 has been described by Warren and Parker,[4] who discuss the solution of the diffusion equation appropriate to their apparatus. The Townsend method of determining the ratio $v_d/\mathscr{D}$ has been critically reviewed by Crompton and Jory.[5] These authors analyze a number of factors influencing the accuracy of the measurements.

Actually, (11-2-2) is strictly correct only for certain electronic energy distributions, which include the Maxwellian distribution. In general, the factor η in (11-2-2) should be replaced by the factor $\eta^* = 3\eta/2F$, where F is a dimensionless ratio given in Ref. 1. Thus the measured quantity is really η^*, from which the true energy factor η can be obtained if F is known; F has the value $\frac{3}{2}$ for the Maxwellian distribution. For the Druyvesteyn distribution, which is shown later to be more realistic for electrons under most conditions, F equals 1.312. For rigorous discussions of the Townsend method the reader is referred to the review by Huxley and Crompton[1] and the paper by Allis and Allen.[6]

It is possible to use the Townsend lateral diffusion method to determine the ratio $v_d/\mathscr{D}$ when ionization is present, provided the value of the ionization coefficient is known from independent growth-of-current experiments.† Therefore the method can be used to determine electron energies when primary ionization is occurring.

2. *Drift velocity measurements.* The determination of drift velocities by the Townsend method requires measurement of the angle of lateral deflection of a steady stream of electrons by a magnetic field normal to the electric field impelling the electrons through the gas. A modified version of the original Townsend apparatus used by Huxley and his colleagues is shown in Fig. 11-2-2. The diffusion chamber is similar to that in Fig. 11-2-1 except for the anode geometry. With no magnetic field applied, the currents I_1 and I_2 received by the two semicircular segments of the anode are equal, but an imbalance is produced by the application of the magnetic field, whose flux density is denoted by B. This imbalance is associated with

† See L. G. H. Huxley, *Australian J. Phys.* **12,** 171 (1959), p. 174.

a lateral deflection of the electron stream through the angle θ, which is defined mathematically by the equation

$$\tan \theta = \frac{v_{dx}}{v_{dz}} \tag{11-2-4}$$

where v_{dx} is the component of the drift velocity in the direction normal to both E and B and v_{dz} is the component along E. The ratio I_1/I_2 with the magnetic field applied may be expressed as a function of $\tan \theta$ and B, so

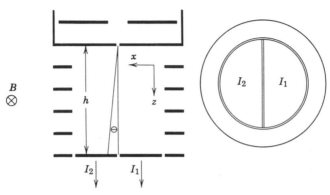

FIG. 11-2-2. The modified Townsend apparatus for the measurement of electronic drift velocities.

that $\tan \theta$ may be obtained from the measured values of this ratio and B. Then $v_{dz} = v_d$ may be obtained from the equation

$$v_{dz} = C \frac{E}{B} \tan \theta \tag{11-2-5}$$

if the quantity C can be calculated. C is a dimensionless factor whose value depends on the form of the electronic energy distribution. It has the value 0.85 for the Maxwellian distribution and equals 0.943 for the Druyvesteyn distribution.

The derivation of (11-2-5) in its correct form is given by Huxley and Crompton,[1] but the following crude analysis will serve to show the approximate dependence of v_{dz} on E, B, and $\tan \theta$. Let us assume that the drift velocity of the electrons in the X direction is proportional to the magnitude of the magnetic force producing the lateral deflection and that the Z component of the drift velocity is proportional to the electric force along the axis of the diffusion chamber. Using (11-2-4), we may then write

$$\tan \theta = \frac{eBv_{dz}}{eE} \quad \text{or} \quad v_{dz} = \frac{E}{B} \tan \theta$$

to establish the approximate form of (11-2-5). The correct form is achieved only by a rather complex analysis.

The method of measuring drift velocities outlined here has been applied in a few experiments to ions as well as electrons. Strong magnetic fields (of the order of thousands of gauss) are required for the ionic measurements, whereas modest fields (of the order of tens of gauss) suffice for the determination of electronic drift velocities. With the advent of modern electronic techniques, the Townsend method of measuring drift velocities has been superseded by time-of-flight techniques, which are to be preferred because they do not require knowledge of the electron energy distribution function for the determination of v_d.

A very thorough survey of the applications of the Townsend method to both ions and electrons is given by Loeb.[2] The most recent survey of the applications to electrons is that of Huxley and Crompton.[1] It is of interest to note that Huxley and his co-workers, in contradistinction to most investigators, have always used the method of free paths in their analyses of electronic motion. It is generally assumed that the formulas derived by this method are restricted in generality and are less precise than those derived by the rigorous but analytically more complex methods of Maxwell and Boltzmann. However, Huxley[7] has shown that both methods lead to equivalent formulas for the diffusion and drift of electrons in gases. It may be inferred therefore that the supposed limitations of the method of free paths in this context are often attributable to imperfections of application rather than to those of principle.

B. THE ELECTRICAL SHUTTER METHOD OF MEASURING DRIFT VELOCITIES. Many ionic and electronic drift velocity measurements have been made with electrical shutters used to time the transit of the charge carriers through the gas. The general method was introduced by Tyndall and his colleagues during the 1920's, and references to the original and much of the subsequent work are given in the first chapter of the book by Loeb.[2] Here we shall discuss only the recent work of Pack, Voshall, and Phelps,[8] who used a modern version of the apparatus employed by Bradbury and Nielsen[9] in their very successful measurements of drift velocities during the 1930's. The Bradbury-Nielsen apparatus has already been described in Section 9-8-B.*

Pack, Voshall, and Phelps's measurements of electronic drift velocities were made with the electrode structure shown schematically in Fig. 11-2-3. Photoelectrons liberated from the cathode by ultraviolet light move

---

* A critical examination of the Bradbury-Nielsen technique has been made by Lowke,[10] who subsequently used the method to produce some of the most accurate data available at present.[23]

downward under the action of a uniform electric field maintained by guard rings. The flow of current to the collector can be reduced by the application of voltage pulses to alternate wires of the grids. In their initial experiments Pack and Phelps utilized a steady light source so that the first shutter was used to inject a pulse of electrons into the drift space. The second shutter measured the transit time of the electrons from the first to the second shutter. In an effort to correct for end effects, drift velocities were measured for two different drift distances, and the difference in the measured transit times was used to calculate the drift velocity.

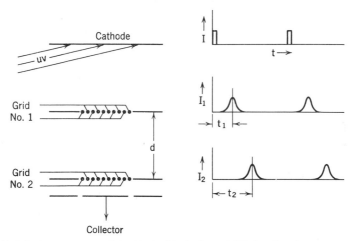

FIG. 11-2-3. Apparatus used by Pack, Voshall, and Phelps for the measurement of electronic drift velocities, shown in the conventional pulsed mode of operation. The widths of the pulses are not to scale.

In the more recent work the need for a grid to provide a time-varying electron current was eliminated by a pulsed light source. Either of the two grids could then determine the time required for the electrons to travel from the cathode to that grid. The difference in transit times gives the time required to travel between grids and should be independent of end effects at the cathode and effects occurring equally at both grids. This operation is shown schematically in Fig. 11-2-3. Light from a pulsed uv source produces a photocurrent leaving the cathode with the waveform marked I. The currents arriving at grid number 1 and grid number 2 are I_1 and I_2, respectively. Two limiting modes of operation of the grids are described.

The "conventional" mode of operation is essentially that used by Bradbury and Nielsen. In this mode a potential is applied between the two halves of grid number 1 to collect electrons. This bias is usually adjusted to reduce the transmitted electron current to about 5% of the value with zero bias. No voltages are applied between the two halves of grid number 2, which is passive during this measurement. In order to open grid number 1, a rectangular voltage pulse is applied symmetrically to each half of the grid to reduce the field between alternate grid wires to zero, that is, to maximize the transmitted electron current when the delay is set at t_1. By varying the time delay between the pulse applied to grid number 1 and the light pulse a collector current versus time plot similar to I_1 can be obtained. In like manner, by making grid number 1 passive and number 2 active, a collector current versus time plot similar to I_2 can be obtained. If t_1 and t_2 are the time locations of the peaks of these waveforms and if the symmetry of the waveform is not badly distorted by diffusion effects,[10] the drift velocity is given by $d/(t_2 - t_1)$, where d is the grid separation.

The alternate "zero-bias" mode of operation was devised by Pack and Phelps to reduce the perturbing effects of voltages applied to the grids by setting the dc bias voltage equal to zero and using only the pulsed voltage to collect some of the electrons near the grid. Thus the transmission of the grids is reduced and the current to the collector goes through a minimum when the gate is closed simultaneously with the arrival of the electrons at the grid. This mode of operation has the advantage that there is no voltage between the grid wires during the period between pulses. Pack and Phelps showed that with equal pulse amplitudes the change in collector current is approximately the same for either method of operation in their experiments and that the computed drift velocities were equal within experimental error. Their results are believed to be free of end effects.

Drift distances of 1 to 4 in. were used in the experiments of Pack, Voshall, and Phelps. The grids consisted of 0.003-in. gold-plated molybdenum wires spaced 0.140 in. apart. The rise and fall times of the pulses applied to the light source (a hot-cathode hydrogen lamp) and to the grids were 0.2 μsec. Space charge effects were negligible because currents of the order of only 10^{-12} amp were utilized. The use of high pressures and low fields permitted the measurements to be extended to lower E/p than those previously reported, and data were taken at temperatures ranging from 77 to 443°K. The drift velocity data are displayed in Section 11-3.

C. SINGLE-ELECTRON TIME-OF-FLIGHT DETERMINATION OF DRIFT VELOCITIES AND DIFFUSION COEFFICIENTS. A new method for obtaining electron transport coefficients has recently been introduced by Hurst and his co-workers[11] at the Oak Ridge National Laboratory. This method differs from Townsend's (Section A) in that it requires pulsed rather than steady-state operation. The technique also differs from the Townsend and electrical shutter methods in that it permits the simultaneous independent evaluation of both the drift velocity and the diffusion coefficient.

In the single-electron time-of-flight method the experimental conditions are arranged to satisfy the boundary conditions applicable to a one-dimensional time-dependent transport equation. Under such conditions the distribution of the times of arrival of individual electrons at a point on a plane separated from another parallel plane releasing electrons at time $t = 0$ may be interpreted in terms of the diffusion coefficient $\mathscr{D}$ and the drift velocity v_d. The experiments are performed in a parallel-plate ionization chamber with a gap separation of 27 cm. Electrons are generated in bursts by the photoelectric action of a diffuse beam of ultraviolet light on the cathode plate. The light is provided by a flash tube operated at 160 flashes per second, and each burst of light has a time width of about 0.5 μsec. Electrons from successive bursts drift across the chamber under the action of a uniform electric field, and a small fraction of them (much less than one electron per burst) passes through an aperture in the anode plate at the opposite side of the chamber. These electrons are individually detected by a Geiger counter mounted directly behind the aperture. The time of flight is measured with a time-to-amplitude converter and a 512-channel pulse height analyzer. The time interval begins when a signal is picked up by a phototube monitoring the uv lamp and ends when a signal is generated in the Geiger tube. The interval between the light signal and the detector signal is the flight time of an individual electron, provided sufficient time is allowed between light flashes for complete recovery of the Geiger counter. The arrival-time distribution may be constructed by repeated measurements of the probability that a single electron will arrive at the detector during the interval between t and $t + \Delta t$.

The main limitations of this method as described here are associated with the fact that a common filling gas must be used in the Geiger counter and the ionization chamber. These limitations may be removed by the substitution of a differentially pumped electron multiplier as the detector.

It may be noted that the approach is somewhat similar to that developed for ion transport studies by McDaniel et al. (see Ref. 56 of Chapter 9).

D. ELECTRICAL PROBE MEASUREMENTS OF ELECTRON ENERGIES. Electrical probes furnish another means of determining the average energy of electrons in a gas and can also provide information concerning the energy distribution functions in certain situations. Probes were first used by Crookes in the 1890's, but the techniques for their use were not well developed until the 1920's, when Langmuir and his co-workers made their extensive theoretical and experimental studies. At the present time probe action is rather well understood, and the limitations of the method are recognized, so that probe studies can yield valuable information. Unfortunately, measurements are limited to situations in which the electronic number densities are rather high, and they have generally been confined to discharges in which n is of the order of $10^{10}/cm^3$ or greater. Probe techniques are discussed at length by Loeb[2] and by Glasstone and Lovberg.[12]*

E. MICROWAVE MEASUREMENTS OF ELECTRON ENERGIES. Another method of determining the mean electronic energy is to study a microwave gas discharge breakdown modified by an applied dc electric field.[13] A gas will break down in a microwave cavity when the losses of electrons to the walls are replaced by ionization in the body of the gas. When an ac field alone is applied, electrons are lost by diffusion. When a small dc sweeping field is added, electrons are lost both by diffusion and dc drift, and the discharge conditions are changed. Observation of the change in the breakdown conditions permits the calculation of the ratio of the electron mobility to the diffusion coefficient; thus the mean energy of the electrons can be obtained. This technique has been applied by Varnerin and Brown to hydrogen.[14]

An indirect determination of the mean energy in helium has been made by Reder and Brown.[15] The energy distribution function was derived, checked for its ability to predict the discharge condition correctly, and then used to obtain the average electronic energy.

The fractional energy loss per collision can be determined in the afterglow of a pulsed discharge by microwave methods. For this determination it is necessary to measure at microwave frequencies the plasma conductivity and its radiation temperature, both with and without an applied microwave heating field. These techniques have been discussed by Formato and Gilardini,[16] who also report the results of their studies of nitrogen and oxygen.

F. THE HORNBECK METHOD OF MEASURING DRIFT VELOCITIES. Hornbeck[17] has used his pulsed Townsend discharge apparatus, shown in Fig. 9-8-3, to measure the electronic drift velocity in helium at low E/p. In this experiment short pulses of photoelectrons were periodically ejected from the cathode C and allowed to drift to the anode A under the influence of a uniform electric field. As soon as the electrons were released from the cathode, the current in the external circuit rose from zero and remained constant until the electrons were collected at the anode. The current dropped sharply to zero when the electrons crossed the gap, permitting the calculation of the electronic drift velocity.

G. THE IONIZATION CHAMBER METHOD OF DRIFT VELOCITY MEASUREMENTS. A number of electronic drift velocity measurements have been made by measuring the time required for collection of electrons produced by a

* See also C. H. Su and S. H. Lam, *Phys. Fluids* **6**, 1479 (1963) and I. M. Cohen, *Phys. Fluids* **6**, 1492 (1963).

burst of ionization in a parallel plate ionization chamber.[18] Sometimes direct ionization of the gas by X rays or alpha particles has been used; at others the gas is ionized by Compton electrons produced by X rays interacting with a gold film on the inner face of a window in the side of the ionization chamber. During the electron transit across the gap between the plates in the imposed electric field, the positive ions formed in the ionization burst move only a negligible distance. Thus by analyzing the shape of the current pulses associated with the electronic motion we may determine the drift velocity.

H. ELECTROMAGNETIC METHODS OF DETERMINING ELECTRON ENERGIES AND NUMBER DENSITIES. The energy and number density of electrons in plasmas may be calculated from observational data on the bremsstrahlung radiated from the plasma. This method is evidently restricted to use on very hot plasmas, in which the effective electron temperature is quite high. The theory and techniques are discussed in several books on plasmas.[19] Another method of measuring electronic number densities in plasmas that are not necessarily hot has already been discussed in Section 10-10, which deals with ambipolar diffusion.

11-3. EXPERIMENTAL DATA ON ELECTRON ENERGIES AND DRIFT VELOCITIES

As we have seen, in an ionized gas not subjected to an electric field, the electrons and ions move at random with an average energy of agitation equal to the average thermal energy of the gas molecules, $3kT/2$. When an electric field is present, the electrons and ions, although still moving with a random component, will in addition undergo a drift in the field direction. At the same time, their agitation energy will be increased above the thermal value. The average energy of the electrons or ions may be characterized by its ratio η to the thermal agitation energy, which is conventionally evaluated at 15°C; η is the *Townsend energy factor*, defined in Section 11-2-A. For low or intermediate values of E/p, $\eta \approx 1$ for ions, and even for $E/p \approx 200$ volts/cm-mm Hg the average ionic energy is only of the order of 1 ev. For electrons, on the other hand, η may be quite high, even for E/p of the order of unity. The actual value of η in a given gas at given E/p is determined by an equilibrium condition between the energy supplied by the field and the energy lost through collisions.

Experimental data on mean electronic energies are presented in Figs. 11-3-1 through 11-3-9. We should stress the point that the energy factor plotted in some of these figures is not the true Townsend factor η but rather the quantity η^* defined in Section 11-2-A, which usually differs from η by a factor close to unity. Plots of $\mathscr{D}/\mathscr{K}$ versus E/N are displayed in

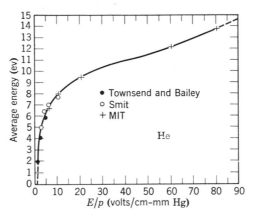

FIG. 11-3-1. The average energy of electrons in helium. The dots represent the data obtained by J. S. Townsend and V. A. Bailey, *Phil. Mag.* **46,** 657 (1923), with the Townsend method. The circles denote the values calculated by J. A. Smit, *Physica* **3,** 543 (1936). The crosses denote the microwave data of F. H. Reder and S. C. Brown, *Phys. Rev.* **95,** 885 (1954). For data on $\mathscr{D}/\mathscr{K}$ versus E/p for He, see Fig. 11-3-5 and Ref. 4.

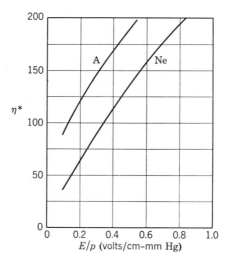

FIG. 11-3-2. The Townsend energy factor for electrons in neon and argon, taken from the book by Healey and Reed,[3] p. 78. These data were obtained by the Townsend method during the 1920's. For additional data on argon see Ref. 4.

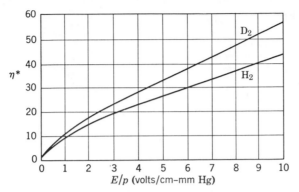

FIG. 11-3-3. The Townsend energy factor for electrons in hydrogen and deuterium. H_2: R. W. Crompton and D. J. Sutton, *Proc. Roy. Soc. (London)* **A-215**, 467 (1952). D_2: B. I. H. Hall, *Australian J. Phys.* **8**, 468 (1955). The Townsend method was employed in these measurements. For data on $\mathscr{D}/\mathscr{K}$ versus E/N see Fig. 11-5-3.

Section 11-5 for H_2 and N_2. Similar data have been obtained by Cochran and Forester[20] for hydrogen, nitrogen, carbon dioxide, methane, ethylene, and cyclopropane. These investigators used the Townsend method and worked in the E/p range extending from 0.2 to 5.0 volts/cm-mm Hg. Warren and Parker[4] have also used the Townsend method to obtain $\mathscr{D}/\mathscr{K}$

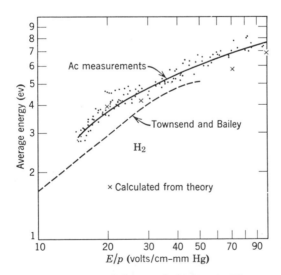

FIG. 11-3-4. The average energy of electrons in hydrogen. The ac measurements were made by L. J. Varnerin and S. C. Brown, *Phys. Rev.* **79**, 946 (1950), who also calculated the theoretical values shown. The dashed curve represents the data of J. S. Townsend and V. A. Bailey, *Phil. Mag.* **42**, 873 (1921), who used the Townsend method.

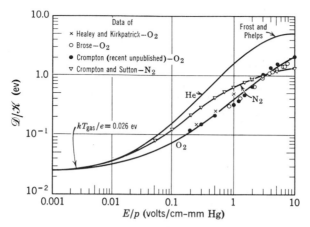

FIG. 11-3-5. The characteristic energy $\mathscr{D}/\mathscr{K}$ for electrons in He, N_2, and O_2 as a function of E/p. This figure is taken from the paper by L. M. Chanin, A. V. Phelps, and M. A. Biondi, *Phys. Rev.* **128**, 219 (1962). For O_2 and N_2 the curves are averages of data obtained by Healey and Kirkpatrick, Brose, Crompton and Sutton, and Crompton. The curve for He was theoretically calculated by L. S. Frost and A. V. Phelps (unpublished).

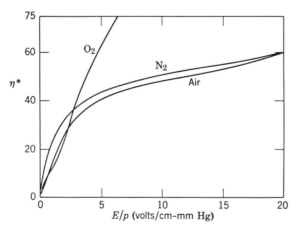

FIG. 11-3-6. The Townsend energy factor for electrons in oxygen, nitrogen, and air, obtained by the Townsend method. O_2: L. G. H. Huxley, R. W. Crompton, and C. H. Bagot, *Australian J. Phys.* **12**, 303 (1959). N_2: R. W. Crompton and D. J. Sutton, *Proc. Roy. Soc.* (*London*) **A-215**, 467 (1952). Air: R. W. Crompton, L. G. H. Huxley, and D. J. Sutton, *Proc. Roy. Soc.* (*London*) **A-218**, 507 (1953).

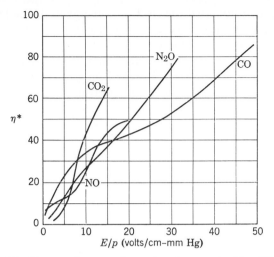

FIG. 11-3-7. The Townsend energy factor for electrons in CO_2, NO, N_2O, and CO, taken from the book by Healey and Reed,[3] p. 80. For additional data on CO and CO_2, see Ref. 4.

for electrons in He, A, N_2, H_2, D_2, CO, and CO_2 at low temperatures and low E/p. Their measurements were extended down to 77°K or to the boiling point of the gas being studied, whichever is higher. The lowest E/p values at which their measurements were made were well within the thermal range where $\mathscr{D}/\mathscr{K} = kT/e$.

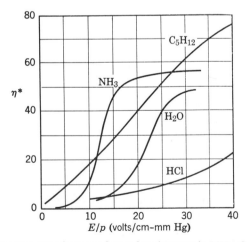

FIG. 11-3-8. The Townsend energy factor for electrons in NH_3, C_5H_{12}, H_2O, and HCl, taken from the book by Healey and Reed,[3] p. 81.

It is interesting to note that the electronic energy in the molecular gases is much lower than in the atomic gases because of the ability of the molecules to absorb energy from the electrons by vibrational and rotational excitation in collisions at low energies (less than 1 ev). Such excitation is impossible in atoms, which can be excited only by electrons possessing energies greater than the threshold for electronic excitation which lies

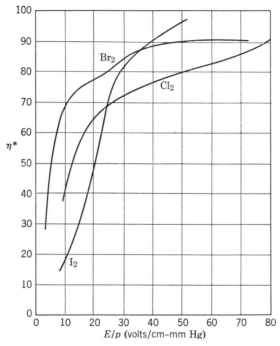

FIG. 11-3-9. The Townsend energy factor for electrons in chlorine, bromine, and iodine, taken from the book by Healey and Reed,[3] p. 52.

somewhere between 2 and 20 ev. Thus an electron starting from rest in a gas in an electric field can rise rapidly to energies of the order of several ev if the gas is monatomic, but if the gas is molecular the electron will have difficulty in building up its energy because of repeated losses experienced in exciting the vibrational and rotational levels of the molecules.

The following equations may facilitate the use of the data presented in this chapter. If we assume a gas temperature of 15°C, we may express the mean electronic energy as

$$\frac{m}{2} v_R^2 = \eta \tfrac{3}{2} kT = \eta(0.037 \text{ ev}) = \frac{\eta}{27} \text{ ev} \qquad (11\text{-}3\text{-}1)$$

where m is the electronic mass and v_R the rms speed. An effective electron temperature T_e may be defined by the equation

$$\frac{m}{2} v_R{}^2 = \tfrac{3}{2}kT_e \qquad (11\text{-}3\text{-}2)$$

The rms speed of the electrons is related to the Townsend energy factor by the expression

$$v_R = 1.15\sqrt{\bar{\eta}} \times 10^7 \text{ cm/sec} \qquad (11\text{-}3\text{-}3)$$

Figures 11-3-10 through 11-3-18 display data on the drift velocity as a function of E/p in a number of gases. The values of E/p are expressed in units of volt/cm-mm Hg for an equivalent density at 300°K, that is, $E/p = (E/N) \times 3.22 \times 10^{16}$ where N is the gas number density. Much of the data shown were obtained by Pack, Voshall, and Phelps,[8] who used the method described in Section 11-2-B. The data of Bowe,[21] which are shown for comparison in some of the figures, were obtained by the Hornbeck method (see Section 11-2-F). Bortner, Hurst, and Stone[22] used an ionization-chamber method to make measurements in argon, nitrogen, methane, carbon dioxide, ethylene, cyclopropane, and some mixtures of these gases. Additional measurements have been made on hydrogen and nitrogen by Lowke,[23] who employed an electrical shutter technique similar to that used by Bradbury and Nielsen. Lowke's measurements extended over an E/p range of 0.001 to 20 volts/cm-mm Hg.

It is interesting to note that the very careful experiments of Pack, Voshall, and Phelps[8] failed to reveal negative ion formation in water vapor anywhere within the range of experimental parameters they covered. Pack et al. state their opinion that all previous measurements of attachment in water vapor at E/p below 10 volts/cm-mm Hg must have been due to impurities in the water vapor. The experiments of Hurst, Stockdale, and O'Kelly[24] appear to confirm this observation.

As we shall see in the following paragraph, the presence of slight traces of impurities, especially of polyatomic types, can have a pronounced effect on the drift velocity of electrons in a supposedly pure gas. For this reason it is essential to use good vacuum techniques and pure gases in these measurements. Many of the early measurements, and even some made in recent years, were in error because of impurities. In general, data obtained before 1950 should be accepted with reserve, although the measurements of Bradbury and Nielsen made during the 1930's are recognized as being among the best ever made.

In order to understand the errors that impurities can introduce, let us refer to (9-2-2), which gives an approximate expression for the drift velocity of a particle of charge e and mass m moving through a gas with an

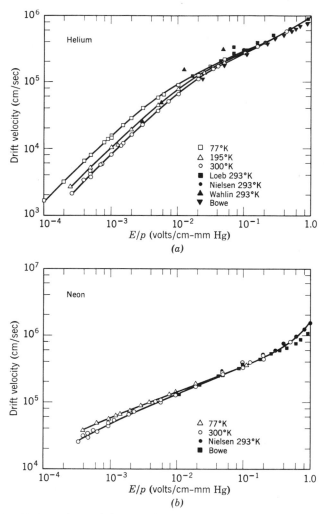

FIG. 11-3-10. Experimental data obtained by Pack, Voshall, and Phelps on the drift velocity of electrons in the noble gases compared with the results of other investigators. J. L. Pack and A. V. Phelps, *Phys. Rev.* **121**, 798 (1961); J. L. Pack, R. E. Voshall, and A. V. Phelps, *Phys. Rev.* **127**, 2084 (1962).

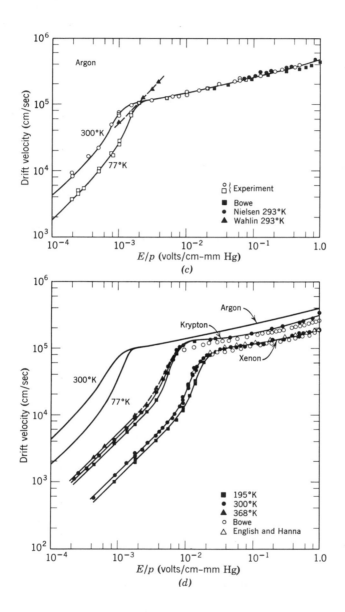

(c)

(d)

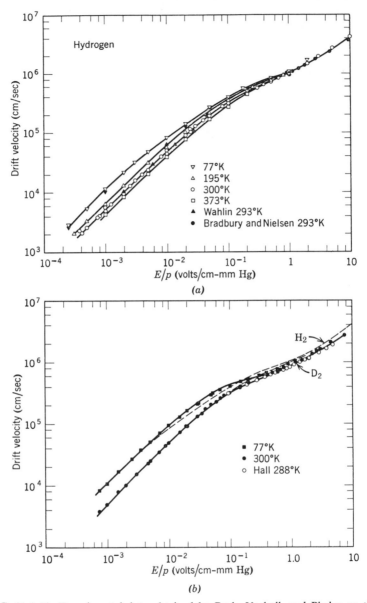

FIG. 11-3-11. Experimental data obtained by Pack, Voshall, and Phelps on the drift velocity of electrons in molecular gases compared with results of other investigators. Note in (d) that the values for H_2O are multiplied by 0.1 so that they will not fall on the NH_3 curve. J. L. Pack and A. V. Phelps, *Phys. Rev.* **121**, 798 (1961); J. L. Pack R. E. Voshall, and A. V. Phelps, *Phys. Rev.* **127**, 2084 (1962). For calculations on nitrogen, oxygen, and air see A. E. D. Heylen, *Proc. Phys. Soc.* (*London*) **79**, 284 (1962).

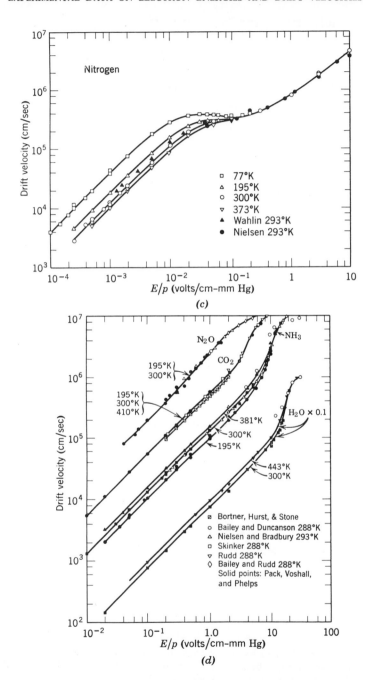

(c)

(d)

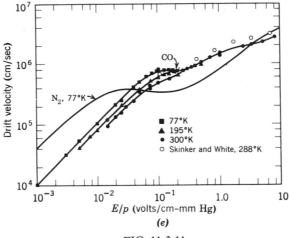

FIG. 11-3-11e.

average velocity $\bar{v}$ and mean free path λ. As we stated in Section 11-1, this equation is only qualitatively correct for electrons, but it will serve to illustrate the point at hand. Since

$$v_d = \frac{Ee\lambda}{m\bar{v}} \qquad (9\text{-}2\text{-}2)$$

we see that $v_d \sim \lambda/\bar{v} \sim \lambda/v_R$, and any factor that tends to change the agitation energy of the electrons will also tend to change their drift velocity. Each gas has its own unique set of excitation levels, and in certain cases slight traces of an impurity may have a strong effect on the

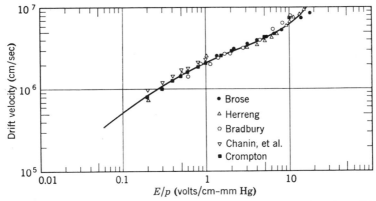

FIG. 11-3-12. The drift velocity of electrons in oxygen as a function of E/p. This figure is taken from a paper by L. M. Chanin, A. V. Phelps, and M. A. Biondi, *Phys. Rev.* **128,** 219 (1962), which contains references to the original investigations.

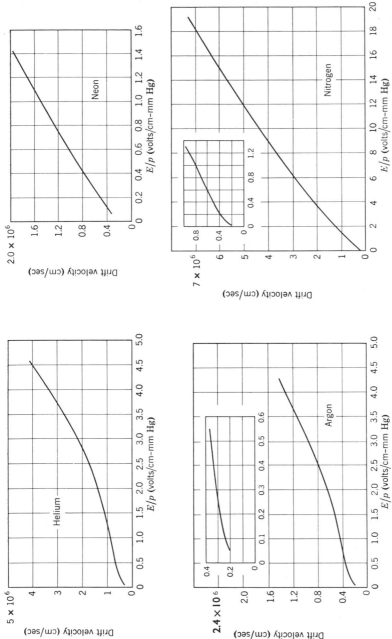

FIG. 11-3-13. Drift velocities of electrons in helium, neon, argon, and nitrogen as a function of E/p. These data were obtained by R. A. Nielsen, *Phys. Rev.* **50**, 950 (1936), using the electrical shutter method.

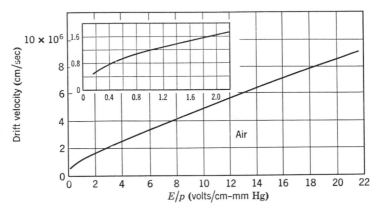

FIG. 11-3-14. The drift velocity of electrons in air, obtained by the electrical shutter method. R. A. Nielsen and N. E. Bradbury, *Phys. Rev.* **51**, 69 (1937).

average electronic energy. This is particularly true when molecular impurities are present in argon and the other heavy noble gases, in which the collision cross section decreases to small values at electron energies of less than 1 ev (the Ramsauer-Townsend Effect—cf. Section 4-1). Sometimes about 5% carbon dioxide is added to an argon-filled ionization chamber to lower the electron energy, decrease the collision cross section, and speed up the electron collection. The introduction of this amount of CO_2 can increase the drift velocity by a factor of about 10 over what it is in pure argon. In fact, the value of the drift velocity in the gas mixture is almost as large as if the chamber contained only the CO_2 to the extent of its partial pressure in the mixture. Figure 11-3-18 shows the effect of adding nitrogen

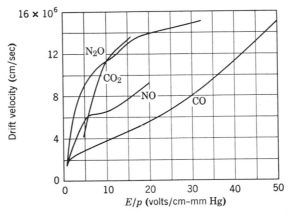

FIG. 11-3-15. Drift velocity data for electrons in N_2O, CO_2, NO, and CO, taken from the book by Healey and Reed,[3] p. 85.

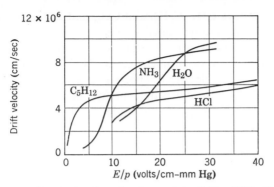

FIG. 11-3-16. Drift velocity data for electrons in C_5H_{12}, NH_3, H_2O, and HCl, taken from the book by Healey and Reed,[3] p. 86.

to argon—a polyatomic gas has an even greater effect on the drift velocity, as shown in recent experiments by Hurst and his co-workers.[24]

Hurst et al. measured the drift velocity of electrons in binary mixtures of water vapor with N_2, CH_4, C_2H_4, and CO_2 and found the drift velocities to be very sensitive to the presence of small quantities of water vapor in all the mixtures. When H_2O was added to N_2, the drift velocity increased markedly. This effect is attributed to the fact that the average electronic agitation energy in pure N_2 is higher than in pure H_2O, and the decrease in electron energy that occurs when H_2O is added is the dominant effect. Addition of small amounts of water vapor has the opposite effect in the other mixtures studied and causes the drift velocity to decrease. The electron energy is

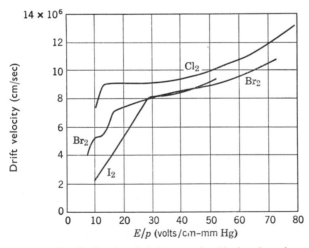

FIG. 11-3-17. Drift velocity data for electrons in chlorine, bromine, and iodine, taken from the book by Healey and Reed,[3] p. 53.

already quite low in pure CH_4, C_2H_4, and CO_2, and the addition of H_2O does little to change the agitation energy. The dominant effect associated with the presence of water vapor in these gases seems to be produced by the rather large permanent dipole moment of the H_2O molecule. (The N_2, CH_4, C_2H_4, and CO_2 molecules are nonpolar.) Indeed, when certain other polar molecules (acetone, heavy water, methyl alcohol, dimethyl ether, hydrogen sulfide, toluene, and nitrous oxide) were mixed with C_2H_4, a

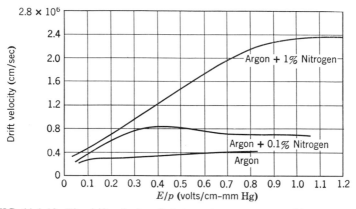

FIG. 11-3-18. The drift velocity of electrons in pure argon and in argon contaminated by nitrogen. These results were obtained by the ionization chamber method. L. Colli and U. Facchini, *Rev. Sci. Instr.* **23**, 39 (1952).

decrease in drift velocity resulted in each instance, and the magnitudes of the decreases correlated well with the magnitudes of the electric dipole moments of the added molecules.

11-4. THE RIGOROUS THEORY OF ELECTRONIC MOTION IN GASES

Pidduck[25] in 1913 made the first theoretical study of the energy of electrons in a gas acted on by an electric field. He used the general method developed by Lorentz[26] in his studies of electronic velocities in metals. A great deal of work was done between Pidduck's study and 1930 when Druyvesteyn[27] attacked the problem, and the reader may consult Loeb[2] for a discussion of these calculations. We shall proceed immediately to the study of Druyvesteyn.

A. DRUYVESTEYN'S CALCULATION OF THE ELECTRONIC ENERGY DISTRIBUTION.   In his analysis Druyvesteyn[27] considered the loss of energy by electrons in elastic impacts with molecules but ignored the effects of inelastic collisions. He further considered the electronic mean free path to be independent of the energy. His result for the energy distribution was

$$\rho(\varepsilon) = C\varepsilon^{1/2} \exp - \frac{3\delta\varepsilon^2}{2\lambda^2 e^2 E^2} \qquad (11\text{-}4\text{-}1)$$

where C is a constant, ε, the energy, $\delta = 2m/M$, m, the electron mass, M, the mass of a molecule, λ, the electronic mean free path, e, the electronic charge, and E, the electric field intensity. Druyvesteyn's distribution is shown in Fig. 11-4-1 compared to the Maxwell distribution for the same mean electron energy. It is seen that the number of fast electrons is much larger in the Maxwell distribution.

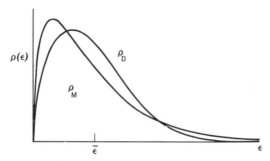

FIG. 11-4-1. The Druyvesteyn energy distribution ρ_D compared with the Maxwell distribution ρ_M for the same mean electron energy $\bar{\varepsilon}$.

B. SUBSEQUENT WORK. The next important calculation was made by Morse, Allis, and Lamar[28] in 1935. They used the same basic approach as Lorentz[26] and obtained the distribution function and drift velocity. Since they made the same assumptions as Druyvesteyn, it is not surprising that they again found the Druyvesteyn law to apply.

Later, in 1937, Allis and Allen[6] extended this work to include an analysis of the Townsend experimental method (discussed in Section 11-2) and considered the effects of a variable electronic mean free path. In addition, Allen[29] made an approximate extension of the calculations to include inelastic collisions.

In 1935 Davydov[30] calculated the energy distribution and drift velocity and considered the case in which E/p is so small that the energies of the molecules cannot be neglected in comparison with the electronic energies. He also obtained the Druyvesteyn distribution under the appropriate assumptions.

Smit[31] in 1937 performed an analysis of electronic motion which made allowances for variable mean free paths and for inelastic collisions. He also computed the energy distribution for electrons in helium at four values of E/p and obtained the results shown in Fig. 11-4-2.

Passing over the intervening years, we finally mention an important paper by Carleton and Megill,[32] who obtained numerically computed solutions to the Boltzmann equation for the electron energy distribution in weakly ionized air in the presence of a static magnetic field and an orthogonal ac electric field. The assumed fields are such that the average electron energy is much larger than the thermal energy of the molecules but that heating of the air by the electrons is negligible. Processes for

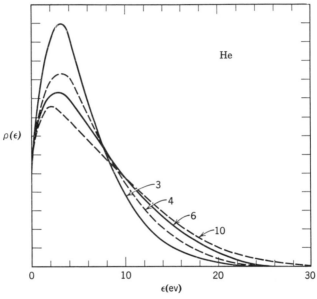

FIG. 11-4-2. Smit's calculated energy distributions for electrons in helium, for E/p of 3, 4, 6, and 10 volts/cm-mm Hg.[31]

creation and removal of free electrons are ignored, but electron energy losses by elastic scattering and by rotational, vibrational, and electronic excitation are taken into account by use of experimental cross sections. The air constituents were taken to be N_2, O_2, and O, the latter being included for upper atmospheric applications.

No attempt is made here to discuss the remainder of the analyses of electronic motion that have been carried out. Most of them are covered by Loeb,[2] who gives an extensive list of references to the work done before 1955. Excellent general discussions of the theory are also provided by Allis[33] and Chapman and Cowling.[34] We shall, however, discuss in some detail a calculation made by Margenau in order to illustrate the application of the Boltzmann transport theory to the analysis of electronic motion.

C. MARGENAU'S CALCULATION OF THE ENERGY DISTRIBUTION AND DRIFT VELOCITY. Margenau's motivation for investigating the problem of electronic motion was an interest in the electrical conductivity of an ionized gas. This quantity plays an important role in microwave research and ionospheric studies. Margenau[35] first derived the energy distribution function, from which he then computed the electronic drift velocity and the conductivity as a function of the gas pressure and the frequency of the electromagnetic waves. In this section we shall reproduce a portion of Margenau's calculation. By setting the frequency equal to zero in his results we can obtain the expressions for the dc case.

The electrical conductivity of an ionized gas σ, is related to the current density $\mathbf{J}$ by the equation

$$\mathbf{J} = \sigma \cdot \mathbf{E} \tag{11-4-2}$$

where $\mathbf{J}$ is given in terms of the electronic number density n and the drift velocity $\mathbf{v}_d$ by the equation

$$\mathbf{J} = ne\mathbf{v}_d \tag{11-4-3}$$

We shall consider here only an isotropic medium, so that the tensor conductivity reduces to scalar form.

There are two limiting situations that are very easy to describe. For low frequencies and high pressures the current density set up by an alternating field $E = E_0 \cos \omega t$ may be calculated by use of the Langevin expression for the drift velocity (9-2-2). Using this equation and the expression (2-2-3) for the mean velocity, we may write

$$J = \frac{e^2 E_0 \lambda n}{(8mkT/\pi)^{1/2}} \cos \omega t \tag{11-4-4}$$

The current expressed here is in phase with the applied field. For high frequencies and low pressures, however, the current is in quadrature with the field and is represented by the formula characteristic of free electrons:

$$J = \frac{e^2 E_0 n}{m\omega} \sin \omega t \tag{11-4-5}$$

For situations between these two extremes it is necessary to consider the effect of electron-molecule collisions on the forced oscillations that the field imposes on the electrons. As we have seen in Sections 4-1 and 9-4, this may be done by including in the equation of motion of the electron a friction, or damping, term of the form cv_d, with the result that the current density becomes

$$J = \frac{e^2 E_0 m\omega n}{m^2 \omega^2 + c^2} \sin \omega t \tag{11-4-6}$$

The constant c has often been treated as an empirical parameter, but it is usually taken to be equal to mv_m, where v_m is the electronic collision frequency for momentum transfer. This approach has been widely used, but it is artificial and furthermore fails to provide a proper average over electron velocities. The following derivation is free from these criticisms.

Let us assume that some external agency other than the electromagnetic waves maintains a steady number density of electrons in the gas. We shall consider only the effects of the applied field and elastic collisions on the electrons—inelastic collisions are to be completely ignored.

1. *The energy distribution.* Of the n electrons per cm³,

$$f(v_x, v_y, v_z)\, dv_x\, dv_y\, dv_z$$

have velocity components about v_x, v_y, v_z. The function f satisfies the Boltzmann equation (2-12-1), which reads

$$\frac{eE}{m}\frac{\partial f}{\partial v_x} + \frac{\partial f}{\partial t} = \left(\frac{\partial f}{\partial t}\right)_e \qquad (11\text{-}4\text{-}7)$$

if the field E is applied in the X direction. Here $\partial f/\partial t$ represents the local time rate of change caused in f by variations of E, and $(\partial f/\partial t)_e$ represents the change due to collisions with gas molecules. Electron-electron interactions are neglected, and a term involving the magnetic field strength may be omitted because the velocity of the electrons is small compared with that of light. Now let

$$E = E_0 \cos \omega t \qquad (11\text{-}4\text{-}8)$$

and put

$$\gamma = \frac{eE_0}{m} \qquad (11\text{-}4\text{-}9)$$

The distribution function $f(\mathbf{v})$ is expanded in spherical harmonics of the components of $\gamma\mathbf{v}$, and all harmonics beyond the first are neglected. Thus

$$f(\mathbf{v}) = f_0(v) + \gamma v_x[f_1(v) \cos \omega t + g_1(v) \sin \omega t] \qquad (11\text{-}4\text{-}10)$$

where the functions f_0, f_1, and g_1 depend only on the magnitude of $\mathbf{v}$. It may be shown[28] that

$$\left(\frac{\partial f_0}{\partial t}\right)_e = \frac{1}{v^2}\frac{m}{M}\frac{\partial}{\partial v}\left(\frac{v^4 f_0}{\lambda}\right) + \frac{kT}{Mv^2}\frac{\partial}{\partial v}\left(\frac{v^3}{\lambda}\frac{\partial f_0}{\partial v}\right) \qquad (11\text{-}4\text{-}11)$$

$$\left(\frac{\partial(v_x f_1)}{\partial t}\right)_e = -\frac{v_x v}{\lambda} f_1 \qquad (11\text{-}4\text{-}12)$$

and

$$\left(\frac{\partial(v_x g_1)}{\partial t}\right)_e = -\frac{v_x v}{\lambda} g_1 \qquad (11\text{-}4\text{-}13)$$

where λ is the mean free path of the electrons and M is the mass of a gas molecule. By inserting these expressions in (11-4-7) and equating coefficients of γv_x we have

$$\frac{\cos \omega t}{v} \frac{\partial f_0}{\partial v} - (\sin \omega t)\omega f_1 + (\cos \omega t)\omega g_1$$

$$= -(\cos \omega t)\frac{v}{\lambda}f_1 - (\sin \omega t)\frac{v}{\lambda}g_1 \quad (11\text{-}4\text{-}14)$$

Terms that are even in v_x yield, after being averaged over all directions,

$$\frac{\gamma^2}{3v^2}(\cos^2 \omega t)\frac{\partial}{\partial v}(v^3 f_1) + \frac{\gamma^2}{3v^2}(\cos \omega t \sin \omega t)\frac{\partial}{\partial v}(v^3 g_1) = \left(\frac{\partial f_0}{\partial t}\right)_e$$

and this equation, when averaged over a period of the wave, becomes, with the use of (11-4-11),

$$\frac{\gamma^2}{6}\frac{\partial}{\partial v}(v^3 f_1) = \frac{m}{M}\frac{\partial}{\partial v}\left(\frac{v^4 f_0}{\lambda}\right) + \frac{kT}{M}\frac{\partial}{\partial v}\left(\frac{v^3}{\lambda}\frac{\partial f_0}{\partial v}\right) \quad (11\text{-}4\text{-}15)$$

Equation 11-4-14, on the other hand, resolves itself, when the coefficients of the sine and cosine terms are equated, into the following two equations:

$$g_1 = \frac{\omega \lambda}{v}f_1 \quad (11\text{-}4\text{-}16)$$

$$\frac{1}{v}\frac{\partial f_0}{\partial v} = -\frac{v}{\lambda}f_1 - \omega g_1 \quad (11\text{-}4\text{-}17)$$

It then follows that

$$f_1 = -\frac{\lambda}{v^2 + \omega^2 \lambda^2}\frac{\partial f_0}{\partial v} \quad (11\text{-}4\text{-}18)$$

This expression for f_1 may be put into (11-4-15), which becomes after integration (the constant of integration being 0)

$$-\frac{\gamma^2}{3}\frac{\lambda v^4}{v^2 + \omega^2 \lambda^2}\frac{\partial f_0}{\partial v^2} = \frac{m}{M}\frac{v^4 f_0}{\lambda} + \frac{2kT}{M}\frac{v^4}{\lambda}\frac{\partial f_0}{\partial v^2}$$

so that

$$\log f_0 = -\int_0^{v^2}\frac{(m/2)\,d(v^2)}{kT + [M\gamma^2\lambda^2/6(v^2 + \omega^2\lambda^2)]} \quad (11\text{-}4\text{-}19)$$

If γ is so small that kT outweighs the second term in the denominator, f is Maxwellian. If the second term is dominant, we obtain a distribution function similar to Druyvesteyn's though differing from it by the presence of the term in ω:

$$f_0 = A \exp - \frac{3m(v^4 + 2\omega^2\lambda^2 v^2)}{2M\gamma^2\lambda^2} \qquad (11\text{-}4\text{-}20)$$

In arriving at this result, we have taken λ to be constant.

A more convenient way of expressing f_0 is by introducing two energy parameters

$$\varepsilon_1 = \tfrac{1}{2}m(\omega\lambda)^2 \quad \text{and} \quad \varepsilon_2 = eE_0\lambda \qquad (11\text{-}4\text{-}21)$$

which are characteristics of the distribution. In terms of these parameters and of $\varepsilon = \tfrac{1}{2}mv^2$, (11-4-20) reads

$$f_0 = A \exp\left[-\frac{6m}{M\varepsilon_2^2}(\varepsilon^2 + 2\varepsilon_1\varepsilon)\right] \qquad (11\text{-}4\text{-}22)$$

It is clear that for sufficiently large ε_1 the distribution differs appreciably from Druyvesteyn's formula even in the limiting case $(\varepsilon_2 \to \infty)$ under consideration.

If we integrate (11-4-19) without approximation, we obtain the accurate distribution law

$$f_0 = Ae^{-\varepsilon/kT}\left[1 + \frac{\varepsilon/kT}{(\varepsilon_1/kT) + \alpha}\right]^\alpha \qquad (11\text{-}4\text{-}23)$$

where

$$\alpha \equiv \frac{M}{12m}\left(\frac{\varepsilon_2}{kT}\right)^2 \qquad (11\text{-}4\text{-}24)$$

To determine the constant A, we use the relation

$$n = 4\pi\int_0^\infty f_0 v^2\, dv = 2\pi\left(\frac{2kT}{m}\right)^{3/2} A \int_0^\infty e^{-x}\left(1 + \frac{x}{x_1 + \alpha}\right)^\alpha x^{1/2}\, dx$$

$$= \left(\frac{2\pi kT}{m}\right)^{3/2} A\left[1 + \frac{3}{2}\frac{\alpha}{\alpha + x_1}\right.$$

$$\left. + \sum_{j=2}^\infty \frac{\alpha(\alpha-1)\cdots(\alpha-j+1)}{j!}\frac{1\cdot3\cdot5\cdots(2j-3)}{(\alpha+x_1)^j}\frac{4j^2-1}{2^j}\right]$$

where

$$x_1 \equiv \frac{\varepsilon_1}{kT} = \frac{m(\omega\lambda)^2}{2kT} \qquad x \equiv \frac{\varepsilon}{kT} \qquad (11\text{-}4\text{-}25)$$

Margenau shows that provided

$$x_1 > \alpha \qquad (11\text{-}4\text{-}26)$$

f_0 is Maxwellian in the ac case, even for values of the field strength which call for the use of the Druyvesteyn formula under dc conditions. If we consider as an example 3-cm waves passing through helium at a pressure of 20 mm Hg and room temperature, x_1 is about 100, and condition (11-4-26) requires that E_0 be less than about 7 volts/cm. For shorter wavelengths and lower pressure, the field strength is allowed to be greater.

2. *The drift velocity and conductivity.*   The drift velocity through the gas is

$$v_d = \bar{v}_x = \frac{\gamma}{n} \int v_x{}^2 (f_1 \cos \omega t + g_1 \sin \omega t) v^2 \, dv \sin \theta \, d\theta \, d\varphi$$

because of (11-4-10). Hence, in view of (11-4-16),

$$J = \frac{4\pi}{3} e\gamma \int_0^\infty f_1 \left(\cos \omega t + \frac{\lambda \omega}{v} \sin \omega t \right) v^4 \, dv \qquad (11\text{-}4\text{-}27)$$

Starting with (11-4-23) and using the quantities defined in (11-4-24) and (11-4-25), we obtain with the use of (11-4-18) and (11-4-19)

$$f_1 = 2A \left(\frac{m}{2kT} \right)^{2/3} \lambda \frac{(x + x_1 + \alpha)^{\alpha-1}}{(x_1 + \alpha)^\alpha} e^{-x} x^{1/2} \qquad (11\text{-}4\text{-}28)$$

When this expression is inserted in (11-4-27) the results, after an appropriate change of variable, are

$$J = \frac{8\pi}{3} \frac{e^2 E \lambda}{m^2} AkT \left[\int_0^\infty \frac{(x + x_1 + \alpha)^{\alpha-1}}{(x_1 + \alpha)^\alpha} e^{-x} x^2 \, dx (\cos \omega t) \right.$$

$$\left. + x_1^{1/2} \int_0^\infty \frac{(x + x_1 + \alpha)^{\alpha-1}}{(x_1 + \alpha)^\alpha} e^{-x} x^{3/2} \, dx (\sin \omega t) \right] \qquad (11\text{-}4\text{-}29)$$

The remaining integrals, as well as A, may be expressed in terms of confluent hypergeometric functions. For small integral values of α the integrands in (11-4-29) can be expanded easily, and the integrals become sums of Γ-functions. When this procedure is possible, it is far less laborious. From the expression for the current density, the conductivity (in general, a complex quantity) is obtained from the equation

$$J = \sigma_{\text{complex}} E_0 e^{i\omega t} \qquad (11\text{-}4\text{-}30)$$

The original Margenau analysis outlined here can lead to negative conductivities. Alternate formulas have been derived which correctly yield only positive results.[36]

11-5. ENERGY LOSSES IN COLLISIONS AND THE TRANSIENT MOTION OF ELECTRONS

It is often of interest to know how rapidly an electron swarm is able to approach steady-state conditions in a gas. The discussion of Section 2-5 indicates that the *energy relaxation time* for electrons in an atomic gas in the absence of inelastic collisions is roughly equal to $M/2m\bar{\nu}$, where M and m are the atomic and electronic masses and $\bar{\nu}$ is the average electronic collision frequency. Approximate values at E/p of the order of 0.1

TABLE 11-5-1. Values of F, the mean fraction of its energy that an electron loses per collision with a molecule, derived from the experiments of Crompton and Sutton[38] on hydrogen and nitrogen. The values labeled F_M were obtained by assuming a Maxwellian distribution of electron energies; those marked F_D were derived on the assumption that a Druyvesteyn distribution applies.

E/p (volts/cm-mm Hg)	Hydrogen		Nitrogen	
	$F_M \times 10^4$	$F_D \times 10^4$	$F_M \times 10^4$	$F_D \times 10^4$
0.05	5.37	6.63	3.33	4.11
0.1	10.6	13.1	3.11	3.84
0.2	16.0	19.9	3.07	3.78
0.3	18.1	22.3	2.90	3.58
0.4	18.2	22.5	3.03	3.74
0.5	18.6	23.0	3.10	3.83
0.6	19.2	23.7	3.28	4.05
0.7	19.1	23.6	3.52	4.35
0.8	18.9	23.4	3.86	4.76
0.9	18.8	23.2	4.20	5.18
1.0	19.3	23.8	4.52	5.58
1.2	19.9	24.5	5.27	6.51
1.5	22.1	27.3	6.73	8.32
1.8	24.5	30.3	8.20	10.1
2.0	25.2	31.3	9.05	11.2
3	30.6	37.8	14.5	18.0
4	35.8	44.2	20.6	25.4
5	41.4	51.0	26.9	33.2
10	61.3	75.6	66.9	82.6
15	81.0	100	114	141
20	111	138	166	205

* The collision frequency is really the quantity directly calculated—the time related to it has meaning only if the frequency is independent of speed.

volt/cm-mm Hg are $5/p$, $100/p$, and $500/p$ μsec for helium, neon, and argon, respectively, where p is the pressure in mm Hg. Estimates of the relaxation time for molecular gases must include the effects of vibrational and rotational excitation. Average values for H_2 and N_2 are about $\frac{1}{10}$ that for He.[8] Some idea of the magnitude of the relaxation time is required for the proper design of a drift velocity experiment. (It is obviously necessary to ensure that the relaxation time be much shorter than the drift time to be measured.) The energy loss experienced by electrons in collisions with molecules is also an important factor in the interaction of radio waves in the ionosphere.[1,37]

The mean fractional energy losses per collision for electrons in hydrogen and nitrogen are tabulated for various values of E/p in Table 11-5-1. These results were computed by Crompton and Sutton[38] from data they obtained in electron swarm diffusion experiments. Values are given for assumed Maxwell and Druyvesteyn electron energy distributions.

Data on electron collision frequencies in hydrogen and nitrogen are presented in Figs. 11-5-1 and 11-5-2, which are taken from a paper by Frost and Phelps.[39] In the energy range covered in these figures the electron distributions in both H_2 and N_2 are intermediate between Maxwellian and Druyvesteyn.[39] Two different collision frequencies, which describe separately the effects of momentum transfer collisions and inelastic collisions, are plotted for each gas. The first of these is ν_m, the *effective frequency for momentum transfer*, or *elastic collisions*; ν_m is defined by the relation

$$\frac{\nu_m}{N} = \frac{e}{m \mathscr{K} N} = \frac{e}{m} \frac{1}{v_d} \frac{E}{N} \qquad (11\text{-}5\text{-}1)$$

[cf. (9-2-2) and (9-4-2)]. If the true frequency of momentum transfer collisions, that is, the product of Nq_m and the electron speed, is independent of electron energy, the collision frequency is given exactly by (11-5-1).* Since in a real gas the true momentum transfer collision frequency is a function of the electron energy, it is convenient to plot the experimental and theoretical values of ν_m/N as functions of an experimental quantity, $\mathscr{D}/\mathscr{K}$, which measures the electron energy (cf. Section 11-2-A). The characteristic energy $\mathscr{D}/\mathscr{K}$ is, in turn, plotted as a function of E/N for hydrogen and nitrogen in Figs. 11-5-3 and 11-5-4. These figures permit the collision frequencies to be evaluated for specified values of E/N, if E/N rather than $\mathscr{D}/\mathscr{K}$ is the independent variable given.

The second collision frequency which Frost and Phelps[39] calculated is obtained by writing the power balance equation for an average electron.

---

* Here we are using q_m rather than q_D to denote the momentum transfer cross section in order to adhere to the notation of Frost and Phelps.

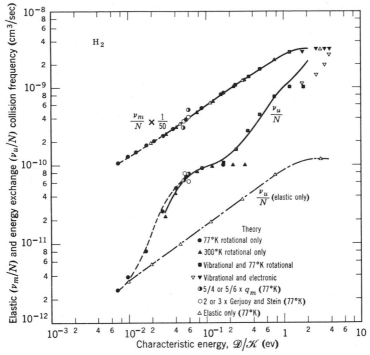

FIG. 11-5-1. Elastic and energy exchange collision frequencies as functions of $\mathscr{D}/\mathscr{K}$ for H_2. The points are the results of theoretical calculations by Frost and Phelps.[39] The solid and dashed curves are average values calculated from the experimental data shown in Fig. 11-5-3 for 300 and 77°K, respectively. The lowest curve gives the energy exchange collision frequency calculated when inelastic collisions are ignored. The energy exchange due to elastic collisions is included in all calculations. The collision frequencies are denoted by ν_m and ν_u and the gas number density, by N.

The power input per electron due to the applied electric field $v_d eE$ is equal to the *frequency of energy exchange collisions* ν_u times the excess of the electron energy over its thermal equilibrium value. If $\mathscr{D}/\mathscr{K}$ is taken to be the measure of the electron energy,

$$\frac{\nu_u}{N} = \frac{v_d E/N}{\mathscr{D}/\mathscr{K} - kT/e} \tag{11-5-2}$$

It is also convenient to plot the energy exchange collision frequency as a function of the characteristic energy, since ν_u/N is a measure of the energy-dependent inelastic collision cross sections divided by the electron speed. Frost and Phelps[39] point out that the energy exchange parameter defined by (11-5-2) offers several advantages over the energy loss per collision parameter usually applied in analyses of swarm experiments. First of all, its definition in terms of experimental and theoretical transport coefficients is independent of assumptions regarding the energy dependence of the distribution function. Second, the parameter characterizing the energy loss

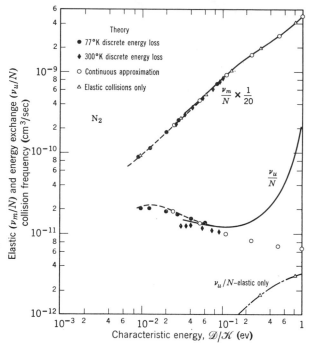

FIG. 11-5-2. Elastic and energy exchange collision frequencies as functions of $\mathcal{D}/\mathcal{K}$ for N_2. The points are the results of theoretical calculations by Frost and Phelps.[39] The solid and dashed curves are average values calculated from the experimental data of Fig. 11-5-4 for 300 and 77°K, respectively. The lowest broken curve gives the values of ν_u/N calculated when inelastic collisions are ignored.

per collision does not as a rule separate the elastic and inelastic effects but instead gives their ratio, a quantity that is seldom evaluated theoretically and generally has little significance in terms of atomic structure.

The form of (11-5-2) makes it clear that a high accuracy must be aimed for in the determination of $\mathcal{D}/\mathcal{K}$ as the electron energy approaches its thermal equilibrium value kT/e. The most recent work of Crompton and Elford[40] has produced data of high accuracy in this energy regime. The results of their investigation show a smaller experimental scatter than the data of Warren and Parker[4] and were obtained without the necessity of an empirical calibration of the apparatus which characterized the earlier

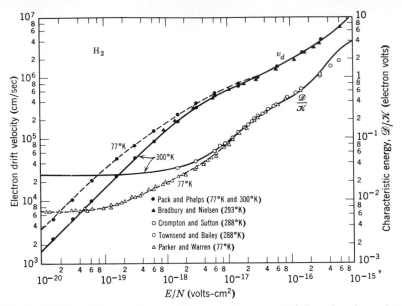

FIG. 11-5-3. The drift velocity v_d and characteristic energy $\mathscr{D}/\mathscr{K}$, as functions of E/N for H_2 at 77°K and room temperature. The points are experimental data, and the curves are the results of theoretical calculations by Frost and Phelps.[39] The $\mathscr{D}/\mathscr{K}$ versus E/N data at 77°K were measured after completion of the theoretical calculations.

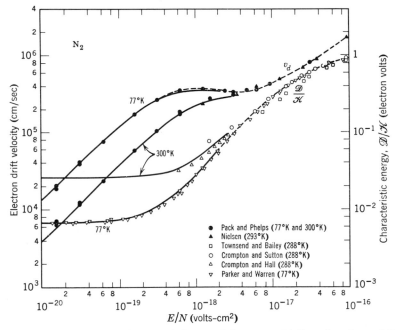

FIG. 11-5-4. The drift velocity v_d and characteristic energy $\mathscr{D}/\mathscr{K}$, as functions of E/N for N_2 at 77°K and room temperature. The points are experimental data, and the solid curves are the results of theoretical calculations by Frost and Phelps.[39]

work. Crompton and Elford[40] used the Townsend diffusion method and obtained data on H_2 and N_2. Their work was conducted at room temperature and at values of E/p_0 down to 0.006 v/cm-mm Hg.

REFERENCES

1. L. G. H. Huxley and R. W. Crompton, "The Motions of Slow Electrons in Gases," in *Atomic and Molecular Processes* (edited by D. R. Bates), Academic, New York, 1962.
2. L. B. Loeb, *Basic Processes of Gaseous Electronics*, Second Edition, University of California Press, Berkeley, 1960, Chapters III and IV.
3. R. H. Healey and J. W. Reed, *The Behavior of Slow Electrons in Gases*, Amalgamated Wireless, Ltd., Sydney (1941).
4. R. W. Warren and J. H. Parker, *Phys. Rev.* **128**, 2661 (1962). For important new theoretical work which bears on the Townsend diffusion method see J. H. Parker, *Phys. Rev.* **132**, 2096 (1963).
5. R. W. Crompton and R. L. Jory, *Australian J. Phys.* **15**, 451 (1962).
6. W. P. Allis and H. W. Allen, *Phys. Rev.* **52**, 703 (1937).
7. L. G. H. Huxley, *Australian J. Phys.* **10**, 118 (1957). See also L. Monchick, *Phys. Fluids* **5**, 1393 (1962).
8. J. L. Pack and A. V. Phelps, *Phys. Rev.* **121**, 798 (1961); J. L. Pack, R. E. Voshall, and A. V. Phelps, *Phys. Rev.* **127**, 2084 (1962).
9. N. E. Bradbury and R. A. Nielsen, *Phys. Rev.* **49**, 388 (1936); R. A. Nielsen, **50**, 950 (1936); R. A. Nielsen and N. E. Bradbury, **51**, 69 (1937).
10. The correction to be applied to the drift time when a variable-frequency voltage control is applied to the grid in a shutter experiment has been discussed by R. A. Duncan, *Australian J. Phys.* **10**, 54 (1957). A more comprehensive analysis of the errors caused by diffusion in drift velocity measurements has been performed by J. J. Lowke, *Australian J. Phys.* **15**, 39 (1962).
11. G. S. Hurst, L. B. O'Kelly, E. B. Wagner, and J. A. Stockdale, *J. Chem. Phys.* **39**, 1341 (1963).
12. S. Glasstone and R. H. Lovberg, *Controlled Thermonuclear Reactions*, Van Nostrand, Princeton, N.J., 1960.
13. S. C. Brown, *Basic Data of Plasma Physics*, Wiley, New York, 1959, pp. 85–86.
14. L. J. Varnerin and S. C. Brown, *Phys. Rev.* **79**, 946 (1950).
15. F. H. Reder and S. C Brown, *Phys. Rev.* **95**, 885 (1954).
16. D. Formato and A. Gilardini, *Proceedings of the Fifth International Conference on Ionization Phenomena in Gases*, Munich, 1961, North-Holland, Amsterdam (1962), Vol. I, p. 660.
17. J. A. Hornbeck, *Phys. Rev.* **83**, 374 (1951); see also J. C. Bowe, **117**, 1411 (1960).
18. See, for example, J. M. Kirshner and D. S. Toffolo, *J. Appl. Phys.* **23**, 594 (1952). L. Colli and U. Facchini, *Rev. Sci. Instr.* **23**, 39 (1952); T. E. Bortner, G. S. Hurst, and W. G. Stone, **28**, 103 (1957).
19. S. Glasstone and R. H. Lovberg, *Loc. cit.* D. J. Rose and M. Clark, *Plasmas and Controlled Fusion*, Wiley, New York, 1961. C. B. Wharton, "Microwave Diagnostics for Controlled Fusion Research," in *Plasma Physics* (edited by J. E. Drummond), McGraw-Hill, New York, 1961.
20. L. W. Cochran and D. W. Forester, *Phys. Rev.* **126**, 1785 (1962).
21. J. C. Bowe, *Phys. Rev.* **117**, 1411 (1960).

22. T. E. Bortner, G. S. Hurst, and W. G. Stone, *Rev. Sci. Instr.* **28,** 103 (1957).
23. J. J. Lowke, *Australian J. Phys.* **16,** 115 (1963).
24. G. S. Hurst, J. A. Stockdale, and L. B. O'Kelly, *J. Chem. Phys.* **38,** 2572 (1963). For more recent measurements of drift velocities in water vapor see J. J. Lowke and J. A. Rees, *Australian J. Phys.* **16,** 447 (1963).
25. F. B. Pidduck, *Proc. Roy. Soc. (London)* **A-88,** 296 (1913).
26. H. A. Lorentz, *The Theory of Electrons*, Second Edition, Dover, New York, 1952.
27. M. J. Druyvesteyn, *Physica* **10,** 61 (1930).
28. P. M. Morse, W. P. Allis, and E. S. Lamar, *Phys. Rev.* **48,** 412 (1935). See also T. Holstein, *Phys. Rev.* **70,** 367 (1946) and J. C. Bowe, *Am. J. Phys.* **31,** 905 (1963).
29. H. W. Allen, *Phys. Rev.* **52,** 707 (1937).
30. B. Davydov, *Physik Z. Sowjetunion* **8,** 59 (1935).
31. J. A. Smit, *Physica* **3,** 543 (1936).
32. N. P. Carleton and L. R. Megill, *Phys. Rev.* **126,** 2089 (1962).
33. W. P. Allis, "Motions of Ions and Electrons," in *Handbuch der Physik*, Vol. XXI, Springer-Verlag, Berlin, 1956, pp. 383–444.
34. S. Chapman and T. G. Cowling, *The Mathematical Theory of Non-uniform Gases*, Second Edition, Cambridge University Press, London, 1952, Chapter 18.
35. H. Margenau, *Phys. Rev.* **69,** 508 (1946).
36. E. A. Desloge, S. W. Matthysse, and H. Margenau, *Phys. Rev.* **112,** 1437 (1958); L. S. Taylor, *Phys. Fluids.* **4,** 1499 (1961).
37. J. D. Craggs and H. S. W. Massey, *Handbuch der Physik*, Springer-Verlag, Berlin, 1959, Vol. XXXVII, pp. 346–350.
38. R. W. Crompton and D. J. Sutton, *Proc. Roy. Soc. (London)* **A-215,** 467 (1952).
39. L. S. Frost and A. V. Phelps, *Phys. Rev.* **127,** 1621 (1962). For an extension of this work, see A. G. Engelhardt and A. V. Phelps, *Phys. Rev.* **131,** 2115 (1963); **133,** 375 (1964).
40. R. W. Crompton and M. T. Elford, *Sixth International Conference on Ionization Phenomena in Gases*, Paris, 1963.

12

RECOMBINATION*

In the present context the term recombination refers to a charge-neutralizing encounter between charge carriers of opposite sign moving about in a gas. If the carriers are both ionic, the process is called *ion-ion recombination*; if one is an electron and the other a positive ion, it is termed *electron-ion recombination*. These terms are misnomers in the sense that rarely does a "recombination" event actually involve the reunion of two particles that were formerly parts of the same structure,† but this terminology is standard and is used throughout this book.

The first studies of recombination were made in 1896 by Thomson and Rutherford at Cambridge. They proposed the mechanism of recombination to explain the gradual decrease in the conductivity of a gas following its ionization by a burst of X rays. Although experimental and theoretical investigations have continued since the late nineteenth century up to the present time,[1,2,3] our understanding of recombination is still far from

---

* An excellent review of this subject has recently been prepared by M. A. Biondi, "Atomic Collisions Involving Low Energy Electrons and Ions," in *Advances in Electronics and Electron Physics*, Vol. 18, Academic, New York, 1963.

† True *recombination*, or parent-ion recapture, may be important at short times after creation of ionization, before the electrons and positive ions can escape their mutual attractive field. See S. G. ElKomoss and J. L. Magee, *J. Chem. Phys.* **36**, 256 (1962).

complete. In fact, this subject is probably less well understood than that in any other chapter in this book. Some of the experimental difficulties and theoretical complexities that retard progress in this field will be brought out as we proceed.

We first define the recombination coefficient and derive expressions for the time dependence of the charge carrier number densities in terms of this coefficient. Then we discuss mechanisms and theories of recombination and derive equations for the recombination coefficient. Finally, experimental methods and data are presented, and comparisons are made with theoretical predictions.

12-1. THE RECOMBINATION COEFFICIENT

The recombination of two oppositely charged carriers is usually described in terms of their *recombination coefficient* α, which is defined as R, the number of recombination events per unit volume and unit time, divided by n^+n^-, the product of the number densities of the charge carriers. Thus

$$R = \alpha n^+ n^- \tag{12-1-1}$$

where α is a positive quantity with cgs units of cm³/sec.

The recombination coefficient is given in terms of the *recombination cross section* $q_r(v_0)$ by the equation

$$\alpha = \int_0^\infty v_0 q_r(v_0) f(v_0) \, dv_0 \tag{12-1-2}$$

where $f(v_0) \, dv_0$ is the fraction of the encounters between positive and negative particles in which the relative velocity lies between v_0 and $v_0 + dv_0$. In most applications α can be satisfactorily approximated by $\bar{v}_0 q_r(\bar{v}_0)$, where $\bar{v}_0$ is the mean value of v_0.

For a simple two-component system the recombination rate equals the loss rate of each of the two carriers, provided diffusion losses may be neglected and the ionization source is passive at the time under consideration. Accordingly, for such a system

$$\frac{dn^+}{dt} = \frac{dn^-}{dt} = -\alpha n^+ n^- \tag{12-1-3}$$

If we suppose that $n^+ = n^- = n$ and that $n = n_0$ at $t = 0$, the solution of (12-1-3) is .

$$\frac{1}{n} = \frac{1}{n_0} + \alpha t \tag{12-1-4}$$

so that the reciprocal of the number density is a linear function of the time with slope α. The recombination coefficient can therefore be obtained from the loss rate of the charge carriers in the gas if the conditions stated are satisfied. The measured value of α will, however, show a time dependence unless the ions were initially produced with random spatial distributions, both microscopic and macroscopic.[1,2] This condition requires that ions of opposite sign be given no preferential distribution in pairs and that there be no significant gradients in the ionic number densities over distances comparable with the apparatus dimensions.

If an ionization source is active in a two-component system, producing Q ions per cm³ per second and if recombination is the only loss mechanism, we have

$$\frac{dn}{dt} = Q - \alpha n^2 \tag{12-1-5}$$

where we again assume that $n^+ = n^- = n$. If we now set $n = 0$ at $t = 0$, integration of (12-1-5) yields

$$n = \left(\frac{Q}{\alpha}\right)^{\frac{1}{2}} \frac{e^{2\sqrt{\alpha Q}\,t} - 1}{e^{2\sqrt{\alpha Q}\,t} + 1} \tag{12-1-6}$$

so the number density of ions rises from zero at $t = 0$ toward an equilibrium value

$$n_\infty = \left(\frac{Q}{\alpha}\right)^{\frac{1}{2}} \tag{12-1-7}$$

12-2. RECOMBINATION IN A MULTIPLE-COMPONENT SYSTEM

Usually a recombination study involves a complex system consisting of electrons and several types of ions, and other processes such as diffusion, ion-molecule reactions, and electron attachment may play important roles. To illustrate the analysis required for realistic descriptions of such complex situations, we summarize a paper by Kunkel[4] which treats several cases of particular interest. Effects of diffusion are discussed in Section 12-8.

A. SECONDARY IONS FORMED IN COLLISIONS BETWEEN PRIMARY IONS AND GAS ATOMS. Kunkel's first analysis was meant to apply to experiments such as that performed by Johnson et al.[5] on the recombination of electrons with atomic and molecular ions of helium. Let n, M, and A denote the number densities of electrons, molecular ions, and atomic ions, respectively; α_1 represents the molecular, α_2, the atomic recombination coefficients, and β, the probability per unit time that an atomic ion will combine with a neutral atom to form a molecular ion (cf. Section 9-9-A).

Johnson et al. took α_1, α_2, and β to be constant, assumed diffusion* and electron attachment losses to be negligible, and described the recombination process by the equations

$$\frac{dn}{dt} = -\alpha_1 M n - \alpha_2 A n \tag{12-2-1}$$

$$\frac{dM}{dt} = -\alpha_1 M n + \beta A \tag{12-2-2}$$

$$\frac{dA}{dt} = -\alpha_2 A n - \beta A \tag{12-2-3}$$

which they solved by numerical integration. The molecular ions, all of which are produced during the measurement at the expense of the atomic ions, have a recombination coefficient that is large compared to that of the atomic ions.

The foregoing set of equations would also apply to the situation in which there is only one species of positive ion present (with number density n) and electrons (number density A) are being converted to negative ions (number density M) with an attachment probability of β per unit time. Whatever the problem under consideration, α_1, α_2, and β will generally be functions of the temperature and pressure and, of course, will depend on the nature of the gas.

One of the variables in this system of equations can at once be eliminated, since

$$\frac{dn}{dt} - \frac{dM}{dt} - \frac{dA}{dt} = 0 \tag{12-2-4}$$

Thus

$$n - M - A = \delta = n_0 - M_0 - A_0 \tag{12-2-5}$$

where the subscripts denote evaluation at time $t = 0$. Nevertheless, since the system of equations (12-2-1–12-2-3) is nonlinear, simple solutions cannot be obtained for all cases. Kunkel,[4] however, has solved these equations for the important case in which $\alpha_2 n \ll \beta$. This condition was satisfied in the microwave experiment of Johnson et al.,[5] in which $n \leq 10^{11}$, $\alpha_2 < 10^{-8}$, and $\beta = 10^4$. For this special case (12-2-3) reduces to

$$\frac{dA}{dt} = -\beta A \tag{12-2-6}$$

with the solution

$$A = A_0 e^{-\beta t} \tag{12-2-7}$$

* Actually diffusion was important in these experiments, and for this reason Kunkel's analysis is not truly applicable here because it ignored diffusion.

Substitution of (12-2-5) and (12-2-7) into (12-2-1) yields

$$\frac{dn}{dt} = -\alpha_1 n^2 + [(\alpha_1 - \alpha_2)A_0 e^{-\beta t} + \alpha_1 \delta]n \tag{12-2-8}$$

which has the solution

$$\frac{1}{n} = \frac{1}{g}\left(\frac{1}{n_0} + \alpha_1 \int_0^t g\, dt\right) \tag{12-2-9}$$

where

$$g = \exp\left[\delta\alpha_1 t + \frac{A_0(\alpha_1 - \alpha_2)}{\beta(1 - e^{-\beta t})}\right] \tag{12-2-10}$$

If $\alpha_1 = \alpha_2$, $A_0 = 0$, or $\beta = 0$, (12-2-9) becomes

$$\frac{1}{n} - \frac{1}{\delta} = \left(\frac{1}{n_0} - \frac{1}{\delta}\right)e^{-\delta\alpha_1 t} \tag{12-2-11}$$

which is the solution for the simple case of just two types of charge carriers, one of which has an excess concentration δ. If $\delta\alpha_1 t \ll 1$, (12-2-11) becomes approximately

$$\frac{1}{n} = \frac{1}{n_0} + \alpha_1\left(1 - \frac{\delta}{n_0}\right)t \tag{12-2-12}$$

Equation 12-2-12 shows how an excess of one carrier affects the apparent recombination coefficient. In the limiting case of equal number densities, we recover (12-1-4).

The integral in (12-2-9) does not have a closed form solution, hence must be expressed as a series. For the case of zero net charge density $\delta = 0$, and the series can be written

$$\int_0^t g\, dt = \left\{t - \frac{1}{\beta}\sum_{k=1}^{\infty}\left[\frac{A_0(\alpha_1 - \alpha_2)^k}{\beta}\frac{1 - e^{-k\beta t}}{kk!}\right]\right\}\exp\frac{A_0(\alpha_1 - \alpha_2)}{\beta} \tag{12-2-13}$$

This series converges rapidly only if $A_0(\alpha_1 - \alpha_2) \leq \beta$. To examine the significance of this condition, we observe from (12-2-5) that $\delta = 0$ implies $A_0 \leq n_0$. We have already required in our linearization process that $\alpha_2 n_0 \ll \beta$. The result is therefore that $\alpha_1 A_0 \leq \beta$. If $\alpha_2 \ll \alpha_1$, this requirement is more severe than the original requirement that $\alpha_2 n_0 \ll \beta$.

If it can be established that $A_0(\alpha_1 - \alpha_2) \ll \beta$, as in the experiment by Johnson et al.,[5] all terms with $k > 1$ in (12-2-13) may be neglected and (12-2-9) may be written

$$\frac{1}{n} \approx \frac{1}{n_0} + \alpha_1 t - \frac{A_0(\alpha_1 - \alpha_2)}{\beta}\left[\left(\frac{1}{n_0} + \frac{\alpha_1}{\beta}\right)(1 - e^{-\beta t}) - \alpha_1 t e^{-\beta t}\right] \tag{12-2-14}$$

This result differs from that for the simple two-component system with $\delta = 0$, described by (12-1-4), only by a small correction term. Equation 12-1-14 is plotted in Fig. 12-2-1, which was taken from the paper by Kunkel.[4] The numerical values in the insert are those of Johnson et al.[5] Note that $1/n$ is linear with t at times greater than about 3×10^{-4} sec but shows a curvature at earlier times. Equation 12-2-14 has the asymptotic form

$$\frac{1}{n} \approx \frac{1}{n_0} - \frac{A_0(\alpha_1 - \alpha_2)}{\beta n_0} + \alpha_1 t \qquad (12\text{-}2\text{-}15)$$

which represents a straight line intersecting the horizontal line $1/n = 1/n_0$ at a time $t_1 \approx A_0(\alpha_1 - \alpha_2)/n_0\alpha_1\beta$. Thus, if n_0 is known from measurements,

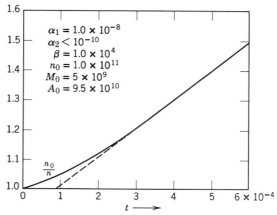

FIG. 12-2-1. Kunkel's solution of the recombination equation for the variation of $1/n$ with t when two positive ions, He^+ and $He_2{}^+$, for example, combine with electrons. He^+, which has a small recombination coefficient, is converted in collisions with helium atoms to $He_2{}^+$, which has a large coefficient.

$(A_0/\beta)(1 - \alpha_2/\alpha_1)$ is found immediately. Since α_1 is known from the slope of (12-2-15), it remains to determine A_0 or β separately.

Equations 12-2-5, 12-2-7, and 12-2-14 provide the basis for plots of n and $M = n - A$, and thus indirectly of $(nM)^{1/2}$, versus t. Since α_2 is negligible, the intensity of the recombination radiation* is proportional to nM. Therefore the maximum intensity should occur when $(nM)^{1/2}$ has its maximum value, that is, at a time given by the equation

$$e^{\beta t} = \left(1 + \frac{\beta}{\alpha_1 M}\right) \frac{A_0}{2n} \qquad (12\text{-}2\text{-}16)$$

* The emission of electromagnetic radiation in recombination events is discussed in Section 12-3.

Since α_1, n_0, and t for maximum radiation can be determined experimentally, (12-2-16) provides an independent means of obtaining a relationship between A_0 and β.

B. ION PRODUCTION DUE TO METASTABLE ATOMS. Kunkel[4] also considered the possibility of ionization in the gas following the removal of the external source. If the atoms of one of the constituents in a gas mixture have metastable states whose excitation energy is greater than the ionization energy of the other constituent, collisions between metastables of the first constituent and ground state atoms of the second may lead to ionization of the second type of atom. Such reactions may take place in mercury-contaminated helium according to the equation

$$Hg + He^m \rightarrow Hg^+ + e^- + He \qquad (12\text{-}2\text{-}17)$$

This reaction is an example of the Penning effect, which we have already discussed in Section 6-4. The cross section for an event such as that described by (12-2-17) may be extremely large.

Ionization may also occur in a pure gas such as helium as the result of the collision of two metastable atoms if the sum of the excitation energies is greater than the ionization energy of the ground state atom. This reaction in helium is described by the equation

$$He^m + He^m \rightarrow He^+ + e^- + He \qquad (12\text{-}2\text{-}18)$$

If we neglect diffusion and assume that only two carriers are involved, the system of recombination equations takes the form

$$\frac{dn}{dt} = \frac{dA}{dt} = -\alpha nA + Q(t) \qquad (12\text{-}2\text{-}19)$$

$Q(t)$ is the production term and depends on the time dependence of the ionizing source. For nonzero net charge density we may write

$$n - A = \delta = n_0 - A_0 \qquad (12\text{-}2\text{-}20)$$

and eliminate A to obtain

$$\frac{dn}{dt} = -\alpha n^2 + \alpha \delta n + Q(t) \qquad (12\text{-}2\text{-}21)$$

Kunkel[4] solved (12-2-21) for two special cases. One of these corresponds to an important class of experiments, and so the results are presented here. Let us suppose that the ionizing source decays exponentially and that we may write

$$Q = be^{-\beta t} \qquad (12\text{-}2\text{-}22)$$

where b is a constant. This assumption is reasonable if the ionization process is governed by (12-2-17) or by (12-2-18), provided the metastable removal is not controlled by (12-2-18). Under this assumption (12-2-21) has the approximate solution

$$\frac{1}{n} \simeq \frac{1}{n_0} + \alpha t - \frac{b}{\beta n_0}\left[\frac{1}{n_0}(1 - e^{-\beta t}) - \alpha t e^{-\beta t}\right] \qquad (12\text{-}2\text{-}23)$$

If we had assumed that n_0 was zero, we would have obtained

$$n \simeq \frac{1 - e^{-\beta t}}{\alpha t + (\beta/b)} \qquad (12\text{-}2\text{-}24)$$

We may note that for $\beta t \gg 1$ the behavior of (12-2-24) is similar to that predicted by the simple two-component result (12-1-4).

12-3. MECHANISMS OF ION-ION RECOMBINATION

If charge carriers of opposite sign are to recombine, their total internal energy must decrease as a result of the reaction. In the case of atomic ions the required energy decrease is equal to the difference between the ionization energy of the positive ion and the electron affinity of the negative ion. Once the oppositely charged ions begin to interact, the ability of the system to dispose of this excess energy determines the probability that recombination will occur. The energy release may be achieved through an increase in the kinetic energy of the neutralized particles, by transfer of energy to a third body, by the emission of electromagnetic radiation, or by electronic excitation of the neutralized atoms (which later become de-excited by some separate process).

The requirement that linear and angular momentum be conserved makes it almost impossible to dispose of the recombination energy by an increase in the kinetic energy of the recombining ions. Hence recombination between positive and negative ions will proceed according to one of the following reactions:

$$X^+ + Y^- + Z \rightarrow XY + Z \qquad (12\text{-}3\text{-}1)$$
$$X^+ + Y^- \rightarrow XY + h\nu \qquad (12\text{-}3\text{-}2)$$
$$X^+ + Y^- \rightarrow X^* + Y^* \qquad (12\text{-}3\text{-}3)$$

Three-body recombination, represented by (12-3-1), is the most important mechanism at pressures above a few mm Hg. Reactions 12-3-2 and 12-3-3, which represent *radiative recombination* and *mutual neutralization through charge exchange*, respectively, will predominate at low pressure, since they involve only two bodies. If one or both of the ions are molecular, the reaction list must be extended to include the possibility of dissociative mutual neutralization, which may be represented by an equation of the form

$$XY^+ + Z^- \rightarrow X + Y + Z \qquad (12\text{-}3\text{-}4)$$

12-4. ION-ION RECOMBINATION THEORY

In this section we shall discuss the theoretical treatments of the various recombination processes indicated in (12-3-1) through (12-3-4).

A. THREE-BODY RECOMBINATION. 1. *The Thomson theory.* Consider two species of ions, one of charge e and the other $-e$, undergoing random motion in a weakly ionized gas whose temperature is T. On the assumption that the ions are in thermal equilibrium with the gas, the average kinetic energy per ion equals $3kT/2$. Thus

$$\tfrac{1}{2}m^+v_R^{+2} = \tfrac{1}{2}m^-v_R^{-2} = \tfrac{3}{2}kT \qquad (12\text{-}4\text{-}1)$$

where $m^\pm$ denotes the ionic mass and $v_R{}^\pm$, the rms ionic velocity. The average kinetic energy of relative motion of a pair of oppositely charged ions also equals $3kT/2$, if the separation distance r is large; that is to say,

$$\tfrac{1}{2}M_r v_{0R}^2 = \tfrac{3}{2}kT \qquad (12\text{-}4\text{-}2)$$

where M_r is the reduced mass of m^+ and m^- and v_{0R} is the rms value of the relative velocity v_0 at large r. This relationship follows from (1-2-12), (2-2-15), and (12-4-1). The mutual potential energy of the ion pair is assumed to be given by the Coulomb expression $-e^2/r$. The potential energy is thus nearly zero when the ions are widely separated.

The Thomson theory[6] is based on the premise that an ion pair will combine if its total relative energy ever becomes negative, that is, if its kinetic energy of relative motion W ever becomes less than the energy required to separate the ions by an infinite distance. This condition is expressed by the inequality $W < e^2/r$. In the absence of collisions with a third body, recombination is therefore impossible according to this model (which does not allow for the possibility of de-excitation by radiation). At very large separation distances the relative energy of an ion pair, on the average, has the positive value $3kT/2$. If the two ions do not collide with molecules as they approach each other, the total relative energy will remain constant, since their relative kinetic energy increases during the approach at the same rate at which their mutual potential energy decreases. However, if one of the ions collides with a molecule and has its kinetic energy restored to the average thermal value within a critical distance r_1 of the other ion, the ions will execute closed orbits about each other and recombination will result. This critical distance is determined by the equation $3kT/2 = e^2/r_1$, so that

$$r_1 = \frac{2e^2}{3kT} \tag{12-4-3}$$

Thomson assumed each of the ions to be surrounded by a sphere of radius r_1. He then calculated the number of collisions of positive ions per second with gas molecules inside the negative ion spheres and the number of collisions of negative ions per second with gas molecules inside the positive ion spheres. The sum of these collision rates should equal the recombination rate, provided each collision results in recombination as assumed.

Following Thomson, let us assume that all directions of motion of the ions are equally probable. The discussion in Section 2-6, together with (2-2-15), shows that within a factor close to unity the number of positive ions passing into the sphere of radius r_1 surrounding each negative ion is

$$\pi r_1^2 n^+ (v_m^{+^2} + v_m^{-^2})^{\frac{1}{2}}$$

per second. Here the subscript m is used to denote the mean value of the velocities. A similar expression applies for the number of negative ions passing per second through the sphere centered at each positive ion:

$$\pi r_1^2 n^- (v_m^{+^2} + v_m^{-^2})^{\frac{1}{2}}$$

Then, if $w^{\pm}$ denotes the probability that an ion entering a sphere will collide with a gas molecule inside that sphere, the number of recombination events per cm^3 per second will be

$$R = \pi r_1^2 n^+ n^- (v_m^{+^2} + v_m^{-^2})^{\frac{1}{2}}(w^+ + w^-) \tag{12-4-4}$$

We must now calculate the probabilities w^+ and w^-. It was shown in Section 1-4 that particles with mean free path λ have a probability of $e^{-x/\lambda}$ of traveling a distance x from a given point without making a collision. If ψ represents the angle between the path of an ion entering a "sphere of possible recombination" and the normal to that sphere, $2r_1 \cos \psi$ will be the distance traveled by the ion while passing through the sphere if no collision occurs and if the curvature of the incident ion path is neglected. As shown in Section 1-5, the probability that the incidence angle will lie between ψ and $\psi + d\psi$ is $\sin \psi \, d\psi$. Therefore the probability that the ion will traverse the sphere without collision is

$$\int_0^{\pi/2} e^{-2r_1 \cos\psi/\lambda} \sin \psi \, d\psi = \frac{\lambda}{2r_1}(1 - e^{-2r_1/\lambda}) \tag{12-4-5}$$

It follows that the probability that a collision will occur is

$$w = 1 - \frac{\lambda}{2r_1}(1 - e^{-2r_1/\lambda}) \tag{12-4-6}$$

The actual collision probability is greater than this, however, because the mutual attraction of the ions increases the path length of the ion traversing the sphere.

If we calculate the probabilities w^+ and w^- by using the mean free paths λ^+ and λ^- for the positive and negative ions, respectively, we can obtain the final expression for the recombination rate R from (12-4-4). This quantity divided by n^+n^- equals the recombination coefficient α, and

$$\alpha = \pi r_1^2 (v_m^{+2} + v_m^{-2})^{1/2}\left[1 - \frac{\lambda^+}{2r_1}(1 - e^{-2r_1/\lambda^+}) + 1 - \frac{\lambda^-}{2r_1}(1 - e^{-2r_1/\lambda^-})\right] \tag{12-4-7}$$

Thomson considered two limiting cases, corresponding to "low" and "high" pressures, respectively. In the "low pressure" case $2r_1/\lambda$ is small, and the collision probabilities are

$$w = 1 - \frac{\lambda}{2r_1}\left(1 - e^{-2r_1/\lambda}\right) \approx \frac{r_1}{\lambda} \tag{12-4-8}$$

The resulting recombination coefficient is

$$\alpha_{rL} = 2\pi r_1^3(v_m^{+2} + v_m^{-2})^{1/2}\left(\frac{1}{\lambda^+} + \frac{1}{\lambda^-}\right) \tag{12-4-9}$$

At "high" pressure $2r_1/\lambda$ is large, the collision probabilities are approximately equal to unity, and the recombination coefficient becomes

$$\alpha_{rH} = 2\pi r_1^2(v_m^{+2} + v_m^{-2})^{1/2} \tag{12-4-10}$$

According to (2-2-15) and (2-2-3),

$$(v_m^{+2} + v_m^{-2})^{1/2} = v_{0m} = \left(\frac{8kT}{\pi M_r}\right)^{1/2} \tag{12-4-11}$$

By substituting (12-4-3) and (12-4-11) into (12-4-9) and (12-4-10), we obtain

$$\alpha_{rL} = \frac{32\sqrt{2\pi}e^6}{27\sqrt{M_r}}\frac{1}{(kT)^{5/2}}\left(\frac{1}{\lambda^+} + \frac{1}{\lambda^-}\right) \tag{12-4-12}$$

and

$$\alpha_{rH} = \frac{16\sqrt{2\pi}e^4}{9\sqrt{M_r}}\frac{1}{(kT)^{3/2}} \tag{12-4-13}$$

The derivation we have given here is that originally due to Thomson.[6] Differences in averaging procedures will lead to results that differ by small numerical factors from those we have presented. Massey and Burhop,[3] for instance, obtain a value for α_{rL} lower than that given by (12-4-12) by a factor of $\frac{2}{3}$.

We observe that the Thomson theory predicts that at constant temperature α should increase linearly with p at low pressures and become pressure-independent at high p. If the possible variation of $\lambda^{\pm}$ with T is ignored, α_{rL} should vary as $T^{-5/2}$ and α_{rH} as $T^{-3/2}$. The critical radius r_1 has the value 4.08×10^{-6} cm at 0°C, whereas the mean free path of an oxygen molecule at 0°C and atmospheric pressure is about 1.7 times this distance. It therefore seems reasonable to expect (12-4-12) to be valid for pressures from about 1 atm down to the level at which three-body collisions become too infrequent for the Thomson mechanism to apply. Experimental data of Sayers[7] for recombination in pure air, presented in Fig. 12-4-1, show reasonable agreement with the Thomson prediction for α_{rL} in the pressure range 100 to 1000 mm Hg. At pressures above 1000 mm Hg the experimental values decrease steadily in contrast with the Thomson prediction of constant α_{rH}.

At very high pressures the Thomson theory is defective because it assumes that recombination will inevitably occur if one of the ions makes an effective collision with a gas atom within a distance r_1 of an ion of the opposite sign. Although this assumption is reasonable at low pressures, it ignores the distinct possibility that at higher pressures a subsequent collision inside the sphere of radius r_1 may restore the ion to a hyperbolic orbit before recombination can take place. Thus we should expect the Thomson theory to overestimate the recombination coefficient at high pressures and that the higher the pressure, the greater the overestimate.*

Before we turn to the Langevin theory, which does prove satisfactory at high pressures, we should discuss the proper calculation and use of the ionic mean free paths in the Thomson theory. Massey and Burhop[3] point out that the mean free path of each ion may be assumed given by its diffusion cross section q_D and that $\lambda^{\pm} = 1/Nq_D{}^{\pm}$, where N is the number density of the gas atoms. However, in the calculation of α this mean free path should be increased by the larger of the two factors $m^{\pm}/M$ or $M/m^{\pm}$, in order to allow for the inefficiency of energy transfer in collisions of ions with gas atoms when their masses are different. Here M denotes the mass of the gas atom.

* The Thomson theory does not necessarily overestimate, however, because it ignores the possibility of stabilization by collisions in which energy is taken up in internal rotational modes. The effects of collisions of this kind in *electron-ion* recombination have been considered by R. C. Stabler, *Phys. Rev.* **131**, 1578 (1963).

2. *The Langevin theory.* According to this theory,[8] which holds only at very high pressures, the Coulomb force of attraction between two neighboring oppositely charged ions causes them to drift toward each other at a rate determined by their mobilities, $\mathscr{K}^+$ and $\mathscr{K}^-$. The electric field in which they move is given by $E = e^2/r^2$, and their relative drift velocity when they are separated by a distance r is $(\mathscr{K}^+ + \mathscr{K}^-)e^2/r^2$. Now assume that each positive ion is surrounded by a sphere of radius r. The net inward radial current density is given by the product of the relative drift velocity and number density of the negative ions. Thus the number of negative ions per second that drift inward across the sphere surrounding each positive ion is

$$4\pi(\mathscr{K}^+ + \mathscr{K}^-)e^2n^-$$

If we assume that none of these ions interacts with an ion other than that at the center of the sphere, we see that the number of recombining ion-pairs per cm³ per second will be

$$R = 4\pi e^2(\mathscr{K}^+ + \mathscr{K}^-)n^+n^- \qquad (12\text{-}4\text{-}14)$$

and the recombination coefficient will be given by

$$\alpha = 4\pi e^2(\mathscr{K}^+ + \mathscr{K}^-) \qquad (12\text{-}4\text{-}15)$$

Since the mobilities vary inversely with the pressure, the Langevin expression for the recombination coefficient decreases steadily as the pressure increases. Equation 12-4-15 has been found to be in general agreement at pressures above 10 atm with the results obtained by Mächler[9] for air at pressures of 5 to 12 atm. Neither the Thomson nor the Langevin theory satisfies the intermediate region between about 1 and 10 atm.

Satisfactory theoretical agreement with experiment throughout the range covered by the combination of Thomson's and Langevin's theories has recently been obtained by Natanson.[10] A detailed discussion of his paper follows.

3. *Natanson's analysis.* We recall from part 1 of this section that the starting point of Thomson's analysis of recombination was the consideration of the kinetic energies of two oppositely charged ions as they come close enough together to interact appreciably. Thomson assumed that if one of the ions collides with a gas molecule during this approach the average kinetic energy of each of the ions after the collision is equal to $3kT/2$ and that the mean kinetic energy associated with the relative motion of the two ions is also $3kT/2$. Natanson assumed, on the other hand, that following the collision of one of the ions with a neutral molecule the mean kinetic energy of the relative ionic motion has a different value, which may

be calculated as follows: when the ions are very far apart, the mean kinetic energy of each ion is $3kT/2$. Of the total kinetic energy $3kT$, half consists of the kinetic energy of the relative motion of the ions and half is the kinetic energy of the center of mass. When the ions approach each other within a distance r, the kinetic energy of their center of mass $3kT/2$ remains unchanged, and the kinetic energy of their relative motion increases to $3kT/2 + e^2/r$. The kinetic energy of each ion is then equal to $3kT/2 + e^2/2r$, provided the ions have equal masses. If, at the time when the ions are at a distance r from one another, one of them collides with a neutral gas molecule of the same mass which has the mean molecular kinetic energy of $3kT/2$, the kinetic energy of this ion will be reduced on the average to the value $\frac{1}{2}(3kT/2 + e^2/2r + 3kT/2) = 3kT/2 + e^2/4r$. (The energy of the ion is reduced to $3kT/2$ only in the case of a head-on collision.) Assuming that all directions of motion are equally probable for the first ion after the collision, we then obtain for the mean kinetic energy of the relative ionic motion after the collision the value

$$W = \frac{1}{2}\left(\frac{3kT}{2} + \frac{e^2}{4r} + \frac{3kT}{2} + \frac{e^2}{2r}\right) = \frac{3kT}{2} + \frac{3e^2}{8r}. \quad (12\text{-}4\text{-}16)$$

The critical recombination radius $r_1{}^*$ is thus determined by the condition

$$\frac{3kT}{2} + \frac{3e^2}{8r_1{}^*} = \frac{e^2}{r_1{}^*} \quad (12\text{-}4\text{-}17)$$

or

$$r_1{}^* = \frac{5e^2}{12kT} \quad (12\text{-}4\text{-}18)$$

Note that this value is $\frac{5}{8}$ of that given by the Thomson analysis in (12-4-3).

Natanson also modified Thomson's requirement that, in order for recombination to occur, the energy of relative motion of the ions W be less than the energy required to separate them by an infinite distance. Natanson imposed the more stringent requirement that the energy of relative motion be less than the energy required to alter the distance of separation of the ions from the value r to $r + \beta\lambda$, where $\beta\lambda$ is a distance of the order of the ionic mean free path λ. (If one of the ions collides with a molecule when the separation distance is $r + \beta\lambda$, it is likely that this ion will undergo another collision and thus gain the additional kinetic energy necessary to overcome the force of attraction.) The Thomson criterion

$$W \leq \int_r^\infty F\, dr \quad (12\text{-}4\text{-}19)$$

is therefore replaced by the requirement that

$$W \leq \int_r^{r+\beta\lambda} F \, dr \qquad (12\text{-}4\text{-}20)$$

where F is the force of interaction between the ions. Equations 12-4-19 and 12-4-20 yield comparable results for $\beta\lambda \gg r$. Recognizing that as the ions approach one another their trajectories are uninterrupted by collisions, on the average, only for separation distances between $r + \beta\lambda$ and r, Natanson obtains in place of (12-4-17) the condition

$$\frac{3kT}{2} + \frac{3}{8} \int_{r_1}^{r_1+\beta\lambda} F \, dr = \int_{r_1}^{r_1+\beta\lambda} F \, dr \qquad (12\text{-}4\text{-}21)$$

if the ionic masses are assumed to be equal. Thus the critical recombination radius is now found to be

$$r_1 = \frac{\beta\lambda}{2}\left[\left(1 + \frac{5e^2}{3kT\beta\lambda}\right)^{\frac{1}{2}} - 1\right] \qquad (12\text{-}4\text{-}22)$$

For the limiting cases of low and high pressures, respectively, we have

$$r_{1L} = \frac{5e^2}{12kT} ; \quad \beta\lambda \gg \frac{e^2}{kT} \qquad (12\text{-}4\text{-}23)$$

$$r_{1H} = \left(\frac{5e^2\beta\lambda}{12kT}\right)^{\frac{1}{2}} ; \quad \beta\lambda \ll \frac{e^2}{kT} \qquad (12\text{-}4\text{-}24)$$

Note that the result expressed by (12-4-23) is identical to the modified Thomson result (12-4-18).

We now proceed to calculate the recombination rate in terms of the value for r_1 given by (12-4-22). Let us circumscribe a sphere of radius r_1 about one of the positive ions, which is referred to as the "central ion." The probability that either this positive ion or a particular negative ion will collide with a gas molecule while the negative ion is inside the sphere is denoted by w. This quantity also equals the probability that a negative ion crossing into the sphere will be neutralized if we assume that the central positive ion is not neutralized by some other negative ion. A diffusion current of negative ions I incident on the sphere will therefore lead to $wI \, dt$ neutralizations of negative ions inside r_1 during the time dt. It follows that $wn^+I \, dt$ is the actual number of ion pairs undergoing recombination per unit volume in the time interval t to $t + dt$, if n^+ is the positive ion number density at the time t. The recombination coefficient is then given by the relation

$$\alpha = \frac{wn^+I}{n^+n^-} = \frac{wI}{n^-} \qquad (12\text{-}4\text{-}25)$$

where I represents the radial diffusion current of negative ions across the surface of a sphere of radius r_1 in a force field whose potential is

$$\varphi = \int_r^\infty F \, dr \qquad (12\text{-}4\text{-}26)$$

In evaluating the diffusion current of negative ions, we make the following three assumptions: (a) the positive ion at the center of the sphere is stationary; (b) the force acting on a diffusing negative ion is determined only by the interaction of that ion with the central positive ion; (c) the diffusion is quasi-stationary. Assumption (c) may be made if $(nr_1{}^3)^{1/2} \ll 1$. For values of r_1 of the order of e^2/kT or less this assumption is always valid when assumption (b) is fulfilled.

On the basis of these assumptions, diffusion theory gives the flow of negative ions toward the sphere for $r - r_1 \gg \lambda$ as

$$I_1 = 4\pi r^2 \left(\mathscr{D}^- \frac{dn}{dr} + \mathscr{K}^- En \right) \qquad (12\text{-}4\text{-}27)$$

where $\mathscr{D}^-$ is the negative ion diffusion coefficient, $\mathscr{K}^-$, the mobility, n, the number density, and E, the electric field intensity. The first term in the parentheses on the right side of (12-4-27) represents the negative ion current arising from diffusion, and the second term the current produced by the drift of the negative ions in the force field of the positive ion. In (12-4-27) we used the definition of mobility which is standard in discussions of gaseous electronics, that is, our mobility $\mathscr{K}$ is defined as the drift velocity per unit of applied electric field intensity. Natanson used a more general concept of mobility, and his coefficient B is equal to the drift velocity per unit of applied force $F = eE$. Evidently

$$B = \frac{\mathscr{K}}{e} \qquad (12\text{-}4\text{-}28)$$

From this point on to the end of Natanson's analysis we shall use his definition of mobility. According to (10-2-5), we may make the substitution

$$B^- = \frac{\mathscr{D}^-}{kT} \qquad (12\text{-}4\text{-}29)$$

Then if we integrate (12-4-27) for constant I_1, subject to the boundary condition that $n = n^-$ when $r = \infty$, we obtain

$$I_1 = \frac{4\pi \mathscr{D}^-(n^- - ne^{-\varphi/kT})}{\displaystyle\int_r^\infty e^{-\varphi/kT} dr/r^2} \tag{12-4-30}$$

which reduces to

$$I_1 = \frac{4\pi \mathscr{D}^- e^2(n^- - ne^{-e^2/rkT})}{kT(1 - e^{-e^2/rkT})} \tag{12-4-31}$$

We may also use kinetic theory to obtain the radial current of negative ions incident on the sphere surrounding the central positive ion. Although determination of a general expression for this current is difficult, approximate expressions applying to the two special cases $\lambda \gg r_1$ and $\lambda \ll r_1$ are readily obtainable.

Case a: low pressure, $\lambda \gg r_1$.

Assume that each of the ions incident on the sphere of radius r_1 underwent its last collision with a gas molecule at a radius $r_1 + \lambda$. Let the fraction of the negative ions with velocities at the beginning of their free paths in the range v_1 to $v_1 + dv_1$ be denoted by $f(v_1)\,dv_1$. Then, if we imagine the ions to move in straight lines, in the absence of interaction forces, the number of negative ions with initial velocities in the range v_1 to $v_1 + dv_1$ which approach the center of the sphere in the time dt at a distance less than r_1 is equal to

$$\pi r_1^2 n_{r_1+\lambda}^- v_1\, f(v_1)\, dv_1\, dt$$

where $n_{r_1+\lambda}^-$ represents the negative ion concentration at $r = r_1 + \lambda$. In order to account for the effect of the interaction between the incoming negative ions and the central positive ion, it is necessary to multiply this expression by the quantity[11]

$$\gamma = 1 + \frac{2\displaystyle\int_{r_1}^{r_1+\lambda} F\, dr}{mv_1^2} \tag{12-4-32}$$

where F denotes the interaction force. Now, for $\lambda \gg r_1$, $\lambda F_{r_1+\lambda}/kT \ll 1$, and the ionic velocity v_1 for $r = r_1 + \lambda$ may be taken to be the most probable velocity corresponding to a Maxwellian distribution at the gas temperature T. From (2-2-5) this velocity is

$$v_p = \left(\frac{2kT}{m}\right)^{1/2} \tag{12-4-33}$$

Therefore the number of ions with velocity in the range v_1 to $v_1 + dv_1$ incident on the spherical surface of radius r_1 in unit time is

$$\pi r_1^{\,2}\left(1 + \frac{1}{kT}\int_{r_1}^{r_1+\lambda} F\,dr\right)n_{r_1+\lambda}^{-}\,v_1 f(v_1)\,dv_1$$

Integration over the velocity distribution yields

$$I_2(\lambda \gg r_1; r = r_1) = \pi r_1^{\,2}\bar{v}\left(1 + \frac{1}{kT}\int_{r_1}^{r_1+\lambda} F\,dr\right)n_{r_1+\lambda} \quad (12\text{-}4\text{-}34)$$

where $\bar{v}$ is the mean velocity of the negative ions.

Case b: high pressure, $r_1 \gg \lambda$.

In order to obtain the current for the high pressure case, we shall calculate the number of negative ions crossing a unit plane surface per unit time. We assume that the velocity component in the direction of the normal y to the surface is constant for all ions and equal to B^-F. This number may be expressed as (cf. Sections 2-6 and 2-9)

$$\int_{-\infty}^{\infty}\int_{B^-F}^{\infty}\int_{-\infty}^{\infty}\left(n_{r_1} + \lambda\cos\theta\,\frac{dn}{dy}\right)\left(\frac{m}{2\pi kT}\right)^{3/2}$$

$$\times \exp\left[\frac{-m(v_x^{\,2} + v_y^{\,2} + v_z^{\,2})}{2kT}\right](v_y + B^-F)\,dv_x\,dv_y\,dv_z \quad (12\text{-}4\text{-}35)$$

where v_x, v_y, and v_z are the components of the thermal velocity of the ions and

$$\cos\theta = \frac{v_y + B^-F}{[v_x^{\,2} + (v_y + B^-F)^2 + v_z^{\,2}]^{1/2}}$$

Calculation to first order in B^-F yields the value

$$\left(\frac{\bar{v}n_{r_1}}{4}\right) + \tfrac{1}{2}\mathscr{D}^-\frac{dn}{dr} + \tfrac{1}{2}B^-Fn_{r_1} + \tfrac{9}{8}B^-F\frac{\mathscr{D}^-}{\bar{v}}\frac{dn}{dr} \quad (12\text{-}4\text{-}36)$$

for the triple integral in (12-4-35), where we have replaced dn/dy by dn/dr and used (2-9-6) to make the substitution

$$\mathscr{D}^- = \frac{\bar{v}\lambda}{3}$$

The first term of (12-4-36) corresponds to the number of crossings per second per unit area calculated by kinetic theory for zero concentration gradient and no interaction between the ions. The expression analogous to (12-4-36) for the number of ions crossing unit area in the reverse direction differs from (12-4-36) only in the signs preceding the second and third terms. Thus the difference between the number of crossings in the forward and reverse directions actually gives the total current corresponding to the expression in parentheses in (12-4-27). In this manner we obtain the following expression for the negative ion current for $r = r_1$ and $r_1 \gg \lambda$:

$$I_2(r_1 \gg \lambda; r = r_1) = 4\pi r_1^2\left[\left(\frac{\bar{v}n_{r_1}}{4}\right) + \frac{1}{2}\mathscr{D}^-\left(\frac{dn}{dr}\right)_{r_1} + \frac{1}{2}B^-F_{r_1}n_{r_1}\right.$$

$$\left. + \frac{9}{8}\frac{B^-F}{\bar{v}}\mathscr{D}^-\left(\frac{dn}{dr}\right)_{r_1}\right] \quad (12\text{-}4\text{-}37)$$

We should emphasize the point that (12-4-37) and indeed the concept of a constant mobility, is correct only if $B^-F/\bar{v} \ll 1$ or $\lambda F_{r_1}/3kT \ll 1$. At the same time, according to (12-4-22), r_1 has been determined, and for $r_1 \gg \lambda$, $\lambda F_{r_1}/3kT = \frac{4}{5}$. Nevertheless, as a rough approximation, we assume that (12-4-37) remains correct even for $\lambda F_{r_1}/kT$ approximately equal to unity. Now, if we replace the coefficient $\frac{9}{8}$ which appears in (12-4-37) by unity and make use of the fact that $\mathscr{D}^- = B^-kT$, we may write

$$I_2(r_1 \gg \lambda; r = r_1) = \pi r_1^2\bar{v}\left(n_{r_1} + \frac{2\mathscr{D}^-}{\bar{v}}\frac{dn}{dr}\right)\left(1 + \frac{2\mathscr{D}^-F}{\bar{v}kT}\right)$$

$$= \pi r_1^2\bar{v}\left(1 + \frac{1}{kT}\int_{r_1}^{r_1+2\mathscr{D}^-/\bar{v}} F\,dr\right)n_{r_1+2\mathscr{D}^-/\bar{v}} \quad (12\text{-}4\text{-}38)$$

Thus we are able to write both (12-4-38), which applies for high pressures, and (12-4-34), the low pressure result, in the same form:

$$I_2 = \pi r_1^2\bar{v}\left(1 + \frac{1}{kT}\int_{r_1}^{r_1+\beta\lambda} F\,dr\right)n_{r_1+\beta\lambda} \quad (12\text{-}4\text{-}39)$$

where $\beta = 2\mathscr{D}^-/\bar{v}\lambda$ for $r_1 \gg \lambda$ and $\beta = 1$ for $\lambda \gg r_1$.

We shall now make the assumption that (12-4-31) for I_1 remains valid for values of $r \geq r_1 + \beta\lambda$. By substituting the values $r = r_1 + \beta\lambda$ and $n = n_{r_1+\beta\lambda}$ in this expression and making use of the fact that under steady-state conditions $I_1 = I_2 = I$, we get from (12-4-31) and (12-4-39)

$$n_{r_1+\beta\lambda} = n^-e^{e^2/(r_1+\beta\lambda)kT}$$

$$\times \left[1 + \frac{r_1^2\bar{v}wkT}{4\mathscr{D}^-e^2}\left(1 + \frac{e^2\beta\lambda}{r_1(r_1 + \beta\lambda)kT}\right)(e^{e^2/(r_1+\beta\lambda)kT} - 1)\right]^{-1} \quad (12\text{-}4\text{-}40)$$

Up to this point we have assumed the central positive ion to be stationary. In order to take the motion of this ion into consideration, we must replace $\mathscr{D}^-$ by $\mathscr{D} = \mathscr{D}^- + \mathscr{D}^+$ and the mean thermal velocity $\bar{v}$ by the mean relative velocity $\bar{v}_0 = [(\bar{v}_-)^2 + (\bar{v}_+)^2]^{1/2}$. By neglecting the difference in the values of the mean free paths of the positive and negative ions and substituting the expression for $n_{r_1+\beta\lambda}$ in either (12-4-39) or (12-4-31), we obtain for the recombination coefficient

$$
\alpha = \frac{wI}{n^-} = \pi r_1^2 \bar{v}_0 w \left(1 + \frac{e^2 \beta \lambda}{r_1(r_1 + \beta\lambda)kT} \right) e^{e^2/(r_1+\beta\lambda)kT}
$$

$$
\times \left[1 + \frac{r_1^2 \bar{v}_0 w kT}{4\mathscr{D}e^2} \left(1 + \frac{e^2 \beta\lambda}{r_1(r_1 + \beta\lambda)kT} \right) (e^{e^2/(r_1+\beta\lambda)kT} - 1) \right]^{-1} \quad (12\text{-}4\text{-}41)
$$

For $\lambda \ll e^2/kT$, $\lambda \ll r_1$ and $r_1 \ll e^2/kT$, according to (12-4-22). Under these conditions (12-4-41) becomes

$$
\alpha = \frac{4\pi \mathscr{D} e^2}{kT} (1 - e^{-e^2/r_1 kT})^{-1} \approx 4\pi e^2 (\mathscr{K}^- + \mathscr{K}^+) \quad (12\text{-}4\text{-}42)
$$

which is the Langevin result (12-4-15) exactly. Note that (12-4-42) is independent of the exact form of the expression for I_2 for $r_1 \gg \lambda$.

For $\lambda \gg e^2/kT$, $\lambda \gg r_1$ and $r_1 = 5e^2/12kT$, according to (12-4-22). Under these conditions (12-4-41) becomes

$$
\alpha = \pi r_1^2 w \bar{v}_0 \left(1 + \frac{e^2}{r_1 kT} \right) e^{e^2/\beta\lambda kT} \sim \frac{17}{5} \pi r_1^2 w \bar{v}_0 \quad (12\text{-}4\text{-}43)
$$

Equation 12-4-43 differs from Thomson's formula by the factor $(1 + e^2/r_1 kT)$, which takes account of the curvature of the ion trajectory, and by the factor $e^{e^2/\beta\lambda kT}$, which accounts for the changes in the ion concentration for ions separated by a distance $r = r_1 + \beta\lambda$. Equation 12-4-43 also contains a different value for r_1. For ions of equal mass the numerical value of α given by (12-4-43) for $\lambda \gg e^2/kT$ is larger than Thomson's result by a factor of $\frac{85}{64}$.

Using (12-4-22), we find that

$$
\int_{r_1}^{r_1+\beta\lambda} F \, dr = \frac{e^2 \beta\lambda}{r_1(r_1 + \beta\lambda)} = \frac{12kT}{5}
$$

for ions of equal mass, and thus $e^2/(r_1 + \beta\lambda)kT = 12r_1/5\beta\lambda$. Even though β is a function of r_1/λ, we shall make the assumption that β is a constant and equal to unity. Then, using (12-4-22) and making the substitution

$$
x = \frac{r_1}{\lambda} = \frac{1}{2}\left[\left(1 + \frac{5e^2}{3kT\lambda} \right)^{1/2} - 1 \right]
$$

we may write (12-4-41), for the case of equal ion masses, in the form

$$
\alpha = \tfrac{17}{5}\pi \bar{v}_0 w \lambda^2 x^2 e^{2x} \left[1 + \frac{17\bar{v}_0 kT}{20e^2} \frac{\lambda}{\mathscr{D}} w\lambda x^2 (e^{2x} - 1) \right]^{-1} \quad (12\text{-}4\text{-}44)
$$

Thomson[6] showed that if the positive and negative ions are assumed to have equal probabilities of colliding with molecules $w = 2w_1 - w_1^2$, where $w_1 = 1 - (1/2x^2)[1 - e^{-2x}(1 + 2x)]$. For high pressures $x \gg 1$ and $w = 1$. At low pressures $x \ll 1$ and $w = 8x/3$. Loeb[12] presents a table of values of w for intermediate values of r_1/λ.

Complete confirmation of (12-4-44) by comparison with experiment is not possible because of the scarcity of the data. Natanson, however, did obtain a partial check with the experimental results obtained by Sayers[7] and Mächler[9] on ion-ion recombination in air. The comparison is illustrated in Figure 12-4-1, which shows a log-log plot of the recombination coefficient

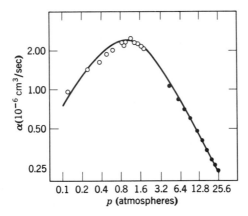

FIG. 12-4-1. Comparison of theoretical results of Natanson (solid curve) with experimental results of Sayers (circles) and Mächler (dots) for ion-ion recombination in air. For recent theoretical work see K. A. Brueckner, *J. Chem. Phys.* **40,** 439 (1964).

versus pressure. Sayers' data are indicated by the circles and Mächler's results, by the dots. The curve represents the results of computations based on (12-4-44). The following values of constants were used: $\bar{v}_0 = 6.2 \times 10^4$ cm/sec, $\lambda = 2.9 \times 10^{-6}$ cm at atmospheric pressure, and $\mathscr{D} = 8.2 \times 10^{-2}$ cm²/sec at atmospheric pressure. The value for $\bar{v}_0$ was chosen to agree with the assumption that the recombining ions were atomic oxygen ions, since this was thought to be the case for very pure air.[13]

Despite the many assumptions evident in Natanson's analysis and the limited opportunities for comparison with experimental results, it appears that his results bridge the gap between the low- and high-pressure regimes formerly describable only in terms of the two distinct theories of Thomson and Langevin. The absolute comparison between Natanson's theory and experimental results is perhaps questionable, but the pressure dependence predicted by the theory appears valid.

B. RADIATIVE RECOMBINATION. In radiative recombination the excess energy of the recombining ions is disposed of by the emission of electromagnetic radiation. This recombination process

$$X^+ + Y^- \rightarrow XY + h\nu \tag{12-3-2}$$

requires a radiative transition between two electronic states of the molecule XY, the final state of XY being one that dissociates into the ions X^+ and Y^- at infinite separation. An estimate of the radiative recombination coefficient may be obtained by the following argument, which is similar to that used in Section 8-2-A in the discussion of radiative electron attachment. Measured lifetimes of ordinary excited states of atoms and molecules indicate that a pair of oppositely charged ions must remain close together for about 10^{-8} sec at least if they are to recombine via a radiative process. If we assume that the ions have thermal energies corresponding to room temperature, their average relative velocity will be about 10^5 cm/sec, and the time required to traverse a typical molecular diameter at this velocity is only about 10^{-13} sec. During this period of time the probability that a photon will be emitted to de-excite the system is only about 10^{-13} sec$/10^{-8}$ sec $= 10^{-5}$, and this probability corresponds to a recombination coefficient of only about 10^{-14} cm^3/sec. For ions of greater than thermal energy, radiative recombination occurs at an even slower rate. Accordingly, one may conclude that radiative recombination will be highly ineffective except at extremely low pressures and that this mode of recombination may normally be neglected in comparison with three-body and mutual neutralization processes.

C. MUTUAL NEUTRALIZATION. As stated earlier, recombination of positive and negative ions at pressures above a few mm Hg proceeds primarily via three-body processes, with the third body serving to remove the excess energy. At reduced pressures the mutual neutralization process

$$X^+ + Y^- \rightarrow X^* + Y^* \tag{12-3-3}$$

becomes significant, in which case the energy of recombination goes into electronic excitation or kinetic energy of the neutral atoms or a combination of these two forms of energy. The neutralizations occurs by a *charge exchange process*. The electron from ion Y^- may be captured into any state of the neutral atom X, with the neutral atom Y being left in any state for which energy is conserved. However, the probability of the charge exchange occurring is a strong maximum for some particular pair of final states of X and Y.[3]

The first quantitative treatment of the process of mutual neutralization was published by Bates and Massey[14] in 1943, and a number of similar calculations have appeared subsequently in the literature.[15] The theory of the process is best considered in relation to the crossing of molecular potential energy curves.* Figure 12-4-2a shows the potential energy curves for two electronic states of a molecule AB, which dissociate into separated atomic states $A_1 + B_1$ and $A_2 + B_2$, respectively, calculated to zero-order approximation. (In the present problem the right-hand side of curve Ia corresponds to the ions X^+ and Y^-, and the right-hand side of IIa corresponds to the neutral atoms X and Y in excited states.) Suppose that these curves intersect at a point S in the absence of interaction. Then if the

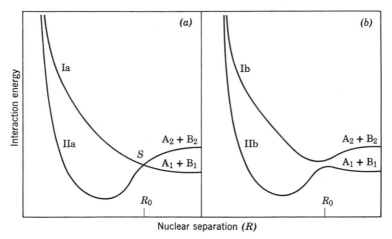

FIG. 12-4-2. Illustration of the interaction of molecular potential energy curves: (a) two curves in the absence of interaction; (b) the curves modified by the interaction.[14]

properties of the states are such that they can interact, this interaction will modify the potential energy diagram to that shown in Fig. 12-4-2b, in which the curves no longer cross. Thus curve Ib has the character of an $A_1 + B_1$ combination at small nuclear separations but the character of an $A_2 + B_2$ combination at large separations. The situation is reversed for curve IIb. This means that if atoms A and B in states A_1 and B_1, respectively, are allowed to come together adiabatically (i.e., with infinite slowness), the interaction between them will follow curve IIb. On the other hand, if the atoms in these states come together with a finite relative velocity v_r, there is a finite probability that a transition will occur near S in which the system jumps from IIb to Ib. If this probability is denoted by $P(v_r)$, the probability that the system will continue along IIb is $1 - P$.

---

* For a general discussion of molecular potential energy curves the reader is referred to Section 8-1-B. Massey and Burhop treat curve crossing on pp. 445–447 of their book,[3] and mutual neutralization on pp. 620–622 of the same reference.

When the atoms reach their distance of closest approach, their relative motion will reverse, and there is again a chance P that a transition will occur at S. Thus, if we imagine the atoms to be brought together from infinite separation with a finite relative velocity v_r and then allowed to separate again, the probability of finding the separated atoms in the initial states A_1 and B_1 is consequently $1 - 2P(1 - P)$, whereas the probability of finding them in the A_2 and B_2 states is $2P(1 - P)$. The net probability, $2P(1 - P)$, that the atoms will finally withdraw from one another in neutral states will be small if P is small or nearly unity. The former case is the nearly adiabatic one of a very slow approach; the latter corresponds to the interaction between the two molecular states being very weak. (In the limit of vanishing interaction the curves actually cross at S, as shown in Fig. 12-4-2a, and the identifications of the curves inside S are interchanged.) The maximum value of the net transition probability is $\frac{1}{2}$.

The transition probability P may be calculated by the *Landau-Zener formula*,[16] which is given below. Let $U_i(R)$ and $U_f(R)$ be the two potential energy functions in zero-order approximation, and let $U_{if}(R)$ be the transition potential energy, in which R denotes the internuclear separation. In terms of the zero-order electronic wave functions ψ_i and ψ_f for the two potential energy curves, these functions are given by the equations

$$U_i = \int \psi_i^* V \psi_i \, d\tau; \qquad U_f = \int \psi_f^* V \psi_f \, d\tau; \qquad U_{if} = \int \psi_i^* V \psi_f \, d\tau$$

$$(12\text{-}4\text{-}45)$$

where $V(r, R)$ is the appropriate interaction energy between the colliding atoms and the integration is performed over the electronic coordinates $\mathbf{r}$. In terms of these quantities, P is given by the expression

$$P = \exp \left[\frac{-(4\pi^2/hv_r)|U_{if}|^2}{|(d/dR)(U_i - U_f)|} \right] \qquad (12\text{-}4\text{-}46)$$

where all the quantities, including the relative velocity of the atoms v_r, are calculated at the crossing point $R = R_0$. If ΔE is the energy difference between the two curves at infinite nuclear separation, R_0 is the solution of the equation

$$U_i - U_f = \Delta E \qquad (12\text{-}4\text{-}47)$$

The Landau-Zener result (12-4-46) was obtained on the assumption that the relative motion of the atoms occurs along their line of centers. If, on the other hand, the atoms have a nonzero relative angular momentum, a centrifugal energy term $l(l + 1)h^2/8\pi^2 M_r R^2$ is introduced into the functions U_i and U_f, where M_r is the reduced mass of the atoms. This additional term reduces the value of the relative velocity v_r, which is now given by the equation

$$\tfrac{1}{2}M_r v_r^2 = E_i - U_i - \frac{l(l+1)h^2}{8\pi^2 M_r R^2} \tag{12-4-48}$$

where E_i is the kinetic energy of relative motion at infinite separation in the initial state. No appreciable transition probability is associated with relative motion in which, at $R = R_0$, the value of v_r given by (12-4-48) is small. The same statement applies if the right-hand side of (12-4-48) is negative.

Since the probability P depends on the relative angular momentum of the two systems, the cross section for mutual neutralization recombination q_r must be obtained by a summation process:

$$q_r = \sum_{l=0}^{\infty} 2P_l(1 - P_l)q_m \tag{12-4-49}$$

Here q_m is the maximum partial cross section* for relative angular momentum $[l(l+1)]^{1/2}h/2\pi$ and is equal to $(2l+1)\pi/\kappa^2$, where κ is the wave number of relative motion of a system composed of masses M_1 and M_2 with a relative velocity v_r; κ is given by the equation

$$\kappa = \frac{2\pi M_r v_r}{h}$$

where M_r is the reduced mass of M_1 and M_2.

In a paper already referred to Bates and Massey[14] applied this theory to the reaction

$$O^+ + O^- \rightarrow O^* + O^*$$

Because it was impossible to determine accurately the interaction between the different sets of potential energy curves at the point S, they did not attempt to calculate the actual value of the mutual neutralization coefficient. Bates and Massey, however, did obtain the possible order of magnitude of the coefficient and an indication of the most likely final states of the atoms. They concluded that a coefficient as high as 10^{-8} cm³/sec at room temperature was probable and that the value could even be an order of magnitude higher. The most probable transition was found to be one in which the atoms are left with a relative kinetic energy of about 1 ev at infinite separation. Magee[17] has also estimated the mutual neutralization coefficient for O^+ and O^- ions by means of a semiclassical impact parameter method. His results agree with those of Bates and Massey.

* See Section 3-15-D.

Unfortunately, there are no experimental data on mutual neutralization with which theoretical calculations can be compared, and such data will evidently be hard to obtain. A further difficulty has been pointed out by Bates,[18] who has demonstrated that the Landau-Zener formula is invalid over much of the energy range for which it was designed and to which it has been applied. Bates particularly emphasizes the severe restrictions that must be imposed if the orbitals involved are not spherically symmetric.

12-5. MECHANISMS AND THEORY OF ELECTRON-ION RECOMBINATION

Electron-ion recombination has traditionally been analyzed in terms of separate reactions of the following types: radiative, dielectronic, dissociative, and three-body recombination. In Section A we discuss each of these mechanisms separately; then in Section B we show the necessity of considering the coupling of these mechanisms in a realistic analysis of the general recombination problem.

A. SEPARATE MECHANISMS. 1. *Radiative recombination.*

$$X^+ + e \rightarrow X^* + h\nu \qquad (12\text{-}5\text{-}1)$$

The energy of recombination is carried off in the form of radiation. This process is the inverse of photoionization, the cross sections for the two processes being related by the *Milne formula*[19] [which simplifies to (7-2-3) when the ionization energy of the neutral species is much larger than kT.] Radiative recombination proceeds at a slow rate and is normally of no significance except in very tenuous plasmas. However, it is surely the most important recombination process in the high atmosphere. For thermal ($\sim 300°K$) electrons the radiative recombination coefficient is calculated to have values in the range 10^{-11} to 10^{-12} cm^3/sec for various positive ions.

The reactions

$$O^+ + e \rightarrow O' + h\nu \qquad (12\text{-}5\text{-}2)$$

(where the prime indicates all the possible final states) have been studied by Bates, Buckingham, Massey, and Unwin,[20] who obtained the rates presented in Table 12-5-1.

The processes

$$H^+ + e \rightarrow H' + h\nu \qquad (12\text{-}5\text{-}3)$$

have been investigated by Burgess[21] and Seaton,[22] whose results are also given in Table 12-5-1. The accuracy of these data is thought to be high. Computed values for the partial radiative recombination coefficients $\alpha_n(Z = 1, T)$ for capture into the states of the hydrogen atom with principal quantum numbers $n = 1$ to 12 are tabulated for temperatures ranging from 250 to 64,000°K in the review by Bates and Dalgarno[19] and in a report by Dalgarno et al.[23] When the mean thermal energy is small compared with the ionization energy of the nth level, the partial coefficient for hydrogen ions varies about as

$$\alpha_n(1, T) \sim (nT^{1/2})^{-1} \qquad (12\text{-}5\text{-}4)$$

TABLE 12-5-1. Calculated rates of radiative recombination processes. The recombination coefficients α_Σ refer to capture of an electron into any of the possible states of the resulting neutral atom. The coefficients are expressed in units of 10^{-12} cm³/sec. These rates were tabulated by A. Dalgarno, *Ann. Géophys.* **17**, 16 (1961).

Electron Temperature (°K)	250	500	1000	2000
$\alpha_\Sigma(O^+ + e \rightarrow O' + h\nu)$	3.4	2.2	1.3	0.8
$\alpha_\Sigma(H^+ + e \rightarrow H' + h\nu)$	4.8	3.1	2.0	1.3

The rate coefficient for hydrogenic ions may be calculated exactly, but the labor required increases rapidly with increasing n. The values for hydrogen ions may be scaled to apply to nuclei of charge Ze by multiplying the entries in the temperature row by Z^2 and the corresponding rate coefficients by Z. For fixed temperature the total recombination coefficient

$$\alpha_\Sigma(Z, T) = \sum_{n=1}^{\infty} \alpha_n(Z, T) \qquad (12\text{-}5\text{-}5)$$

varies approximately as $Z^{2.4}$.[19] The contribution of the excited levels to the total coefficient is greater when T is low than when T is high. The temperature variation of the total coefficient $\alpha_\Sigma(1, T)$ for H$^+$ ions is about as $T^{-0.7}$.[19]

2. *Dielectronic recombination.*

$$X_i^+ + e \rightarrow X_d^* \rightarrow X_b + h\nu \qquad (12\text{-}5\text{-}6)$$

In this reaction the electron is captured by the ion X_i^+ into some excited state of the atom X, and the excess energy of recombination is taken up by a second electron which then also occupies an excited state. The doubly excited neutral state X_d^* thus formed lies in the continuum and is energetically unstable. It may revert to the ionic state X_i^+ by the process of autoionization,* in which one electron is ejected and the other is left

* Autoionization is discussed in Section 8-2-A. Dielectronic recombination is the process of inverse autoionization.

in a bound state. However, it is possible that before this reversal occurs the doubly excited atom X_a^* may undergo a radiative transition and drop to some state X_b which is not subject to autoionization. If this occurs, *dielectronic recombination* is said to have taken place. The lifetime associated with emission of the line $d \rightarrow b$ is in general much longer than the lifetime for autoionization ($d \rightarrow i$), which may be of the order of 10^{-13} sec or even less.[19] Thus the rate of dielectronic recombination will usually be small because of the relative inefficiency of the second step of the reaction (12-5-6) compared with the inverse of the first step.

The dielectronic recombination coefficients for the normal N^+ and O^+ ions have been shown by Bates[24] to be much smaller than the corresponding values for radiative recombination, but dielectronic recombination may be faster for certain other ions.[19] Of course, dielectronic recombination cannot take place with H^+ ions.

3. *Dissociative recombination*

$$(XY)^+ + e \rightarrow (XY)^* \rightarrow X^* + Y^* \qquad (12\text{-}5\text{-}7)$$

(The asterisks on X and Y indicate the possibility that these atoms may be left in excited states.) Dissociative recombination takes place when a radiationless transition occurs to some state of the molecule XY in which the atoms recede one from the other and gain kinetic energy under the action of their mutual repulsion so that the neutralization is made permanent by the requirement imposed by the Franck-Condon principle.* The lifetime for this stabilization process is extremely short, and in most cases it is likely that the rate-limiting step is the radiationless transition.[19]

Figure 12-5-1, taken from a paper by Biondi and Holstein,[25] illustrates schematically the dissociative recombination reaction

$$X_2^+ + e \rightarrow (X_2)^* \rightarrow X^* + X + \text{kinetic energy}$$

Initially, the system is composed of a molecular positive ion and an electron (state A). If the repulsive curve ($B - C$) of an excited state of the molecule crosses the molecular ion-electron curve at the appropriate point, the system may jump to this state of the molecule and begin to dissociate. Once the internuclear separation has increased slightly, the system can no longer revert to its original state by autoionization, and the electron is trapped as the molecule continues to dissociate (state C).

It may be of interest to trace the development of the present ideas concerning this mode of recombination. During the 1940's investigations of the night time decay of the electron density in the E layer of the ionosphere led to the deduction of large effective recombination coefficients

* For a discussion of the Franck-Condon principle see Section 8-1-B.

(10^{-8} to 10^{-7} cm³/sec) for the electrons. The failure of attempts to explain this rapid rate in terms of electron capture to neutral species and subsequent ion-ion recombination prompted the suggestion by Bates and Massey[26] that a new process, dissociative recombination between electrons and molecular positive ions, might explain the observations. Shortly afterward Bates[27] again invoked this mechanism to explain the surprisingly high values of the recombination coefficient reported by Biondi and Brown[28]

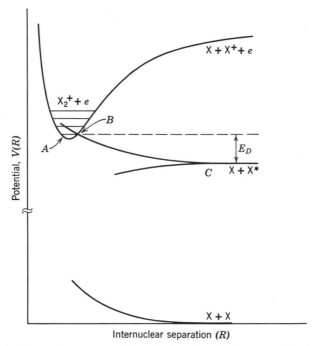

FIG. 12-5-1. Schematic representation of the dissociative recombination process, $X_2^+ + e \rightarrow (X_2)^*$ unstable $\rightarrow X^* + X +$ kinetic energy.[25]

in laboratory studies of decaying helium plasmas. (Molecular ions of the noble gases were known to exist at that time.[29]) Further microwave investigations by Biondi and Brown[30] and others also showed recombination to occur in Ne, A, H_2, N_2, and O_2 at rates several orders of magnitude too rapid to be explained on the basis of radiative processes, and the rapid recombination was again ascribed by Bates[31] to dissociative reactions. More recent experimental studies appear to support Bates's hypothesis and there seems to be little doubt that dissociative recombination can occur rapidly enough (with $\alpha \sim 10^{-6}$ to 10^{-8} cm³/sec) to account for the observed decay rates. We return to this subject in Section 12-7.

4. *Three-body recombination.*

$$X^+ + e + Z \rightarrow X^* + Z \qquad (12\text{-}5\text{-}8)$$

$$X^+ + e + e \rightarrow X^* + e \qquad (12\text{-}5\text{-}9)$$

Early considerations of three-body electron-ion recombination were directed primarily toward the reaction (12-5-8) in which a *heavy particle* Z acts as the third body. The theory for this process was based on the Thomson theory of three-body ion-ion recombination (Section 12-4-A), with allowance being made for the fact that an electron can lose only a small fraction of its energy to the heavy third body in an elastic collision. At ordinary pressures reaction (12-5-8) should be very slow because atoms or molecules are relatively ineffective in degrading the energy of electrons so that they may be readily captured by positive ions. Massey and Burhop[3] estimate that for helium the coefficient of recombination by this process is about $10^{-11} p$ cm^3/sec, where p is the gas pressure in mm Hg. Recent work, however, has shown that reaction (12-5-9), in which the third body is an *electron*, may be quite fast at high electron and positive ion densities (above about 10^{+14}/cm^3).

The process (12-5-9) was discussed some time ago by Fowler[32] and Giovanelli[33] in connection with stellar atmospheres. More recently it was suggested independently and almost simultaneously by D'Angelo,[34] Bates and Kingston,[35] and McWhirter[36] that the electron third-body reaction might account for the very large recombination coefficients for hydrogen and other gases observed in the laboratory under conditions in which they could not be ascribed to dissociative recombination, for which, as we have seen, the coefficient may be extremely large.* In these cases recombination coefficients of the order of 10^{-10} cm^3/sec have been reported, and the radiative process is known to proceed with a coefficient about two orders of magnitude smaller. However, the three-body reaction (12-5-9), with an electron serving as the third body, has been shown to give results compatible with the experimental results. We discuss some experimental studies of this type of recombination in Section 12-7. Here we outline the theoretical work of D'Angelo.

D'Angelo[34] considered the case of a fully ionized hydrogen plasma. A collision may occur between two electrons, one of which may lose enough of its energy to be captured into a bound state about one of the hydrogen ions. Once the electron is bound, either of two processes can occur: (a) the electron may be re-ejected into the continuum by a collision with another electron, or (b) the electron may make a radiative transition to a

---

* Three-body electron-ion recombination has also been treated recently by B. Makin and J. C. Keck, *Phys. Rev. Letters* **11,** 281 (1963), who used a classical variational method.

lower level, from which it may still be re-ejected into the continuum or make another downward radiative transition. (Collisional transitions between quantized states are ignored in D'Angelo's calculation.) Recombination is considered accomplished when a neutral hydrogen atom is formed in the ground state.

Calculation of the final or net three-body recombination coefficients required knowledge of the rates of three-body recombination to each level of the structure into which the electron is initially captured, the probabilities of collisional ionization, and the probabilities of radiative transitions from each level. The ionization probabilities were calculated from the classical theory of Thomson and Bohr, and the rates of recombination to the various levels were obtained from these probabilities by use of the principle of detailed balancing.* The first nine states of the hydrogen atom were considered in D'Angelo's calculation. Transition probabilities for states up to principal quantum number $n = 6$ were taken from the review by Bethe and Salpeter;[37] the remainder were obtained by extrapolation.

D'Angelo calculated the three-body recombination coefficients for three electron temperatures, 1000, 3000, and 10,000°K, and for electron densities in the range 10^{12} to 10^{13} cm^{-3}. His procedure consisted in following an electron which, as the result of a collision with another electron, has been captured into one of the substates of the nth level and in determining the probability that it ultimately ends in the ground state. In his calculation the maximum contribution to the net recombination rate comes from initial capture into states with n around 6 or 7. For smaller n the rate of collisional captures decreases because larger and larger energy exchanges are required in the collision between the two electrons. (Recombination directly into the ground state makes only a very small contribution.) For higher n the re-ejection of the captured electron into the continuum becomes more and more probable.

The results of D'Angelo's calculations have been compared by Hinnov and Hirschberg[38] with experimental data they obtained on magnetically confined plasma in the quiescent afterglow of the B-1 stellarator discharge at Princeton. The agreement was not good, apparently because collisional transitions were neglected by D'Angelo. The experimental results are in substantial agreement, however, with the predictions of Bates and Kingston[35] and McWhirter,[36] whose work is discussed in Section B. Minor discrepancies are probably attributable to differences in assumed inelastic collision cross sections. Calculations made by Hinnov and

* See page 281 of Ref. 33 for the equations used in the calculation of the ionization probabilities and the recombination rates. See Fowler's book (Ref. 32) for a discussion of detailed balancing.

Hirschberg predict a considerably stronger dependence of the recombination coefficient on both the electron density and temperature than do the calculations of D'Angelo. Although D'Angelo's investigation reveals the importance of the three-body recombination processes (12-5-9), his method of solution is laborious to apply, since he considers the complicated reaction paths followed by the individual electrons. Furthermore, as already pointed out, D'Angelo ignores collisional excitation and de-excitation processes. The theory developed by Bates, Kingston, and McWhirter is more accurate and properly takes into account excitation and de-excitation by electron impact, which turn out to be very important.

B. COLLISIONAL-RADIATIVE RECOMBINATION. As we have seen, when an electron recombines with an atomic ion in the absence of a third body, the recombination energy is carried off by radiation. Molecular ions may also be lost by the process of dissociative recombination. However, as pointed out by Bates and his colleagues,[19,39] the rate coefficients for these separate processes describe the actual recombination that occurs only if the plasma is sufficiently tenuous. In general, the possibility must be acknowledged that part of the released energy may be imparted to a neighboring electron in a collision, and, as pointed out earlier, collisional processes may control the recombination if the plasma is sufficiently dense. The loss mechanism in very tenuous plasmas is generally referred to as *radiative recombination*, and the term *collisional recombination* may be applied to the loss mechanism in very dense plasmas. These two mechanisms are really the two limiting cases of a more general loss mechanism which Bates et al. have termed *collisional-radiative recombination*. This general loss mechanism is not simply the sum of the two limiting types, for it results from the combination of interacting collisional and radiative processes. This coupling greatly complicates the analysis of recombination, which in general can be described only in terms of a complex sequence of reactions[34] or by a statistical picture.[39] The methods of analyzing the general type of recombination occurring in optically thin plasmas are discussed by Bates, Kingston, and McWhirter[39] and by Bates and Dalgarno.[19] Recombination between electrons and atomic ions in optically thick plasmas has also been investigated by Bates, Kingston, and McWhirter.[40]

The initial work on electron-electron-ion recombination done by Bates, Kingston, and McWhirter was described in brief notes cited in Refs. 35 and 36. Both papers dealt with collisional-radiative recombination and were quite similar in approach. Consequently, these investigators collaborated when preparing papers[39,40] to describe their work on the problem more fully. A portion of their statistical treatment of optically thin plasmas is reproduced here in its original form to indicate the way in which their analysis proceeds.

Bates, Kingston, and McWhirter[39] confine their discussion to the recombination of electrons e with bare nuclei N^{Z+} of charge Ze to form hydrogen atoms or hydrogenic ions. Let $p, q, \ldots$ denote the principal quantum numbers of the discrete levels and c, the continuum. Write $n(p), n(q), \ldots$ for the number densities of atoms or ions in the indicated levels and $n(c)$ and $n(N^{Z+})$ for the number densities of free electrons and bare nuclei. Let $K(c, p)$ be the rate coefficient for the three-body recombination process

$$N^{Z+} + e + e \rightarrow N^{(Z-1)+}(p) + e \qquad (12\text{-}5\text{-}10)$$

(This rate coefficient is defined to give $n(c)\, n(N^{Z+})\, K(c, p)$ as the number of events that occur per cm³ per second); $K(p, c)$ is the rate coefficient for the inverse process

$$N^{(Z-1)+}(p) + e \rightarrow N^{Z+} + e + e \qquad (12\text{-}5\text{-}11)$$

$K(p, q)$ denotes the rate coefficient for the collisional excitation or de-excitation process

$$N^{(Z-1)+}(p) + e \rightarrow N^{(Z-1)+}(q) + e \qquad (12\text{-}5\text{-}12)$$

and $\beta(p)$ is the rate coefficient for radiative recombination

$$N^{Z+} + e \rightarrow N^{(Z-1)+}(p) + h\nu \qquad (12\text{-}5\text{-}13)$$

All of these rate coefficients correspond to the electron temperature T of the plasma. Finally let $A(p, q)$ denote the spontaneous transition probability for the process

$$N^{(Z-1)+}(p) \rightarrow N^{(Z-1)+}(q) + h\nu \qquad (12\text{-}5\text{-}14)$$

A uniform distribution among the degenerate states of a level is assumed. Elastic collisions must be sufficiently numerous to ensure such a distribution if inelastic and superelastic* collisions populate and deplete the level at a rate comparable with or greater than the rate at which radiative processes do so. The distribution cannot influence the collisional-radiative recombination coefficient if inelastic and superelastic collisions are much less effective than radiative processes.

We make the justifiable assumption that electronic transitions caused by atom-atom, atom-ion, or ion-ion collisions can be neglected. If we further ignore boundary effects and assume that the plasma is optically thin so that all emitted radiation escapes the plasma without being

---

* A *superelastic* collision is one in which a particle increases its kinetic energy in a collision at the expense of the excitation energy of the structure with which it collides.

absorbed, we may express the rate of increase of $n(p)$ with time t by the equation

$$\frac{dn(p)}{dt} = -n(p)[n(c)\,\mathscr{K}(p) + \mathscr{A}(p)] + n(c)\sum_{q \neq p} n(q)\,K(q, p)$$

$$+ \sum_{q > p} n(q)\,A(q, p) + \frac{n(c)^2}{X}\,[K(c, p) + \beta(p)], \quad (12\text{-}5\text{-}15)$$

where

$$\mathscr{K}(p) = K(p, c) + \sum_{q \neq p} K(p, q), \qquad\qquad (12\text{-}5\text{-}16)$$

$$\mathscr{A}(p) = \sum_{q < p} A(p, q), \quad\text{and}\quad X = \frac{n(c)}{n(N^{Z+})}$$

It will prove convenient to introduce the ratios

$$\rho(p) = \frac{n(p)}{n_E(p)} \qquad\qquad (12\text{-}5\text{-}17)$$

where $n_E(p)$ is the number density of hydrogen atoms or hydrogenic ions in level p in Saha equilibrium* at temperature T with free electrons and bare nuclei of number densities $n(c)$ and $n(N^{Z+})$, so that†

$$\frac{X n_E(p)}{n(c)^2} = p^2 \left(\frac{h^2}{2\pi m k T}\right)^{3/2} \exp \frac{I_p}{kT} \qquad\qquad (12\text{-}5\text{-}18)$$

I_p denotes the ionization potential, which we may take, with sufficient accuracy, to be that of an isolated atom or ion. Then since

and

$$n_E(q)\,K(q, p) = n_E(p)\,K(p, q)$$

$$\frac{n(c)}{X}\,K(c, p) = n_E(p)\,K(p, c) \qquad\qquad (12\text{-}5\text{-}19)$$

we see that (12-5-15) may be written in the form

$$\frac{dn(p)/dt}{n_E(p)} = -\rho(p)[n(c)\,\mathscr{K}(p) + \mathscr{A}(p)] + \sum_{q \neq p} \rho(q)\,n(c)\,K(p, q)$$

$$+ \sum_{q > p} \rho(q)\frac{n_E(q)}{n_E(p)}\,A(q, p) + n(c)\,K(p, c) + \frac{n(c)^2}{X n_E(p)}\,\beta(p) \quad (12\text{-}5\text{-}20)$$

The total recombination process is described by an infinite set of coupled differential equations such as (12-5-20).

* See Fowler, Ref. 32.
† Bates et al. point out that (12-5-18) is not valid for very large values of p, but the high levels to which these large values correspond are not important in collisional-radiative recombination except at low electron temperatures.

Numerical substitution into (12-5-18) gives

$$\frac{Xn_E(p)}{n(c)} = 4.2 \times 10^{-16}\left[\frac{n(c)p^2}{T^{3/2}}\right]\exp\frac{157,890Z^2}{p^2T} \qquad (12\text{-}5\text{-}21)$$

which shows that over a wide range of plasma conditions the Saha equilibrium number density of excited systems is very much smaller than the number densities of free electrons and bare nuclei. Thus for a much wider range of conditions

$$n(p) \ll n(c) \qquad (p \neq 1) \qquad\qquad (12\text{-}5\text{-}22)$$

which condition Bates et al. show is violated only in the case of extremely dense plasmas.

The problem is greatly simplified when the plasma conditions are such that (12-5-22) is satisfied and the mean thermal energy is much smaller than the first excitation energy, so that in addition

$$n(p) \ll n(1) \qquad (p \neq 1) \qquad\qquad (12\text{-}5\text{-}23)$$

when the steady state is reached. Under these conditions, a quasi-equilibrium number density of excited systems is established almost immediately without the number densities of free electrons and bare nuclei being appreciably altered. Thereafter the rates at which excited states are produced and destroyed by collisional and radiative processes are much faster than the rates at which the number densities of these rare systems change as the plasma decays. Under these conditions the derivatives on the left side of (12-5-20) for $p \neq 1$ can be set equal to zero without appreciable error. The resulting set of simultaneous equations determines $\rho(p)$ for $p \neq 1$, in terms of $n(c)$, $\rho(1)$, T, and various atomic parameters. Equation 12-5-20 for $p = 1$ determines $dn(1)/dt$, which is the rate of disappearance of free charges, and

$$\frac{dn(1)}{dt} = -\frac{dn(N^{Z+})}{dt} = \gamma n(c)\, n(N^{Z+}) \qquad (12\text{-}5\text{-}24)$$

where γ is an effective two-body rate coefficient which depends on $n(c)$, $n(1)$, X, and T and which Bates et al. call the *collisional-radiative decay coefficient*.

Bates and his co-workers emphasize the point that the decision to express the results in terms of a two-body rate coefficient does not imply that two-body processes predominate; the decision is purely a matter of convenience. They feel that the description of the coefficient by the "noncommittal" adjective decay is desirable, since both recombination and ionization occur. When the steady state is reached, these opposing processes balance, and γ vanishes.

When p is large enough, collisional processes are much more important than radiative processes so that $n(p)$ satisfies the Saha equation and we avoid an infinite matrix. It is convenient to group the levels with p greater than some value s so that $\rho(s)$ is very nearly unity. If we denote this group by the symbol σ, write

$$\rho(\sigma) = 1 \qquad (12\text{-}5\text{-}25)$$

and

$$K(p, \sigma) = \sum_{q>s} K(p,q) \qquad (12\text{-}5\text{-}26)$$

we can reduce (12-5-20) to

$$\rho(p)[n(c)\,\mathcal{K}(p) + \mathcal{A}(p)] - \sum_{\substack{q \neq p \\ \leq s}} \rho(q)\, n(c)\, K(p,q) - \sum_{\substack{q > p \\ \leq s}} \rho(q) \frac{n_E(q)}{n_E(p)} A(q, p)$$

$$= n(c)[K(p, \sigma) + K(p, c)] + \frac{n(c)^2\, \beta(p)}{X n_E(p)} + \sum_{q>s} \frac{n_E(q)}{n_E(p)} A(q, p) \qquad (12\text{-}5\text{-}27)$$

for

$$p \neq 1, \qquad \leq s \qquad (12\text{-}5\text{-}28)$$

If we take $\rho(1)$ to be known, we may write the solutions to this set of $s - 1$ equations in the form

$$\rho(p) = r_0(p) + r_1(p)\, \rho(1) \qquad (12\text{-}5\text{-}29)$$

where $r_0(p)$ and $r_1(p)$, which are functions of $n(c)$ and T but not of X, are positive definite.

Using (12-5-20) with $p = 1$ and (12-5-24), we may express the decay coefficient γ by the equation

$$\frac{\gamma}{X} = \frac{dn(1)/dt}{n(c)^2} = \frac{n_E(1)}{n(c)} \left[\sum_{\substack{q>1 \\ \leq s}} \rho(q)\, K(1,q) + K(1, \sigma) + K(1, c) \right]$$

$$+ \left[\sum_{\substack{q > p \\ \leq s}} \rho(q) \frac{n_E(q)}{n(c)^2} A(q, 1) + \sum_{q>s} \frac{n_E(q)}{n(c)^2} A(q, 1) + \frac{\beta(1)}{X} \right]$$

$$- \left[\frac{n_E(1)}{n(c)} \rho(1)\, \mathcal{K}(1) \right] \qquad (12\text{-}5\text{-}30)$$

In (12-5-30) the first term in square brackets represents the population of the ground level by collisional de-excitation and by three-body recombination. The second term represents the population of the ground level by cascading and radiative recombination, and the third describes the evacuation of the ground level by collisional excitation and ionization. Because of the form of (12-5-29), (12-5-30) may be written

$$\gamma = \alpha - \frac{SXn(1)}{n(c)} \qquad (12\text{-}5\text{-}31)$$

where α and S are positive quantities that depend only on $n(c)$, T, and various atomic parameters.

In plasmas of density low enough for radiative processes to be important,

$$\frac{\alpha n(c)}{X} \gg Sn_E(1) \qquad (12\text{-}5\text{-}32)$$

In plasmas dense enough for collision processes to predominate

$$\frac{\alpha n(c)}{X} \approx Sn_E(1) \qquad (12\text{-}5\text{-}33)$$

During at least the early part of the decay from a state in which $n(1)$ is very small γ may be put equal to α and the term in S neglected. Bates et al. refer to α as the *collisional-radiative recombination coefficient* and to S as the *collisional-radiative ionization coefficient*. These two coefficients do not give the rates at which electrons enter and leave the ground level. These rates are larger than α and S because they include transitions between excited levels and the ground level in an internal cycle that does not involve passage through the continuum.

Bates, Kingston, and McWhirter[39] used the foregoing theory to carry out detailed calculations on optically thin atomic hydrogen plasmas. They took the required spontaneous transition probabilities $A(p, q)$ from tables of Baker and Menzel[41] and Green, Rush, and Chandler.[42] The radiative recombination coefficients $\beta(p)$ were obtained from tables prepared by Seaton.[43] They used rate coefficients for collisional excitation and ionization and the reverse processes, based on the calculations of Gryziński[44] for hydrogen atoms and on the work of Burgess[45] and Seaton[46] for hydrogenic ions. The available data on the radiative processes are considered very reliable, but the situation with respect to the collisional processes is much less satisfactory.

The results they computed for α in atomic hydrogen plasmas are tabulated in Table 12-5-2. [This table extends to higher values of $n(c)$ than condition (12-5-22) permits. For the lower of these values the theory underestimates α during an initial period when the electron reservoir formed by the excited levels is being filled but overestimates α at later times when this reservoir is being emptied.] If $n(c)$ is low, α is seen to be a slowly decreasing function of the temperature, but a rapidly decreasing function if $n(c)$ is high; α is a rapidly increasing function of $n(c)$ if T is low, but a slowly increasing function if T is high.

TABLE 12-5-2. Collisional-radiative recombination coefficients α (in cm³/sec) at temperature T for optically thin H$^+$ ion plasma.[39] The indices give the power of 10 by which the entries must be multiplied

$n(c)$ (cm^{-3}) \ T(°K)	250	500	1000	2000	4000	8000	16000	32000	64000
Limit $n(c) \to 0$	$4 \cdot 8^{-12}$	$3 \cdot 1^{-12}$	$2 \cdot 0^{-12}$	$1 \cdot 3^{-12}$	$7 \cdot 9^{-13}$	$4 \cdot 8^{-13}$	$2 \cdot 9^{-13}$	$1 \cdot 7^{-13}$	$1 \cdot 0^{-13}$
10^8	$8 \cdot 8^{-11}$	$1 \cdot 4^{-11}$	$4 \cdot 1^{-12}$	$1 \cdot 8^{-12}$	$9 \cdot 2^{-13}$	$5 \cdot 1^{-13}$	$3 \cdot 0^{-13}$	$1 \cdot 8^{-13}$	$1 \cdot 0^{-13}$
10^9	$4 \cdot 0^{-10}$	$3 \cdot 8^{-11}$	$7 \cdot 5^{-12}$	$2 \cdot 5^{-12}$	$1 \cdot 0^{-12}$	$5 \cdot 3^{-13}$	$3 \cdot 0^{-13}$	$1 \cdot 8^{-13}$	$1 \cdot 0^{-13}$
10^{10}	$2 \cdot 8^{-9}$	$1 \cdot 6^{-10}$	$1 \cdot 9^{-11}$	$4 \cdot 1^{-12}$	$1 \cdot 4^{-12}$	$6 \cdot 1^{-13}$	$3 \cdot 2^{-13}$	$1 \cdot 8^{-13}$	$1 \cdot 0^{-13}$
10^{11}	$2 \cdot 7^{-8}$	$1 \cdot 0^{-9}$	$6 \cdot 9^{-11}$	$9 \cdot 1^{-12}$	$2 \cdot 2^{-12}$	$8 \cdot 1^{-13}$	$3 \cdot 4^{-13}$	$1 \cdot 8^{-13}$	$1 \cdot 0^{-13}$
10^{12}	$2 \cdot 6^{-7}$	$9 \cdot 0^{-9}$	$3 \cdot 9^{-10}$	$2 \cdot 9^{-11}$	$4 \cdot 4^{-12}$	$1 \cdot 2^{-12}$	$4 \cdot 3^{-13}$	$2 \cdot 0^{-13}$	$1 \cdot 0^{-13}$
10^{13}	$2 \cdot 6^{-6}$	$8 \cdot 9^{-8}$	$3 \cdot 1^{-9}$	$1 \cdot 4^{-10}$	$1 \cdot 2^{-11}$	$2 \cdot 1^{-12}$	$6 \cdot 2^{-13}$	$2 \cdot 4^{-13}$	$1 \cdot 1^{-13}$
10^{14}	$2 \cdot 6^{-5}$	$8 \cdot 8^{-7}$	$2 \cdot 9^{-8}$	$9 \cdot 8^{-10}$	$5 \cdot 1^{-11}$	$5 \cdot 1^{-12}$	$1 \cdot 0^{-12}$	$3 \cdot 1^{-13}$	$1 \cdot 2^{-13}$
10^{15}	—	$8 \cdot 8^{-6}$	$2 \cdot 9^{-7}$	$8 \cdot 7^{-9}$	$2 \cdot 7^{-10}$	$1 \cdot 7^{-11}$	$2 \cdot 3^{-12}$	$4 \cdot 9^{-13}$	$1 \cdot 6^{-13}$
10^{16}	—	—	$2 \cdot 9^{-6}$	$8 \cdot 5^{-8}$	$2 \cdot 3^{-9}$	$8 \cdot 4^{-11}$	$5 \cdot 0^{-12}$	$7 \cdot 3^{-13}$	$1 \cdot 9^{-13}$
10^{17}	—	—	—	$8 \cdot 4^{-7}$	$2 \cdot 1^{-8}$	$3 \cdot 4^{-10}$	$1 \cdot 4^{-11}$	$1 \cdot 8^{-12}$	$4 \cdot 4^{-13}$
10^{18}	—	—	—	—	$2 \cdot 0^{-7}$	$2 \cdot 5^{-9}$	$9 \cdot 6^{-11}$	$1 \cdot 2^{-11}$	$2 \cdot 8^{-12}$
Limit $n(c) \to \infty$	$2 \cdot 6^{-19} n(c)$	$8 \cdot 8^{-21} n(c)$	$2 \cdot 9^{-22} n(c)$	$8 \cdot 4^{-24} n(c)$	$1 \cdot 9^{-25} n(c)$	$2 \cdot 4^{-27} n(c)$	$9 \cdot 1^{-29} n(c)$	$1 \cdot 1^{-29} n(c)$	$2 \cdot 7^{-30} n(c)$

12-6. EXPERIMENTAL STUDIES OF ION-ION RECOMBINATION

In this section we discuss the two principal methods which have been used for the experimental investigation of ion-ion recombination.

A. X-RAY IONIZATION EXPERIMENTS ON THREE-BODY RECOMBINATION. The earliest recombination experiments were those of Thomson and Rutherford,[1] who utilized X rays as the source of ionizing radiation in studies at relatively high pressures, at which three-body recombination is dominant. Their pioneering work was published in 1896, the year after the discovery of X rays. Many similar experiments were subsequently performed, but the results of most of them were unreliable because of the poor vacuum and gas purification techniques that were used and because of the failure of the investigators to consider properly the effects of spatial nonuniformity of the ionization, excessive X-ray intensities, and other factors. Only the carefully performed experiments of Sayers[7] and Mächler[9] for clean dry air and Gardner[47] for oxygen appear to be valid. The techniques of these three investigators were similar, for each was based on Rutherford's "flash method."[48] A description of Sayers' work alone will suffice here.

Sayers' ionization chamber was built in a cylindrical pyrex envelope, which could be baked at 500°C, and the interior metal electrodes were induction heated. A mercury diffusion pump and liquid air traps were employed during the envelope evacuation. For recombination measurements the chamber was filled with air at a pressure in the range 100 to 1500 mm Hg. X rays were admitted to the sensitive volume of the chamber by a slotted rotating brass disk, which served as a synchronous shutter, and the air was ionized by these X rays and by the secondary electrons they ejected from gas molecules and surfaces within the chamber. The electrons thus produced were captured by oxygen molecules to form negative ions before any significant amount of electron-ion recombination could occur. The ion concentration could be measured at any instant after one of the X-ray bursts by applying a high potential to one of the electrodes of the ionization chamber and collecting the ions that remained at that time. This collecting voltage was applied by a commutator device mounted on the same shaft as the rotating disk, and the phase relation between the two could be varied to give different intervals between the cessation of the X-ray burst and application of the collection voltage. This process was cyclic and was repeated at the shaft rotation frequency. The charge collected on the electrode each time the collection voltage was applied was integrated and measured as a current. By multiplying this current by the period (0.7 sec) of the cycle the collected charge could be estimated. Plots of the reciprocal of the positive and negative charge densities versus time permitted the evaluation of α from an equation such as (12-1-4), when appropriate consideration was given to diffusion effects.

The recombination coefficient evaluated in this manner was found to have a constant value except for a very short time following the removal of the ionizing source. During this brief interval an unusually large value of α was obtained. This initial value was the result of abnormally rapid "columnar recombination" along the densely ionized path of the incident

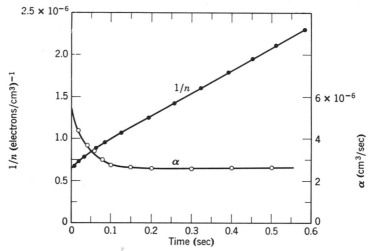

FIG. 12-6-1. Curves illustrating the initial high value of the recombination coefficient α at short intervals after the cessation of the X-ray ionizing burst. The values of α are obtained by graphical differentiation of the curve of reciprocal ionic number density $(1/n)$ versus time.[7]

radiation and along the ionization tracks produced by secondary electrons. The recombination coefficient attained its proper constant value following a time interval sufficient to allow diffusion to distribute the positive and negative charges uniformly throughout the sensitive volume of the chamber. This "aging effect" is illustrated in Fig. 12-6-1. Similar high values for α were obtained by Sayers when he used Rümelin's method,[49] which involves measurement of the equilibrium value of the ionization established by a continuous source of X rays. The source of the error is the same in both methods—extreme care must be observed to ensure uniformity of the charge distribution at the time the measurement is performed.

A final observation made by Sayers and others is that erroneous values of α can be obtained if the intensity or the energy of the X-ray beam is excessive. Under these conditions other than the normal species of ions may be produced, and the composition of the gas may be affected. The formation of appreciable amounts of ozone in oxygen under intense irradiation is an example of this effect.

The results obtained by Sayers and Mächler on air were presented as functions of pressure in comparison with the Natanson theory in Fig. 12-4-1 and therefore are not repeated here. Gardner's value[47] for the recombination coefficient in pure oxygen at 760 mm Hg and 25°C was $(2.08 \pm 0.05) \times 10^{-6}$ cm^3/sec.

B. PULSED-DISCHARGE AFTERGLOW EXPERIMENTS ON TWO-BODY RE-COMBINATION. The techniques described in the last section are not applicable at pressures below a few mm Hg, where two-body recombination is dominant. However Yeung,[50] in Sayers' laboratory, has developed a new technique that appears to be satisfactory for such studies. Yeung's method involves the measurement of the time variation of the dielectric constant of a highly electronegative gas produced by changes in the free charge density. In these gases free electrons are rapidly attached to form negative ions, which in turn undergo volume recombination with positive ions while diffusing toward the walls of the confining vessel. Yeung's method is closely akin to the microwave afterglow discharge experiments in the study of electron-ion recombination (Section 12-7).

Yeung produced a pulsed rf discharge in a pyrex tube containing a cylindrical electrode whose axis was coincident with the axis of the discharge tube. A second cylindrical electrode, concentric with the first, served as the second plate of a cylindrical capacitor. The properties of the dielectric of this capacitor varied in accordance with the changes in the ionic charge density of the contained plasma. By incorporating the capacitor in the tuned circuit of an oscillator it was possible to measure the change in plasma charge density in terms of the oscillator resonant frequency shift. The oscillator driving power was held to a low level to avoid perturbation of the plasma by the sampling field.

Values of the two-body recombination coefficient were obtained by Yeung for bromine and iodine at room temperature and at pressures in the range 0.07 to 1.00 mm Hg. As expected, α was observed to be independent of p over this range; its values were 1.47×10^{-8} cm^3/sec and 1.85×10^{-8} cm^3/sec for iodine and bromine, respectively. However, Greaves[51] later discovered a calibration error in one of Yeung's amplifiers which is believed to have existed during the period of Yeung's measurements. Sayers[52] has accordingly revised Yeung's data, but the results are still approximately 50% high compared with more recent unpublished work of Greaves.[51]

Although the abovementioned discrepancy cannot be explained with certainty at the present time, recent work by Gray and Kerr[53] (discussed in detail in Section 12-8) may provide the answer. Gray and Kerr solved the diffusion equation for the charge density in plasmas of cylindrical and spherical geometries, taking into account an additional recombination term. They find that a linear plot of the reciprocal of the charge density versus time can be obtained even for plasma afterglow experiments that are *diffusion-dominated*. A value of α deduced from a $(1/n)$ versus t plot will be excessively large if the plasma decay is not *recombination-dominated*, and Gray and Kerr's analysis indicates that this criterion was not fulfilled in Yeung's experiment.

Yeung[54] has also applied his technique to the study of recombination between positive cesium ions and negative ions of iodine.

One cannot avoid being impressed with the paucity of reliable data on ion-ion recombination, and, as we shall see, the situation is equally bad with respect to electron-ion recombination. Real progress is to be expected, however, now that the effects of diffusion in recombination experiments are better understood[53] and the importance of gas purity and mass spectrometric identification of the recombining ions is appreciated.

12-7. EXPERIMENTAL STUDIES OF ELECTRON-ION RECOMBINATION

Accurate values for the electron-ion recombination coefficient are difficult to obtain experimentally because electrons are lost by diffusion (and in some cases by attachment), as well as by recombination, and because electrons may continue to be produced after the primary ionizing discharge is turned off (see Section 12-2). Furthermore, measured values of α are not very meaningful unless the identity of the recombining ions is definitely known, and positive identification can be obtained only by mass spectrometric probing or spectroscopic observations of the plasma while the recombination is occurring. Ion-molecule reactions involving the parent plasma gas, together with ion-molecule reactions, charge transfer, and Penning ionization with impurities, may eliminate the initially formed ions and replace them with new species which are frequently of quite unexpected types.

Most measurements of the electron-ion recombination coefficient are made by observing the diminution of the electron density in decaying plasma. Microwave techniques are generally employed both for breaking down the sample gas and for probing the resulting plasma. Since the microwave method appears to be the most reliable in current use, it is the only one discussed in detail here. Other methods treated by Loeb,[1,2] Massey and Burhop,[3] Massey,[14] and Bates and Dalgarno[19] are mentioned briefly in this chapter.

A. TECHNIQUES USED IN MICROWAVE EXPERIMENTS. The initial application of microwave techniques* to the determination of recombination coefficients was made in 1949 by Biondi and Brown.[28] The apparatus used by Biondi[55,56] in more recent recombination studies is shown schematically in Fig. 12-7-1. High-purity gas is admitted at a pressure of about 1 to 25 mm Hg into the cylindrical quartz bottle located inside a cylindrical microwave cavity, which is resonant at 3000 Mc. A pulsed discharge of

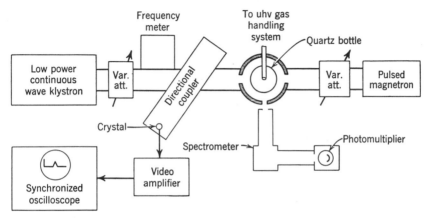

FIG. 12-7-1. Simplified block diagram of the microwave and optical apparatus used in afterglow recombination studies by Biondi.[56]

variable time duration (10 μsec to $>$1 msec) is then produced by microwave energy fed from the magnetron at the right side of the figure. Under proper experimental conditions for the study of recombination, the chief effect of the free electrons produced in the discharge is to change the resonant frequency of the cavity. If the spatial distribution of the electrons in the bottle is known, absolute values of the average electron density can be obtained from the measured frequency shifts.

To determine the changing electron density during the afterglow following the cessation of the discharge, a low-level probing signal is fed into the cavity by the continuous wave klystron to excite the cavity in the TM_{010} mode. The level of this signal is low enough to preclude any appreciable perturbation of the plasma electron energy distribution. The dielectric effect of the electrons leads to a shift in resonant frequency of the cavity which is dependent on the average of the electron density weighted by the square of the electric field intensity. The low-level CW probing signal is partly reflected from the cavity, and a minimum in the reflected signal

* The use of microwave methods in other measurements on plasmas is discussed in Sections 4-1-C, 10-10-B, and 11-2-E.

occurs when the resonant frequency of the cavity-plus-electrons coincides with the signal frequency. Measurements of the times of occurrence of minimum reflections for various frequencies of the probing signal provide the time dependence of the frequency shift, from which the time dependence of the average electron density can be obtained. The time measurements are made with the directional coupler, amplifier, and oscilloscope shown in the drawing.

The shift in the resonant frequency of the cavity is related to the electron number density n by the equation[19,57]

$$\frac{\Delta f}{f} = \frac{1}{2}\frac{\bar{n}}{1 + (\nu/\omega)^2 n_p} \tag{12-7-1}$$

where ν is the electron collision frequency, ω is the angular frequency of the probing signal, and n_p equals $m\omega^2/e^2$.* The weighted mean electron density $\bar{n}$ is defined by the equation

$$\bar{n} = \frac{\int nE^2\, dv}{\int E^2\, dv} \tag{12-7-2}$$

where E is the electric field of the probing signal and the integration is performed over the volume of the cavity. Persson[57] has pointed out that (12-7-1) is not valid at high electron densities because of the macroscopic polarization of the plasma, and Oskam[58] has emphasized the inapplicability of this equation at high power levels of the CW probing signal because of heating effects and the possibility of secondary electron production.

The spectral distribution and temporal variation of the light emitted from the plasma have also been studied with the apparatus in Fig. 12-7-1. In principle, simultaneous determinations of the electron density and the absolute intensity of the recombination radiation could yield the recombination coefficient, although this method has provided only qualitative results to date. Observations of the spatial distribution of the emitted radiation have shown that the radiation does not arise from *wall recombination* between electrons and positive ions (see Fig. 12-7-2), and intensity measurements show that the radiation does not result from electron impact excitation processes. To demonstrate this fact, the electron energy is momentarily increased during the afterglow by applying a moderately high-level probing signal, and the effect of the energy increase is observed. As expected, raising the electron energy decreases the intensity of the observed radiation, since the recombination rate decreases with increasing

---

* Equation 12-7-1 is valid only if the collision frequency is independent of energy.

energy. If, on the other hand, the afterglow radiation were caused by excitation processes involving electron impact, the light intensity should increase as the electron energy is raised. These observations indicate that electron-ion *volume recombination* is indeed the source of the light emitted from the decaying plasmas in Biondi's experiments.

Observations on the emitted radiation also permit conclusions to be drawn concerning the nature of the volume recombination. In cases in

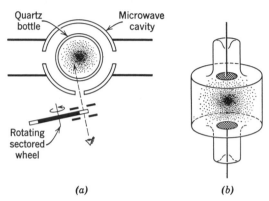

(a)   *(b)*

FIG. 12-7-2. Sketches of the visually observed spatial distribution of the afterglow radiation from (*a*) the microwave discharge and (*b*) a pulsed dc discharge in recombination studies of Biondi.[56]

which the recombination process is associated with the dominant positive ion and negative ion formation is absent $n \approx n^+$, and we would expect the intensity of the recombination radiation to be proportional to n^2 if two-body recombination is occurring (n denotes the electron number density). This expectation was fulfilled in Biondi's measurements on neon and argon under conditions in which a single positive ion is expected to predominate.

Other papers describing techniques similar to those we have discussed are cited by Biondi[56] and by Bates and Dalgarno.[19] In addition, the reader's attention is directed particularly to a recent series of papers by Kerr and his colleagues.[59–61] The electron number density can also be determined in recombination experiments by measurements of changes in microwave beams transmitted through a decaying plasma.[62]

B. RESULTS OF LOW-DENSITY MICROWAVE RECOMBINATION STUDIES. Biondi's latest results on recombination in neon and argon are discussed in the paper[56] in which the foregoing techniques are described. Biondi observed that the time and pressure dependences of the electron density decays in these gases follow a two-body volume electron-ion recombination law over a wide range of variables and yield recombination coefficients of

10^{-7} to 10^{-6} cm³/sec. (In his experiments the gas pressure was in the range 1 to 25 mm Hg, the electron temperature was about 300°K, and the electron number densities were of the order of 10^8 to 10^9/cm³.) Dissociative recombination

$$X_2^+ + e \rightarrow X^* + X \tag{12-7-3}$$

was shown to be the mechanism responsible for the large values of the observed recombination rates.

To show this, measurements were first made on helium containing only about 1 part in 10^3 of argon. In this case ionization during the discharge is predominantly of the Penning type (see Section 12-2-B):

$$He^m + A \rightarrow He + A^+ + e \tag{12-7-4}$$

where the superscript m denotes helium in a metastable state. This reaction is possible because the metastable levels of the helium atom lie above the ionization limit of argon. Because of the low concentration of argon atoms used, conversion of A^+ to A_2^+ by the reaction

$$A^+ + A + A \rightarrow A_2^+ + A \tag{12-7-5}$$

or by the reaction

$$A^+ + A + He \rightarrow A_2^+ + He \tag{12-7-6}$$

(see Section 9-9-A) should be too slow to produce significant argon molecular ion concentrations during the afterglow measuring period. Thus A^+ ions are expected to predominate in the afterglow, and dissociative recombination should not be possible to any appreciable extent. Under these conditions, Biondi observed *only* ambipolar diffusion loss of the ions and electrons. The recombination which was occurring was of the radiative type and was characterized by a coefficient too small to be determined by microwave methods. Biondi states that the coefficient had to be at least 1000 times smaller than that normally measured in pure argon. When the measurements were repeated with pure argon, A_2^+ ions were expected to be produced by reaction (12-7-5) and to be the most abundant ionic species present in the afterglow. Dissociative recombination should then assume its usual importance, and, indeed, in pure argon the usual high recombination loss rate was observed.

Kerr and his colleagues[59-61] have studied the afterglow of very pure, weakly ionized helium plasmas at pressures of 0.25 to 21.4 mm Hg. The early afterglow was dominated by the generation of new ionization. Between 3 and 21.4 mm Hg the charge removal process at late times appeared to be ambipolar diffusion with a single positive ion characterized by $(\mathscr{D}_a p) = 697$ cm²-mm Hg/sec at 300°K, corresponding to a mobility of 16.2 cm²/v-sec (see Sections 9-9-A and 10-10-B). This ion is He_2^+.

Below 2 or 3 mm Hg no such simple situation exists. Between about 0.2 and 2 or 3 mm Hg there is a mixture of He^+ and He_2^+ ions, although at pressures below about 0.7 mm Hg nearly all the ions are He^+. The measured mobility of the He^+ ions is 10.6 cm^2/v-sec. The radiation emitted by the decaying plasma consisted primarily of atomic spectral lines at low pressures and molecular bands at high pressures. The light intensity was proportional to the square of the average electron density only for molecular light at 15 mm Hg and higher; no simple relationship was observed between the atomic light and the electron density. The absolute intensities of the molecular radiation place a lower limit of 3×10^{-10} cm^3/sec on the recombination coefficient at 15 mm Hg. Kerr et al. were able to show that two-body radiative recombination could not account for their observations. Other types of recombination would lead to behavior that agrees in some respects with the experimental data, disagrees in others, and is inconclusive or ambiguous in still others. No single process was considered to offer a satisfactory explanation of the radiation. Kerr et al. assign a tentative upper limit of 2×10^{-9} cm^3/sec to the recombination coefficient in helium at 15 mm Hg. They point out that this value depends on unresolved aspects of metastable collisions and higher mode diffusion.

Kasner, Rogers, and Biondi[63] have combined microwave and mass spectrometric techniques to study electron-ion recombination in nitrogen and oxygen. These measurements are of special interest, for they permit identification of the ions present at various times in the afterglow. Their apparatus consists of a rectangular stainless steel microwave cavity containing in one wall a quartz iris for coupling microwave energy and in the opposite wall a 0.008-in. diameter effusion orifice leading to a Boyd-type rf mass spectrometer and its differential pumping system.

In order to carry out measurements at low concentrations of nitrogen or oxygen, Kasner et al. used an inert buffer gas to inhibit particle loss by diffusion to the walls. They observed that in pure nitrogen or nitrogen-helium mixtures the predominant afterglow ions for nitrogen pressures in the range 0.1 to 7.0 mm Hg were N_3^+ and N_4^+, whereas at nitrogen pressures less than 0.01 mm Hg N_2^+ was the only significant ion in the afterglow. In oxygen O_2^+ predominated at partial pressures of less than 0.005 mm Hg, whereas O_3^+ was the dominant ion at higher pressures.

Measurements on electron-ion recombination were carried out under conditions in which one particular ionic species predominated during the afterglow, except in nitrogen at the higher N_2 pressures, at which both N_3^+ and N_4^+ were present in significant quantities, as stated earlier. Table 12-7-1 shows the results obtained by Kasner, Rogers, and Biondi[63] after corrections were made for diffusion effects and for an error in the electron density calibration. Also shown in this table are very recent data on molecular noble gas ions obtained by Oskam and Mittelstadt in microwave afterglow studies.

C. OTHER TYPES OF EXPERIMENTAL ELECTRON-ION RECOMBINATION STUDIES. The first experimental studies of electron-ion recombination were made by Kenty, Mohler, Boeckner, and Sayers, who used interrupted arcs in

TABLE 12-7-1. Recombination coefficients for various molecular ions in their parent gases at $T^+ = T^- = T_{gas} = 300°K$. These values refer to *dissociative electron-ion recombination* and were deduced from measurements on microwave afterglows. In general, the dissociative recombination rate is expected to depend on the electron temperature, and the temperature dependence may be different for different ions. This mode of recombination is much faster than radiative recombination, for which coefficients of about 5×10^{-12} cm³/sec are predicted by theory

System	α in cm³/sec	Reference
$He_2^+ + e$	$\leq 4 \times 10^{-9}$	
$Ne_2^+ + e$	$(2.2 \pm 0.2) \times 10^{-7}$	H. J. Oskam and V. R. Mittelstadt,
$A_2^+ + e$	$(6.7 \pm 0.5) \times 10^{-7}$	*Phys. Rev.* **132**, 1445 (1963).
$Kr_2^+ + e$	$(1.2 + 0.1) \times 10^{-6}$	
$Xe_2^+ + e$	$(1.4 \pm 0.1) \times 10^{-6}$	
$N_2^+ + e$	$(2.8 \pm 0.5) \times 10^{-7}$	M. A. Biondi, Symposium on Aero-
$O_2^+ + e$	$(1.7 \pm 1) \times 10^{-7}$	nomy, sponsored by the IAGA of the
$N_4^+ + e$	$\geq 1 \times 10^{-6}$	IUGG (Berkeley, California, August 1963), to be published in *Annales de Géophysique*.

argon, cesium, and mercury vapor and measured the electron densities by probes and photometric methods.[1,3] The electron densities in these experiments were rather high (of the order of $10^{12}/cm^3$) and the electron temperatures were several thousand deg K. Apparent values for the recombination coefficients of about 2×10^{-10} cm³/sec were obtained, but these results may not be very meaningful because the identity of the ions was uncertain and the effects of ambipolar diffusion were not taken into account in the analysis of the data.

More recently, electron-ion recombination has been studied in high current spark channels in hydrogen, argon, and helium by Craggs and his co-workers, who used photomultipliers and fast oscilloscopes. Recombination coefficients have also been deduced indirectly by Griem and his associates from observations of line profiles in very dense plasmas

($n \approx 10^{17}/cm^3$). References to all of this work are given by Bates and Dalgarno.[19]

Fowler and Atkinson[64] have studied electron recombination in atomic hydrogen by measuring the absolute intensity of the continuum radiation associated with the Balmer lines in a shock tube containing an expanding hydrogen plasma in a field-free region. The ion density was about $6 \times 10^{16}/cm^3$ and the temperature about $4500°K$. They deduced a recombination coefficient of 10^{-12} cm^3/sec, which is appropriate for radiative recombination under the indicated conditions.

A number of studies on electron-ion recombination in dense helium and hydrogen plasmas have been made by the Stellerator group at Princeton with both microwave and optical techniques.[65] The results of these studies are in general agreement with the theory of collisional-radiative recombination developed by Bates, Kingston, and McWhirter[39,40] and with the results of similar calculations by Byron, Stabler, and Bortz.[66]

Wada and Knechtli[67] have used a double-probe technique to study electron-ion recombination in thermal cesium plasma, at electron temperatures of 2000 to $2500°K$. Their results are in qualitative agreement with the theory of collisional-radiative recombination.

12-8. THE EFFECTS OF DIFFUSION IN RECOMBINATION EXPERIMENTS

In the simple case of a decaying two-component system the experimental methods outlined in Sections 12-6 and 12-7 might be expected to yield a linear decrease in the reciprocal charge density with increasing time [cf. (12-1-4)]. As we have seen, however, complications may arise because of secondary ionization, ion-molecule reactions, and electron attachment. These complications may be taken into account in the analysis of multiple-component recombination by the methods discussed in Section 12-2. In addition, we should consider the effects of diffusion on the apparent recombination rate. Some of these effects have been analyzed by Oskam[58] for infinite parallel plane geometry and by Gray and Kerr[53] for recombination in plasmas confined in infinitely long cylinders and in spherical vessels. One important conclusion gained from these studies is that linearity of the plot of reciprocal number density versus time does not in itself imply that a meaningful value for the recombination coefficient can be deduced from the slope of the plot; in fact, linearity may be observed even when the decay is controlled by diffusion. Gray and Kerr's analysis is outlined here.

A. GRAY AND KERR'S ANALYSIS. Gray and Kerr considered the afterglow of a microwave discharge in which diffusion and electron-ion recombination compete for the loss of charged particles. The model they used was one in which the loss of electrons is attributable only to *volume recombination with a single species of positive ion* or to *ambipolar diffusion to the walls followed by surface neutralization*. Thermal equilibrium is assumed, and the possibility of electron attachment or electron generation following removal of the microwave field is excluded. Under the assumption that the electron loss rate is quadratic in the electron concentration, the conservation equation for the electron number density $n(\mathbf{r}, t)$ is

$$\frac{\partial n}{\partial t} = \mathscr{D}_a \nabla^2 n - \alpha n^2 \tag{12-8-1}$$

where $\mathscr{D}_a$ is the ambipolar diffusion coefficient and α is the electron-ion recombination coefficient. This equation is recognized as the same as (10-10-7) with constant $\mathscr{D}_a$ and a term added to account for the recombination. The boundary condition to be imposed on (12-8-1) is

$$n_{\text{wall}} = 0 \tag{12-8-2}$$

(see Section 10-7).

Complete specification of the solution of (12-8-1) requires knowledge of an initial distribution $n(\mathbf{r}, t_0)$, where t_0 may be any time following the removal of the microwave field at which (12-8-1) correctly describes the electron loss. The afterglow period following the discharge starts with "hot" electrons distributed in space in a manner determined by the character of the discharge. The precise form of this distribution is not important. Evidently t_0 must be chosen to be late enough after cessation of the microwave discharge that the hot electrons will have cooled down approximately to the ambient gas temperature.

Either the diffusion loss term $\mathscr{D}_a \nabla^2 n$ or the recombination loss term αn^2 may be dominant over most of the plasma volume at any particular time, except at late times in the afterglow when diffusion must dominate the electron loss. Thus the plasma may be *diffusion-controlled* or *recombination-controlled* at any given instant. If either of these two conditions obtains for a sufficiently long period during the decay, an electron distribution will be achieved which is a solution of (12-8-1) with the recombination or the diffusion term absent. These distributions may be called the *diffusion* and the *recombination distributions*, respectively. Gray and Kerr point out that a plasma which at a given time is recombination-controlled need not have a recombination spatial distribution, and likewise diffusion control does not necessarily imply a diffusion distribution at that instant.

If the plasma is recombination-controlled at time t_0, the electron density will tend to redistribute itself in such a way as to establish a recombination distribution, which however will be attained only if the plasma remains recombination-dominated long enough. On the other hand, if the plasma is diffusion-controlled at $t = t_0$, the electron distribution will immediately tend toward a diffusion distribution. As we have already pointed out, this distribution will be attained ultimately, regardless of the initial distribution.

Gray and Kerr performed their analysis for each of the two following initial distributions: (1) the *diffusion distribution corresponding to the fundamental mode of diffusion*, described by (12-8-1) with $\alpha = 0$, subject to the boundary condition (12-8-2), and (2) the *recombination distribution*, by which they mean a distribution uniform throughout the container but with a discontinuity at the walls where $n = 0$. Boundary surfaces in the form of spheres and infinitely long cylinders were chosen because numerical solutions are much easier to obtain in situations that can be described in terms of a single spatial coordinate. Fortunately, these geometries provide good approximations to the cavities used in many microwave recombination studies.

For the cylindrical surface (12-8-1) has the form

$$\frac{\partial n}{\partial t} = \frac{\mathscr{D}_a}{r} \frac{\partial}{\partial r}\left(r \frac{\partial n}{\partial r}\right) - \alpha n^2 \qquad (12\text{-}8\text{-}3)$$

and

$$\frac{\partial n}{\partial t} = \frac{\mathscr{D}_a}{r^2} \frac{\partial}{\partial r}\left(r^2 \frac{\partial n}{\partial r}\right) - \alpha n^2 \qquad (12\text{-}8\text{-}4)$$

is the appropriate equation for spherical geometry. In each of these cases

$$n(R, t) = 0 \qquad (12\text{-}8\text{-}5)$$

where R is the radius of the container. Thus, according to Section 10-8, the diffusion distribution has the form

$$n(r, t_0) = n_0 J_0\left(\frac{\lambda_1 r}{R}\right) \qquad (12\text{-}8\text{-}6)$$

for the infinite cylinder, where $\lambda_1 = 2.405$ is the first root of $J_0(x)$. For the sphere the diffusion distribution is

$$n(r, t_0) = n_0 \frac{\sin \pi r/R}{\pi r/R} \qquad (12\text{-}8\text{-}7)$$

The recombination distribution has the form

$$n(r, t_0) = \begin{cases} n_0 & (0 \leq r < R) \\ 0 & (r = R) \end{cases} \qquad (12\text{-}8\text{-}8)$$

for both geometries.

In order to reduce the number of parameters from four ($\mathscr{D}_a$, α, n_0, and R) to one, Gray and Kerr introduce the dimensionless variables

$$N = \frac{n}{n_0}, \qquad \rho = \frac{r}{\Lambda}, \qquad \tau = \frac{\mathscr{D}_a t}{\Lambda^2} \tag{12-8-9}$$

Here Λ is the fundamental diffusion length, which is

$$\Lambda = \frac{R}{\lambda_1} \quad \text{for the infinite cylinder}$$

and

$$\Lambda = \frac{R}{\pi} \quad \text{for the sphere.} \tag{12-8-10}$$

Then the differential equations can be written

$$\frac{\partial N}{\partial \tau} = \frac{1}{\rho} \frac{\partial}{\partial \rho} \left(\rho \frac{\partial N}{\partial \rho} \right) - \beta N^2 \tag{12-8-11}$$

for the infinite cylinder and

$$\frac{\partial N}{\partial \tau} = \frac{1}{\rho^2} \frac{\partial}{\partial \rho} \left(\rho^2 \frac{\partial N}{\partial \rho} \right) - \beta N^2 \tag{12-8-12}$$

for the sphere. The one remaining (dimensionless) parameter β, together with the shape of the initial electron spatial distribution, determines the nature of the solution; β is given by the equation

$$\beta = \frac{\alpha n_0 \Lambda^2}{\mathscr{D}_a} = \frac{\alpha n_0^2}{\mathscr{D}_a n_0 / \Lambda^2} \tag{12-8-13}$$

The second form of (12-8-13) shows that β is the ratio of the initial axial or central electron loss rate which would apply in the absence of diffusion, to the corresponding loss rate which would result solely from diffusion in the fundamental mode. Thus β is a measure of the extent to which the plasma is initially recombination-controlled ($\beta \gg 1$) or diffusion-controlled ($\beta \ll 1$). The boundary condition becomes

$$N(\lambda_1, \tau) = 0 \tag{12-8-14}$$

for the cylinder and

$$N(\pi, \tau) = 0 \tag{12-8-15}$$

for the sphere. The diffusion distribution becomes

$$N(\rho, \tau_0) = J_0 \left(\frac{\rho \Lambda \lambda_1}{R} \right) \tag{12-8-16}$$

for the infinite cylinder and

$$N(\rho, \tau_0) = \frac{\sin (\pi \rho \Lambda / R)}{\pi \rho \Lambda / R} \tag{12-8-17}$$

for the sphere. The recombination distribution becomes

$$N(\rho, \tau_0) = \begin{cases} 1, & 0 \leqq \rho < \dfrac{R}{\Lambda} \\ \\ 0, & \rho = \dfrac{R}{\Lambda} \end{cases} \tag{12-8-18}$$

Gray and Kerr obtained numerical solutions to (12-8-11) and (12-8-12) by replacing the differential equations by difference equations and applying the methods they describe in their paper.[53] The results of some of their calculations are shown in Figs. 12-8-1 through 12-8-4, which illustrate the time development of N for several values of β for the two initial conditions and cylindrical geometry. In each figure the solid lines represent the change in spatial distribution of the electron number density up to the time when the recombination distribution is most nearly approached. The dashed lines illustrate the approach to the diffusion distribution. Special note should be made that an initial diffusion distribution can approach a recombination distribution only for very large values of β.

B. APPLICATION OF GRAY AND KERR'S CONCLUSIONS TO INTERPRETATION OF MICROWAVE RECOMBINATION EXPERIMENTS. Most experimental studies of electron-ion recombination have been made in cylindrical microwave cavities by the frequency shift method described in Section 12-7-A. The shift in the resonant frequency of the cavity produced by the free electrons in the decaying plasma is measured by an interrogating microwave signal, usually of a type to excite the cavity in the simplest (TM_{010}) mode. In this mode the electric field intensity E is directed along the axis of the cylinder, and its magnitude is independent of the axial coordinate but varies with radius as $J_0(\lambda_1 r/a)$, where a denotes the cavity radius. According to (12-7-1), the frequency shift is proportional to the spatial average $\bar{n}(t)$ of the electron density defined by (12-7-2). The recombination coefficient α is determined by comparing the measured time dependence of $\bar{n}$ with the time dependence of $\bar{n}$ calculated from the solution of (12-8-1).

If the diffusion loss term in (12-8-1) is set equal to zero, the solution is given by (12-1-4), which becomes

$$\frac{1}{N(\tau)} = 1 + \beta\tau \tag{12-8-19}$$

in terms of the dimensionless variables we have defined. This solution is called the *recombination approximation*. Its simplicity makes the determination of α straightforward if the plasma is truly recombination-controlled. In this case n does not depend on r at any time, so that $n(t) = \bar{n}(t)$, and a plot of $1/\bar{n}(t)$ versus t will be linear with slope α. Likewise, a plot of $1/\bar{N}(\tau)$ versus τ will be linear with slope β. Equation 12-4-1

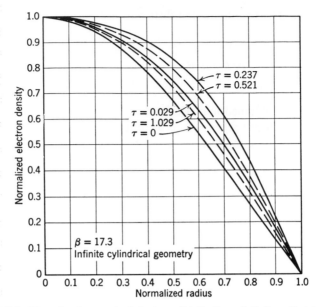

FIG. 12-8-1. Time development of electron distribution. Infinite cylindrical geometry. Initial diffusion distribution. $\beta = 17.3$.

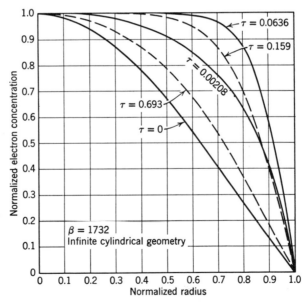

FIG. 12-8-2. Time development of electron distribution. Infinite cylindrical geometry. Initial diffusion distribution. $\beta = 1730$.

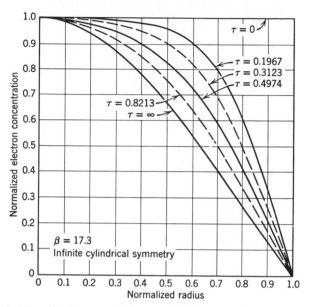

FIG. 12-8-3. Time development of electron distribution. Infinite cylindrical geometry. Initial recombination distribution. $\beta = 17.3$.

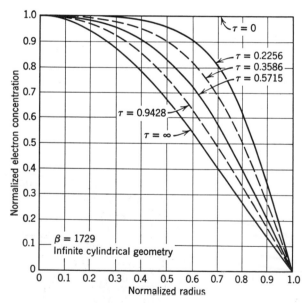

FIG. 12-8-4. Time development of electron distribution. Infinite cylindrical geometry. Initial recombination distribution. $\beta = 1730$.

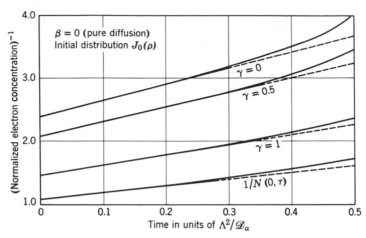

FIG. 12-8-5. $1/\bar{N}$ and $1/N(0)$ versus τ. Infinite cylindrical geometry. Initial diffusion distribution. $\beta = 0$; $\gamma = 0, 0.5$, and 1.

or 12-8-19 has been used for the determination of α in most microwave experiments.

Gray and Kerr computed the dependence of $\bar{N}$ on τ for cylindrical geometry at various values of β and various values of $\gamma = R/a$, the ratio of the plasma and cavity radii. TM_{01} mode excitation of the infinite cylinders was assumed in the calculation of $\mathbf{E}$. Some of their results are shown in Figs. 12-8-5 through 12-8-8. Also shown is the reciprocal of the

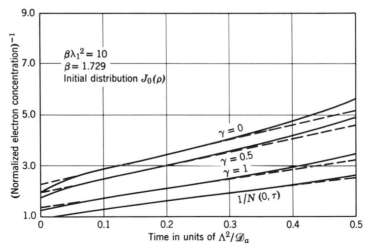

FIG. 12-8-6. $1/\bar{N}$ and $1/N(0)$ versus τ. Infinite cylindrical geometry. Initial diffusion distribution. $\beta = 1.73$; $\gamma = 0, 0.5$, and 1.

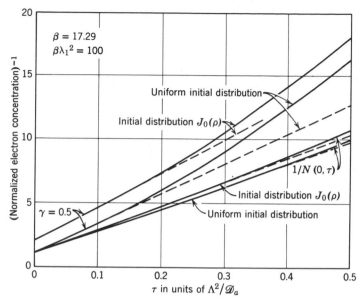

FIG. 12-8-7. $1/\bar{N}$ and $1/N(0)$ versus τ. Infinite cylindrical geometry. Initial diffusion and recombination distribution. $\beta = 17.3$; $\gamma = 0.5$.

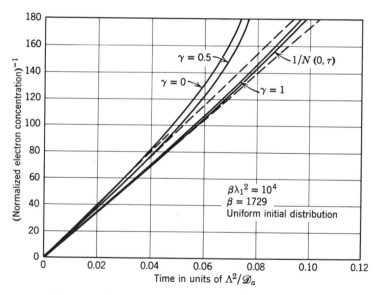

FIG. 12-8-8. $1/\bar{N}$ and $1/N(0)$ versus τ. Infinite cylindrical geometry. Initial recombination distribution. $\beta = 1730$; $\gamma = 0, 0.5,$ and 1.

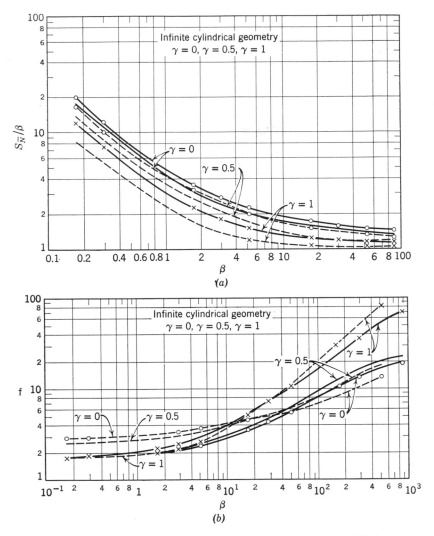

FIG. 12-8-9. (*a*) Factor by which slope exceeds β versus β. Infinite cylindrical geometry. Solid lines are for initial diffusion distribution, dashed lines for initial recombination distribution. $\gamma = 0$, 0.5, and 1. The points represent the computed values used to draw the curves. (*b*) f versus β. Infinite cylindrical geometry. Solid line is for initial diffusion distribution, dashed line for initial recombination distribution. $\gamma = 0$, 0.5, and 1. The points represent the computed values used to draw the curves.

axial density, $1/N(0, \tau)$. The dashed lines represent the best linear approximation to the high-density parts of these curves. We note that the region of linearity is relatively small, even for values of β as large as 17. In order to obtain a quantitative measure of the extent of the linear region, Gray and Kerr define a quantity f, which is the factor by which $\bar{N}$ changes over the region where $1/\bar{N}$ is approximated by the straight line to within 2%.

In a recombination-controlled plasma the slope of the $1/N$ versus τ plot is β. Thus the accuracy of the recombination approximation for determining α may be tested by comparing β with the slope $S_{\bar{N}}$ of the linear approximation. Plots of $S_{\bar{N}}/\beta$ and f versus β for cylindrical geometry are shown in Fig. 12-8-9. Plots of $S_{\bar{N}}/\beta$ versus f are presented in Fig. 12-8-10. Similar graphs for spherical geometry are provided by Gray and Kerr.

Several conclusions are to be drawn from this analysis. (1) The slope $S_{\bar{N}}$ of the linear approximation to $1/\bar{N}$ versus τ is a good approximation to β only for very large β. (2) A linear region in a $1/\bar{N}$ versus τ plot does not in itself constitute proof that the plasma decay is recombination-controlled unless f is as large as about 3 or 4. (3) f is large only if β is very large. (4) $S_{\bar{N}}$ and f are both sensitive to γ and to some extent to the initial distribution. (5) $S_{\bar{N}}$ is always larger than β, and values of α deduced from $1/\bar{n}$ versus t plots of experimental data will always be too large.

Returning now to Figs. 12-8-5 through 12-8-8, we see that the reciprocal of the axial electron density $1/N(0, \tau)$ is linear with time over a considerably wider range of τ than is the reciprocal of the average density over the total volume $1/\bar{N}(\tau)$. This feature derives from the fact that the distribution in the vicinity of the walls is always diffusion-controlled under the assumed boundary condition of this analysis. The parameter β is a measure of the degree of recombination control only for the central region of the plasma at the initial time, and very large values of β are essential if recombination is to be dominant over most of the volume of the cavity for a significant time during the afterglow. The strong influence of wall neutralization suggests that the calculated values of β for a spherical cavity will exhibit greater deviations from the true β values than those for an infinite cylindrical container with the same diffusion length Λ.

Gray and Kerr[53] have applied the preceding analysis to the results of a number of microwave electron-ion recombination experiments. In a few cases the criteria for obtaining accurate values of α appeared to have been met. In many, however, the criteria were definitely not fulfilled, whereas in others no decision can be made. The results obtained by Biondi and Brown[30] on neon, by Biondi[25] on argon, and by Gray and Kerr[68] on helium appear to be accurate to within 10 or 15%, when judged by the criteria established. This work by Biondi, Brown, and Gray and Kerr has been discussed in more recent papers by Biondi[56] and by Kerr and his

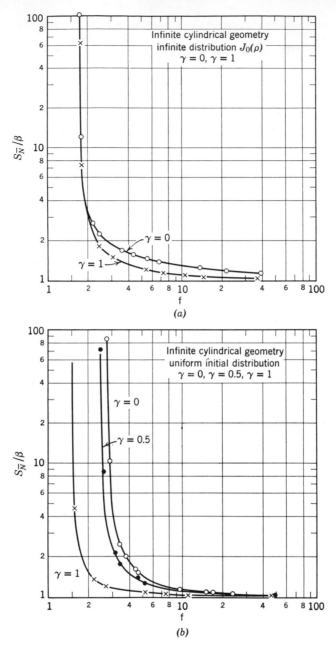

FIG. 12-8-10. (*a*) Factor by which slope exceeds β versus f. Infinite cylindrical geometry. Initial diffusion distribution. $\gamma = 0$ and 1. The points represent the computed values used to draw the curves. (*b*) Factor by which slope exceeds β versus f. Infinite cylindrical geometry. Initial recombination distribution. $\gamma = 0$, 0.5, and 1. The points represent the computed values used to draw the curves.

co-workers,[59–61] to which reference was made in Section 12-7-B. The data presented in Table 12-7-1 also appear to be accurate when judged by the Gray-Kerr criteria.

REFERENCES

1. L. B. Loeb, *Basic Processes of Gaseous Electronics*, Second Edition, University of California Press, Berkeley, 1960, Chapter VI.
2. L. B. Loeb, "The Recombination of Ions," in *Handbuch der Physik*, Vol. XXI, Springer-Verlag, Berlin, 1956, pp. 471–503.
3. H. S. W. Massey and E. H. S. Burhop, *Electronic and Ionic Impact Phenomena*, Oxford University Press, Oxford, 1952, Chapters VI and X.
4. W. B. Kunkel, *Phys. Rev.* **84,** 218 (1951).
5. R. A. Johnson, B. T. McClure, and R. B. Holt, *Phys. Rev.* **80,** 376 (1950).
6. J. J. Thomson, *Phil. Mag.* **47,** 337 (1924).
7. J. Sayers, *Proc. Roy. Soc.* (*London*) **A-169,** 83 (1938).
8. P. Langevin, *Ann. Chim. Phys.* **28,** 289, 433 (1903).
9. W. Mächler, *Z. Physik* **104,** 1 (1936).
10. G. L. Natanson, *Soviet Phys.-Tech. Phys.* **4,** 1263 (1959).
11. J. J. Thomson and G. P. Thomson, *Conduction of Electricity Through Gases*, Cambridge University Press, Cambridge, 1928, Vol. I, pp. 43–44.
12. L. B. Loeb, *Basic Processes of Gaseous Electronics*, Second Edition, University of California Press, Berkeley, 1960, p. 549.
13. R. Maushart, *Ann. Phys.* **1,** 264 (1958).
14. D. R. Bates and H. S. W. Massey, *Phil. Trans. Roy. Soc.* (*London*) **A-239,** 269 (1943). See also H. S. W. Massey, *Advan. Phys.* **1,** No. 4, 395 (1952).
15. See, for example, D. R. Bates and J. T. Lewis, *Proc. Phys. Soc.* (*London*) **A-68,** 173 (1955); D. R. Bates and T. J. M. Boyd, **A-69,** 910 (1956).
16. D. R. Bates, "Transitions," in *Quantum Theory-Vol. I: Elements* (edited by D. R. Bates), Academic, New York, 1961, pp. 293–296.
17. J. L. Magee, Discussions Faraday Soc. **12,** 33 (1952).
18. D. R. Bates, *Proc. Roy. Soc.* (*London*) **A-257,** 22 (1960). See also D. R. Bates, "Collisions Between Atomic Systems," in *Atomic and Molecular Processes* (edited by D. R. Bates), Academic, New York, 1962, pp. 608–613.
19. D. R. Bates and A. Dalgarno, "Electronic Recombination," in *Atomic and Molecular Processes* (edited by D. R. Bates), Academic, New York, 1962, pp. 245–271.
20. D. R. Bates, R. A. Buckingham, H. S. W. Massey, and J. J. Unwin, *Proc. Roy. Soc.* (*London*) **A-170,** 322 (1939).
21. A. Burgess, *Mon. Not. Roy Astron. Soc.* **118,** 477 (1958).
22. M. J. Seaton, *Mon. Not. Roy. Astron. Soc.* **119,** 81 (1959).
23. See Section 2 and Appendix A of the Geophysics Corporation of America Report GCA 62-4-A, entitled "Study of Recombination Phenomena, Vol. II–Recombination in Plasma" (February 1962).
24. D. R. Bates, *Planetary Space Sci.* **9,** 77 (1962).
25. M. A. Biondi and T. Holstein, *Phys. Rev.* **82,** 962 (1951); see also M. A. Biondi, **83,** 1078 (1951).
26. D. R. Bates and H. S. W. Massey, *Proc. Roy. Soc.* (*London*) **A-192,** 1 (1947).
27. D. R. Bates, *Phys. Rev.* **77,** 718 (1950).
28. M. A. Biondi and S. C. Brown, *Phys. Rev.* **75,** 1700 (1949).

29. The existence of diatomic noble gas ions was first demonstrated by O. Tüxen, *Z. Physik* **103,** 463 (1936). For discussion of the formation of these ions, see Section 9-9-A of this book.
30. M. A. Biondi and S. C. Brown, *Phys. Rev.* **76,** 1697 (1949).
31. D. R. Bates, *Phys. Rev.* **78,** 492 (1950).
32. R. H. Fowler, *Statistical Mechanics,* Second Edition, Cambridge University Press, Cambridge, 1936, pp. 726–727. R. H. Fowler, *Phil. Mag.* **47,** 257 (1924).
33. R. G. Giovanelli, *Australian J. Sci. Res.* A-1, 275, 289 (1948).
34. N. D'Angelo, *Phys. Rev.* **121,** 505 (1961).
35. D. R. Bates and A. E. Kingston, *Nature* **189,** 652 (1961).
36. R. W. P. McWhirter, *Nature* **190,** 902 (1961).
37. H. A. Bethe and E. E. Salpeter, *Quantum Mechanics of One- and Two-Electron Atoms,* Academic, New York, 1957.
38. E. Hinnov and J. G. Hirschberg, *Phys. Rev.* **125,** 795 (1962).
39. D. R. Bates, A. E. Kingston, and R. W. P. McWhirter, *Proc. Roy. Soc. (London)* **A-267,** 297 (1962). See also D. R. Bates and A. E. Kingston, *Planetary Space Sci.* **11,** 1 (1963); D. R. Bates, *Third International Conference on the Physics of Electronic and Atomic Collisions,* London, 1963; R. W. P. McWhirter and A. G. Hearn, *Proc. Phys. Soc. (London)* **82,** 641 (1963); F. Robben, W. B. Kunkel, and L. Talbot, *Phys. Rev.* **132,** 2363 (1963); D. R. Bates and A. E. Kingston, *Proc. Phys. Soc. (London)* **83,** 43 (1964).
40. D. R. Bates, A. E. Kingston, and R. W. P. McWhirter, *Proc. Roy. Soc. (London)* **A-270,** 155 (1962).
41. J. G. Baker and D. H. Menzel, *Astrophys. J.* **88,** 52 (1938).
42. L. C. Green, P. P. Rush, and C. D. Chandler, *Astrophys. J. Suppl.* **3,** 37 (1957).
43. M. J. Seaton, *Mon. Not. Roy. Astron. Soc.* **119,** 81 (1959).
44. M. Gryziński, *Phys. Rev.* **115,** 374 (1959).
45. A. Burgess, *Mem. Soc. Roy. Sci. Liége* (5) **4,** 299 (1961).
46. M. J. Seaton, "The Theory of Excitation and Ionization by Electron Impact," in *Atomic and Molecular Processes* (edited by D. R. Bates), Academic, New York, 1962.
47. M. E. Gardner, *Phys. Rev.* **53,** 75 (1938).
48. E. Rutherford, *Phil. Mag.* **44,** 422 (1897). For a modern version of Rutherford's technique and for very recent results see B. H. Mahan and J. C. Person, *J. Chem. Phys.* **40,** 392 (1964).
49. G. Rümelin, *Ann. Phys.* **43,** 821 (1914).
50. T. H. Y. Yeung, *Proc. Phys. Soc. (London)* **71,** 341 (1958).
51. C. Greaves, Thesis, University of Birmingham (1959), quoted in Ref. 52.
52. J. Sayers, "Ionic Recombination," in "Atomic and Molecular Processes" (edited by D. R. Bates), Academic, New York, 1962, pp. 272–279.
53. E. P. Gray and D. E. Kerr *Ann. Phys.* (New York) **17,** 276 (1962). Oskam (Ref. 58) has performed a similar analysis for infinite parallel plate geometry.
54. T. H. Y. Yeung, *J. Electron. Control* **5,** 307 (1958).
55. M. A. Biondi, *Rev. Sci. Instr.* **22,** 500 (1951).
56. M. A. Biondi, *Phys. Rev.* **129,** 1181 (1963).
57. K. B. Persson, *Phys. Rev.* **106,** 191 (1957); S. J. Buchsbaum and S. C. Brown, **106,** 196 (1957).
58. H. J. Oskam, *Philips Res. Rept.* **13,** 335, 401 (1958).
59. D. E. Kerr and E. F. Tubbs, to be published.
60. C. S. Leffel, M. N. Hirsh, and D. E. Kerr, to be published.

61. D. E. Kerr and C. S. Leffel, to be published.
62. See, for example, R. F. Whitmer, *Phys. Rev.* **104,** 572 (1956). S. Takeda and E. H. Holt, *Rev. Sci. Instr.* **30,** 722 (1959). R. W. Motley and A. F. Kuckes, *Proceedings of the Fifth International Conference on Ionization Phenomena in Gases*, Munich, 1961, North-Holland, Amsterdam, 1962, Vol. I, 651.
63. W. H. Kasner, W. A. Rogers, and M. A. Biondi, *Phys. Rev. Letters* **7,** 321 (1961).
64. R. G. Fowler and W. R. Atkinson, *Phys. Rev.* **113,** 1268 (1959).
65. A. F. Kuckes, R. W. Motley, E. Hinnov, and J. G. Hirschberg, *Phys. Rev. Letters* **6,** 337 (1961). E. Hinnov and J. G. Hirschberg, *Proceedings of the Fifth International Conference on Ionization Phenomena in Gases*, Munich, 1961, North-Holland, Amsterdam, 1962, Vol. I, 638; R. W. Motley and A. F. Kuckes, *op. cit.*, 651. E. Hinnov and J. G. Hirschberg, *Phys. Rev.* **125,** 795 (1962).
66. S. Byron, R. C. Stabler, and P. I. Bortz, *Phys. Rev. Letters*, **8,** 376 (1962). See erratum, *ibid.*, p. 497.
67. J. Y. Wada and R. C. Knechtli, *Phys. Rev. Letters* **10,** 513 (1963).
68. E. P. Gray and D. E. Kerr, *Bull. Am. Phys. Soc.* **5,** 372 (1960).

13

SURFACE PHENOMENA

Surface phenomena encompass a broad and complex area. We discuss here only those phenomena that are particularly important in experimental studies of atomic collisions and ionized gases. Our treatment includes the adsorption of gases on surfaces, the surface impact of heavy particles and electrons, photoemission of electrons, thermionic emission, and surface ionization.

13-1. THE ADSORPTION OF GASES ON SURFACES

Let us define an *atomically clean*, or simply *clean*, surface as one whose atoms are of the same type as those of the bulk material beneath. Gas atoms striking a clean surface have a high probability of sticking (0.3–0.6) until a *monolayer* is formed, that is, until all available adsorption sites corresponding to the maximum binding energy per atom are occupied.[1] This condition obtains when one gas atom is adsorbed for about four surface atoms and corresponds to a coverage of roughly 2.5×10^{14} adsorbed atoms/cm². For a monolayer the energy of adsorption is generally between 2 and 4 ev per adsorbed atom. For additional layers both the sticking probability and the binding energy drop rapidly. At room temperature several layers of atoms may be attached to a surface.

The binding energy per gas atom in the outermost layer is perhaps a few tenths of an electron volt, which is typical of a van der Waals polarization interaction, and the sticking probability of an atom impinging upon this layer may be about 10^{-3}. Under equilibrium conditions gas atoms leave the surface because of thermal agitation at the same rate at which others are adsorbed.

With this background information, we shall now consider in more detail the formation of adsorbed layers, the effects of these layers on various surface phenomena, and the methods of obtaining atomically clean surfaces.

A. THE FORMATION OF ADSORBED GAS LAYERS.   The first monolayer forms quickly on an atomically clean surface unless its temperature is kept high. To show this, let us estimate the monolayer formation time for nitrogen at a pressure of 1 mm Hg and room temperature. From the discussion of Section 2-6 it follows that $N\bar{v}/4$ molecules per second strike each unit area of a surface bounding a gas which is in thermal equilibrium and which has number density N and mean molecular velocity $\bar{v}$. At room temperature and 1 mm Hg, $N \approx 3.7 \times 10^{16}$ molecules/cm^3 and $\bar{v} \approx 45 \times 10^3$ cm/sec. If the sticking probability is assumed to have the constant value 0.5, then 2.5×10^{20} molecules/cm^2-sec stick to the surface. Thus the first monolayer is formed in about 10^{-6} sec. If the pressure were 10^{-6} mm Hg, the formation time would still be only about one second. However, because of the decrease in sticking probability following the formation of the first layer, the second layer would take several seconds to form at 10^{-6} mm Hg, and minutes would be required to approach equilibrium.

The examples cited make it apparent that even if atomically clean surfaces can be produced, pressures of the order of 10^{-9} mm Hg or lower are necessary if experiments conducted at room temperature are to be performed before the surfaces of the apparatus become badly contaminated. Techniques for achieving vacua of this quality in the laboratory were developed only in the late 1940's.[2] Experimental work reported before about 1950 was of necessity performed with surfaces contaminated at least to the extent of a monolayer, unless the surfaces were maintained at a very high temperature during the experiment.

The amount and tenacity of adsorption of a gas is determined in large measure by the structure of its molecules. The hydrogen molecule, for example, is strongly adsorbed because of its small size. Hagstrum[3] observed that although he could produce an atomically clean tungsten surface in the presence of nitrogen he could not do so in the presence of hydrogen. The noble gases, because of their chemical inactivity, are not strongly adsorbed, although the heavier noble gases, which are highly polarizable, are adsorbed to the extent of a monolayer or two.*

The nature of the surface is also important. Hagstrum[4] found that he could not produce an atomically clean tantalum surface at room temperature, despite the fact that a clean tungsten surface could be achieved under the identical experimental conditions. Adsorbed gas molecules apparently penetrate into the body of the metal when tantalum is heated, and they reappear at the surface when the metal is allowed to cool.

B. THE EFFECTS OF ADSORBED GASES.   Even though gases to be admitted to an experimental apparatus can be made extremely pure (in some cases pure to within a few parts per million), they may become contaminated soon after admission to the system by impurity molecules desorbed from interior surfaces. The release of a single monolayer from the interior faces of a 10-cm cubical container would result in a pressure increase of about 4×10^{-3} mm Hg inside the vessel. The number density of impurities thus introduced might well equal the number density of the gas molecules deliberately introduced for the purpose of the experiment.

Many surface phenomena are sensitive to impurities. For instance, the work function of atomically clean tantalum is 4.1 ev, and a value of 4.9 ev has been obtained for the metal when it was coated with gas molecules.[4] According to Rose and Clark,[1] the magnitude of the work function is generally increased by adsorption of atoms with high ionization potentials and decreased by coverage with those of low ionization potentials. As shown in Section 13-2, the emission of secondary electrons by slow positive ions is also sensitive to surface contamination. In fact, Hagstrum and D'Amico[5] have made use of this fact to determine the degree of contamination of metal surfaces.

C. THE PRODUCTION OF ATOMICALLY CLEAN SURFACES.   As mentioned earlier, adsorbed gases may be driven off a surface by raising its temperature. Rose and Clark[1] state that heating a metal to 700°K in a good vacuum will remove all but the last few monolayers, whereas heating to 1300°K will drive off all but the last one. Hagstrum and D'Amico[5] present extensive evidence supporting the premise that flashing a tungsten surface to 2200°K for times of a few seconds produces an atomically clean condition. Refractory materials such as tungsten can be cleaned in this manner because of their high binding energy (up to about 8 ev per atom of the refractory material). On the other hand, materials such as the alkalis,

---

* Helium behaves somewhat differently from the other noble gases in that He atoms can penetrate a solid to relatively great depths because of their small size. See J. H. Carmichael and P. M. Waters, *J. Appl. Phys.* **33,** 1470 (1962).

which have very low binding energies, are vaporized as the temperature is raised before complete desorption of contaminants occurs.

Using as a standard the secondary electron emission characteristics of a tungsten surface which had been proved atomically clean, Hagstrum and D'Amico[5] were able to show that positive ion bombardment utilized under rigorous experimental conditions is also capable of producing atomically clean surfaces. Although this technique is considerably more complicated to use than the heating method, it offers the advantage that clean surfaces may be produced on materials that might not survive a high temperature flash.* Hagstrum,[6] for example, was able to achieve atomically clean germanium surfaces by ion bombardment, but not by heating even for three hours at $1170°K$, a temperature within $40°K$ of the melting point of germanium.

13-2. THE IMPACT OF HEAVY PARTICLES ON SURFACES

In this section we treat the ejection of secondary electrons and heavy particles from surfaces under the impact of ions and neutral particles. The reflection of heavy particles incident on surfaces and the emission of electromagnetic radiation from surfaces bombarded by fast ions are also discussed briefly.

A. EJECTION OF SECONDARY ELECTRONS.   Electrons may be ejected from a surface bombarded by electrons, ions, or neutral molecules. The yield of "secondary" electrons produced in this manner is usually expressed by the *secondary electron emission coefficient*, which is defined as the average number of electrons ejected per incident particle. We use the symbol γ_i to denote the coefficient for incident ions and other heavy particles; δ designates the corresponding quantity for incident electrons.

Secondary electron emission plays a variety of roles in the experimental study of atomic collisions and plasmas. This phenomenon at times can be put to good use by the experimenter; at other times it is merely a possible source of error.

Electron and photomultipliers, whose action depends on the production of secondary electrons, are useful as detectors of charged and neutral particles and of photons. Certain metallic alloys have unusually high secondary emission coefficients which make them particularly useful in the construction of multipliers (see Section 3). An electron multiplier with 12 or more stages of secondary multiplication can provide unexcelled

---

* This technique has been used recently in studies of electron ejection from metals by 1- to 10-kev noble gas ion bombardment. See G. D. Magnuson and C. E. Carlston, *Phys. Rev.* **129**, 2403, 2409 (1963).

sensitivity for the measurement of beam currents. Charged or neutral particles are easily detected above the noise background by a multiplier operated as a discrete particle counter, provided they have energies above about 5 kev. The ability to register the arrival of individual projectiles in a beam permits the routine measurement of particle currents of less than one per second, corresponding to electric currents of less than 10^{-19} amp in the case of singly-charged ions.*

Sufficiently intense beams of projectiles may be detected by allowing them to strike an ordinary metallic surface and measuring the current of electrons thus produced in a single stage of secondary ejection. Usually no effort is made to prepare a clean target surface for such a "secondary emission detector"; it is found[7] that gas-covered surfaces become stable after a short period of use and that the secondary yield thereafter remains constant with time. On the other hand, if it is intended that the number of charged particles striking a metallic surface be determined by measurement of the primary current to that surface, a suitable electric field perpendicular to the surface or a magnetic field parallel to the surface must be provided to ensure suppression of secondaries. For example, if a 100 μamp beam of positive ions strikes a surface for which γ_i is 0.5, and if the ejected electrons are not then returned to that surface, measurement of the current to the target electrode would indicate a beam current of 150 μamp. A properly designed Faraday cup[7] obviates this difficulty.

The unintentional production of "stray" electrons by secondary emission from surfaces within an experimental apparatus can cause a great deal of trouble, and this possibility must always be reckoned with. Also, any critically located insulating surfaces within the apparatus must be shielded from fast particle impact lest they acquire a surface charge because of secondary emission and thus produce spurious electric fields.

1. *The theory of secondary electron ejection by heavy particles.* Ejection of an electron from a surface proceeds by excitation of the electron into the kinetic energy continuum above the surface potential barrier. In a heavy particle incident on a surface the source of this excitation energy might be either the kinetic or internal potential energy of the projectile. These two possibilities may be distinguished as kinetic and potential ejection, respectively. The potential energy of the projectile might be due to its being in an ionized or a metastable state, or both. (The lifetimes of

---

* For an illustration of such counting techniques, see E. W. McDaniel, D. W. Martin, and W. S. Barnes, *Rev. Sci. Instr.* **33,** 2 (1962). For a general discussion of the detection of ion beams by multipliers see A. I. Akishin, *Soviet Phys.-Uspekhi* **1,** 113 (1958). Pulse-counting techniques for detecting very weak beams with essentially 100% efficiency are described by N. R. Daly, *Rev. Sci. Instr.* **31,** 264 (1960); **34,** 1116 (1963); V. V. Afrosimov et al., *Soviet Phys.-Tech. Phys.* **5,** 1378 (1961).

ordinary excited states are so short, about 10^{-8} sec, that atoms in such states usually become de-excited by emitting radiation before they strike a surface). Since an electron cannot acquire potential energy of internal excitation, kinetic ejection is the only ejection process possible for an incident electron. Electron impact is discussed in Section 13-3.

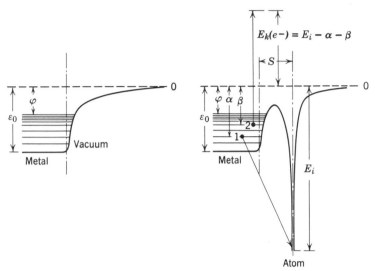

FIG. 13-2-1. (*a*) The normal electron energy diagram of a metal; φ is the work function, and ε_0 is the depth of the conduction band with respect to the level of zero kinetic energy in the continuum. (*b*) The energy diagram modified by the approach of an ion within a distance S of the surface. Here the ion undergoes *direct Auger neutralization*. Electron (1) tunnels directly to the ground state of the ion, and the excess energy is given to electron (2). If the electron (2) escapes, its kinetic energy outside the surface is $E_k(e^-)$.

Potential ejection. According to Hagstrum, on whose papers[4,8,9] the following treatment is based, potential ejection from metals involves electronic interaction between the incoming ion and the conduction electrons of the metal while the ion is at a distance of a few angstroms from the surface. Potential ejection can occur when the ionization energy is greater than twice the work function of the surface material.

Figure 13-2-1 shows (a) the electron energy diagram for a metal which applies while the incident ion is still far from the surface and (b) the diagram modified by the approach of the ion to within a distance S (a few angstroms) of the surface. Note the deep potential crevasse produced by the ion. The dashed line at the horizontal level marked 0 represents zero kinetic energy in the continuum. The work function of the metal is φ, and the lowest available level in the metal conduction band has energy

$-\varepsilon_0$. Thus the width of the filled portion of the conduction band is $\varepsilon_0 - \varphi$. The solid horizontal lines represent the density of energy states within the conduction band; E_i is the ionization energy of the incident ion.

As the ion approaches within a few angstroms of the surface, it is likely to be neutralized. The process involved may be *direct Auger neutralization,* which is illustrated in Fig. 13-2-1b. In this process an electron (1) tunnels through the reduced potential barrier directly to the ground state of the ion, neutralizing it and simultaneously giving up its excess energy to another electron (2) in the conduction band. If this excess energy $E_i - \alpha$ is greater than the minimum escape energy β, then the second electron may be ejected into the continuum with kinetic energy $E_i - \alpha - \beta$. It is apparent that the maximum and minimum values of the ejected electron's kinetic energy are $E_i - 2\varphi$ and $E_i - 2\varepsilon_0$, respectively.* It is also apparent that the production of an external secondary electron is energetically impossible if $E_i < 2\varphi$, although neutralization of the ion by this process can, and almost always does, occur if $E_i > \varphi$.

Potential ejection may also take place in a *two-stage Auger process,* as described in Fig. 13-2-2. This process depends on the existence of a metastable level of the ion isoenergetic to some level ε in the metal conduction band. Here a metal conduction electron (1) tunnels through the barrier to the metastable level, neutralizing the ion but leaving it in an excited state. The atom subsequently decays to its ground state in an Auger de-excitation process wherein a second metal electron (2) tunnels to the ground state of the atom, simultaneously giving up its excess energy to the "metastable" electron. The kinetic energy of the ejected metastable electron is $E_i - \varepsilon - \beta$. The corresponding maximum and minimum values of the kinetic energy are $E_i - \varepsilon - \varphi$ and $E_i - \varepsilon - \varepsilon_0$, respectively. Note that this process is energetically impossible if $E_i < \varepsilon + \varphi$.

It might appear that if the energy requirements are satisfied one electron would be ejected for each incident ion, so that the secondary emission coefficient could not be less than unity. Such is not the case. Although theory predicts that one electron is excited for each incident ion, this electron must still escape from the metal. Those electrons having velocities initially directed into the interior of the metal may not even reach the surface, and there is also the possibility of internal reflection at the surface barrier. Thus the yield may be substantially less than unity.

Our simplified treatment predicts a maximum kinetic energy of $E_i - 2\varphi$ for the secondary electrons. If we include the effects of energy level shifts in the ion as it comes under the influence of the metal surface, we find that the maximum kinetic energy can slightly exceed $E - 2\varphi$. Hagstrum[9] considers these effects in a quantitative discussion of the theory of potential

* Collisions will actually reduce the minimum ejection energy to zero.

ejection from metals. Hagstrum[10] has also developed a theory of Auger ejection of electrons from semiconductor surfaces.

The foregoing qualitative discussion of potential ejection indicates that the secondary electron yield should depend primarily on the excitation

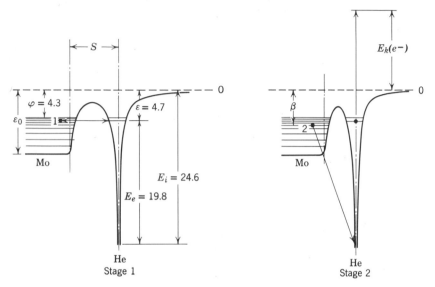

FIG. 13-2-2. Electronic transitions characteristic of the *two-stage process* of potential ejection, illustrated for the case of He+ ions incident on molybdenum. Stage 1 consists of the resonance capture of a conduction electron (1) into the ^3S metastable level of the He atom, the only excited state isoenergetic to a filled level in the metal. In stage 2, the excited atom thus formed is deexcited by capture of a second metal electron (2) with the simultaneous excitation of the "metastable" electron into the continuum. $E_k(e^-)$ is the kinetic energy which the excited electron possesses if it leaves the metal. This process involves *resonance neutralization and Auger deexcitation*. The decay of the excited atom may also occur without electron exchange between the metal and ion. This mode of decay, which involves dropping of the "metastable" electron to the ground state and excitation of the second metal electron into the continuum, is much less likely than the first mode described.[8]

energy of the ion. Dependence on ion kinetic energy is secondary. Thus we would expect the yield to be higher for a doubly charged ion than for a singly charged ion of the same species, even though the singly charged ion might have considerably higher kinetic energy. The kinetic energy of the incident ions does, however, become an important factor at energies above a few kev. Furthermore, if $E_i < 2\varphi$, kinetic ejection is the only mechanism possible for secondary emission of electrons.

· *Kinetic ejection.* The theory of kinetic ejection of electrons from surfaces is not so well established as that of potential ejection. Petrov[11] explains kinetic ejection on the basis of excitation of bound surface electrons. Parilis and Kishinevskii[12] have developed a theory in which the electron yield from a metal is considered to be the result of an Auger recombination of a conduction electron with a hole, with a second conduction electron receiving the energy resulting from this recombination. These authors claim that this mechanism gives good agreement with experimental results. Neither Parilis and Kishinevskii nor Petrov included in their papers a prediction of the energy distribution of the ejected electrons, a prediction which would be helpful in evaluating the merit of the theory.

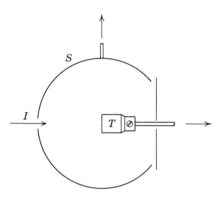

FIG. 13-2-3. Schematic diagram of target T and electron collector S, used by Hagstrum in experiments on secondary electron emission. The target is a metal ribbon, bent such that the portion of its surface struck by the incident ion beam I is flat and lies in a plane perpendicular to the plane of the drawing.

2. *Apparatus used for measurements.*   Conceptually, the measurement of secondary electron yield is quite simple, as shown by Fig. 13-2-3, taken from a paper by Hagstrum.[8] A target, shown as a ribbon T bent perpendicular to the plane of the drawing, is bombarded by an ion beam I, and the resulting currents to the target and the spherical collector S are measured. Variation of a retarding potential applied between S and T permits the determination of the energy distribution of the ejected secondaries. Proper analysis of the currents must, however, include the effects of unneutralized ions reflected from the target surface, ions which become resonance-neutralized and are reflected as metastable atoms, as well as secondary electrons liberated at the target, and in addition, tertiary electrons ejected from the collector by all three of the foregoing types of particles.

Figure 13-2-4 displays a complete experimental tube designed by Hagstrum.[3] The target surface can either be made atomically clean or covered with a monolayer of known composition. Hagstrum used this

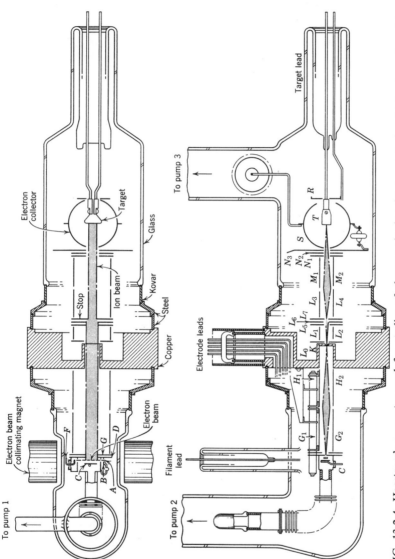

FIG. 13-2-4. Hagstrum's apparatus used for studies of electron ejection from metals by singly charged positive ions. H. D. Hagstrum, *Phys. Rev.* **104**, 1516 (1956).

tube for studies of singly charged noble gas ions in the kinetic energy range between 10 and 1000 ev. The target-collector arrangement is like that in Fig. 13-3-3. The target has two leads attached and thus can be electrically heated to the temperature (about 2200°K) necessary to produce an atomically clean surface.

An electron beam is used to produce the noble gas ions. Filament A supplies electrons for the ionizing beam which passes through slits in electrodes B and C to the collector F. Ions formed in the electron beam inside the chamber C are drawn out and focused by the lens $G–H$ on the narrow slit in K. (The barrier at K permits differential pumping between the source and target chambers.) The ion beam then passes through the lens $L–M$ and is focused on the target T. Source gas is admitted to the source chamber through the lead to pump 1. Magnetic analysis of the ion beam is not provided in this instrument, but charge-state homogeneity is achieved by keeping the energy of the electrons in the ionizing beam below the threshold for double ionization. A typical ion current is 5×10^{-10} amp, obtained with an electron beam current of 0.5 ma and a source gas pressure of about 3×10^{-5} mm Hg.

In all of his experiments on electron ejection Hagstrum used bakeable apparatus and ultrahigh-vacuum techniques.[2] His experimental procedures are discussed in detail in a lengthy review,[13] which also describes other versions of his apparatus. One of Hagstrum's instruments provided e/m analysis of the ion beam and was used for experiments on multiply charged ions.[8]

3. *Data on electron yield versus bombarding energy.* A great deal of data is available on secondary electron ejection by heavy particles, although much of this data pertains to surfaces contaminated to unknown extents by gases of unknown types. Hagstrum's papers represent the best single source of reliable data on surfaces of known composition. The review article by Little[14] also represents an excellent source of information on this and related subjects.

In this section we are mainly concerned with the energy dependence of electron yields. Figure 13-2-5 shows the yields of atomically clean tungsten and molybdenum under the impact of singly charged ions of the noble gases. At energies up to the maximum reached here (1000 ev) the yields of A^+, Kr^+, and Xe^+ are nearly independent of the kinetic energy of the ions, and we infer that the mechanism of electron production here is potential ejection. (Other evidence indicates that only the direct Auger process is involved to a significant extent.) If this is indeed the case, we would expect the yield from a given metal to be a monotonically increasing function of the potential energy of the projectile, that is, the ionization energy of the noble gas atom from which the ion was formed. The ionization energy of the noble gases decreases monotonically as we proceed from the lightest to the heaviest atom, and we see that the A^+, Kr^+, and Xe^+ data of Fig. 13-2-5 have the expected dependence on potential energy.

At the lowest energy that Hagstrum reached (10 ev) the direct Auger process is thought to be dominant for He^+ and Ne^+ as well as for the

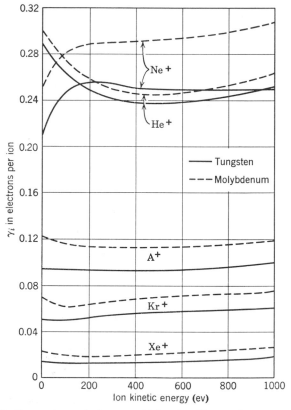

FIG. 13-2-5. Comparison of electron yields of noble gas ions on atomically clean tungsten and molybdenum. H. D. Hagstrum, *Phys. Rev.* **104**, 672 (1956).

heavier ions. Differences appear, however, as the energy is raised. The initial drop in γ_i with increasing energy of the He^+ ion is explained by the theory of Auger neutralization.[9] It is the result of a reduction in the effective ionization potential and the broadening of the energy distribution as the He^+ ion is Auger-neutralized nearer the surface, on the average, as it approaches with greater velocity. However, the theory predicts a steady drop in γ_i for He^+ and cannot account for the observed rise above 500 ev which has been attributed to another process setting in at high energy. In Ne^+ indications are that as the ion energy is increased to about 200 ev the two-stage electronic transition process described earlier occurs in about 10% of the impacts. The higher probability of electron escape associated with this process causes a rise in γ_i. We may note that neon also exhibits anomalous behavior in the case of photoabsorption, as shown in Fig. 7-2-1.

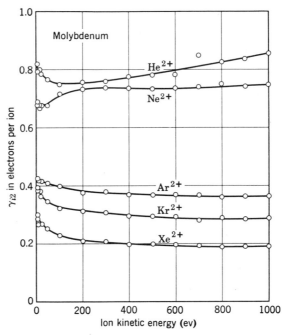

FIG. 13-2-6. Electron yields for doubly charged ions of the noble gases incident on atomically clean molybdenum. H. D. Hagstrum, *Phys. Rev.* **104**, 672 (1956).

Figures 13-2-6 and 13-2-7 exhibit secondary electron yields for multiply charged ions. Again the electron yield is seen to increase with an increase of ionization energy. Figure 13-2-8 charts electron yields of gas-covered tantalum. Hagstrum was unable to produce an atomically clean tantalum surface at room temperature.

As we have already mentioned, the effect of adsorbed gases on secondary electron yield is quite important; in fact, it is large enough that secondary electron yield can be used as a sensitive measure of surface purity.[3,5] Figure 13-2-9 shows the change of γ_i, as a monolayer of nitrogen forms on a tungsten surface. The monolayer adsorption time is seen from the lower graph to be about 10 minutes. Figures 13-2-10 through 13 illustrate the effect of various gas monolayers as a function of ion kinetic energy.

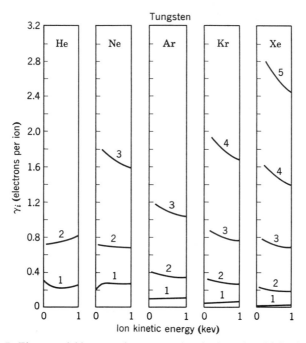

FIG. 13-2-7. Electron yields versus ion energy for singly and multiply charged positive ions of the noble gases incident on atomically clean tungsten. The charge of the ion is indicated at each curve. H. D. Hagstrum, *Phys. Rev.* **96**, 325 (1954).

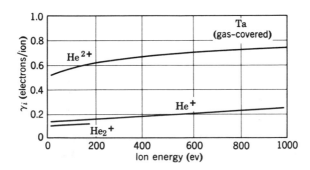

FIG. 13-2-8. Electron yields for He^+, He^{2+}, and He_2^+ ions on gas-covered tantalum. H. D. Hagstrum, *Phys. Rev.* **91**, 543 (1953).

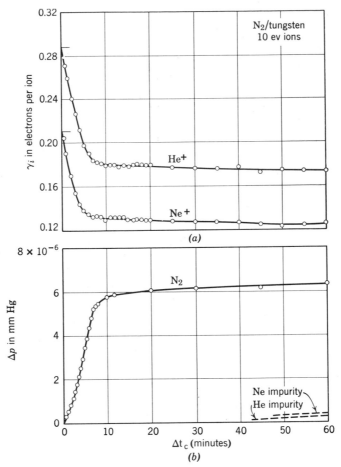

FIG. 13-2-9. (*a*) Plots of electron yields for He$^+$ and Ne$^+$ ions and (*b*) pressure rise on target flash as functions of cold interval as a monolayer of N_2 forms on tungsten. The horizontal lines on the ordinate axis indicate the values of the yield for clean tungsten measured when N_2 was not admitted. The break in the N_2 plot represents the sudden decrease in the sticking probability as the first monolayer is completed. H. D. Hagstrum, *Phys. Rev.* **104**, 1516 (1956).

Data are shown in Figs. 13-2-14 and 13-2-15 for several metal alloys; Ag-Mg and Cu-Be are frequently used as dynode materials in electron and photomultipliers because of their high yields.

Waters[16] and Petrov[17] have performed experiments with ions, such as Cs$^+$, which have low potential energies. Data for these ions are quite useful in the evaluation of theoretical predictions concerning kinetic ejection. Since potential ejection is energetically impossible with these

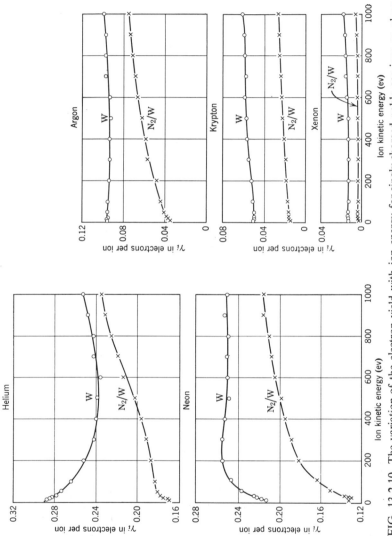

FIG. 13-2-10. The variation of the electron yield with ion energy for singly charged noble gas ions on clean tungsten (W) and tungsten covered with a monolayer of N_2 (N_2/W). H.D. Hagstrum, *Phys. Rev.* **104**, 1516 (1956).

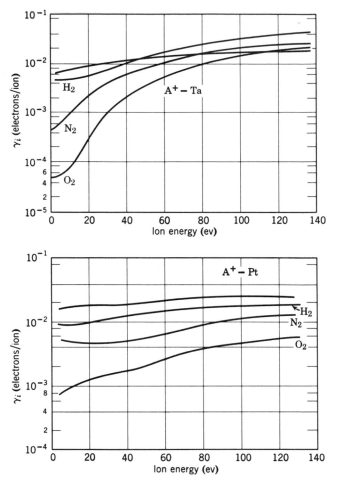

FIG. 13-2-11. Electron yields for A^+ ions on outgased tantalum and platinum and on these metals after treatment with hydrogen, nitrogen, and oxygen. J. H. Parker, *Phys. Rev.* **93**, 1148 (1954).

projectiles, the observed yields must be due entirely to kinetic ejection. Kinetic ejection is also the dominant mechanism at very high ion energies. Data for such energies are displayed in Figures 13-2-16 and 13-2-17.

Oliphant[18] and Allen[19] have investigated the dependence of γ_i on the angle of incidence of the bombarding ions. Figure 13-2-18 shows the behavior observed by Oliphant for 1000 ev He^+ ions on nickel. The angle made by the ions with the normal to the surface is denoted by θ. Allen employed ions in the energy range 48 to 212 kev and observed a yield

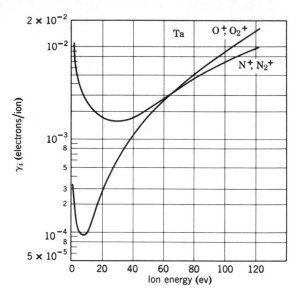

FIG. 13-2-12. Electron yields for mixtures of O^+ and O_2^+ ions on oxygen-covered tantalum and for mixtures of N^+ and N_2^+ ions on nitrogen-covered tantalum. J. H. Parker, *Phys. Rev.* **93**, 1148 (1954).

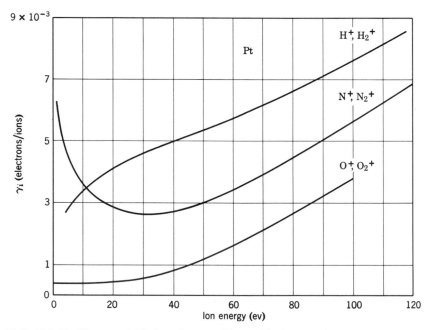

FIG. 13-2-13. Electron yields for mixtures of ions of hydrogen, nitrogen, and oxygen on platinum covered with molecules of the parent gas in each case. J. H. Parker, *Phys. Rev.* **93**, 1148 (1954).

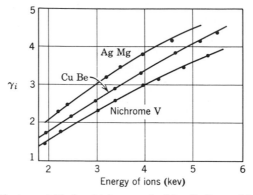

FIG. 13-2-14. Electron yields for A$^+$ ions on Ag-Mg, Cu-Be, and Nichrome V alloys. M. J. Higatsberger, H. L. Demorest, and A. O. Nier, *J. Appl. Phys.* **25**, 883 (1954).

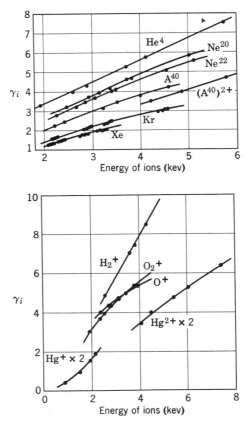

FIG. 13-2-15. Electron yields of various ions on Ag-Mg targets. M. J. Higatsberger, H. L. Demorest, and A. O. Nier, *J. Appl. Phys.* **25**, 883 (1954).

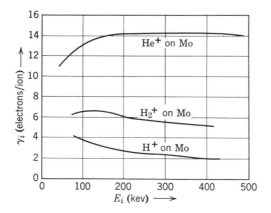

FIG. 13-2-16. Electron yields for high-energy ions on molybdenum. A. G. Hill, W. W. Buechner, J. S. Clark, and J. B. Fisk, *Phys. Rev.* **55**, 463 (1939).

proportional to secant θ. Oliphant's results do not depart far from proportionality to secant θ over the angular range shown in Fig. 13-2-18.

4. *Energy and angular distributions of secondary electrons.* By use of retarding potential techniques,[13] Hagstrum has measured energy distributions of ejected secondaries. Figure 13-2-19 displays the distributions for 40-ev noble gas ions incident on atomically clean molybdenum; the vertical marks on the abscissa represent the $E_i - 2\varphi$ kinetic energy

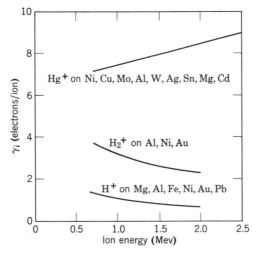

FIG. 13-2-17. Electron yields for high-energy ions. Hg^+ ions: L. H. Linford, *Phys. Rev.* **47**, 279 (1935). H^+ and H_2^+ ions: B. Aarset, R. W. Cloud, and J. G. Trump, *J. Appl. Phys.* **25**, 1365 (1954).

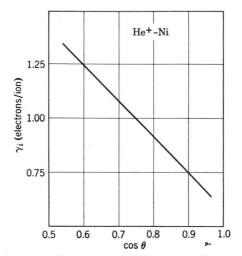

FIG. 13-2-18. Electron yield dependence on the angle of incidence for helium ions on nickel. M. L. E. Oliphant, *Proc. Roy. Soc.* (*London*) **A-127**, 373 (1930).

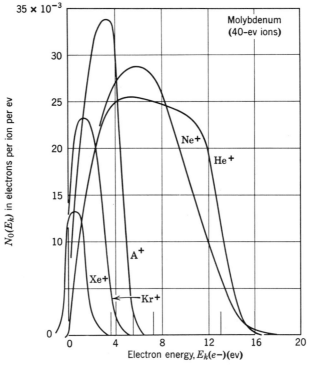

FIG. 13-2-19. Energy distributions of secondary electrons ejected from Mo by 40-ev ions of the noble gases. H. D. Hagstrum, *Phys. Rev.* **104**, 672 (1956).

maximum predicted for each ion by theory. The agreement is quite good in every case except that of neon. These data are interpreted as meaning that He^+, A^+, Kr^+, and Xe^+ ions are neutralized in the process of direct Auger neutralization but that some 10% of the Ne^+ ions are resonance-neutralized near the surface and form excited atoms that go to the ground state by Auger de-excitation. This two-stage process can produce faster electrons and has a higher yield per ion than the direct process. At

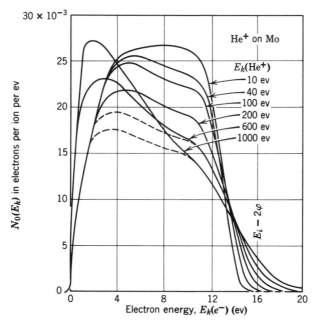

FIG. 13-2-20. Energy distributions of secondary electrons ejected from Mo by He^+ ions of various energies. H. D. Hagstrum, *Phys. Rev.* **104**, 672 (1956).

Hagstrum's lowest energy, 10 ev, the maximum observed electron energy was $E_i - 2\varphi$ for Ne^+ as well as for the other ions.

Figure 13-2-20 illustrates the energy distributions of secondary electrons ejected from atomically clean molybdenum by helium ions as a function of ion kinetic energy. The energy distributions in the ion energy range 10 to 200 ev are explained in terms of Auger neutralization. The low-energy peaks for the 600-ev and 1000-ev ions must come from another process. The dashed portions of these curves describe the behavior expected if only an Auger process were operative. These "excess" low-energy secondaries are probably the result of kinetic ejection.

Kronenberg et al.[20] have recently established the presence of high energy

(2000-ev) secondaries in the spectrum of electrons ejected from various metal targets bombarded by 1 Mev protons. These electrons apparently were overlooked by earlier workers.

Abbott and Berry[21] have studied the angular distributions of the ejected secondary electrons as a function of the ion kinetic energy and incidence angle for He+ ions on tungsten. Their investigations covered situations in which kinetic ejection and potential ejection, respectively, were the dominant mechanisms. In all cases the ejected secondaries displayed a cosine distribution, with maximum ejection occurring normal to the target surface.

5. *Ejection of electrons by metastables.*   Metastable ions or atoms incident on a surface are capable of ejecting electrons from the surface by virtue of their excitation energy, provided this energy is sufficiently high. The mechanism in the case of a metastable atom does not necessarily involve direct Auger de-excitation of the atom. If the energy levels are appropriately located, the "metastable" electron may tunnel to an unfilled level in the conduction band of the metal surface, with the formation of a ground state singly charged ion. This ion may undergo Auger neutralization by the process discussed in the section on theory.

The ejection of electrons by a metastable singly charged ion is similar to that by a ground state doubly charged ion.[22] Hagstrum[22,23] makes use of this fact to determine the fraction of metastables present in a beam of singly charged ions. By use of a retarding potential to cancel out the contributions of reflected ions and electrons ejected by ground state ions,[23] Hagstrum produced a sensitive device for detecting metastable ions.

Stebbings[24] has measured the secondary yield for He (2^3S) metastable atoms incident on a contaminated gold surface. Hasted[25] has extended this work to include flashed W, Mo, and Pt surfaces, although he did not employ ultrahigh-vacuum techniques. His measured yields for metastable atoms are somewhat lower than would be expected from consideration of Hagstrum's results for singly charged ions.

The ejection of secondary electrons from surfaces by metastable atoms can be a matter of particular concern. Since metastable atoms are uncharged, they cannot be swept out to electrodes by an applied electric field, and consequently they may diffuse through an apparatus and eject secondaries from surfaces not accessible to ions. Furthermore, their arrival times at a surface are unpredictable. This fact can lead to the production of spurious counts in a Geiger tube containing a noble gas unless a small admixture of a molecular gas is present to de-excite the metastables.[26]

The de-excitation process referred to immediately above takes place by what is called the "Penning effect," which involves a "collision of the

second kind" between a neutral metastable and a molecule whose ionization energy is less than the excitation energy of the metastable.* The
metastable is de-excited to the ground state by transferring its excitation
energy to the molecule, which is ionized in the process. In a neon metastable (with excitation energy of 16.62 ev) colliding at thermal velocity
with an argon atom in the ground state (ionization energy 15.76), the
ionization process occurs with close to unit probability. The Penning
effect can lead to a reduction in the starting potential of ac discharges.[27] It
can also lead to spurious determinations of the Townsend coefficient[28]
and the average energy required to form an ion pair.[29]

B. EJECTION OF HEAVY PARTICLES—SPUTTERING.   Heavy particles incident on a surface may eject other heavy particles as well as secondary
electrons. The ejected heavy particles may be neutrals, positive ions, or
negative ions. This phenomenon, which is called sputtering, was first
observed by Grove in 1852.

The erosion of a surface due to sputtering can be very undesirable.
In controlled thermonuclear experiments,† for instance, atoms sputtered
from interior surfaces of the apparatus contaminate the plasma and have
a pronounced cooling effect. Sputtering of the exposed surfaces of space
vehicles by the solar wind or by swept-up particles is also a matter of
concern.‡ In vacuum tubes with indirectly heated cathodes the erosion of
the cathode that results from its bombardment by ions of residual gas can
greatly reduce the tube lifetime. There are, however, a number of important uses of sputtering. This phenomenon has been applied, for example,
in the deposition of thin films,[30] cleaning of semiconductor surfaces,[6] and
in ion getter pumps.[2]

Two distinct kinds of sputtering can occur: chemical and physical.
Chemical sputtering is confined to certain reactive projectile-target combinations, such as hydrogen on carbon, in which volatile compounds are
formed at the target surface; the material loss from the surface occurs as
these compounds vaporize. The kinetic energy of the incident particles
is therefore not essential in chemical sputtering. In *physical sputtering*,
however, atoms are ejected from the target surface as the result of momentum transfer from the incident particles to atoms of the target. As
expected, the kinetic energy of the projectiles is an important parameter

* For further discussion of the Penning effect the reader is referred to Section 6-4.
† A general discussion of surface effects in controlled thermonuclear research appears
in an article by J. L. Craston and co-workers, *Proceedings of the Second International
Conference on Peaceful Uses of Atomic Energy*, Vol. 32, United Nations, Geneva
(1958), p. 414.
‡ See G. Wehner, C. Kenknight, and D. L. Rosenberg, *Planetary Space Sci.* **11**, 885
(1963).

in physical sputtering, and the charge state of the projectiles is of little concern here. In most experiments chemical sputtering plays no significant role; for this reason, the remainder of our discussion is concerned solely with physical sputtering.

For reasons of convenience experimental studies of sputtering generally involve the use of ions, rather than neutrals, as projectiles. Two different methods of study are in common use. In the first method an ion beam impinges obliquely on the target surface, and a mass spectrometer oriented near the angle of specular reflection is employed to identify and determine the yield of the ejected particles.[31] When the ion energies are less than 1 kev, the greatest current densities that may be used are not high enough to keep the target surface atomically clean. Therefore the mass spectrum includes contributions from material adsorbed on the surface as well as from the target material and its bulk impurities. Studies of this kind are of special interest to workers in atomic collisions, for they describe sputtering under conditions prevalent in many low-current experiments.

The second extensively used method of studying sputtering involves insertion of the target into a highly ionized low-pressure plasma so that it acts like a negative Langmuir probe.[32] The ion current densities resulting at the target surface are high enough to keep the surface atomically clean, even for low ion energies. This approach is yielding the basic data necessary for clarification of the mechanism of physical sputtering. We shall now consider each of these techniques separately.

1. *Mass spectrometric studies of sputtering.* Mass spectrometric studies of sputtering from contaminated surfaces show that complex patterns of positive ions, negative ions, and neutrals are ejected from a surface under positive ion bombardment. Honig,[33] for example, observed 13 species of neutrals, 21 species of positive ions, and 21 species of negative ions when he bombarded a SiC surface with 600-ev noble gas ions. Similar results were obtained in studies of silver, germanium, and a Ge-Si alloy[31,34] and in experiments on coal, diamond, and graphite.[35] About 1% of the ejected heavy particles were found to be ions. The apparatus[33,34] used in Honig's recent experiments consists primarily of an oscillating-electron ion source and a 180° mass analyzer. Either positive or negative ions may be observed directly by proper biasing of the analyzer; an auxiliary electron beam is available to ionize ejected neutrals so that they may be detected in the analyzer. Projectile current densities up to 50 μamp/cm^2 are employed, and the energy of the projectiles may be varied from 50 to 600 ev.

An important parameter in sputtering is the *sputtering yield*, which for a particular ejected species is defined as the average number of particles of that species ejected per bombarding particle. The total yield is the total number of atoms, regardless of type, ejected per incident projectile.

Honig's yields for several species of negative ions ejected from a SiC surface by Kr^+ projectiles are shown as functions of the kinetic energy of the bombarding ions in Fig. 13-2-21.

Bradley and his colleagues[36] have studied the positive ion emission from molybdenum, tantalum, platinum, and copper under the bombardment of ions of the inert gases. They found between 0.1 and 1% of the ejected

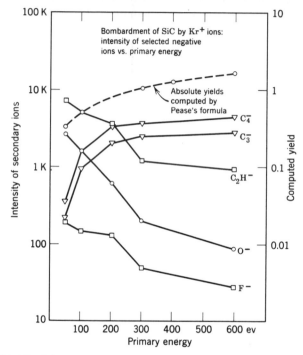

FIG. 13-2-21. Honig's measured negative ion yields from SiC as a function of the energy of the bombarding Kr^+ ions.[33]

heavy particles to be charged. Investigation of the "reflected" inert gas ions present in the mass spectra led Bradley and his co-workers to the conclusion that these ions were actually atoms that had been adsorbed on the target surface and subsequently sputtered as ions.

Fogel et al.[37] have developed a mass spectrometric method which allows simultaneous determination of the yields of positive and negative ions and the reflection coefficient for the incident ions. Using this method, they have studied Mo, Ta, W, Cu, and Fe targets under the bombardment of several types of ions in the energy range 5 to 40 kev.

2. *High current density studies of sputtering.*   As stated earlier, the high bombarding current densities required to keep the target surface free from

adsorbed material may be obtained by extracting ions from a dense low-pressure plasma. Since the target surface is clean and very few ions are ejected, the total yield, which is the quantity experimentally determined here, is nearly equal to the yield of neutral atoms of the target material. In the remainder of this section we shall see how the yield is affected by the characteristics of the bombarding particles and those of the surface material. We shall also look briefly at the velocity and angular distributions of the ejected particles. Further details can be found in recent papers by Wehner.[38,39]

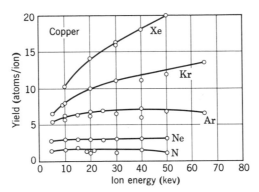

FIG. 13-2-22. Sputtering yields of copper bombarded by various ions. O. Almèn and G. Bruce, *Nuclear Instr. Methods* **11**, 257, 279 (1961).

· *Influence of bombarding energy on yield.* The variation of yield with kinetic energy of the bombarding particle has a characteristic shape.[38] At energies below a certain value (the "threshold," generally 8–25 ev[38]) no substantial sputtering takes place. As the energy is increased above this level, the yield rises linearly, then approaches a broad maximum in the region of kev or tens of kev and finally decreases slowly at very high energies. The yield maximum and the later decrease are related to the depth of penetration of the incident projectiles into the target.* As the projectile energy is increased, the penetration depth increases, and a larger fraction of the energy is expended in collisions that do not lead to sputtering. Small ions, such as H^+, penetrate the surface readily and reach their maximum yield at low energies. Large heavy ions such as Xe^+ may not attain their maximum yield until their energies are well above 50 kev. Figures 13-2-22 and 13-2-23 illustrate this behavior for several heavy and light projectile ions.

* For discussions of the depth of penetration of heavy particles into solids, see M. T. Robinson, *Appl. Phys. Letters* **1**, 49 (1962); D. K. Holmes, "The Ranges of Energetic Atoms in Solids," appearing in *Radiation Damage in Solids*, International Atomic Energy Agency, Vienna, 1962, pp. 3–42.

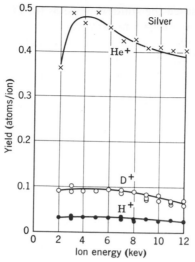

FIG. 13-2-23. Sputtering yields of silver for H^+, D^+, and He^+ ions. F. Grønlund and W. J. Moore, *J. Chem. Phys.* **32**, 1540 (1960).

Note that the yields can be very large. For instance, according to Fig. 13-2-22, 50-kev xenon ions incident on copper eject 20 atoms per projectile! Figure 13-2-24 depicts the yields of lower energy Xe^+ ions incident on several materials. The data presented here are intended only to be representative; the papers of Wehner and his colleagues[40–42] furnish much additional information. Data of particular relevance to controlled thermo-nuclear research is to be found in the paper by Yonts, Normand, and

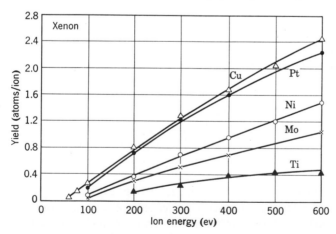

FIG. 13-2-24. Sputtering yields for Cu, Pt, Ni, Mo, and Ti bombarded by xenon ions. D. Rosenberg and G. K. Wehner, *J. Appl. Phys.* **33**, 1842 (1962).

Harrison,[43] who measured the sputtering yields for D^+, He^+, and A^+ ions on copper in the energy range 5 to 40 kev.

The data in Figs. 13-2-22 through 13-2-24 pertain to ions impinging normally on the surface. As the angle of incidence is increased, the ion spends more of its energy in collisions near the surface, and a higher yield may be anticipated. Figure 13-2-25 shows this effect for 45 kev Kr^+ ions on various materials.

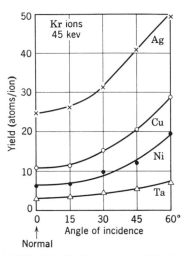

FIG. 13-2-25. Sputtering yields of various metals bombarded with 45 kev Kr^+ ions as a function of the angle of ion incidence. O. Almèn and G. Bruce, *Nuclear Instr. Methods* **11**, 257, 279 (1961).

• *Influence of the atomic structure of the target.* Figure 13-2-26 shows the sputtering yields of 28 elements under 400 ev A^+ bombardment as a function of the atomic number of the target element. There is a characteristic rise in the yield within the different periods. According to Wehner,[38] the increase is associated with the filling of the electron shells, especially the *d* shells. As the shells fill, the target surface will look more opaque to a given incident particle. Again, we see that the depth of penetration is quite important and that those target materials that appear the most opaque (Cu, Ag, Au) will have the highest sputtering yields.

• *Influence of the target crystal structure.* In 1955 Wehner observed that atoms are ejected from single crystal targets in preferred crystallographic directions. Since that time, this aspect of sputtering has received a considerable amount of study.[44,45] It has been observed that atoms are sputtered from single-crystal targets primarily in nearest-neighbor directions. This observation invalidates an early theory of sputtering, according to which the ion gives its energy to a small portion of the crystal lattice, with atoms being evaporated subsequently. This process cannot be the dominant one in sputtering, since a dependence on crystallographic direction has never been observed when material is evaporated from a single crystal.[45]

The abovementioned observation is strong evidence in favor of a momentum transfer theory based on focused collision sequences, such as that developed by Thompson[46] for sputtering by high energy light ions. This theory is based on a model in which an energetic ion penetrates the target surface and produces atomic recoils within the target as a result of ion-atom collisions. These collisions produce atomic collisions cascades, which arrive at the surface and eject atoms. The cascades travel most readily in nearest-neighbor (close-packed) directions. Other important contributions to sputtering theory have been made recently by Harrison[47] and Pease.[48]

• *Velocity and angular distributions of sputtered particles.* Wehner[49] has measured the average energy of atoms ejected from several metals by Hg^+ ions. The average energies are in the range 10 to 30 ev. They increase as

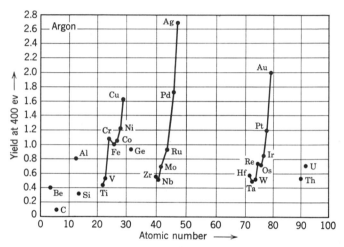

FIG. 13-2-26. Sputtering yields for 400-ev argon ions on 28 elements plotted against the atomic number of the element. N. Laegreid and G. K. Wehner, *J. Appl. Phys.* **32**, 365 (1961).

the ion kinetic energy increases and as the ion beam incidence becomes more oblique. Wehner and Rosenberg[50] have also measured the angular distribution of particles ejected from a polycrystalline surface under Hg^+ bombardment in the energy range 100 to 1000 ev. With normal Hg^+ incidence, the angular distribution approaches a cosine form at high energies. Under oblique ion incidence atoms are sputtered preferentially in the forward direction.

C. REFLECTION OF POSITIVE IONS FROM SURFACES. Positive ions incident on a surface may be reflected either as ions or as neutral atoms. If the ionization energy is greater than the surface work function, most of the ions are Auger-neutralized at the surface and the reflected fraction of the incident ions is small. On the other hand, ions with low potential energy, such as those of the alkalis, are found to have high reflection coefficients.[17,51]

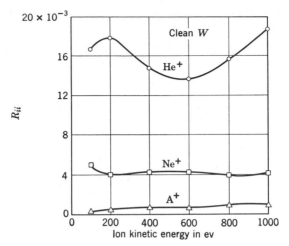

FIG. 13-2-27. R_{ii} versus ion kinetic energy for He$^+$, Ne$^+$, and A$^+$ on clean tungsten. H. D. Hagstrum, *Phys. Rev.* **123**, 758 (1961).

Hagstrum[52] has investigated the reflection of the lighter noble gas ions from atomically clean and slightly contaminated surfaces. The apparatus he used is basically that described earlier[3] in this chapter. Hagstrum determined the fraction R_{ii} of the incident ion beam reflected as ions, and the fraction R_{im} reflected as metastables. Figure 13-2-27 shows the variation of R_{ii} with ion energy for He$^+$, Ne$^+$, and A$^+$ on a clean tungsten surface. Note that the fraction reflected is quite small and is almost independent of the kinetic energy of the ions. Figure 13-2-28 illustrates the variation of R_{im} with the ion velocity for the same ions incident on a clean tungsten surface. The fraction of the ions reflected as metastables

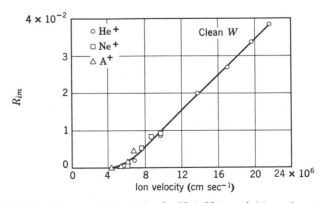

FIG. 13-2-28. R_{im} versus ion velocity for He$^+$, Ne$^+$, and A$^+$ on clean tungsten. H. D. Hagstrum, *Phys. Rev.* **123**, 758 (1961).

is strongly energy-dependent. Furthermore, the curves for the three ions coincide when plotted as functions of the ion velocity. The noble gas ions observed by Hagstrum actually appear to be reflected from the surface rather than adsorbed onto the surface and subsequently sputtered, as concluded by Bradley et al.[36] for Xe⁺ ions on platinum.

D. EMISSION OF ELECTROMAGNETIC RADIATION BY SURFACES UNDER PARTICLE BOMBARDMENT. The production of X rays by electron bombardment of surfaces has been exhaustively investigated and fully described

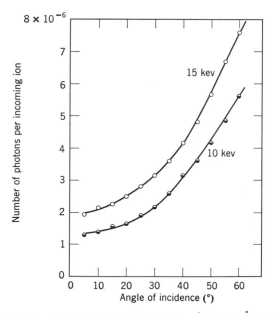

FIG. 13-2-29. Photon production at the CuI line $\lambda = 3247$ Å as a function of the angle of incidence of an argon ion beam on a polycrystalline Cu target. The angle of incidence is measured with respect to the normal to the surface. Fluit et al.[54]

in the literature.* This phenomenon is so familiar that its effects are unlikely to be overlooked in any experiment utilizing a beam of fast electrons. On the other hand, the production of electromagnetic radiation by heavy particle impact on surfaces has received much less attention, and its importance is perhaps not fully appreciated. It may be well to emphasize that significant amounts of radiation may be produced by fast ion or neutral beams and that this radiation may, through photoionization and photoexcitation processes, seriously interfere with the measurements being made.

* See, for example, Vol. XXX, *Handbuch der Physik*, Springer-Verlag, Berlin, 1957

Merzbacher and Lewis[53] have recently reviewed the production of X rays by heavy charged particles incident on a surface. Their article is concerned mainly with the line radiation resulting from innershell ionization of the target by protons and alpha particles in the Mev range. The production of continuous X rays (bremsstrahlung) is not so important here as in the electron case because the intensity of the continuous radiation is inversely proportional to the square of the mass of the bombarding projectile.

A few experiments have been performed recently to measure the radiation emitted from surfaces under heavy particle bombardment.[54] Fluit et al.[54] studied the photons and metastable atoms produced when copper targets were sputtered by Cu^+, A^+, and Ne^+ ion bombardment. The radiation from the target was measured with a grating spectrometer. With 15 kev projectiles, the total photon yield was approximately 7×10^{-5} photon per sputtered copper atom. Most of these photons are from the CuI resonance lines with wavelengths of 3247 and 3274 Å. The photon yield is strongly affected by the angle of incidence of the ion beam, as shown by Fig. 13-2-29. The rapid increase in the photon yield as the angle between the beam and the normal to the surface is made larger indicates that the production of excited states in the target takes place near the surface, whereas normal sputtering takes place deeper within the material. Fluit et al. observed a large yield of metastable copper atoms: 3×10^{-2} ejected metastables per sputtered copper atom. The energy distribution of the sputtered metastables had a maximum at about 11 ev.

13-3. THE IMPACT OF ELECTRONS ON SURFACES

A number of important phenomena are associated with the impact of electrons on surfaces. In this section our attention is focused on the ejection of secondary electrons* by electron impact and on the reflection of primary electrons by the target material. Although secondary emission was discovered as long ago as 1902,[55] it is still the subject of vigorous research. Much also remains to be learned about electron reflection. Another phenomenon of great importance is the emission of electromagnetic radiation by surfaces under electron bombardment (see Section 13-2-D). This subject, however, is essentially well understood and is so thoroughly treated elsewhere that it need not be discussed here.

Some indication of the practical importance of secondary emission was given in Section 13-2-A. Additional interest centers on electron-produced secondary emission because this phenomenon is responsible for the "negative resistance" portion of tetrode vacuum tube characteristics.

---

* Electrons will not generally eject heavy particles from a surface because of the unfavorable mass ratio for the two types of particles.

Secondary electrons may also give rise to disturbing effects in X-ray tubes by producing X rays and causing electrolysis of the glass insulators and envelopes. Many applications of secondary emission in electronics are discussed by Bruining.[56]

A. EJECTION OF SECONDARY ELECTRONS. The subject of electron-produced secondary emission has been reviewed by Bruining,[56] Hachenberg and Brauer,[57] Dekker,[58] and Kollath.[59] Our treatment is much less detailed than any of these reviews, to which the reader is referred if additional information is desired. All of these works contain extensive bibliographies.

The physics of surface reflection and secondary emission is quite complicated. Some of the primary electrons impinging on a target are reflected at the surface barrier.* Most of them, however, cross the barrier and interact with the nuclei and electrons in the target material. As the result of these interactions, the primary electrons lose energy and are scattered. (The similarity to the problem of fast neutrons slowing down and diffusing in a scattering medium is obvious.) In low-Z targets the energy degradation is rapid compared with the diffusion process; the opposite situation prevails in high-Z targets. Some of the rediffused primaries sooner or later are scattered back to the surface, and if they have enough energy remaining they may climb the potential barrier at the surface and escape. In the process of slowing down, however, the primary electrons produce excitation and ionization within the solid, principally by interaction with outershell electrons. The electrons freed within the solid by this process are called *true secondaries*. These secondary electrons themselves slow down and diffuse as the result of collisions, and the fraction that manages to reach the surface and escape the target consists of the observed true secondaries.

Figure 13-3-1 illustrates a typical energy distribution for secondary electrons. Three distinct regions are apparent in this distribution. In region I the electrons have essentially the same energy as the incident electrons. They are primary electrons which have been elastically back-scattered at the target surface. Region III contains a large number of electrons whose energy distribution is peaked around a few electron volts. The number of these electrons, which are true secondaries, may exceed the number of primary electrons. Region II contains a few energetic true secondaries, but mainly primary electrons which have suffered multiple

---

* As is well known, quantum mechanics predicts that a beam of projectiles will be partially reflected whenever it encounters a significant change in potential. This is true whether the potential increases or decreases in the direction of motion of the particles. An electron entering a solid experiences a decrease in potential energy of a few ev as it crosses the surface barrier.

collisions within the target. These electrons are the "rediffused primaries" just referred to. Separation of the rediffused primaries and true secondaries is not possible, and the boundary between regions II and III is arbitrary. It is usually taken at 50 ev.

The *total secondary electron yield* δ is defined as the average number of external electrons produced per incident electron. The *true secondary electron yield* δ_{true} is the average number of external electrons in the energy range 0 to 50 ev produced per primary electron. The *backscattering*

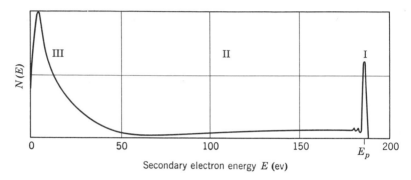

FIG. 13-3-1. A typical energy distribution for secondary electrons; E_p denotes the energy of the primary electrons which produce the secondary emission.

coefficient η is defined as the average number of external electrons with energies greater than 50 ev per incident electron. From these definitions it follows that

$$\delta = \delta_{\text{true}} + \eta \qquad (13\text{-}3\text{-}1)$$

Although η may be small in some cases, it certainly is not always small in relation to δ. In spite of this fact, the terms "secondaries" and "true secondaries" are frequently used interchangeably, and most data on secondary emission are expressed in terms of δ rather than δ_{true}.*

1. *Dependence of δ on the energy of the primary electrons.* The secondary yield δ varies with the energy of the primary electrons E_p in approximately the same manner for *all* target materials. Figure 13-3-2 shows the shape of a typical yield curve. At very low and very high energies few secondaries are ejected, but the yield is substantial at intermediate energies and may exceed unity there. At low primary energies the energy of many of the secondaries at the surface is less than the work function of the target, and they cannot escape. At high energies most of the secondaries

* Some Russian authors have attempted to remove this ambiguity by using different letter symbols for the total and true yields. They denote the total yield by σ and the true yield by δ. The relation involving these symbols which is equivalent to (13-3-1) is $\sigma = \delta + \eta$.

are produced deep within the target and lose so much energy in collisions with other electrons before they reach the surface that they too cannot escape. We let E_{p0} denote the energy at which the yield reaches its maximum value δ_{max}; E_{p+} and E_{p-} are the primary electron energies at which the yield curve crosses the line $\delta = 1$ with positive and negative slopes, respectively.

Values of δ_{max}, E_{p0}, E_{p+}, and E_{p-} for 31 different metals are listed in Table 13-3-1. Note that δ_{max} varies only from 0.5 to 1.7 in this table, whereas other properties of these metals, such as density and electrical conductivity, vary over a much wider range.

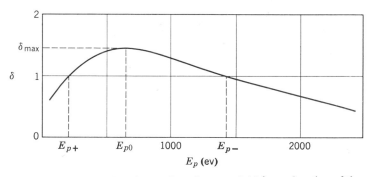

FIG. 13-3-2. A typical plot of secondary electron yield δ as a function of the energy of the primary electrons E_p. The numerical values of the yield shown here are representative of pure metals and many semiconductors, although intermetallic compounds and insulators may have considerably higher yields (see Table 13-3-2).

The secondary electron yield is sensitive to surface contamination and roughness, and values of δ_{max} obtained for metals by various investigators may differ by 10%. Determination of yields for insulators is more difficult than for metals, and discrepancies in the data are considerably wider. The principal difficulty in making measurements on an insulator arises because its low conductivity permits the bombarded surface to acquire a net electrical charge. Thus, if $E_p < E_{p+}$, the surface will charge negatively until it approaches the primary electron accelerating potential and no more primary electrons can strike it. If $E_{p+} < E_p < E_{p-}$, the surface will charge positively to a potential near that of the secondary electron collector, and space charge effects will reduce the effective yield to unity. If $E_p > E_{p-}$, the surface will charge negatively until the yield is increased to unity.

In order to avoid the charging effects experienced with insulators, it is necessary to determine the yield by a pulsed beam technique,[60] in which the surface is allowed to recover completely between pulses of electron

TABLE 13-3-1. Values of the peak secondary electron yields δ_{max} and the primary electron energies E_{p0} at which they occur for different metals. The electron energies E_{p+} and E_{p-} for which the yields equal unity are also indicated. This table is taken from the review by Hachenberg and Brauer.[57]

Atomic Number	Chemical Symbol	δ_{max}	E_{p0}	E_{p+}	E_{p-}
3	Li	0.5	85	–	–
4	Be	0.5	200	–	–
11	Na	0.82	300	–	–
12	Mg	0.95	300	–	–
13	Al	0.95	300	–	–
19	K	0.7	200	–	–
22	Ti	0.9	280	–	–
26	Fe	1.3	(400)	120	1400
27	Co	1.2	(500)	200	–
28	Ni	1.35	550	150	1750
29	Cu	1.3	600	200	1500
37	Rb	0.9	350	–	–
40	Zr	1.1	350	175	(600)
41	Cb	1.2	375	175	1100
42	Mo	1.25	375	150	1300
46	Pd	>1.3	>250	120	–
47	Ag	1.47	800	150	>2000
48	Cd	1.14	450	300	700
50	Sn	1.35	500	–	–
51	Sb	1.3	600	250	2000
55	Cs	0.72	400	–	–
56	Ba	0.82	400	–	–
73	Ta	1.3	600	250	>2000
74	W	1.35	650	250	1500
78	Pt	1.5	750	350	3000
79	Au	1.45	800	150	>2000
80	Hg	1.3	600	350	>1200
81	Tl	1.7	650	70	>1500
82	Pb	1.1	500	250	1000
83	Bi	1.5	900	80	>2000
90	Ta	1.1	800	–	–

bombardment. Even so, the yield of insulators is so sensitive to surface conditions and method of preparation that results may be quite misleading. The yield of MgO, for example, varies from 2.4 to 25, depending on the method of target preparation, surface treatment, and even the past history of the sample. Table 13-3-2, prepared from data compiled by Hachenberg

TABLE 13-3-2. Maximum secondary electron yields from semiconductors and insulators under electron bombardment. These data are taken from the review by Hachenberg and Brauer.[57]

Group	Substance	δ_{max}	E_{p0}
Semiconductive elements	Ge (single crystal)	1.2–1.4	400
	Si (single crystal)	1.1	250
	Se (amorphous)	1.3	400
	Se (crystal)	1.35–1.40	400
	C (diamond)	2.8	750
	C (graphite)	1	250
	B	1.2	150
Semiconductive compounds	Cu_2O	1.19–1.25	400
	PbS	1.2	500
	MoS_2	1.10	
	MoO_2	1.09–1.33	
	Ag_2O	0.98–1.18	
	ZnS	1.8	350
Intermetallic compounds	$SbCs_3$	5–6.4	700
	SbCs	1.9	550
	$BiCs_3$	6–7	1000
	Bi_2Cs	1.9	1000
	GeCs	7	700
Insulators	LiF (evaporated layer)	5.6	
	NaF (layer)	5.7	
	NaCl (layer)	6–6.8	600
	NaCl (single crystal)	14	1200
	NaBr (layer)	6.2–6.5	
	NaBr (single crystal)	24	1800
	NaI (layer)	5.5	
	KCl (layer)	7.5	1200
	KCl (single crystal)	12	
	KI (layer)	5.5	
	KI (single crystal)	10.5	1600
	RbCl (layer)	5.8	
	KBr (single crystal)	12–14.7	1800
	BeO	3.4	2000
	MgO (layer)	4	400
	MgO (single crystal)	23	1200
	BaO (layer)	4.8	400
	BaO—SrO (layer)	5–12	1400
	Al_2O_3 (layer)	1.5–9	350–1300
	SiO_2 (quartz)	2.4	400
	Mica	2.4	300–384
Glasses	Technical glasses	2–3	300–420
	Pyrex	2.3	340–400
	Quartz-glass	2.9	420

and Brauer,[57] presents information on the yields of semiconductors and insulators. In the light of the preceding example, however, these data should be considered only as representative of what is to be expected in any given situation.

It may be noticed that insulators generally have extremely high yields. As pointed out by Rose and Clark,[1] the reason for this is that, apart from the few secondaries present, there are no electrons in the conduction band of an insulator, and there is a quantum mechanically forbidden energy gap between the bottom of the conduction band and the next allowed band below. This lower band is completely filled and can accommodate no more electrons because of the exclusion principle. Therefore the secondary electrons are unable to dissipate their energy in small steps by colliding with other electrons as they move toward the surface. As a consequence, the secondary electrons reach the surface with greater energy, on the average, than in metals, and they thus have a better chance of escaping the target.

2. *Dependence of δ on the angle of incidence of the primary electrons.* For a given target material and primary electron energy, the more oblique the angle of incidence, the higher the secondary yield. The reason for this is obvious: the more oblique the incidence of the primaries, the nearer the secondaries are produced to the surface, on the average. Thus for more oblique incidence the secondaries have a higher probability of reaching the surface, and, furthermore, those that arrive at the surface have higher energy and a correspondingly better chance of escaping. Secondaries produced deeper than about 100 Å within a metal have little chance of escaping.[57] In KCl the corresponding depth is about 500 Å.

3. *Other factors influencing secondary yields.* When the secondary electron yields of various metals are compared, it is found that high yields are correlated with high densities and that metals with larger work functions generally have larger yields.[61] This observation does not imply, however, that increasing the work function of a given metal* will increase the yield. In fact, the opposite effect is usually produced. The correlation between the yield and work function must be the result of another correlation between the work function and some more fundamental property of the metal. Sternglass[62] has also found a correlation between the maximum value of the true secondary yield and the atomic shell structure of the elements. The yield increases steadily as long as successive shells are

---

* The work function of a metal may be changed by allowing a monolayer of gas to be absorbed on the surface. [See, for example, M. P. Hill and B. A. Pethica, *J. Chem. Phys.* **36,** 3095 (1962)]. The resulting change in work function can be measured independently. Secondaries from the absorbed layer itself contribute a negligible amount to the secondary yield.

filled without leaving an inner shell vacant. Whenever a new shell is begun outside one that is subsequently filled, the yield drops discontinuously. Likewise, when an inner shell is completed and a new subshell is begun, the yield drops to a lower value. The yield varies as the number of outer-shell electrons, so that it appears to be a true atomic property.

The secondary electron yield for metals is very nearly independent of the temperature over the range 20 to 400°C. For some semiconductors and insulators, however, the yield decreases with increasing temperature. This fact is justified by Dekker[58] in terms of the decrease in the mean free path for scattering by lattice vibrations.

The charging of an insulating surface under certain conditions can lead to thin-film field emission, which is known as the *Malter effect*.[56,58,63] A surface suitable for demonstration of this effect may be prepared by electrolytic oxidation of aluminum to form a layer of Al_2O_3 approximately 2000 Å thick. This layer is then coated with cesium and oxidized. If the resulting surface is bombarded with several hundred ev electrons, secondary yields as high as 1000 may be observed. The yield drops rapidly when the primary beam is cut off but persists at a nonzero value for many hours. The emission is the result of polarization of the oxide film by positive ions formed at the surface. The electric field gradient across the Al_2O_3 thin film is of the order of 10^6 volts/cm and is high enough to cause field emission from the Al_2O_3.

4. *Energy and angular distributions of secondary electrons.* For primary energies between 20 and 1000 ev the energy distribution of the true secondaries from metals is almost independent of the primary energy[57] and has the shape shown in Fig. 13-3-1. The maximum in the distribution function for metals generally lies between 1.4 and 2.2 ev.[64] The energy distributions for metals are all very similar to one another and to the distributions of typical semiconductors, such as Ge, Se, and PbS. The angular distribution of the rediffused primaries and true secondaries is close to cos θ, where θ is the angle of emission measured with respect to the normal to the surface.[65] This is true regardless of the angle of incidence of the primaries. On the other hand, elastically reflected primaries are preferentially scattered in a direction determined by the angle of incidence of the primaries.

The secondary electron energy distribution is generally obtained by retarding potential measurements, such as those made by Hagstrum and described in Section 13-2-A, or by means of a magnetic selector, such as that developed by Kollath[66] and shown in Fig. 13-3-3. The RPD measurements give the energy distribution for electrons emitted from the surface at all angles. Measurements made with the magnetic analyzer give the distribution for particular values of the angle of emission from the surface.

In Kollath's magnetic analysis apparatus electrons from the cathode travel parallel to a longitudinal magnetic field and strike the target at normal incidence. The slits shown in Fig. 13-3-3 permit only those electrons emitted at some particular angle to reach the collector. If a point source emits electrons with the same energy all at the same angle

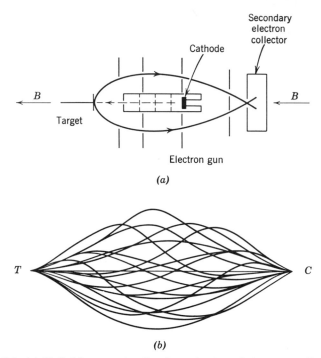

(a)

(b)

FIG. 13-3-3. (a) Kollath's apparatus for determination of the energy distribution of secondary electrons. The ejected electrons spiral about the lines of the axial magnetic induction B. Those electrons which leave the target at the proper angle and with a particular speed (determined by the magnitude of B) negotiate the slit system and reach the collector. (b) Actual trajectories of a group of secondary electrons which leave the target T at the same angle and with the same speed, and which are focused on the collector C.

with respect to a uniform magnetic field, then the electrons will be focused at a point on the axis of symmetry. The distance from the source to this point is directly proportional to the velocity of the electrons and inversely proportional to the magnetic induction. Kollath's apparatus thus provides velocity selection for the secondary electrons, so that measurement of the secondary current to the collector as a function of the magnetic induction will permit evaluation of the energy distribution for the angle of emission determined by the slit positions. The resolution of this device is better than 0.5 ev.

5. *The elementary theory of secondary electron emission.* Two distinct stages are generally recognized in a theoretical treatment of secondary electron emission. The first corresponds to the excitation of secondaries; the second pertains to the diffusion of these electrons through the target material and their escape from the surface. The detailed quantum mechanical theory is treated by Hachenberg and Brauer;[57] we shall discuss briefly a theory based on the Sommerfeld free-electron model of solids.

The independence of the yield on the temperature for metals suggests that the lattice vibrations play a minor role in secondary emission from metals. Thus a logical initial approach would be to consider the metal electrons as a completely free gas. However, such a description would negate the possibility of secondary emission, for a primary electron cannot be backscattered in the laboratory system of coordinates when it strikes a free electron (see Section 1-5). If the electrons, on the other hand, are considered to be free in the excitation event but able to be scattered by the lattice after excitation, a more realistic picture of secondary emission emerges. This is the model applied by Baroody[67] in his "free electron theory." Baroody assumed a Coulomb interaction between the incident electron and the free electrons. He further assumed that the speed of the incident electron is large compared with the velocities of the conduction electrons. Baroody's results are in qualitative agreement with observational data. The general shape of the yield curve and that of the energy distribution are correctly predicted. References to other theoretical treatments of secondary emission are given in Baroody's paper[67] and in the reviews already cited.[56–59]

B. REFLECTION OF ELECTRONS FROM SURFACES. The backscattering coefficient η is determined from a curve such as that shown in Fig. 13-3-1 by an integration over regions I and II. The elastically reflected electrons forming the large peak at I normally compose a small portion of the total backscattered electrons, and this fraction decreases with increasing primary energy. The shape of the curve in region II is similar to the energy distribution of a beam of electrons which has passed through a thin film. The small peaks near E_p represent electrons that have undergone inelastic collisions in the target. Thus the location of these peaks should be characteristic of the target material. The energy losses in the inelastic collisions may be associated with the excitation of plasma oscillations in the electron gas.[68]

Figure 13-3-4 shows the variation of η with primary electron energy for a number of metals and carbon. To obtain this figure, smooth curves

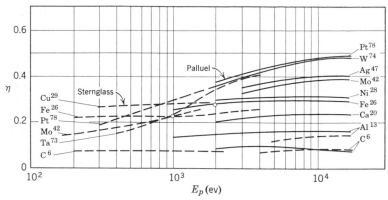

FIG. 13-3-4. The backscattering coefficient η as a function of primary electron energy for various materials bombarded by low- and intermediate-energy electrons.

were drawn through data points of Sternglass[69] (energies between about 0.2 and 4 kev) and those of Palluel[70] (energies between about 2 and 16 kev). At primary energies above about 2 kev the backscattering coefficient at a given energy is higher, the larger the value of the atomic number Z of the target. This correlation is also observed at Mev energies.[71] In the energy ranges covered by Sternglass and Palluel η is observed to be nearly independent of the primary energy for targets with $Z \lesssim 30$, whereas η increases with E_p for elements with $Z \gtrsim 30$. At somewhat higher energies

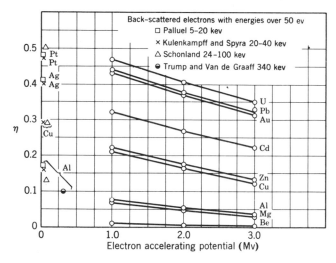

FIG. 13-3-5. The backscattering coefficient η as a function of the primary electron energy for various materials bombarded by high-energy electrons. K. A. Wright and J. G. Trump, *J. Appl. Phys.* **33**, 687 (1962).

the η versus E_p curves become flat for all metals studied, and then at still higher primary energies η begins to decrease monotonically, as shown in Fig. 13-3-5, which is taken from the paper by Wright and Trump.[71] The heaviest metals have a maximum reflection coefficient approaching 0.5. This means that in the heavy metals the primaries become distributed nearly isotropically within the target before they slow down to the point at which they cannot escape the surface, for if a normally incident beam is "totally diffused" without considerable "absorption" half the primary electrons should eventually escape. For light targets the diffusion is slight before the absorption becomes strong, and η_{max} has values much less than 0.5.

Figure 13-3-6, also from the paper by Wright and Trump,[71] shows the variation of the average energy per backscattered electron as a function

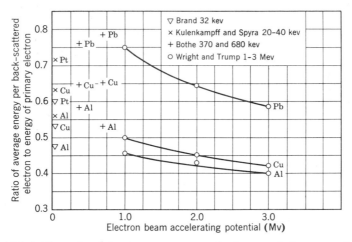

FIG. 13-3-6. The ratio of the average energy per backscattered electron to the energy of the primary electron for electrons normally incident on Al, Cu, and Pb with energies up to 3 Mev. K. A. Wright and J. G. Trump, *J. Appl. Phys.* **33**, 687 (1962).

of E_p. The total fraction of the incident beam energy which is reflected from the surface increases with increasing Z and decreases with increasing E_p. This fraction varies from 34% in 1-Mev electrons on Pb to 1% for 3.5-Mev electrons on Al.

Everhart[72] has developed a theory concerning the reflection of electrons which agrees quite well with experimental data. The theory is based on the following assumptions: (1) the primary cause of electron reflection is Rutherford scattering through angles greater than 90°; (2) the energy loss of electrons penetrating a solid target is given by the *Thomson-Whiddington law*, or a modified version of it; (3) no multiple scattering is allowed. The Thomson-Whiddington law gives the variation of the electron velocity v with distance x traveled in the target as

$$v^4 = v_0^4 - c\rho x = c\rho(R - x) \tag{13-3-2}$$

where v_0 is the initial electron velocity, c is a constant, ρ is the target density, and R is the range of the electrons in the target.

13-4. PHOTOEMISSION

Electromagnetic radiation incident on a solid may excite electrons of the solid into the kinetic energy continuum above the surface barrier. This phenomenon, which is called photoemission or the external photoelectric effect, was first observed by Hertz in 1887 in the course of experiments on electrical resonance. The early work on this subject is described in the book by Hughes and DuBridge,[73] and the field has been reviewed recently by Weissler,[74] Görlich,[75] and Maurer.[76] In this section we shall concern ourselves mainly with photoemission from metals. Photoemission from semiconductors and insulators, although of great interest to workers in other fields,[77] is not particularly relevant to the subject of this book, hence is not covered here. Photoeffects in nonmetals are discussed in the general references given here and in numerous journal publications, among which the papers by Apker and his colleagues at the General Electric Research Laboratory are particularly important.

A. GENERAL CONSIDERATIONS. The aspect of photoemission which is of the greatest interest to us is the *photoelectric yield* γ_p, which is defined as the average number of external photoelectrons produced per incident quantum of radiation. The number of photoelectrons ejected per unit time from unit surface area of a given material is proportional to the intensity of the incident radiation, that is, it is proportional to the number of photons impinging upon it in unit time. Hence the photoelectric yield is independent of the intensity of the radiation. The maximum kinetic energy with which electrons are ejected is also found to be independent of the intensity. These observations led Einstein[78] to formulate his famous photoelectric equation, which expresses the maximum kinetic energy of the ejected photoelectrons in terms of the quantum energy of the incident radiation and the surface work function φ:

$$\left(\frac{mv^2}{2}\right)_{\max} = h\nu - \varphi \tag{13-4-1}$$

The magnitude of the photoelectric yield depends on the frequency and incidence angle of the radiation, and, of course, on the nature of the target material and the condition of its surface. The yield may also depend on the state of polarization of the radiation, particularly for those cases in which most of the incident radiation is absorbed near the surface of the target. In some instances the yield is larger by a factor as great as 10 for radiation polarized with the electric vector in the plane of incidence than when the electric vector is perpendicular to the plane of incidence and therefore parallel to the surface.

Pure metals have yields of only 10^{-4} to 10^{-3} electron per photon in the visible and quartz ultraviolet regions (7000 to 1800 Å). Certain other materials have much higher yields in these spectral ranges; for example, the semiconductor Cs_3Sb has a maximum yield of 0.25 electron per photon at a wavelength of 3600 Å. One reason that metals have very low yields in the long wavelength regions is that much of the radiation incident on them is reflected at the surface. Another reason is that a photon cannot impart its energy to a completely free electron, since it is impossible to conserve both energy and momentum in such a process. If an electron is bound to an atom, the other electrons in the atom can participate in the momentum transfer, but conduction electrons in a metal are relatively free and are therefore not readily excited by incident photons. At short wavelengths the reflectivity of metallic surfaces is small, and the photons are energetically capable of exciting more tightly bound electrons. Both factors are responsible for the high yields (10^{-2} to 10^{-1} electron per photon) observed in the extreme ultraviolet.

There are certain similarities between photoemission and secondary emission. Both processes are viewed as consisting of two steps: the excitation of electrons and their subsequent escape over the surface barrier. In either process the ejected electrons may have been excited near the surface or as deep as about 100 Å within the solid. If the excitation event takes place deep within the target, the electrons make many collisions as they diffuse through the solid, and only those electrons that reach the surface with sufficient energy remaining and with properly oriented velocity vectors will escape. Even though the incident radiation (particle or electromagnetic) may penetrate the target to a much greater depth than the "maximum escape depth" indicated, very few secondary or photo-electrons originating deeper within the solid will have the ability to surmount the surface barrier even if they reach the surface.

B. THE PHOTOELECTRIC THRESHOLD AND DETERMINATION OF WORK FUNCTIONS. Electrons in a metal have a Fermi-Dirac distribution of energies.[79] At 0°K the highest occupied level is the *Fermi level at absolute zero*, $E_F(0)$, which lies between about 2 and 7 ev above the bottom of the conduction band (see Fig. 13-2-1). The work function of the metal is the energy that must be given an electron which initially has the energy $E_F(0)$ in order to remove it from the metal. Thus φ equals the difference between $E_F(0)$ and the energy of a stationary electron outside the metal. The photoelectric threshold is therefore φ ev, since photons of lower energy are incapable of producing photoelectrons.

When the temperature is raised above absolute zero, the Fermi energy drops very slightly to the value

$$E_F \cong E_F(0)\left[1 - \frac{\pi^2}{12}\left(\frac{kT}{E_F(0)}\right)^2\right] \tag{13-4-2}$$

The Fermi level no longer represents a sharp energy cutoff and indeed no longer has a simple physical significance. At $T > 0°K$, E_F is simply that energy level for which the probability of occupation is exactly $\frac{1}{2}$. As the temperature is raised from $0°K$, a small fraction of the more energetic electrons have their energies raised above the original maximum $E_F(0)$, but very few electrons have energies greater than $E_F(0)$ or E_F by more than about $4kT$, which amounts only to about 0.1 ev at room temperature. (The electron distribution is such that the density of electrons decreases from 99% of its maximum value to 1% of this value as the energy varies from $E_F - 4kT$ to $E_F + 4kT$.) We see that at nonzero temperatures the photoelectric threshold is not sharply defined, but the observed photo-current does drop rapidly toward zero as the energy of the incident photons is decreased below φ ev.

Fowler's treatment of the photoemission problem[80,76] makes it possible to reduce data taken at finite temperatures to absolute zero and thus obtain accurate values for the work function. Fowler derived the following equation for the photoelectric current Y:

$$Y = CIT^2\chi\left[\frac{h(\nu - \nu_0)}{kT}\right] \tag{13-4-3}$$

Here C is a constant that depends on the properties of the solid, I is the intensity of the incident radiation, and ν_0 is the threshold frequency defined by the relation

$$h\nu_0 = \varepsilon_0 - E_F = \varphi \tag{13-4-4}$$

where ε_0 is the height of the surface barrier above the bottom of the conduction band, as indicated in Fig. 13-2-1. Let us denote the argument of the function χ by x; $\chi(x)$ is a universal function which Fowler expressed in series form and tabulated as a function of x. Extensive measurements have shown that (13-4-3) gives an adequate description of the temperature and frequency dependence of the yield near threshold. For the analysis of experimental data, it is convenient to write (13-4-3) in the form

$$\log \frac{Y}{T^2} = \log CI + \log \chi(x) \qquad (13\text{-}4\text{-}5)$$

A graph of log Y/T^2 versus x is called a *Fowler plot*, an example of which is shown in Fig. 13-4-1. Note that Y/T^2 is a universal function of x. If experimental data for constant I are plotted in the form log Y/T^2 versus hv/kT, the horizontal shift required to make the experimental curve

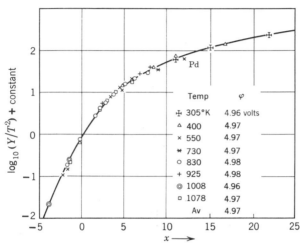

FIG. 13-4-1. Photoelectric emission data for palladium at eight different temperatures fitted to a Fowler plot. L. A. DuBridge and W. W. Roehr, *Phys. Rev.* **39**, 99 (1932).

coincide with the theoretical plot will give hv_0/kT and thus the photoelectric threshold. The threshold frequency defined in this manner is the minimum frequency that can produce photoemission if the temperature of the solid is reduced from the level at which the measurements were made to absolute zero without ε_0 or E_F being changed. At absolute zero a true threshold exists, and the yield rises parabolically as the frequency is raised above the threshold value. Values of work functions, $\varphi = hv_0$, obtained from Fowler plots are listed by Weissler[74] for many different metals and compared with values obtained from thermionic emission data. The Fowler theory cannot be used to obtain work functions for semiconductors and insulators.

C. SPECTRAL DISTRIBUTIONS. The photoelectric threshold for most metals occurs at around 4 ev, and the maximum of the spectral distribution curve usually falls in a relatively inaccessible region of the ultraviolet spectrum. However, the alkali metals and alkaline earths have low thresholds, and their maxima lie at sufficiently low frequencies to permit the spectral distribution curves to be obtained easily. Because of their low threshold energies and high yields, compounds containing the alkalis are frequently used in phototubes.

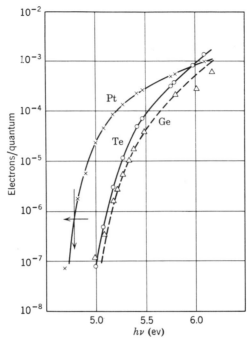

FIG. 13-4-2. Spectral distribution curves for platinum, tellurium, and germanium near threshold. The solid curve through the platinum data was obtained from Fowler's theory. The three surfaces studied here had the same thermionic work function, 4.76 ev. L. Apker, E. Taft, and J. Dickey, *Phys. Rev.* **74**, 1462 (1948).

Comparatively little work has been done on photoemission from metals in recent years; in fact, the bulk of the available data was obtained before 1940. Most of the experiments covered the spectral range from the visible into the quartz ultraviolet because of the ease of work in this range. Little work has been done below the quartz cutoff in the vacuum ultraviolet. Only a small fraction of the available data are presented here. Weissler's article[74] is the best single source of additional information.

Figures 13-4-2 through 13-4-5 illustrate spectral yields for various metals and nonmetals. Because of the difficulty of preparing gas-free surfaces, it is unlikely that any of these data pertain to atomically clean targets. The presence of adsorbed gases may have a large influence on the observed yield, as indicated by Fig. 13-4-6. Figures 13-4-7 through 13-4-10, taken

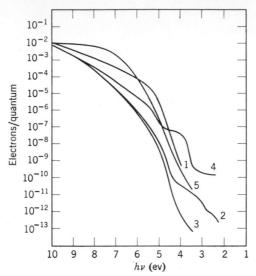

FIG. 13-4-3. Spectral distributions for various materials: Curve 1—platinum; curve 2—beryllium bronze oxidized once; curve 3—beryllium bronze after second oxidation; curve 4—strontium fluoride; curve 5—copper treated with iodine (CuI). A. M. Tyutikov and Yu. A. Shuba, *Optics and Spectroscopy* **9**, 332 (1960).

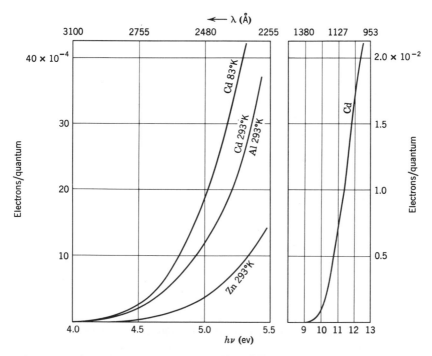

FIG. 13-4-4. Photoelectric yields from Al, Cd, and Zn. R. F. Baker, *J. Opt. Soc. Am.* **28**, 55 (1938); R. Suhrmann and J. Pietrzyk, *Z. Phys.* **122**, 600 (1944).

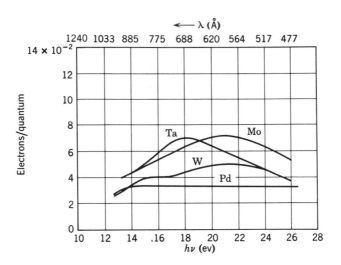

FIG. 13-4-5. Photoelectric yields from Ta, Mo, W, and Pd in the extreme utlraviolet, after heating at 1100°C for two minutes. N. Wainfan, W. C. Walker, and G. L. Weissler, *J. Appl. Phys.* **24**, 1318 (1953); W. C. Walker, N. Wainfan, and G. L. Weissler, *J. Appl. Phys.* **26**, 1366 (1955).

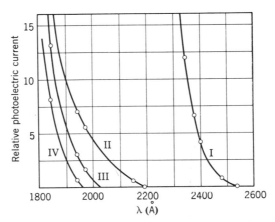

FIG. 13-4-6. Spectral distribution curves for Pt during outgassing. I. Before heating. II. After 50 hr heating. III. After 100 hr. IV. After 300 hr. L. A. Dubridge, *Phys. Rev.* **31**, 236 (1928).

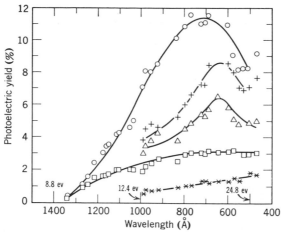

FIG. 13-4-7. Photoelectric yield of Ni. ○ Untreated cathode. □ Heat-treated cathode in equilibrium with residual gases at about 10^{-5} mm Hg. * Cathode maintained at 900°C in a vacuum of 10^{-5} mm Hg. △ Heat-treated cathode at room temperature after exposure to O_2 at 0.1 mm Hg for one half hour. + Heat-treated cathode, heated in 0.05 mm Hg of O_2 at 800°C for one minute.

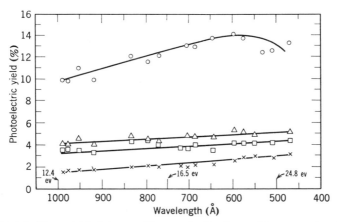

FIG. 13-4-8. Photoyield of Au. ○ Untreated cathode. △ Heat-treated cathode. The cathode was treated for 40 sec at 900°C in a vacuum of about 10^{-5} mm Hg. □ Heat-treated cathode in equilibrium with residual gases at 10^{-5} mm Hg. The cathode was heated for several minutes at 900°C. * Cathode maintained at 800°C in a vacuum of 10^{-5} mm Hg.

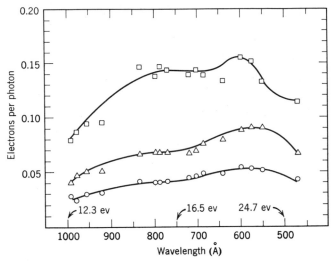

FIG. 13-4-9. Photoyield of W. □ Untreated cathode. △ Cathode heated for five minutes at a temperature above 1000°C in a vacuum of 10^{-5} mm Hg. ○ Cathode heated at a temperature above 1000°C until yield reproducibility was established.

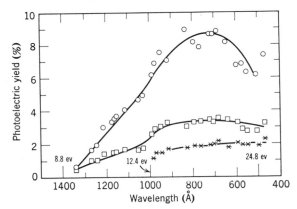

FIG. 13-4-10. Photoelectric yield of Cu. ○ Untreated cathode. □ Heat treated cathode in equilibrium with residual gases at about 10^{-5} mm Hg. ✳ Cathode maintained at 500°C in a vacuum of 10^{-5} mm Hg.

from the paper by Walker, Wainfan, and Weissler,[81] show the spectral distributions of nickel, gold, tungsten, and copper in the vacuum ultraviolet, with various amounts of adsorbed gases. Note that the yields shown here are of the order of 10 to 100 times higher than those usually obtained for visible or ultraviolet light. In addition, it should be noted that the dependence of the yield on adsorbed gases is far greater near threshold than in the vacuum ultraviolet. This observation indicates that near threshold most of the photoelectrons are produced near the surface, whereas at higher energies most of them originate deep within the material.

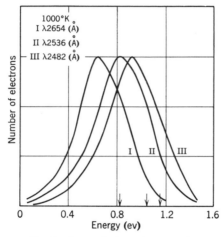

FIG. 13-4-11. Energy distributions of photoelectrons from molybdenum at 1000°K. The arrows indicate the maximum energies at 0°K. W. W. Roehr, *Phys. Rev.* **44**, 866 (1933).

D. ENERGY DISTRIBUTIONS OF PHOTOELECTRONS. At absolute zero the maximum energy of the photoelectrons ejected from a metal of work function φ by a quantum of energy E is $(E - \varphi)$ ev, but at nonzero temperatures the maximum energy is higher than this value. Figure 13-4-11 shows energy distributions characteristic of partially outgassed molybdenum. Energy distributions of photoelectrons from gold are shown in Fig. 13-4-12, which is taken from the paper by Walker and Weissler.[82] Theoretical expressions for the energy distribution of photoelectrons have been developed by DuBridge[83] and Mitchell.[84] Their results agree well with experimental data as a rule.

13-5. THERMIONIC EMISSION

Thermionic emission refers to thermally induced flow of particles from the surface of a solid. The current from any solid at room temperature is too small to be of any practical interest, and thermionic emitters are always operated at a high temperature, generally between 1000 and 2500°K. The emitted particles may be electrons or ions or both, depending on the nature of the material and the temperature to which it is heated. Both metals and semiconductors are useful as emitters. Tungsten, usually in thoriated form, is by all odds the most important metallic emitter; a great variety of semiconducting materials is widely used.

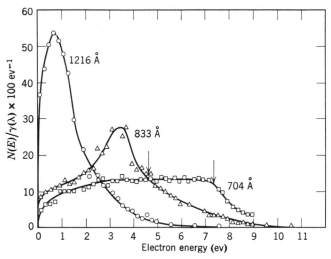

FIG. 13-4-12. Energy distributions of photoelectrons from gold. This sample had a work function of about 4 ev. W. C. Walker and G. L. Weissler, *Phys. Rev.* **97,** 1178 (1955).

A. THERMIONIC EMISSION OF ELECTRONS. This phenomenon is the principal source of electrons in vacuum tubes and in laboratory experiments, but because it is of interest to us mainly as a tool we shall not treat it in any detail. Introductory discussions are also to be found in the texts by Sproull[85] and Van der Ziel.[86] Smith[87] has prepared a short authoritative summary of the subject, and Nottingham[88] has written a comprehensive and critical review of the field up through 1955. A list of several hundred references also appears in Nottingham's bibliography.[89]

The basic physical principles of thermionic electron emission are rather simple: an energy barrier a few ev high exists at the surface of any solid and prevents most of the electrons that impinge upon it from the interior from crossing the surface and escaping from the solid. Some of the electrons, however, have enough energy to pass over the barrier at any nonzero temperature, although, as already mentioned, an insignificant number have the required energy at room temperature. The thermionic emission current is a rapidly increasing function of temperature.

Thermionic emission is extremely sensitive to the atomic composition and crystallographic structure of the solid and to the condition of its surface. Nottingham in his review[88] distinguishes between four surface classifications:

1. clean crystallographically homogeneous surfaces
2. clean heterogeneous surfaces
3. simple composite surfaces
4. complex surfaces.

The only emission experiments amenable to precise theoretical interpretation are those performed on *clean, homogeneous (single-crystal) surfaces*. Since the rate and temperature dependence of the emission depends on the crystallographic structure of the emitter, as well as on its atomic composition, studies of *clean, heterogeneous (polycrystalline) substances* yield data characteristic only of the specimen being investigated, and the structure of such a specimen can never be accurately described. An otherwise clean homogeneous or polycrystalline material covered with about a monolayer, or less, of absorbed atoms or molecules, is said to have a simple composite surface. A small fraction of a monolayer, especially if it is composed of highly polarizable molecules, can drastically affect the thermionic emission from a surface. Complex surfaces are the least understood of all the types of emitting surfaces but are of the greatest practical importance because the oxide-coated cathode[90] falls in this category.

This emitter consists of a metallic support (usually nickel or platinum) on which is placed a processed layer of alkaline earth oxide crystals (usually solid solutions of barium and strontium oxides). Such layers provide copious emission of electrons at very low operating temperatures, a typical yield being about 0.5 amp/cm² at 1000°K. By contrast, the current density from pure tungsten at its normal operating temperature of 2500°K is only about 0.3 amp/cm², and thoriated tungsten will provide about 1.0 amp/cm² at its normal operating temperature of 1900°K. Because of its low emission efficiency, pure tungsten is used only when other types of emitters are unsuitable, as, for example, in high voltage X-ray and transmitter tubes, in which bombardment of the emitter by positive ions of the residual gas is severe.

For a given clean homogeneous surface at absolute temperature T the thermionic emission current density has a limiting value J given by the *Richardson equation*:

$$J = AT^2 \, e^{-\varphi/kT} \tag{13-5-1}$$

where A is the universal thermionic constant

$$A = \frac{4\pi m k^2 e}{h^3} = 120 \text{ amp/cm}^2 \ T^2 \tag{13-5-2}$$

and φ is the electronic work function, which may be temperature-dependent. The Richardson equation does not give directly the emission current observed in a laboratory experiment, since the equation does not allow for the internal reflection of electrons from the surface barrier, for the effects of space charge outside the material, or for other phenomena such as the *Schottky effect*,[88] which is caused by an externally applied electric field. Richardson's equation was first derived by a general thermodynamic argument[91] and thus could hardly be expected to account properly for specific effects (such as boundary reflection), which are different for different materials. Equation 13-5-1 may also be derived by the application of quantum (Fermi) statistics to the free electrons in the solid.[88]

Little or no theoretical significance can be attached to the use of the Richardson equation in the form of (13-5-1) for heterogeneous surfaces, even though they may be clean; (13-5-1) really applies only to clean homogeneous emitters. However, nearly all of the available experimental data relate to other surfaces, and the application of (13-5-1) to them really involves its use as an empirical equation containing two empirically determined constants. Nottingham[88] suggests that a better procedure is to use an empirical equation of the form

$$J = ae^{-\Phi/kT} \tag{13-5-3}$$

where a is a thermionic constant that is determined for each emitter to fit the observational data. The constant Φ is called the work factor and is dependent on the detailed nature of the specimen and its surface configuration. Equation 13-5-3 is easier to use as an empirical equation than (13-5-1). Although the computation necessary to determine the emission for a given temperature is simple with either equation, the reverse calculation, to find the temperature at which a specified current density is expected, is difficult with (13-5-1) but easy with (13-5-3) Nottingham gives tables of empirical constants suitable for use in equations of the form (13-5-1) and (13-5-3) and also with equations for conversion from one representation to the other.

A more nearly complete expression for the saturation current density is[92]

$$J = AT^2(1 - r)e^{-\Phi/kT}e^{-(E)^{\frac{1}{2}}(e)^{\frac{3}{2}}/kT} \text{ amp/cm}^2 \tag{13-5-4}$$

where r is the reflection coefficient of the electrons at the potential barrier (usually about 0.05 for pure metals). The factor $e^{-(E)^{\frac{1}{2}}(e)^{\frac{3}{2}}/kT}$ gives the effect on the emission caused by an electric field at the surface.

Thermionic emission from semiconductors also follows the form of the Richardson equation. The true work function depends on the position of the Fermi level; therefore, the emission current density will depend on the temperature and conductivity of the semiconductor, since these quantities determine the position of the Fermi level.

Before leaving the subject of thermionic electron emission, we shall mention a fact that may be of practical interest. As is well known, the standard thermionic emitters cannot be used in gases at pressures above about 10^{-3} mm Hg. Deleterious chemical effects and the destructive action of positive ion bombardment of the surface limit the lifetimes to unsuitably short values. Thoriated iridium, however, can be used in gases at rather high pressures. Filaments made of this material have operating lifetimes of months, even in corrosive gases at pressures of several mm Hg.[93]

B. THERMIONIC EMISSION OF IONS. Thermionic emission of positive and negative ions from coated filaments is a phenomenon which has been known for decades, and ion sources operating on this principle have been used for many experiments in gaseous electronics.[94] Some metals also emit positive ions of the base material when heated almost to their melting points. This process is not of much practical interest, however, since the number of ions thus produced is small compared with the number of atoms evaporated from the filament. Compton and Langmuir,[95] for instance, find that tungsten at 2800°K emits one positive ion for every 4000 neutral atoms evaporated. A substantial literature exists on the subject of thermionic emission of ions, and many references may be found in the earlier books on thermionic emission[91,96-98] and in the article by Smith.[87] Two experimental studies are mentioned specifically here.

Blewett and Jones[99] produced efficient filament sources of ions of the alkali metals by heating synthetic alkali aluminum silicates to around 1000°C. They also showed that ions of Mg, Ca, Sr, Ba, Al, Ga, In, Ti, V, Mn, Y, and Ce are emitted when the oxide of the metal in question is heated to a white heat on a tungsten filament. The positive ion currents from these emitters ranged from 10^{-10} to 10^{-3} amp. Impurity ions represented a few per cent or less of the total ion current and were separated out with a mass spectrometer. Blewett and Jones found that for lithium ion sources the mineral β-eucryptite (Li_2O: Al_2O_3: $2SiO_2$) appears to be the best emitter. They display a figure showing the emission of such a source as a function of temperature and of the per cent of Li emitted. The emission holds up fairly well even when 60% of the initial Li content of the filament has been emitted. Allison and Kamegai[100] describe a method of preparing artificial β-eucryptite and discuss the design of a lithium ion source. At an ion current of 100 μa the useful emission lifetime of one of their filaments is on the order of 100 hours.

13-6. SURFACE IONIZATION

Surface ionization is the phenomenon in which atoms or molecules are adsorbed on a heated surface and then quickly evaporated in an ionic state. It is possible for both positive and negative ions to be formed in this manner. Langmuir and Kingdon[101] found, for example, that every cesium atom striking a tungsten surface that has been heated above 1200°K gives up an electron to the surface and evaporates as a positive ion. Similar results were obtained with potassium and rubidium. This property gives rise to a useful technique for measuring the absolute intensities of certain atomic and molecular beams and is also the basis of operation of the so-called surface ionization ion sources.

In the surface ionization detector developed by Taylor[102] a tungsten wire filament is enclosed in a metal cylinder held at a negative potential in relation to the filament. A small window is provided in the wall of the cylinder for the entry of the neutral beam. The filament is mounted eccentrically on a rotatable joint, so that it may be made to traverse the incident beam. The negative cylinder serves to collect the positive ions formed at the filament. If the diameter of the wire is small compared with the beam width, it is possible to determine accurately the beam profile.[103] An example of the use of a surface ionization detector is given in Section 4-6-A; other techniques are discussed in the books by Fraser[104] and Ramsey[105] and in reviews by Kusch and Hughes[106] and Datz and Taylor.[107]

A. THEORY OF SURFACE IONIZATION. If the ionization potential of an electropositive atom incident on a hot metal surface is less than the surface work function, then it is quite probable that the atom will be adsorbed on the surface and lose an electron to the surface material. Depending on the temperature of the surface, the ion may remain adsorbed, or evaporate as a positive ion or as a neutral atom.

The phenomenon can be treated mathematically by assuming that the adsorbed particles come to equilibrium with the surface. Under this assumption, the ratio of the number of positive ions (n_+) to the number of neutral atoms (n_a) leaving the surface per unit time is given by the *Saha-Langmuir equation*:[107]

$$\frac{n_+}{n_a} = \frac{(1 - r_+)}{(1 - r_a)} \frac{\omega_+}{\omega_a} e^{(\varphi - I)/kT} \tag{13-6-1}$$

where r_+ and r_a are the reflection coefficients for ion and atom, ω_+/ω_a, the ratio of the statistical weights ($\frac{1}{2}$ for alkali atoms), I, the ionization energy of the atoms, and φ the surface work function. Actually, the charge state of an evaporating particle is determined not only by the energetic requirements of the Saha-Langmuir equation but also by the probability of the incident beam atom reaching equilibrium with the surface. This probability may be taken into account by the insertion of a reflection coefficient r_i for the incident atoms. Then the probability that an incident atom will leave the surface as an ion is[107]

$$\frac{n_+}{n_i} = (1 - r_i)\left[1 + \frac{\omega_a}{\omega_+}\frac{(1 - r_a)}{(1 - r_+)}e^{-(\varphi - I)/kT}\right]^{-1} \qquad (13\text{-}6\text{-}2)$$

where n_i is the number of incident atoms. This ratio is called the ionization efficiency. As we shall see later, the predictions of (13-6-2) agree quite well with experiment, provided that the work function of the surface is accurately known.

A similar treatment is valid for negative ion formation. Negative ions may be formed if the electron affinity of the incident atom is greater than the surface thermionic work function. A much more detailed theoretical treatment of surface ionization may be found in the review by Zandberg and Ionov.[108]

B. EXPERIMENTAL INVESTIGATIONS. Since the work function of pure tungsten is 4.54 ev, a tungsten filament can be used to detect Cs ($I = 3.87$ ev). Rb ($I = 4.16$ ev) and K ($I = 4.3$ ev). Thorium-free tungsten must be employed, since the work function of thoriated tungsten is 2.6 ev, which would result in almost no ionization, according to (13-6-2). Atoms with higher ionization energies may be detected by employing oxidized tungsten, whose work function is about 6 ev. Such an arrangement[105] could be used to detect Na ($I = 5.12$ ev), Li ($I = 5.36$ ev), In ($I = 5.76$ ev), and Ga ($I = 5.97$ ev).

It has been observed experimentally that for alkali metals on tungsten (13-6-2) is satisfied with all reflection coefficients zero. Figure 13-6-1 depicts n_+/n_i as a function of temperature for various alkali metals on tungsten. The dashed lines represent (13-6-2) with $r_+ = r_a = r_i = 0$. The agreement is quite good. Figure 13-6-2 shows the same metals incident on a platinum surface, but in this case the no-reflection theoretical predictions do not agree so well. Datz and Taylor[109] conclude that r_i is the only reflection coefficient significantly different from zero and calculate what r_i must be in order to bring (13-6-2) into agreement with experimental results. Their calculation of r_i is shown in Fig. 13-6-3.

The lower limit in sensitivity for the surface ionization beam detector appears to be set by the thermal emission of positive ions from the hot filament (the anomalous flicker effect in vacuum tubes). This emission has been considered in detail by Datz.[110]

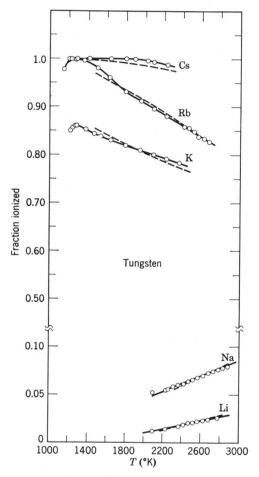

FIG. 13-6-1. Ionization efficiency of alkali metals on tungsten. S. Datz and E. H. Taylor, *J. Chem. Phys.* **25**, 389 (1956).

It is also possible to detect molecules such as KCl with a surface ionization detector. In this process the molecule apparently dissociates on contact with the filament, and the atoms interact with the surface in the same manner as individual atoms incident on the surface.[107]

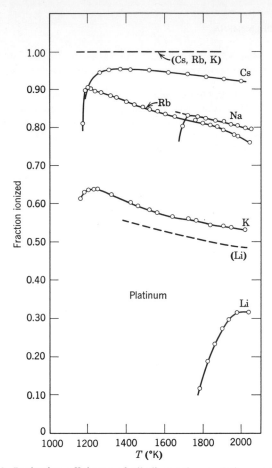

FIG. 13-6-2. Ionization efficiency of alkali metals on platinum. S. Datz and E. H. Taylor, *J. Chem. Phys.* **25,** 389 (1956).

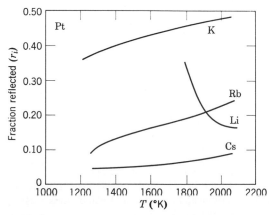

FIG. 13-6-3. Reflection of alkali metals on platinum. S. Datz and E. H. Taylor, *J. Chem. Phys.* **25,** 389 (1956).

REFERENCES

1. D. J. Rose and M. Clark, *Plasmas and Controlled Fusion*, Wiley, New York, 1961, pp. 43–52; H. D. Hagstrum, *Phys. Rev.* **96**, 325 (1954), footnote 4. For results of recent measurements of sticking probabilities see R. T. Brackmann and W. L. Fite, *J. Chem. Phys.* **34**, 1572 (1961); J. N. Smith and W. L. Fite, **37**, 898 (1962); F. S. Baker and G. O. Brink, **37**, 1012 (1962).

2. S. Dushman, *Scientific Foundations of Vacuum Technique*, Second Edition (edited and revised by J. M. Lafferty et al.), Wiley, New York, 1962.

3. H. D. Hagstrum, *Phys. Rev.* **104**, 1516 (1956).

4. *Ibid.*, **91**, 543 (1953).

5. H. D. Hagstrum and C. D'Amico, *J. Appl. Phys.* **31**, 715 (1960).

6. H. D. Hagstrum, *J. Phys. Chem. Solids* **14**, 33 (1960).

7. P. M. Stier, C. F. Barnett, and G. E. Evans, *Phys. Rev.* **96**, 973 (1954); C. F. Barnett and H. K. Reynolds, **109**, 355 (1958). V. J. Vanhuyse, E. D. Wattecamps, R. E. Van de Vijver, and G. J. Vanpraet, *Nucl. Instr. Methods* **15**, 59 (1962).

8. H. D. Hagstrum, *Phys. Rev.* **89**, 244 (1953).

9. *Ibid.*, **96**, 325, 336 (1954).

10. *Ibid.*, **122**, 83 (1961).

11. N. N. Petrov, *Soviet Phys.-Solid State* **2**, 1182 (1960).

12. E. S. Parilis and L. M. Kishinevskii, *Soviet Phys.-Solid State* **3**, 885 (1960).

13. H. D. Hagstrum, *Rev. Sci. Instr.* **24**, 1122 (1953).

14. P. F. Little, *Handbuch der Physik*, Vol XXI, Springer-Verlag, Berlin, 1956, pp. 638–662.

15. H. D. Hagstrum, *Phys. Rev.* **104**, 672 (1956).

16. P. M. Waters, *Phys. Rev.* **111**, 1053 (1958).

17. N. N. Petrov, *Soviet Phys.-Solid State* **2**, 857, 865 (1960).

18. M. L. E. Oliphant, *Proc. Roy. Soc.* (*London*) **A-127**, 373 (1930).

19. J. S. Allen, *Phys. Rev.* **55**, 336 (1939).

20. S. Kronenberg, K. Nilson, and M. Basso, *Phys. Rev.* **124**, 1709 (1961).

21. R. C. Abbott and H. W. Berry, *J. Appl. Phys.* **30**, 871 (1959).

22. H. D. Hagstrum, *Phys. Rev.* **104**, 309 (1956).

23. H. D. Hagstrum, *J. Appl. Phys.* **31**, 897 (1960).

24. R. F. Stebbings, *Proc. Roy. Soc.* (*London*) **A-241**, 270 (1957).

25. J. B. Hasted, *J. Appl. Phys.* **30**, 22 (1959).

26. S. A. Korff, *Electron and Nuclear Counters* Second Edition, Van Nostrand, Princeton, N.J., 1955, pp. 122–123.

27. G. Francis, *Ionization Phenomena in Gases*, Academic, New York, 1960, Chapter 4.

28. L. B. Loeb, *Basic Processes of Gaseous Electronics*, Second Edition, University of California Press, Berkeley, 1960, p. 686, 762.

29. A. Von Engel, *Ionized Gases*, Oxford University Press, Oxford, 1955, Chapter 3.

30. R. B. Belser and W. H. Hicklin, *Rev. Sci. Instr.* **27**, 293 (1956).

31. See, for example, the article by R. E. Honig, appearing in *Advances in Mass Spectrometry*, Pergamon, New York, 1959, p. 162.

32. See, for example, G. K. Wehner, *Phys. Rev.* **108**, 35 (1957); N. Laegreid, G. K. Wehner, and B. Meckel, *J. Appl. Phys.* **30**, 374 (1959).

33. R. E. Honig, *Proceedings of the Fifth International Conference on Ionization Phenomena in Gases*, Munich, 1961, North-Holland, Amsterdam (1962), Vol. I, 106.

34. R. E. Honig, *J. Appl. Phys.* **29**, 549 (1958).
35. R. E. Honig, paper presented at the Mass Spectrometry Conference, Oxford, Sept. 1961.
36. R. C. Bradley, *J. Appl. Phys.* **30**, 1 (1959); R. C. Bradley, A. Arking, and D. S. Beers, *J. Chem. Phys.* **33**, 764 (1960); R. C. Bradley and E. Ruedl, *Proceedings of the Fifth International Conference on Ionization Phenomena in Gases*, Munich, 1961, North-Holland, Amsterdam (1962), Vol. I, 150; R. C. Bradley and E. Ruedl, *J. Appl. Phys.* **33**, 880 (1962).
37. Ya. M. Fogel, R. P. Slabospitskii, and A. B. Rastrepin, *Soviet Phys.-Tech. Phys.* **5**, 58 (1960); Ya. M. Fogel, R. P. Slabospitskii, and I. M. Karnaukhov, **5**, 777 (1960).
38. G. K. Wehner, *Proceedings of the Fifth International Conference on Ionization Phenomena in Gases*, Munich, 1961, North-Holland, Amsterdam (1962), Vol. II, 1141.
39. G. K. Wehner, *1961 Transactions of the Eighth Vacuum Symposium and Second International Congress*, Pergamon, New York, 1962, Vol. I, p. 239.
40. N. Laegreid and G. K. Wehner, *J. Appl. Phys.* **32**, 365 (1961).
41. D. Rosenberg and G. K. Wehner, *J. Appl. Phys.* **33**, 1842 (1962).
42. R. V. Stuart and G. K. Wehner, *J. Appl. Phys.* **33**, 2345 (1962).
43. O. C. Yonts, C. E. Normand, and D. E. Harrison, *J. Appl. Phys.* **31**, 447 (1960).
44. G. Anderson, *J. Appl. Phys.* **33**, 2017 (1962).
45. G. S. Anderson and G. K. Wehner, *J. Appl. Phys.* **31**, 2305 (1961).
46. M. W. Thompson, *Proceedings of the Fifth International Conference on Ionization Phenomena in Gases*, Munich, 1961, North-Holland, Amsterdam (1962), Vol. I, 85. See also A. L. Southern, W. R. Willis, and M. T. Robinson, *J. Appl. Phys.* **34**, 153 (1963).
47. D. E. Harrison, *Phys. Rev.* **102**, 1473 (1956); *1961 Transactions of the Eighth Vacuum Symposium and Second International Congress*, Pergamon, New York, 1962, Vol. I, p. 259.
48. R. S. Pease, *Rend. Scuola Intern. Fis.*, Varenna, 1959, Corso **13**, 158 (Italian Physical Society, Bologna, 1960).
49. G. K. Wehner, *Phys. Rev.* **114**, 1270 (1959).
50. G. K. Wehner, and D. Rosenberg, *J. Appl. Phys.* **31**, 177 (1960).
51. C. Brunnée, *Z. Physik* **147**, 161 (1957).
52. H. D. Hagstrum, *Phys. Rev.* **123**, 758 (1961).
53. E. Merzbacher and H. W. Lewis, "X-ray Production by Heavy Charged Particles," in *Handbuch der Physik*, Vol. XXXIV, Springer-Verlag, Berlin, 1958, pp. 166–192.
54. J. M. Fluit, L. Friedman, J. van Eck, C. Snoek, and J. Kistemaker, *Proceedings of the Fifth International Conference on Ionization Phenomena in Gases*, Munich, 1961, North-Holland, Amsterdam (1962), Vol. I, p. 131; R. M. Chaudhri and M. Y. Khan, *op. cit.*, Vol. II, 1195; R. C. Jopson, H. Mark, and C. D. Swift, *Phys. Rev.* **127**, 1612 (1962).
55. L. Austin and H. Starke, *Ann. Phys. Chem.* **9**, 271 (1902).
56. H. Bruining, *Physics and Applications of Secondary Electron Emission*, Pergamon, London, 1954.
57. O. Hachenberg and W. Brauer, "Secondary Electron Emission from Solids," in *Advances in Electronics and Electron Physics*, Vol. XI, 413–499 (1959), Academic New York.
58. A. J. Dekker, "Secondary Electron Emission," in *Solid State Physics*, Vol. 6, 251–311 (1958), Academic, New York.

59. R. Kollath, "Sekundärelektronen-Emission fester Körper bei Bestrahlung mit Elektronen," in *Handbuch der Physik*, Vol. XXI, 232–303, Springer-Verlag, Berlin, 1956.

60. See, for example, J. B. Johnson and K. G. McKay, *Phys. Rev.* **91**, 582 (1953); N. R. Whetten and A. B. Laponsky, **107**, 1521 (1957), and *J. Appl. Phys.* **30**, 432 (1959).

61. K. G. McKay, "Secondary Electron Emission," in *Advances in Electronics*, Vol. I, 65–130 (1948), Academic, New York.

62. E. J. Sternglass, *Phys. Rev.* **80**, 925 (1950).

63. L. Malter, *Phys. Rev.* **50**, 48 (1936); see also H. Jacobs, J. Freely, and F. A. Brand, **88**, 492 (1952); F. A. Brand and H. Jacobs, **97**, 81 (1955).

64. R. Kollath, *Ann. Physik* **1**, 357 (1947).

65. J. L. H. Jonker, *Philips Res. Rept.* **6**, 372 (1951); **12**, 249 (1957).

66. R. Kollath, *Z. Tech. Phys.* **21**, 328 (1940), and *Ann. Physik* **39**, 59 (1941).

67. E. M. Baroody, *Phys. Rev.* **78**, 780 (1950).

68. L. Marton, L. B. Leder, and H. Mendlowitz, "Characteristic Energy Losses of Electrons in Solids," in *Advances in Electronics and Electron Physics*, Vol. VII, 183–238 (1955), Academic, New York; R. D. Birkhoff, "The Passage of Fast Electrons Through Matter," in *Handbuch der Physik*, Vol. XXXIV, 53–138, Springer-Verlag, Berlin, 1958.

69. E. J. Sternglass, *Phys. Rev.* **95**, 345 (1954).

70. P. C. R. Palluel, *Compt. rend.* **224**, 1492, 1551 (1947); **225**, 383 (1947).

71. K. A. Wright and J. G. Trump, *J. Appl. Phys.* **33**, 687 (1962).

72. T. E. Everhart, *J. Appl. Phys.* **31**, 1483 (1960).

73. A. L. Hughes and L. A. DuBridge, *Photoelectric Phenomena*, McGraw-Hill, New York, 1932.

74. G. L. Weissler, "Photoionization in Gases and Photoelectric Emission from Solids," in *Handbuch der Physik*, Vol. XXI, Springer-Verlag, Berlin, 1956, pp. 342–382.

75. P. Görlich, "Recent Advances in Photoemission," in *Advances in Electronics and Electron Physics*, Academic, New York, Vol XI, 1959, pp. 1–30.

76. R. J. Maurer, "Photoelectric Effect," in *Handbook of Physics* (edited by E. U. Condon and H. Odishaw), McGraw-Hill, New York, 1958, pp. 8-66–8-73.

77. See, for example, A. Van der Ziel, *Solid State Physical Electronics*, Prentice-Hall, Englewood Cliffs, N.J., 1957, Chapter 9; V. K. Zworykin and E. G. Ramberg, *Photoelectricity and Its Applications*, Wiley, New York, 1949.

78. A. Einstein, *Ann. Phys.* **17**, 132 (1905); **20**, 199 (1906).

79. R. L. Sproull, *Modern Physics*, Wiley, Second Edition, New York, 1963, Chapters 9 and 12; C. Kittel, *Introduction to Solid State Physics* Second Edition, Wiley, New York, 1956, Chapter 10.

80. R. H. Fowler, *Phys. Rev.* **38**, 45 (1931).

81. W. C. Walker, N. Wainfan, and G. L. Weissler, *J. Appl. Phys.* **26**, 1366 (1955).

82. W. C. Walker and G. L. Weissler, *Phys. Rev.* **97**, 1178 (1955).

83. L. A. DuBridge, *New Theories of the Photoelectric Effect*, Hermann, Paris, 1935; *Phys. Rev.* **43**, 727 (1933).

84. K. Mitchell, *Proc. Roy. Soc.* (*London*) **A-146**, 442 (1934); **A-153**, 513 (1936).

85. R. L. Sproull, *ibid.*

86. A. Van der Ziel, *op. cit.*, Chapters 6 and 7.

87. L. P. Smith, "Thermionic Emission," in *Handbook of Physics* (edited by E. U. Condon and H. Odishaw), McGraw-Hill, New York, 1958, pp. 8-74–8-82.

88. W. B. Nottingham, "Thermionic Emission," in *Handbuch der Physik*, Vol. XXI, Springer-Verlag, Berlin, 1956, pp. 1–175.

89. W. B. Nottingham, *Bibliography on Physical Electronics*, Addison-Wesley, Cambridge, Mass., 1954.

90. G. Herrmann, *The Oxide-Coated Cathode*, Vol. II (translated by S. Wagener), Chapman and Hall, London, 1951.

91. O. W. Richardson, *The Emission of Electricity from Hot Bodies*, Second Edition, Longmans, Green, London, 1921.

92. D. H. Menzel, *Fundamental Formulas of Physics*, Dover, New York, 1960, p. 353.

93. For examples of the use of thoriated iridium filaments in ion sources, see C. E. Melton, "Ion-Molecule Reactions," in *Mass Spectrometry of Organic Ions* (edited by F. W. McLafferty), Academic, New York, 1963.

94. A. M. Tyndall, *The Mobility of Positive Ions in Gases*, Cambridge University Press, Cambridge, 1938.

95. K. T. Compton and I. Langmuir, *Rev. Mod. Phys.* **2,** 140 (1930).

96. E. Bloch, *Thermionic Phenomena*, E. P. Dutton, New York, 1928.

97. A. L. Reimann, *Thermionic Emission*, Chapman and Hall, London, 1934.

98. T. J. Jones, *Thermionic Emission*, Methuen, London, 1936.

99. J. P. Blewett and E. J. Jones, *Phys. Rev.* **50,** 464 (1936).

100. S. K. Allison and M. Kamegai, *Rev. Sci. Instr.* **32,** 1090 (1961).

101. I. Langmuir and K. H. Kingdon, *Proc. Roy. Soc. (London)* **A-107,** 61 (1925).

102. J. B. Taylor, *Z. Physik* **57,** 242 (1929).

103. J. B. Taylor, *Phys. Rev.* **35,** 375 (1930).

104. R. G. J. Fraser, *Molecular Rays*, Cambridge University Press, Cambridge, 1931; *Molecular Beams*, Methuen, Ltd., London, 1937.

105. N. F. Ramsey, *Molecular Beams*, Oxford University Press, Oxford, 1956.

106. P. Kusch and V. W. Hughes, "Atomic and Molecular Beam Spectroscopy," in *Handbuch der Physik*, Vol. XXXVII, Springer-Verlag, Berlin, 1959, pp. 1–172.

107. S. Datz and E. H. Taylor, "Some Applications of Molecular Beam Techniques to Chemistry," in *Recent Research in Molecular Beams* (edited by I. Estermann), Academic, New York, 1959.

108. E. Ya. Zandberg and N. I. Ionov, *Soviet Phys. Uspehki* **67,** (2), 255 (1959).

109. S. Datz and E. H. Taylor, *J. Chem. Phys.* **25,** 389, 395 (1956).

110. S. Datz, R. E. Minturn, and E. H. Taylor, *J. App. Phys.* **31,** 876 (1960); **31,** 880 (1960).

THE DISTINCTION

BETWEEN A PLASMA

AND AN ORDINARY IONIZED GAS

1. THE DEBYE LENGTH

As indicated in Chapter 1, it is convenient to introduce the concept of the debye length in order to distinguish a true plasma from an ordinary ensemble of ions and electrons. It was stated that for an ionized gas to be a plasma its physical extent must be much greater than its debye shielding length. Exactly how the debye length serves to define a plasma is shown in the following paragraphs.

The concept of the shielding length arose from studies of strong electrolytes made by Debye and Hückel[1] in 1923. An expression for the shielding length may be readily obtained, as seen in the following derivation.[2] Consider an electrolyte containing several types of positive and negative ions, there being n_{j0} ions per cm³ of type j with charge $Z_j e$. Let us assume the following:

(a) The ions of each type j are in a Boltzmann distribution at an equilibrium temperature T_j.

(b) The potential energy of the charges due to their separation is small compared with their thermal energy, so that $|Z_j eV| \ll kT$, where V represents the electrostatic potential.

(c) The microscopic variations of potential resulting from the discrete nature of the particles may be neglected.·

Since the electrolyte as a whole is electrically neutral, each of the ions must create around itself an ion cloud whose net charge is equal and opposite to that of the ion itself. This cloud must be spherically symmetric about the ion, and the number density of each species of ion about any particular ion will depend only on the distance r from this ion. We can now determine the potential $V(r)$ effecting this distribution, subject to the boundary conditions that V vanish for large r and approach the Coulomb potential for small r. If ρ_j is the charge density of ions of type j in the cloud, then we may write

$$\rho_j = Z_j e n_{j0} e^{-Z_j eV/kT_j} \tag{1}$$

Assumption (b) allows us to linearize the problem by considering only the first two terms of the series expansion of ρ_j, and we may write

$$\rho_j = Z_j e n_{j0}\left(1 - \frac{eVZ_j}{kT_j}\right) \tag{2}$$

Since the electrolyte as a whole is electrically neutral, $\sum_j Z_j e n_{j0} = 0$. The total charge density ρ is given by

$$\rho = \sum_j \rho_j = -e^2 V \sum_j \frac{n_{j0}Z_j^2}{kT_j} \tag{3}$$

The charge density and the potential V are related by Poisson's equation

$$\nabla^2 V = -\frac{4\pi\rho}{\varepsilon} \tag{4}$$

where ε is the dielectric constant of the electrolyte. Equation 4 may be written in spherically symmetric form as

$$\frac{\partial^2 V}{\partial r^2} + \frac{2}{r}\frac{\partial V}{\partial r} = \left(\frac{4\pi e^2}{\varepsilon} \sum_j \frac{n_{j0}Z_j^2}{kT_j}\right) V \tag{5}$$

Let us define

$$\lambda_D^2 = \left(\frac{4\pi e^2}{\varepsilon} \sum_j \frac{n_{j0}Z_j^2}{kT_j}\right)^{-1} \tag{6}$$

noting that λ_D has the dimensions of length. The general solution to (5) is

$$V(r) = A\frac{e^{-r/\lambda_D}}{r} + B\frac{e^{r/\lambda_D}}{r} \tag{7}$$

If the origin of coordinates is a particle of charge $Z_a e$, then application of the boundary conditions that $V(r) \to 0$ for large r and $V(r) \to Z_a e/\varepsilon r$ for small r yields as the solution

$$V(r) = \frac{Z_a e}{\varepsilon r} e^{-r/\lambda_D} \tag{8}$$

This screened Coulomb potential becomes quite small at distances much greater than λ_D, which is called the *Debye-Hückel radius* or the *Debye shielding length*. It may be considered to be a measure of the size of the screening ion cloud surrounding the given ion. We see that the shielding length varies directly with the square root of the temperature and inversely with the square root of the number density of the ions. This behavior is in accord with the interpretation that the Debye-Hückel radius is that distance at which the electrostatic forces, which tend to impose charge neutrality, are balanced by the kinetic forces, which tend to produce non-neutrality. Thus an increase in the number density decreases the mean distance between particles and increases the electrostatic forces that maintain electrical neutrality. Evidently, in order to have the requisite electrostatic interaction between particles, the debye length must be considerably less than the minimum dimensions of the ionized medium. If this condition is not satisfied, the medium behaves like a collection of free charges. The foregoing derivation assumes, of course, that the debye length is large compared with the interparticle distances. In a more recent study by Liboff[3] it was shown that a similar argument is also valid for ionized gases.

It should be noted that the assumptions in this derivation result in a single quantity, the Debye-Hückel radius, which characterizes the potential decay about any of the ionized particles in the medium. If we alter our assumptions, it is possible to arrive at what might be called a shielding length for each species of particle. To do this, let us consider an electrically neutral ionized gas consisting of positive ions of one type and electrons. We now replace assumption (a) by the following:

(a′) The electrons are in a Boltzmann distribution at an equilibrium temperature T_e; the ions are uniformly distributed throughout the gas. (Although the assumption of a uniform ion distribution may not be entirely realistic, the result is of sufficient interest to justify the assumption.)

Let $Z_i e$ be the charge of each ion and $-e$ that of each electron; let n_{i0} be the uniform number density of the ions. Choosing one of the ions as our center of coordinates, we see that the electron charge density is given by

$$\rho_e = -e n_{e0} e^{eV/kT_e} \tag{9}$$

Electrical neutrality requires that

$$Z_i n_{i0} = n_{e0} \tag{10}$$

Thus the total charge density is given by

$$\rho = \rho_e + \rho_i = e n_{e0} - e n_{e0} e^{eV/kT_e} \tag{11}$$

Expansion of the exponential term as before yields

$$\rho = -\left(\frac{e^2 n_{e0}}{kT_e}\right) V \tag{12}$$

The potential and charge density are again related by Poisson's equation in spherically symmetric form:

$$\frac{\partial^2 V}{\partial r^2} + \frac{2}{r}\frac{\partial V}{\partial r} = \left(\frac{4\pi e^2 n_{e0}}{\varepsilon k T_e}\right) V \tag{13}$$

We now define

$$\lambda_{De}^2 = \left(\frac{4\pi e^2 n_{e0}}{\varepsilon k T_e}\right)^{-1} \tag{14}$$

With this substitution (14) is now in the same form as before, and the solution is the same as (7) with λ_D replaced by λ_{De}. We see that λ_{De} has dimensions of length and that it depends only on the parameters of the electrons. This length is called the shielding length for ions by electrons or, more simply, the electron shielding length. It would, of course, be possible to assume instead that the electrons were uniformly distributed in space and that the ions were in a Boltzmann distribution. Such an assumption leads to an ion shielding length, λ_{Di}, given by

$$\lambda_{Di}^2 = \left(\frac{4\pi e^2 n_{i0}}{\varepsilon k T_i}\right)^{-1} \tag{15}$$

Thus a shielding length can be determined for each of the species of particle in the gas. These lengths are different from the shielding length associated with the gas as a whole, given by (6). In a gas consisting of singly charged positive ions and electrons at the same temperature (T) we see that $n_{e0} = n_{i0} = n$, and the relationship of the various shielding lengths is

$$\lambda_{De} = \lambda_{Di} = \sqrt{2}\lambda_D \tag{16}$$

When in contact with a physical boundary, a plasma forms a protective sheath about itself. The sheath, in effect, separates the main body of the plasma from its environment. Unlike the main body, the sheath is not electrically neutral and strong electric fields may be present in it. The thickness of the sheath is of the order of a debye length. In order to demonstrate this fact, let us consider a thin slablike region, with half-width x_0, perpendicular to the X axis and centered about the origin. We assume that the electron number density greatly exceeds the ion number density. The resulting net charge gives rise to a potential difference between the center of the slab and its boundaries given by the equation

$$\frac{d^2V}{dx^2} = \frac{4\pi n_e e}{\varepsilon} \tag{17}$$

which integrates to

$$V = \frac{2\pi}{\varepsilon} n_e e x_0^2 \tag{18}$$

if we put $V = 0$ at $x = 0$. The potential appears as a "hill" to electrons and as a "trough" to ions. Clearly, the region over which $n_e \gg n_i$ cannot be arbitrarily large or a point would be reached at which the electrical potential energy would exceed the mean thermal energy and ions would then flow in such a way as to restore neutrality. If we seek that value of x which gives rise to a change in potential energy just equal to the mean kinetic energy in one direction, we find

$$\frac{kT_e}{2} = \frac{2\pi n_e e^2 x_0^2}{\varepsilon} \tag{19}$$

or

$$x_0 = \left(\frac{\varepsilon k T_e}{4\pi n_e e^2}\right)^{1/2} \tag{20}$$

This expression may be recognized as being equivalent to that derived earlier for the debye length, λ_{De}. We conclude then that the distance over which a plasma can have an appreciable departure from charge equilibrium is of the order of a debye length.

2. MULTIPLE SMALL-ANGLE COULOMB SCATTERING*

The expression for the differential cross section for Coulomb scattering was derived in Section 3-8. Using this cross section, we may obtain an expression for the probability of a charged particle being scattered through an angle greater than $90°$ in a single Coulomb collision while penetrating to a given depth in a plasma. It is of interest to compare this expression for the probability of a single large angle Coulomb scattering to the probability of many small angle deflections resulting in a net large angle deflection. An expression for the probability of multiple small-angle

* For a recent general discussion of the small-angle scattering of fast particles see W. T. Scott, *Rev. Mod. Phys.* **35**, 231 (1963).

scattering resulting in a large-angle deflection may be derived as follows:

Consider a particle of charge ze with mass m and velocity v impinging at an impact parameter b on a scattering center of charge Ze and infinite mass. Since nearly all of the deflection of the projectile occurs in the immediate vicinity of the scattering center, we may assume for computational purposes that the incident particle experiences a lateral deflecting force of magnitude zZe^2/b^2 for a period $2b/v$.[4] Thus the momentum change of the projectile is

$$\Delta(mv) = \frac{2zZe^2}{bv} \tag{1}$$

and if we exclude large angle deflections so that $\Delta(mv)$ is small compared with the initial momentum mv, the corresponding angular deflection is

$$\Delta\vartheta = \frac{\Delta(mv)}{mv} = \frac{2zZe^2}{mv^2 b} \equiv \frac{D}{b} \tag{2}$$

The quantity

$$D = \frac{2zZe^2}{mv^2} \tag{3}$$

defined in (2) is the distance of closest approach of the projectile to the scattering center in the special case of a head-on trajectory.

Now suppose that the projectile, rather than encountering a single scattering center, passes through a plasma containing N scattering centers per cm³. Since the individual deflections are completely random, the average deflection must be zero. The mean square deflection will not vanish, however, for there exists a random walk in angle away from the direction of initial incidence.[5] The total mean square deflection associated with the projectile penetrating a depth λ into the medium is

$$\overline{\Delta\vartheta^2} = \int_{\Delta\vartheta_j \min}^{\Delta\vartheta_j \max} \Delta\vartheta_j^2 n(\Delta\vartheta_j)\, d(\Delta\vartheta_j) \tag{4}$$

where $\Delta\vartheta_j = D/b_j$ (the angular deflection in a collision of impact parameter b_j), $\Delta\vartheta_j \max = D/b_j \min$, and $\Delta\vartheta_j \min = D/b_j \max$. The extreme values of the impact parameter b_j used here are defined later. The quantity $n(\Delta\vartheta_j)\, d(\Delta\vartheta_j)$ represents the number of collisions resulting in scattering with changes of direction between $\Delta\vartheta_j$ and $\Delta\vartheta_j + d(\Delta\vartheta_j)$. It is convenient to carry out this integration with respect to the variable b_j. Thus, since $N\lambda 2\pi b\, db$ equals the number of scattering centers in a cylindrical shell of length λ, radius b, and thickness db, we have

$$\overline{\Delta\vartheta^2} = \int_{b_j \max}^{b_j \min} -\left(\frac{D}{b_j}\right)^2 N\lambda 2\pi b_j\, db_j = 2\pi N\lambda D^2 \ell n \frac{b_j \max}{b_j \min} \tag{5}$$

We must now determine suitable limits for the impact parameter b_j. The upper limit $b_{j\,max}$ must reflect the mutual shielding effect of the scattering centers; it is therefore taken to be equal to the debye length characterizing the plasma. The lower limit may be the classical distance of closest approach or the de Broglie wavelength, whichever is smaller. In most cases of interest $\ell n\,(b_{j\,max}/b_{j\,min})$ lies between about 10 and 20.[6]

It is important to note the dependence of $\sqrt{\overline{\Delta\vartheta^2}}$ on $\lambda^{1/2}$. If the rms deflection of a particle is 90° during passage through a distance of $\lambda_{90°}$ in the medium, the particle will undergo about ten 90° deflections in traversing a distance equal to 100 $\lambda_{90°}$.

Now consider N_0 particles incident on a scattering medium of depth λ. The fraction of these particles which have been scattered at a net angle between Φ and $\Phi + d\Phi$ upon exit from the medium is from the theory of statistics[5]

$$\frac{N(\Phi)\,d\Phi}{N_0} = \frac{2\Phi}{\overline{\Phi^2}} e^{-\Phi^2/\overline{\Phi^2}}\,d\Phi$$

$$= \frac{\Phi}{\pi N\lambda D^2\,\ell n\,(b_{j\,max}/b_{j\,min})}\exp\left[\frac{-\Phi^2}{2\pi N\lambda D^2\,\ell n\,(b_{j\,max}/b_{j\,min})}\right]d\Phi$$
(6)

Therefore the fraction of the incident particles scattered through angles greater than $\sqrt{\overline{\Phi^2}}$ is given by

$$\int_{\sqrt{\overline{\Phi^2}}}^{\infty}\frac{2\Phi}{\overline{\Phi^2}}e^{-\Phi^2/\overline{\Phi^2}}\,d\Phi = \frac{1}{e}$$
(7)

We now wish to compare the probability of multiple Coulomb scattering through large angles to the probability of single-collision large-angle Coulomb scattering. This comparison must of necessity involve the depth of the scattering medium. If the medium is very thin, as in a Rutherford scattering experiment, there can be few multiple deflections through large net angles, and we expect that single large-angle collisions will be dominant. On the other hand, if the medium is very thick, the probability of either type of scattering occurring is unity. In the intermediate range of thickness it turns out that multiple small-angle collisions produce most of the large-angle scattering.

Let us first calculate from (5) the thickness $\lambda_{90°}$ for which $\sqrt{\overline{\Delta\vartheta^2}} = \pi/2$. We find that

$$\lambda_{90°} = \frac{\pi}{8ND^2\,\ell n\,(b_{j\,max}/b_{j\,min})}$$
(8)

According to (7), if a group of particles traverses this distance, $1/e$ of them will be scattered through angles greater than 90° as the result of multiple small-angle scattering.

The probability of a particle undergoing a single Coulomb deflection through an angle greater than 90° while traversing the same distance $\lambda_{90°}$ in the medium is*

$$P_s(\Phi > 90°) = N\lambda_{90°} \frac{\pi D^2}{4} = \frac{\pi^2}{32 \ln (b_{j\,max}/b_{j\,min})} \tag{9}$$

Thus the multiple scattering process is $(32/\pi^2 e) \ln (b_{j\,max}/b_{j\,min}) \approx 12$ to 24 times more probable in this case.

It may be pointed out that some writers[7] use (5) directly as the basis for the "mean free path for a random walk scattering through an angle of $\pi/2$." If we put $\overline{\Delta\vartheta^2}$ equal to unity in (5), we obtain the desired result:

$$\lambda_{90°} = [8\pi N(zZe^2/mv^2)^2 \ln (b_{max}/b_{min})]^{-1} \tag{10}$$

An "effective cross section" for a 90° deflection by multiple collisions can then be defined by the equation

$$q_{90°} = \frac{1}{N\lambda_{90°}} \tag{11}$$

This quantity, however, is not a cross section in the usual sense because, according to (5), the relation between the net deflection angle and the number density of scattering centers is not linear.

REFERENCES

1. P. Debye and E. Hückel, *Phys. Z.* **24**, 185, 305 (1923).
2. L. D. Landau and E. M. Lifshitz, *Statistical Physics*, Addison-Wesley, Reading, Mass., 1958, pp. 229–236.
3. R. L. Liboff, *Phys. Fluids* **2**, 40 (1959).
4. It is interesting to note that this commonly used approximation gives the same change in momentum obtained when the exact force function is integrated along the entire flight path. See S. Glasstone and R. H. Lovberg, *Controlled Thermonuclear Reactions*, Van Nostrand, Princeton, N.J., 1960, p. 91.
5. R. M. Eisberg, *Fundamentals of Modern Physics*, Wiley, New York, 1961, pp. 94–98.
6. See Ref. 4 and L. Spitzer, *Physics of Fully Ionized Gases*, Second Edition, Wiley, New York, 1962, Chapter 5.
7. See, for example, A. Simon, *An Introduction to Thermonuclear Research*, Pergamon, New York, 1959, pp. 14–15.

* This expression is derived by computing the area presented by a single target particle for scattering through angles greater than 90° and multiplying this area $\pi D^2/4$ by the total number of scattering centers in a slab of the medium $\lambda_{90°}$ cm thick with a 1-cm² cross sectional area. This number represents the ratio of the total area presented for scattering to the normal surface area 1 cm². For fairly thin targets the resulting expression is also the probability of single scattering through angles greater than 90° as given by (9). This expression is not a true probability, however, as it approaches infinity instead of unity as λ approaches infinity.

APPENDIX II

LANGEVIN'S CALCULATION

OF THE DIFFUSION

AND MOBILITY COEFFICIENTS*

This appendix consists of Paul Langevin's calculation of the coefficients of mutual diffusion and mobility. It is taken from his classic paper "Une Formule fondamentale de théorie cinétique," which appeared in *Annales de chimie et de physique*, Series 8, **5**, 245–288 (1905). Many changes in notation and terminology have been made in order to put the material in a form more familiar to the modern reader. A similar treatment of the problem of mutual diffusion is to be found in the kinetic theory text by Present.[1]

1. THE MOMENTUM TRANSFER EQUATION

Consider a mixture of gases containing molecules of two species, of masses m_1 and m_2, in numbers equal, respectively, to N_1 and N_2 per unit volume. The number densities N_1 and N_2 are assumed to vary from point to point in the gas. Suppose the velocities of the molecules of species 1 with components (ξ_1, η_1, ζ_1) are distributed according to the Maxwell distribution about their mean value, which represents the velocity of mass

* Langevin's paper, which is the subject of this appendix, was translated by E. W. McDaniel and published in Air Force Office of Scientific Research Document No. TN-60-865 (1960) [Georgia Institute of Technology, Atlanta, Ga.].

motion of the first gas. Likewise, the velocities of the molecules m_2, with components (ξ_2, η_2, ζ_2), are distributed according to the same law about their mean value, the velocity of mass motion of the second gas, which is different, in general, from that of the first. The difference in these velocities of mass motion, that is, the mass velocity of one gas relative to the other, is a measure of the intensity of the diffusive flow which results from the gradients in the number densities.

Let (u_1, v_1, w_1) be the velocity of mass motion of the first gas and (u_2, v_2, w_2) that of the second. The distribution law gives the number of molecules per unit volume of the first species whose velocities lie between (ξ_1, η_1, ζ_1) and $(\xi_1 + d\xi_1, \eta_1 + d\eta_1,$ and $\zeta_1 + d\zeta_1)$ as

$$dN_1 = c_1 \exp\{-hm_1[(\xi_1 - u_1)^2 + (\eta_1 - v_1)^2 + (\zeta_1 - w_1)^2]\}\, d\xi_1\, d\eta_1\, d\zeta_1$$
$$= f_1\, d\tau_1 \tag{1}$$

where

$$d\tau_1 = d\xi_1\, d\eta_1\, d\zeta_1$$
$$f_1 = c_1 \exp -hm_1[(\xi_1 - u_1)^2 + (\eta_1 - v_1)^2 + (\zeta_1 - w_1)^2] \tag{2}$$
$$c_1 = N_1 \left(\frac{hm_1}{\pi}\right)^{3/2} \tag{3}$$

and

$$h = \frac{1}{2kT} \tag{4}$$

We may easily verify that

$$\bar{\xi}_1 = \frac{\int \xi_1\, dN_1}{\int dN_1} = u_1 \quad \text{and} \quad \tfrac{1}{2}m_1 \overline{(\xi_1^2 + \eta_1^2 + \zeta_1^2)} = \frac{3kT}{2}$$

We have a similar expression for the molecules of the second species:

$$dN_2 = c_2 \exp\{-hm_2[(\xi_2 - u_2)^2 + (\eta_2 - v_2)^2 + (\zeta_2 - w_2)^2]\}\, d\xi_2\, d\eta_2\, d\zeta_2$$
$$= f_2\, d\tau_2$$

The partial pressure of the first gas on an element of surface equals the momentum transferred during unit time across unit area of this surface by the molecules of this gas, the surface element, of course, being supposed to move with the velocity of mass motion of the gas. For a surface element perpendicular to the X axis at a point at which the number density of molecules is N_1 and the partial mass density is $\rho_1 = N_1 m_1$, the components of the partial pressure are

$$p_{1xx} = \rho_1 \overline{(\xi_1 - u_1)^2} = m_1 \int f_1 (\xi_1 - u_1)^2\, d\tau_1$$
$$p_{1xy} = \rho_1 \overline{(\xi_1 - u_1)(\eta_1 - v_1)} = m_1 \int f_1 (\xi_1 - u_1)(\eta_1 - v_1)\, d\tau_1 \tag{5}$$
$$p_{1xz} = \rho_1 \overline{(\xi_1 - u_1)(\zeta_1 - w_1)} = m_1 \int f_1 (\xi_1 - u_1)(\zeta_1 - w_1)\, d\tau_1$$

The relations necessary for the equilibrium of an element of volume of the gas are

$$p_{1xy} = p_{1yx}; \qquad p_{1xz} = p_{1zx}; \qquad p_{1yz} = p_{1zy}$$

The mean pressure of the gas is defined by $p_1 = \frac{1}{3}(p_{1xx} + p_{1yy} + p_{1zz})$. It is easy to show that if the distribution law is Maxwellian the tangential pressure vanishes and

$$p_{1xx} = p_{1yy} = p_{1zz} = p_1 = N_1 kT \tag{6}$$

Consider now a fixed element of volume ($dx\,dy\,dz$) with its center (x, y, z) at a point at which the partial density is ρ_1. The conservation of matter is expressed by the equation

$$\frac{\partial \rho_1}{\partial t} + \frac{\partial(\rho_1 u_1)}{\partial x} + \frac{\partial(\rho_1 v_1)}{\partial y} + \frac{\partial(\rho_1 w_1)}{\partial z} = 0 \tag{7}$$

Let us seek the time rate of change of momentum of the molecules contained in this volume element. Considering first only the x component of the momentum, we see that there will be an increase due to the flow of molecules into the volume element through one of the faces $dy\,dz$. The increase is $dy\,dz \int \xi_1 f_1 m_1 \xi_1\, d\tau_1$. If we express this quantity in the algebraically identical form $m_1 dy\,dz[\int f_1(\xi_1 - u_1)^2\, d\tau_1 + 2u_1 \int f_1(\xi_1 - u_1)\, d\tau_1 + N_1 u_1^2]$, the use of (5) shows its magnitude to be $dy\,dz(p_{1xx} + \rho_1 u_1^2)$. The middle term has vanished, since the average value of $(\xi_1 - u_1)$ is zero by definition.

The excess of the x component of momentum entering the volume element through one $dy\,dz$ face over that leaving through the opposite face, per unit volume and unit time, is thus

$$-\frac{\partial p_{1xx}}{\partial x} - \frac{\partial(\rho_1 u_1^2)}{\partial x}$$

On taking the analogous quantities for the other dimensions, we have for the momentum increase provided by the flow of molecules per unit volume and unit time

$$-\frac{\partial p_{1xx}}{\partial x} - \frac{\partial p_{1xy}}{\partial y} - \frac{\partial p_{1xz}}{\partial z} - \frac{\partial(\rho_1 u_1^2)}{\partial x} - \frac{\partial(\rho_1 u_1 v_1)}{\partial y} - \frac{\partial(\rho_1 u_1 w_1)}{\partial z}$$

Any externally applied force will make another contribution to the momentum change. If X_1, Y_1, Z_1 denote the components of the applied force per unit mass, this contribution to the net increase of the x component of the momentum, per unit volume and unit time, is evidently $\rho_1 X_1$.

If a single gas is present, there will be only the two above mentioned factors in the increase of the momentum; but, if two gases are mixed, collisions between molecules of the two species produce an exchange of momentum in the x direction which is proportional to the difference $(u_2 - u_1)$ of the x components of the velocities of mass motion of the two gases, that is, to their relative velocities of mass motion. Without making any hypothesis concerning its form at the present time, let us designate by $\mathscr{B}(m_1 \xi_1)$ the x component of momentum transferred per unit volume and unit time to the molecules of the first species during their collisions against molecules of the second species. Collisions between molecules of the same species evidently do not change the total momentum. This quantity $\mathscr{B}$ plays the essential role in the theory of diffusion, and it is on its exact calculation that we now turn our effort.

The x component of momentum per unit volume is $m_1 \int f_1 \xi_1 \, d\tau_1 = \rho_1 u_1$. On equating its time derivative to the total increase due to the various causes, we obtain

$$\frac{\partial(\rho_1 u_1)}{\partial t} = -\frac{\partial p_{1xx}}{\partial x} - \frac{\partial p_{1xy}}{\partial y} - \frac{\partial p_{1xz}}{\partial z}$$

$$-\frac{\partial(\rho_1 u_1^2)}{\partial x} - \frac{\partial(\rho_1 u_1 v_1)}{\partial y} - \frac{\partial(\rho_1 u_1 w_1)}{\partial z} + \rho_1 X_1 + \mathscr{B}(m_1 \xi_1)$$

Using the conservation equation (7) and introducing the mobile time derivative

$$\frac{Du_1}{Dt} = \frac{\partial u_1}{\partial t} + u_1 \frac{\partial u_1}{\partial x} + v_1 \frac{\partial u_1}{\partial y} + w_1 \frac{\partial u_1}{\partial z}$$

to express the time rate of change of u_1 in a moving element following the mass motion of the gas, we find the time rate of change of the x component of momentum of the moving element to be

$$\rho_1 \frac{Du_1}{Dt} + \frac{\partial(p_{1xx})}{\partial x} + \frac{\partial(p_{1xy})}{\partial y} + \frac{\partial(p_{1xz})}{\partial z} = \rho_1 X_1 + \mathscr{B}(m_1 \xi_1) \tag{8}$$

This is the momentum transfer equation that determines the motion of the first gas. If this mass motion is sufficiently slow, (u_1, v_1, w_1) will be very small compared with the average values of (ξ_1, η_1, ζ_1), the thermal agitation velocities of the molecules. Under these conditions, deviations from the Maxwell distribution are extremely small, and we may say that the distribution is Maxwellian and thus isotropic about the velocity of mass motion. Equation 8 then becomes

$$\rho_1 \frac{Du_1}{Dt} + \frac{\partial p_1}{\partial x} = \rho_1 X_1 + \mathscr{B}(m_1 \xi_1) \tag{9}$$

Likewise, for the second gas we have

$$\rho_2 \frac{Du_2}{Dt} + \frac{\partial p_2}{\partial x} = \rho_2 X_2 - \mathscr{B}(m_1 \xi_1) \tag{10}$$

2. CALCULATION OF THE MOMENTUM TRANSFER
PRODUCED BY COLLISIONS

Now let us calculate the quantity $\mathscr{B}(m_1\xi_1)$, which represents the exchange of momentum in collisions between molecules of the different species. Without altering the equations of motion of the molecules, and consequently without changing the results, we may give the axes a uniform translational motion (u_1, v_1, w_1) to annul the velocity of mass motion of

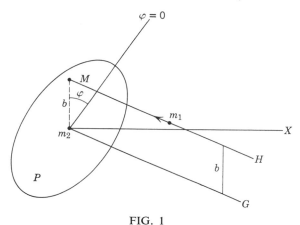

FIG. 1

the first gas; (u_2, v_2, w_2) then represents the relative velocity of mass motion, and we thus simplify the form of the equations.

Boltzmann[2] showed that $\mathscr{B}(m_1\xi_1)$ may be written in the form

$$\mathscr{B}(m_1\xi_1) = m_1 \iiint_0^\infty \int_0^{2\pi} f_1 f_2 (\xi_1' - \xi_1) v_0 b \, d\tau_1 \, d\tau_2 \, db \, d\varphi \tag{11}$$

where $(\xi_1', \eta_1', \zeta_1')$ is the velocity assumed after the collision by a molecule (ξ_1, η_1, ζ_1) which encounters a molecule (ξ_2, η_2, ζ_2). The relative velocity of the molecules before the collision is v_0, its magnitude being

$$v_0 = \sqrt{(\xi_2 - \xi_1)^2 + (\eta_2 - \eta_1)^2 + (\zeta_2 - \zeta_1)^2}$$

The dynamics of the collision are determined by the relative velocity and the impact parameter b as follows: referring to Fig. 1, the line m_2X passes through molecule m_2 and is parallel to the X axis. The molecule m_1 moves with respect to m_2 along the line MH, which is parallel to m_2G. The plane P is drawn through m_2 and is perpendicular to m_2G. In the absence of forces m_1 would pass within a distance b of m_2 and would encounter the plane P at point M, the azimuth angle having the value φ. The $\varphi = 0$ axis is defined by the intersection of planes P and m_2GX. When a central force is introduced, the relative trajectory of m_1 is curved but lies entirely in the plane Gm_2M. Its shape is determined by the relative velocity and the law of force between the molecules.

The relative trajectory of m_1 is composed of two branches that are symmetrical with respect to the line joining the apses, points A and E in

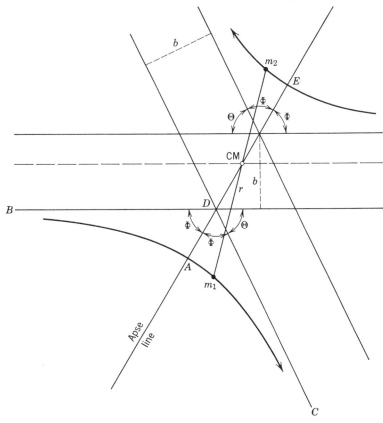

FIG. 2. $\Theta = \pi - 2\Phi =$ scattering angle in CM system; $b =$ impact parameter; CM = center of mass; and $r =$ distance between m_1 and m_2.

Fig. 2. The apses are the points of closest approach to the center of mass for m_1 and m_2, respectively. After the collision the relative velocity DC makes the same angle Φ with respect to AE as the initial relative velocity BD. The change in the velocity component ξ_1 is given as a function of Φ and the initial velocities by

$$\xi_1' - \xi_1 = \frac{m_2}{m_1 + m_2}\left[2(\xi_2 - \xi_1)\cos^2\Phi + \sqrt{v_0{}^2 - (\xi_2 - \xi_1)^2}\sin 2\Phi\cos\varphi\right]$$

If we introduce the reduced mass

$$M_r = \frac{m_1 m_2}{m_1 + m_2} \tag{12}$$

and let V represent the mutual potential energy of m_1 and m_2, we may calculate Φ by the equation (see Chapter 3, Section 3-4)

$$\Phi = \int_0^{\rho_0} \frac{d\rho}{\sqrt{1 - \rho^2 - (2V/M_r v_0^2)}} \tag{13}$$

Here $\rho = b/r$, where r is the distance of separation of the molecules, and ρ_0 is the smallest positive root of the expression under the radical, that is, the outermost zero of the denominator. It is assumed here that the force law is a continuous function of r and that m_1 and m_2 do not actually collide.

If, on the other hand, we suppose m_1 and m_2 to collide elastically but assume that they interact only at the instant of impact, we find that the relative trajectory consists simply of two straight line segments and that Φ is given by

$$\Phi = \sin^{-1} \frac{b}{D_{12}} \tag{14}$$

where D_{12} is the sum of the radii of the molecules m_1 and m_2, both of which are considered to be spherical.

If, finally, it is assumed that the molecules attract one another and then collide elastically, the relative trajectory remains symmetrical, but it has a discontinuity in the first derivative at A at the instant of collision; Φ is now given by

$$\Phi = \int_0^{\rho^*} \frac{d\rho}{\sqrt{1 - \rho^2 - (2V/M_r v_0^2)}} \tag{15}$$

ρ^* being equal to b/D_{12} and corresponding to the value of ρ at the instant when the impact occurs.

If $(\xi_1' - \xi_1)$ in (11) is replaced by its value above, the result is

$$\mathscr{B}(m_1 \xi_1) = 4\pi M_r \iiint_0^{\infty} f_1 f_2 v_0 (\xi_2 - \xi_1) \cos^2 \Phi b \, d\tau_1 \, d\tau_2 \, db$$

We have here seven consecutive integrations to perform, since $d\tau_1$ and $d\tau_2$ each correspond to a product of three differentials.

To simplify further the expressions for f_1 and f_2, we may choose the X axis, until now undetermined, to be parallel to the relative velocity of the two gases. The relative velocity is then written as $(u_2{}^*, 0, 0)$, and we have for f_1 and f_2

$$f_1 = c_1 \exp -hm_1(\xi_1{}^2 + \eta_1{}^2 + \zeta_1{}^2)$$
$$f_2 = c_2 \exp -hm_2[(\xi_2 - u_2{}^*)^2 + \eta_2{}^2 + \zeta_2{}^2]$$

The angle Φ, for a given law of force, depends uniquely on b and v_0, which determine the relative trajectory. Define a cross section* $q(v_0)$ by the equation

$$q(v_0) = \int_0^\infty \cos^2 \Phi b \, db \tag{16}$$

Then

$$\mathscr{B}(m_1\xi_1) = 4\pi M_r \iint f_1 f_2 \, v_0 q(v_0)(\xi_2 - \xi_1) \, d\tau_1 \, d\tau_2 \tag{17}$$

In the special case of the inverse-fifth-power force law treated by Maxwell $v_0 q(v_0)$ is a constant and the relative velocity v_0 disappears from the integral. Nothing remains but

$$\iint f_1 f_2(\xi_2 - \xi_1) \, d\tau_1 \, d\tau_2 = N_1 N_2 u_2{}^* = N_1 N_2(u_2 - u_1)$$

The problem is then reduced to the calculation of the constant $v_0 q(v_0)$, which does not present any particular difficulty.

In the general case the presence of v_0 in the integral necessitates the following artifice: hold v_0 constant and associate with each velocity (ξ_2, η_2, ζ_2) only those values of (ξ_1, η_1, ζ_1) that correspond to the values of v_0 between v_0 and $v_0 + dv_0$. This domain of (ξ_1, η_1, ζ_1) depends on two parameters, and we can without difficulty perform the five integrations that correspond to variations of these two parameters and of (ξ_2, η_2, ζ_2) and reserve until last the sixth integration with respect to v_0. It is important to choose a convenient order for performing the integrations.

The discussion is simplified if we represent each velocity by a point with coordinates (ξ_1, η_1, ζ_1) or (ξ_2, η_2, ζ_2) with respect to an origin 0 (Fig. 3). Let v_2 be the point (ξ_2, η_2, ζ_2). The points (ξ_1, η_1, ζ_1) which we can associate with it are contained between two spheres with center v_2 and radii v_0 and $v_0 + dv_0$. Let r_1 and r_2 be the distances Ov_1 and Ov_2,

---

* This cross section equals the diffusion cross section $q_D = 2\pi \int_0^\infty (1 - \cos \Theta) \, b \, db$ divided by 4π (see Section 9-2).

which are the magnitudes of the velocities (ξ_1, η_1, ζ_1) and (ξ_2, η_2, ζ_2), respectively.

The angles α (between Ov_2 and $O\zeta$), β (between the planes v_1Ov_2 and ζOv_2), γ (between v_2v_1 and Ov_2), and the azimuth δ of v_2 with respect to

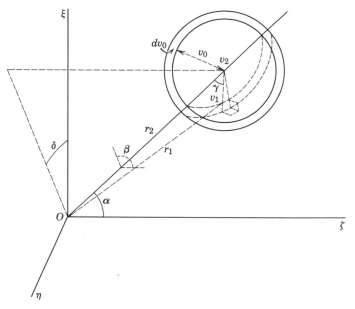

FIG. 3

$O\zeta$ comprise with r_2 the five parameters that we associate with v_0. We then write

$$d\tau_1 = v_0^2 \sin \gamma \, d\gamma \, d\beta \, dv_0$$

$$\xi_1^2 + \eta_1^2 + \zeta_1^2 = r_1^2 = r_2^2 + v_0^2 - 2r_2v_0 \cos \gamma$$

and

$$\xi_2 - \xi_1 = v_0 \cos \gamma \, \frac{\xi_2}{r_2} + v_0 \sin \gamma \cos \beta \left(1 - \frac{\xi_2^2}{r_2^2} \right)^{1/2}$$

Then

$$\frac{\mathscr{B}(m_1\xi_1)}{4\pi M_r} = \iint (\xi_2 - \xi_1)v_0 q(v_0) f_1 f_2 \, d\tau_1 \, d\tau_2$$

$$= \int f_2 \, d\tau_2 \int v_0^3 q(v_0)(\xi_2 - \xi_1)c_1$$

$$\times \exp \left[-hm_1(r_2^2 + v_0^2 - 2r_2v_0 \cos \gamma) \right] \sin \gamma \, d\gamma \, d\beta \, dv_0$$

Replacing $(\xi_2 - \xi_1)$ by its value given above and noting that the term in $\cos \beta$ disappears, we have

$$\frac{\mathscr{B}(m_1\xi_1)}{4\pi M_r} = 2\pi c_1 \int f_2 \frac{\xi_2}{r_2} d\tau_2 \int v_0^4 q(v_0) e^{-hm_1(r_2^2+v_0^2)} dv_0$$

$$\times \int e^{2hm_1r_2v_0 \cos \gamma} \sin \gamma \cos \gamma \, d\gamma$$

$$= \frac{\pi c_1}{2h^2 m_1^2} \int v_0^2 q(v_0) \, dv_0 \int \frac{\xi_2}{r_2^3} [(2hm_1r_2v_0 - 1)e^{-hm_1(r_2-v_0)^2}$$

$$+ (2hm_1r_2v_0 + 1)e^{-hm_1(r_2+v_0)^2}] f_2 \, d\tau_2$$

Now write

$$\xi_2 = r_2 \cos \alpha$$

and

$$d\tau_2 = 2\pi r_2^2 \cos \alpha \, dr_2 \, d\alpha$$

where we have integrated over δ between 0 and 2π.
Also write

$$f_2 = c_2 \exp -hm_2[r_2^2 - 2r_2u_2^* \cos \alpha + u_2^{*2}]$$

Then

$$\frac{\mathscr{B}(m_1\xi_1)}{4\pi M_r} = \frac{\pi^2 c_1 c_2}{h^2 m_1^2} \int_0^\infty v_0^2 q(v_0) \, dv_0$$

$$\times \int_0^\infty [(2hm_1r_2v_0 + 1) e^{-hm_1(r_2+v_0)^2} + (2hm_1r_2v_0 - 1)e^{-hm_1(r_2-v_0)^2}]$$

$$\times e^{-hm_2(r_2^2+u_2^{*2})} dr_2 \int_0^\pi e^{2hm_2r_2u_2^* \cos \alpha} \cos \alpha \sin \alpha \, d\alpha$$

or

$$\frac{\mathscr{B}(m_1\xi_1)}{4\pi M_r} = \frac{\pi^2 c_1 c_2}{4h^4 m_1^2 m_2^2 u_2^2} \int_0^\infty v_0^2 q(v_0) \, dv_0$$

$$\times \int_0^\infty [(2hm_1r_2v_0 + 1)e^{-hm_1(r_2+v_0)^2} + (2hm_1r_2v_0 - 1)e^{-hm_1(r_2-v_0)^2}]$$

$$\times [(2hm_2r_2u_2^* + 1)e^{-hm_2(r_2+u_2^*)^2} + (2hm_2r_2u_2^* - 1)$$

$$\times e^{-hm_2(r_2-u_2^*)^2}] \frac{dr_2}{r_2^2}$$

The integration with respect to r_2 is effected by developing the product in the parentheses, utilizing the formula

$$\int_{-\infty}^\infty e^{-(ax^2+2bx+c)} \, dx = \frac{e^{(b^2/a)-c}}{\sqrt{a}} \int_{-\infty}^\infty e^{-x^2} \, dx = \sqrt{\pi} \frac{e^{(b^2/a)-c}}{\sqrt{a}}$$

and noting that

$$\int_{-\infty}^{\infty} e^{-(ax^2+2bx+c)} \frac{dx}{x^2} = -2b \int_{-\infty}^{\infty} e^{-(ax^2+2bx+c)} \frac{dx}{x} - 2a \int_{-\infty}^{\infty} e^{-(ax^2+2bx+c)} \, dx$$

To finish the calculation, it remains after this fivefold integration to replace c_1 and c_2 by their values given in (3). Then

$$\mathscr{B}(m_1\xi_1) = 2N_1 N_2 \left(\frac{\pi m_1 m_2}{h(m_1 + m_2)}\right)^{\frac{1}{2}} \frac{1}{u_2^{*2}}$$

$$\times \int_0^\infty \left\{ \left(2h \frac{m_1 m_2}{m_1 + m_2} v_0 u_2^* + 1\right) \exp\left[\frac{-hm_1 m_2}{m_1 + m_2}(v_0 + u_2^*)^2\right]\right.$$

$$+ \left. \left(\frac{2hm_1 m_2}{m_1 + m_2} v_0 u_2^* - 1\right) \exp\left[-\frac{hm_1 m_2}{m_1 + m_2}(v_0 - u_2^*)^2\right]\right\} v_0^2 q(v_0) \, dv_0$$

Putting

$$z = v_0 \left(\frac{hm_1 m_2}{m_1 + m_2}\right)^{\frac{1}{2}} = \left(\frac{M_r v_0^2}{2kT}\right)^{\frac{1}{2}}$$

and

$$\varepsilon = u_2^* \left(\frac{hm_1 m_2}{m_1 + m_2}\right)^{\frac{1}{2}} = \left(\frac{M_r u_2^{*2}}{2kT}\right)^{\frac{1}{2}} \tag{18}$$

we have

$$\mathscr{B}(m_1\xi_1) = 2N_1 N_2 \sqrt{2\pi M_r kT} \; u_2^* \int_0^\infty q(v_0) e^{-(z^2+\varepsilon^2)}$$

$$\times [(2\varepsilon z - 1)e^{2\varepsilon z} + (2\varepsilon z + 1)e^{-2\varepsilon z}] \frac{z^2 \, dz}{\varepsilon^3}$$

It is easy to show that εz is always a very small quantity except for very large values of the relative velocity v_0. These values do not interest us because the number of molecules with such velocities is small due to the fact that the exponential term in the Maxwell distribution decreases so rapidly above the mean square velocity. We have

$$\varepsilon z = v_0 u_2^* \frac{M_r}{2kT}$$

The mean square value of v_0 is such that

$$\tfrac{1}{2} M_r \overline{v_0^2} = \frac{3kT}{2} \quad \text{and} \quad \varepsilon z = u_2^* \frac{3v_0}{2\overline{v_0^2}}$$

It would be necessary that v_0 attain the enormous value $v_0 = 2\overline{v_0^2}/3u_2^*$ in order that εz cease to be extremely small. Therefore we may replace the function of εz by its expansion in a series cut off at its first term and write finally

$$\mathcal{B}(m_1\xi_1) = \tfrac{3\cdot2}{3}N_1N_2\sqrt{2\pi M_r kT}\,u_2{}^* \int q(v_0)e^{-z^2}z^5\,dz \qquad (19)$$

(Here we take account of the fact that ε^2 is very small in comparison with z^2.)

Equation 19 properly gives for the exchange of momentum between the molecules of the two gases an expression proportional to the relative velocity of mass motion, $u_2{}^*$, as it should when $u_2{}^*$ is small in relation to the mean molecular agitation velocity. It remains to perform a single integration which ordinarily requires a graphical calculation similar to that Maxwell performed in the case of the inverse-fifth-power repulsive force.

Before passing to the applications of this general formula, let us first verify that it leads exactly to the result obtained by Maxwell for the case of the inverse-fifth-power force. To recover Maxwell's result, assume a repulsive force inversely proportional to the $(n + 1)$th power of the separation distance:

$$f(r) = \frac{c}{r^{n+1}}, \quad \text{and} \quad V = \frac{c}{nr^n}$$

(Here $n = 4$). Then if we put

$$\alpha = \left(\frac{M_r v_0{}^2}{c/b^n}\right)^{1/n}$$

(13) gives the angle Φ as a function of α alone:

$$\Phi = \int_0^{\rho_0} \frac{d\rho}{\sqrt{1 - \rho^2 - (2/n)(\rho/\alpha)^n}} = \Phi(\alpha)$$

and we have

$$q(v_0) = \int_0^\infty \cos^2\Phi b\,db = \left(\frac{c}{M_r v_0{}^2}\right)^{2/n} \int_0^\infty \cos^2\Phi\,\alpha\,d\alpha$$

The integral remaining is a numerical constant, calculated graphically by Maxwell for the case $n = 4$ and called A_1 when multiplied by 4π:

$$q(v_0) = \left(\frac{c}{M_r v_0{}^2}\right)^{2/n} \frac{A_1}{4\pi}$$

We proceed here, in the same manner as Maxwell, to calculate this constant for arbitrary n. Maxwell[3] put

$$A_3 = A_1\left[\frac{c}{m_1 m_2(m_1 + m_2)}\right]^{2/n}$$

from which

$$q(v_0) = \left(\frac{m_1 + m_2}{v_0}\right)^{4/n} \frac{A_3}{4\pi} = \frac{A_3}{4\pi}\left[\frac{m_1 m_2(m_1 + m_2)}{2kT}\right]^{2/n} z^{-4/n}$$

Substituting in the general formula (19), we obtain

$$\mathscr{B}(m_1\xi_1) = \frac{8A_3}{3\pi} N_1 N_2 \sqrt{2\pi M_r kT} \left[\frac{m_1 m_2(m_1 + m_2)}{2kT}\right]^{2/n} u_2^* \int_0^\infty e^{-z^2} z^{(5-4/n)} \, dz$$

Note that this expression contains T to the power $(\frac{1}{2} - 2/n)$ and that if the gases are maintained under constant pressure as the temperature varies N_1 and N_2 vary inversely with the absolute temperature. The value of $\mathscr{B}(m_1\xi_1)$ is thus proportional to $T^{-(3/2+2/n)}$. We use this result later.

If we put $n = 4$ to recover Maxwell's result, the equation for $\mathscr{B}(m_1\xi_1)$ becomes

$$\mathscr{B}(m_1\xi_1) = \frac{8A_3}{3\sqrt{\pi}} \rho_1 \rho_2 u_2^* \int_0^\infty e^{-z^2} z^4 \, dz$$

Now

$$\int_0^\infty e^{-z^2} z^4 \, dz = \frac{3\sqrt{\pi}}{8}$$

so

$$\mathscr{B}(m_1\xi_1) = A_3 \rho_1 \rho_2 u_2^* = A_3 \rho_1 \rho_2 (u_2 - u_1)$$

which is exactly the result obtained by Maxwell.

3. THE MUTUAL DIFFUSION COEFFICIENT FOR THE ELASTIC SPHERE MODEL

Let us compare the predictions of the mean free path and momentum transfer methods for the mutual diffusion of two gases whose molecules are assumed to be elastic spheres which interact only at the instant of impact. Using the mean-free-path method, Boltzmann[4] obtained for the diffusion of molecules m_1 in gas m_2 the expression

$$(\mathscr{D}_{12})_0 = \frac{2}{3\pi D_{12}^2 N_2}\left(\frac{2kT}{\pi(m_1 + m_2)}\right)^{1/2} \tag{20}$$

where the concentration of m_1 is assumed to be negligible in comparison with that of m_2.

We now apply the momentum transfer method to this problem. We assume that no external forces are applied and that the mass motion is slow enough to allow neglect of the acceleration term in the equation of motion (9), which then becomes

$$\frac{\partial p_1}{\partial x} = \mathscr{B}(m_1\xi_1)$$

To calculate the cross section $q(v_0)$ for the elastic sphere model, put

$$\Phi = \sin^{-1}\frac{b}{D_{12}}$$

Then

$$q(v_0) = \int_0^\infty \cos^2 \Phi b\, db = \int_0^\infty \left(1 - \frac{b^2}{D_{12}^2}\right)b\, db = \frac{D_{12}^2}{4}$$

and

$$\mathcal{B}(m_1\xi_1) = \tfrac{32}{3}N_1 N_2\sqrt{2\pi M_r kT}\,(u_2 - u_1)\frac{D_{12}^2}{4}\int_0^\infty e^{-z^2}z^5\, dz$$

or

$$\mathcal{B}(m_1\xi_1) = \tfrac{8}{3}N_1 N_2\, D_{12}^2\sqrt{2\pi M_r kT}\,(u_2 - u_1) = AN_1 N_2(u_2 - u_1)$$

Then we have for the diffusion equation:

$$u_1 - u_2 = -\frac{1}{AN_1 N_2}\frac{\partial p_1}{\partial x}$$

But from (6) $p_1 = N_1 kT$, and

$$u_1 - u_2 = -\frac{kT}{AN_2}\frac{1}{p_1}\frac{\partial p_1}{\partial x}$$

When compared to the equation defining the diffusion coefficient $\mathcal{D}_{12}$,

$$u_1 - u_2 = -\frac{\mathcal{D}_{12}}{p_1}\frac{\partial p_1}{\partial x}$$

this gives

$$\mathcal{D}_{12} = \frac{kT}{AN_2} = \frac{3}{16D_{12}^2 N_2}\left(\frac{2kT}{\pi M_r}\right)^{1/2} \tag{21}$$

Except for the numerical coefficient, which is of little importance, (21) differs from (20) principally in the substitution of M_r for $(m_1 + m_2)$. The difference is most pronounced when the masses m_1 and m_2 are very different, for the diffusion coefficient furnished by the momentum transfer method is much larger. We have, in fact,

$$\frac{\mathcal{D}_{12}}{(\mathcal{D}_{12})_0} = \frac{9\pi}{32}\left(x + \frac{1}{x}\right) \quad \text{where} \quad x^2 = \frac{m_1}{m_2}$$

The minimum of this ratio corresponds to $x = 1$, that is, to equality between the masses m_1 and m_2. The minimum value is $\mathcal{D}_{12}/(\mathcal{D}_{12})_0 = 9\pi/16 = 1.767$. Thus the coefficient furnished by the mean-free-path method is much too small, and the difference is increased when x departs from 1 in either direction, increasing indefinitely with the difference between the masses m_1 and m_2.

A formula similar to (21) can be deduced from the results obtained by Maxwell[5] in one of his early papers on the kinetic theory, where for the first time the dynamical conditions of the collision were introduced to complete the purely statistical arguments of the method of free paths. The formula to which these results lead can be written, in the notation used here,

$$\mathscr{B}(m_1\xi_1) = 2N_1N_2D_{12}^2\sqrt{2\pi M_r kT}\,(u_2 - u_1)$$

From this we get the diffusion coefficient

$$\mathscr{D}_{12} = \frac{1}{4D_{12}^2N_2}\left(\frac{2kT}{\pi M_r}\right)^{\frac{1}{2}}$$

which differs from the exact value only in the ratio $\frac{4}{3}$. This numerical difference is due to Maxwell's assumption that the velocity is the same for all molecules of the same species. It is evident that the argument used by Maxwell is rigorous, since it makes use of the dynamical conditions of the collision and leads to the correct result if we take account of the distribution of velocities, as we have done for an arbitrary force law.

4. THE INFLUENCE OF TEMPERATURE

Equation 21 indicates proportionality to $T^{\frac{3}{2}}$ for the variation of the diffusion coefficient with temperature at constant pressure. This is the same kind of variation as in a law of force inversely proportional to a very high power of the distance. We have, in fact, seen that in a force inversely proportional to the $(n + 1)$th power of the distance the quantity $\mathscr{B}(m_1\xi_1)$ varies for a constant total pressure of the gas mixture as $T^{-(\frac{3}{2}+2/n)}$, that is, that $\mathscr{D}_{12}$, being inversely proportional to $\mathscr{B}$, varies as $T^{(\frac{3}{2}+2/n)}$, which gives $T^{\frac{3}{2}}$ for very large n. For the fifth-power law $n = 4$, and we find, with Maxwell, proportionality to T^2.

The method of integration which has permitted this solution of the problem of the mutual diffusion of two gases does not appear to be applicable to the calculation of the viscosity or the thermal conductivity of a gas. The difference is that in diffusion the departures from the Maxwellian velocity distribution are not essentially important. On the contrary, these differences play a significant role in the other phenomena.

5. CALCULATION OF THE MOBILITY

We have demonstrated a formula generalizing the results of the dynamical method introduced by Maxwell in the kinetic theory of gases and applied it to the particularly simple case in which the molecules repel each other according to the inverse-fifth power of the distance. We have shown that it is possible, whatever the interaction, to calculate the exchange of momentum in a mixture of two gases due to molecular collisions by the formula

$$\mathscr{B}(m_1\xi_1) = \tfrac{3\,2}{3}N_1N_2\sqrt{2\pi M_r kT}(u_2 - u_1)\int_0^\infty q(v_0)\, e^{-z^2}z^5\, dz \qquad (19)$$

Let us now apply this formula to the calculation of the mobility of an ion of finite size moving through a gas whose molecules are attracted toward the ion because of polarization forces. In those cases in which the number of ions is extremely small in comparison with the number of neutral molecules, there is no reason to consider mutual collisions between the ions in calculating their mobility.

If K represents the dielectric constant of the gas m_1, at pressure p_1, containing N_1 molecules per unit volume, the attractive force on a molecule by an ion of charge e at distance r is approximately

$$f = \frac{K-1}{2\pi N_1}\frac{e^2}{r^5}$$

and corresponds to a potential energy

$$V = -\frac{K-1}{8\pi N_1}\frac{e^2}{r^4}$$

If we ascribe to the ion of mass m_2 a finite size, so that the sum of its radius and that of a molecule is D_{12}, we must consider the curvature in the trajectory due to the attraction as well as the deflection that is produced at the instant of impact.

It is necessary to calculate $\mathscr{B}(m_1\xi_1)$ in order to obtain the mobility of the ions. If we neglect the effects of acceleration and diffusion, (10) becomes

$$p_2 X_2 = \mathscr{B}(m_1\xi_1) = \tfrac{3\,2}{3}N_1N_2\sqrt{2\pi M_r kT}\,(u_2 - u_1)\int_0^\infty q(v_0)e^{-z^2}z^5\, dz$$

where $p_2 X_2$ is the external force acting on the N_2 ions contained in unit volume of the gas. If E is the electric field intensity and e is the ionic charge,

$$p_2 X_2 = N_2 eE$$

Then, $(u_2 - u_1)$ being the relative velocity of the ions with respect to the gas, the mobility $\mathscr{K}$ of the ions is given by

$$\mathscr{K} = \frac{u_2 - u_1}{E} = \frac{e}{A}$$

where

$$A = \tfrac{32}{3} N_1 \sqrt{2\pi M_r kT} \int_0^\infty q(v_0) e^{-z^2} z^5 \, dz$$

Now

$$q(v_0) = \int_0^\infty \cos^2 \Phi b \, db$$

where the angle Φ is given by (13):

$$\Phi = \int_0^{\rho^*} \frac{d\rho}{\sqrt{1 - \rho^2 + (2V/M_r v_0^2)}}$$

The smallest positive root ρ_0 of the quantity under the radical (i.e., the outermost zero of the denominator) is equal to ρ^* if an elastic impact does not take place, whereas ρ^* assumes the value b/D_{12} in the contrary case, since r, the distance between centers, cannot be less than D_{12}.

Now

$$\frac{2V}{M_r v_0^2} = \frac{(K-1)}{8\pi N_1 kT} \frac{e^2 \rho_1^4}{z^2 b^4} = \frac{K-1}{8\pi p_1} \frac{e^2 \rho_1^4}{z^2 b^4}$$

and, putting

$$\mu^2 = \frac{K-1}{8\pi p_1} \frac{e^2}{D_{12}^4} \quad \text{and} \quad b^2 = \frac{2\mu D_{12}^2}{z} \beta^2 = \frac{2}{z}\left[\frac{(K-1)e^2}{8\pi p_1}\right]^{1/2} \beta^2 \quad (22)$$

we obtain

$$\Phi = \int_0^{\rho^*} \frac{d\rho}{\sqrt{1 - \rho^2 + (\rho^4/4\beta^4)}}$$

There are two cases to distinguish, according to whether or not an elastic impact takes place, that is according to the value of ρ_0, the root of the radical, with respect to

$$\frac{b}{D_{12}} = \beta \left(\frac{2\mu}{z}\right)^{1/2} \quad (23)$$

Changing the variable ρ by putting

$$\rho = y\sqrt{2\beta^2}$$

we get

$$\Phi = \sqrt{2\beta^2} \int_0^{y^*} \frac{dy}{\sqrt{1 - 2\beta^2 y^2 + y^4}}$$

y^* being equal to the smallest root of the radical if it exists and is less than $\sqrt{\mu/z}$; y^* being equal to $\sqrt{\mu/z}$ in the contrary case, which corresponds to an elastic impact.

We have for the calculation of the integral Φ two different methods, according to whether the quantity under the radical has real or imaginary roots, that is, whether $\beta > 1$ or $\beta < 1$. In the first case the calculation of Φ gives elliptic functions and can be carried out by using tables that give values of

$$F_\psi(\varphi) = \int_0^\varphi \frac{d\varphi}{\sqrt{1 - \sin^2 \psi \sin^2 \varphi}}$$

for all values of φ and ψ, in particular the values of the complete function

$$F_\psi' = \int_0^{\pi/2} \frac{d\varphi}{\sqrt{1 - \sin^2 \psi \sin^2 \varphi}}$$

(1) If an elastic impact does not take place, we shall have, on putting $2\beta^2 = \sin \psi + (1/\sin \psi)$ and $y = \sqrt{\sin \psi} \sin \varphi$,

$$\Phi = \sqrt{1 + \sin^2 \psi} \int_0^{\pi/2} \frac{d\varphi}{\sqrt{1 - \sin^2 \psi \sin^2 \varphi}} = \sqrt{1 + \sin^2 \psi}\, F_\psi'$$

(2) If an elastic impact does take place, the limiting value φ^* of φ is given by

$$\sqrt{\sin \psi} \sin \varphi^* = y^* = \left(\frac{\mu}{z}\right)^{1/2} \quad \text{or} \quad \varphi^* = \sin^{-1}\left(\frac{\mu}{z \sin \psi}\right)^{1/2}$$

Then

$$\Phi = \sqrt{1 + \sin^2 \psi} \int_0^{\sin^{-1}\sqrt{\mu/z \sin \psi}} \frac{d\varphi}{\sqrt{1 - \sin^2 \psi \sin^2 \varphi}}$$

$$= \sqrt{1 + \sin^2 \psi}\, F_\psi\left[\sin^{-1}\left(\frac{\mu}{z \sin \psi}\right)^{1/2}\right]$$

In the second case, if the roots y_0 are imaginary, an elastic impact will always take place, for otherwise the ion and molecule draw indefinitely closer together if they are considered reduced in size to points located at their centers. We always have

$$\Phi = \sqrt{2\beta^2} \int_0^{\sqrt{\mu/z}} \frac{dy}{\sqrt{1 - 2\beta^2 y^2 + y^4}}$$

The values for the integral have been calculated for various values of β between 0 and 1 and $\sqrt{\mu/z}$ between the same limits. When $\sqrt{\mu/z}$ is greater than 1, we may utilize the result of the same calculation, since it is easy to verify that

$$\int_0^{\sqrt{\mu/z}} \frac{dy}{\sqrt{1 - 2\beta^2 y^2 + y^4}} = 2\int_0^1 \frac{dy}{\sqrt{1 - 2\beta^2 y^2 + y^4}} - \int_0^{\sqrt{z/\mu}} \frac{dy}{\sqrt{1 - 2\beta^2 y^2 + y^4}}$$

$\sqrt{z/\mu}$ being less than unity when $\sqrt{\mu/z}$ is larger than unity.

For real roots the occurrence of an elastic impact depends on the value of $\sqrt{\mu/z}$ in relation to the smallest root of the equation

$$1 - 2\beta^2 y^2 + y^4 = 0$$

which is

$$y_0 = \sqrt{\sin \psi}$$

This quantity is always less than one. Therefore an elastic impact will occur for all values of ψ if $\mu/z > 1$. On the contrary, if $\mu/z < 1$ and we put $\mu/z = \sin \varepsilon$, elastic impacts will not take place if $\psi < \varepsilon$ but will occur if $\psi > \varepsilon$.

We then obtain the following table of calculations:

$$\frac{\mu}{z} = \sin \varepsilon < 1 \begin{cases} \beta < 1, \quad 2\Phi = \sqrt{2\beta^2} \int_0^{\sqrt{\mu/z}} \dfrac{dy}{\sqrt{1 - 2\beta^2 y^2 + y^4}} \\[2ex] \beta = \sqrt{\tfrac{1}{2}}\left(\sin \psi + \dfrac{1}{\sin \psi}\right) > 1 \\[2ex] \text{where} \begin{cases} \psi < \varepsilon, \quad \Phi = \sqrt{1 + \sin^2 \psi}\, F_\psi' \\[1.5ex] \psi > \varepsilon, \quad \Phi = \sqrt{1 + \sin^2 \psi}\, F_\psi\left[\sin^{-1}\left(\dfrac{\sin \varepsilon}{\sin \psi}\right)^{1/2}\right] \end{cases} \end{cases}$$

$$\frac{\mu}{z} > 1 \begin{cases} \beta < 1, \quad 2\Phi = \sqrt{2\beta^2}\left(2\int_0^1 \dfrac{dy}{\sqrt{1 - 2\beta^2 y^2 + y^4}} + \int_0^{\sqrt{z/\mu}} \right. \\[2ex] \hspace{4cm} \left. \times \dfrac{dy}{\sqrt{1 - 2\beta^2 y^2 + y^4}}\right) \\[2ex] \beta = \sqrt{\tfrac{1}{2}}[\sin \psi + (1/\sin \psi)] > 1, \quad \Phi = \sqrt{1 + \sin^2 \psi}\, F_\psi' \end{cases}$$

For an ion and molecule of given dimensions D_{12} is determined, and μ follows from (22):

$$\mu^2 = \frac{K - 1}{8\pi p_1} \frac{e^2}{D_{12}^4}$$

Under these conditions, a value of z from (18) corresponds to each value of the relative velocity v_0:

$$z = \left(\frac{M_r v_0^2}{2kT}\right)^{1/2}$$

Similarly, to each value of v_0 there corresponds a value of μ/z.

Then, varying β from 0 to ∞, we have values of Φ for the various

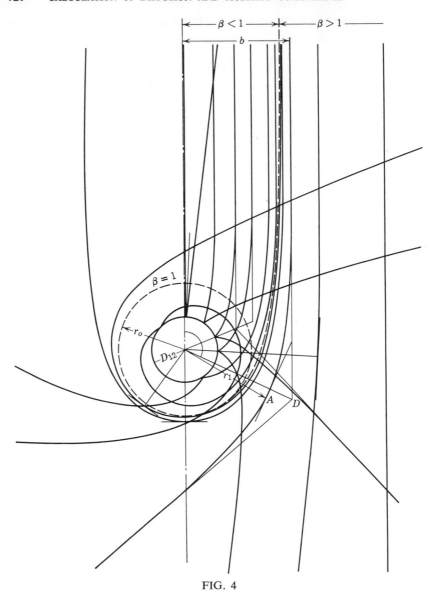

FIG. 4

trajectories that correspond to the same value of the relative velocity. Figures 4, 5, and 6 give the form of these trajectories for very different values of μ/z.

Take first of all a small value for the relative velocity, such as $\sqrt{\mu/z} = 2$, which corresponds to a reduced relative velocity $\mu/z = 4$. The attractions then play an important role, and the relative trajectories are strongly

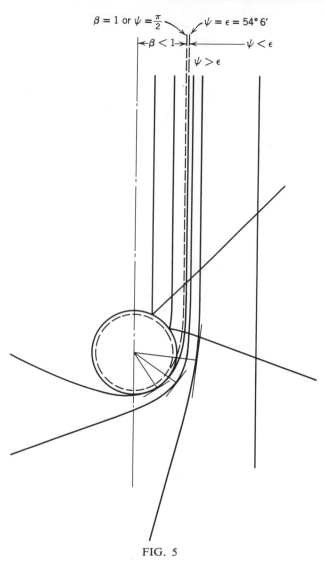

$\beta = 1$ or $\psi = \frac{\pi}{2}$ $\psi = \epsilon = 54° 6'$

$\leftarrow\beta < 1\rightarrow$ $\psi < \epsilon$

$\psi > \epsilon$

FIG. 5

curved inward, as in Fig. 4. This figure shows curves for various values of β, each of which corresponds, according to (23), to a reduced initial distance

$$\frac{b}{D_{12}} = \beta \left(\frac{2\mu}{z}\right)^{\frac{1}{2}}$$

Now assume that the ion is stationary. The relative trajectory gives the motion of the molecule when it is considered to be reduced to point

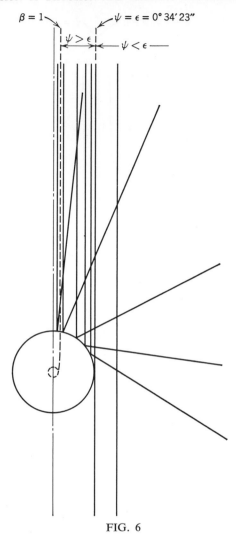

FIG. 6

size and the ion is assumed to have for its radius the sum D_{12} of the real radii. The circle of radius D_{12} is drawn with a full line.

For a sufficiently large β an elastic impact does not take place—the trajectory is simply curved inward and consists of two symmetrical portions separated by the apse A whose position is determined by the value Φ given in the preceding table and by the corresponding value r_1 of the distance to the center of attraction:

$$\frac{r_1}{D_{12}} = \left(\frac{\mu}{z \sin \psi}\right)^{1/2}$$

For a value of $\mu/z > 1$ an elastic impact does not take place for any value of β greater than unity.

For $\beta = 1$ or $\psi = \pi/2$ the molecule revolves about the ion following a dotted circle of radius r_0, where

$$\frac{r_0}{D_{12}} = \left(\frac{\mu}{z}\right)^{\frac{1}{2}}$$

The trajectories corresponding to $\beta > 1$ lie entirely outside this circle.

For $\beta < 1$ the molecule penetrates the interior of the circle and, if an elastic impact does not occur, draws indefinitely nearer the center of attraction. An elastic impact produces a deflection that gives to the trajectory a second branch symmetrical with the first about the radius passing through the point of impact.

As the relative velocity increases, μ/z decreases, the trajectories are less curved, and elastic impacts become more important than the attraction from the point of view of exchange of momentum. Figure 5 corresponds to $\mu/z = 0.9$. The dotted circle penetrates inside the circle of radius D_{12}, so that a molecule may undergo an elastic impact even when, in the absence of this impact, it does not approach indefinitely close to the center of attraction. As indicated in the table, this requires the decomposition of the variation of β into three regions: the region $\beta < 1$, for which an elastic impact takes place in all cases, then a second region ($\psi > \varepsilon$), in which an elastic impact takes place before the molecule attains the apse, and finally a third ($\psi < \varepsilon$), in which an elastic impact does not occur.

Finally, if the velocity becomes very large, as in Fig. 6, in which $\mu/z = 0.01$ and $\sqrt{\mu/z} = 0.1$, elastic impacts play the essential role and the curvature of the trajectories due to the attractive force is no longer significant.

To obtain the total momentum exchange between the two gases, it is necessary to calculate the quantity $q(v_0)$ for each velocity. From (16) we have

$$q(v_0) = \int \cos^2 \Phi b \, db = \frac{\mu D_{12}^2}{2} \int \cos^2 \Phi \, d\beta^2$$

For each value of μ/z we calculate the values of Φ for all values of β and construct a curve with β^2 as the abscissa and $\cos^2 \Phi$ as the ordinate. The area under this curve is $y = \int \cos^2 \Phi \, d\beta^2$, the area being measured by a graphical procedure.

In drawing a similar curve for different values of μ/z, we have y as a function of μ/z or of z if μ is given by

$$q(v_0) = \mu D_{12}^2 \frac{Y}{z}$$

Then

$$A = \tfrac{3}{3}\tfrac{2}{3}N_1\sqrt{2\pi M_r kT}\mu D_{12}^2 \int_0^\infty ye^{-z^2}z^4\, dz \tag{24}$$

and putting

$$Y = f(\mu) = \int_0^\infty ye^{-z^2}z^4\, dz \tag{25}$$

we finally get the mobility

$$\mathscr{K} = \frac{e}{A} = \frac{3}{16Y\sqrt{(K-1)}\rho_1}\left(\frac{m_1 + m_2}{m_2}\right)^{\frac{1}{2}} \tag{26}$$

To each value of μ, that is, to each size of the ion since

$$\mu = \left[\frac{(K-1)}{8\pi p_1}\frac{e^2}{D_{12}^4}\right]^{\frac{1}{2}}$$

there corresponds a value of Y and, consequently, of $\mathscr{K}$. The graph in Fig. 7 represents the results of all these calculations, that is, it gives $3/16Y$ on the ordinate and

$$\frac{1}{\mu} = \left[\frac{8\pi p_1}{(K-1)e^2}\right]^{\frac{1}{2}}D_{12}^2 \tag{27}$$

on the abscissa.

In order to verify the results of this calculation, note that, for small values of μ, μ/z is very small throughout the range of interesting values of z; that is, impacts play the essential role, for the polarization attraction

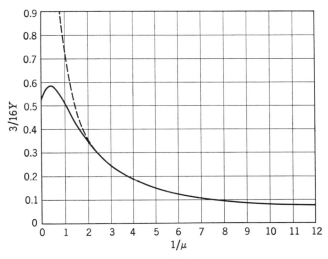

FIG. 7

becomes very weak. In this case we have, as for pure elastic impacts,

$$\int \cos^2 \Phi b \, db = \frac{D_{12}^2}{4}$$

Then

$$Y = \int \cos^2 \Phi \, d\beta^2 = \frac{z}{4\mu}$$

so

$$Y = \int_0^\infty y e^{-z^2} z^4 \, dz = \frac{1}{4\mu} \int_0^\infty e^{-z^2} z^5 \, dz = \frac{1}{4\mu}$$

Finally

$$\frac{3}{16Y} = \frac{3\mu}{4} = \frac{3}{4(1/\mu)} \tag{28}$$

On the contrary, when μ is very large, Y then takes a limiting value Y_p which corresponds to the ordinate of the origin of the full curve in Fig. 7. Then $3/16 Y_p = 0.505$. This extreme case corresponds to a negligible influence of elastic impacts, that is, to motion in the gas of a charged particle of extremely small dimensions whose drift is impeded principally by its attraction for the molecules. We have for the corresponding mobility

$$\mathscr{K}_p = \frac{0.505}{\sqrt{(K-1)\rho_1}} \left(\frac{m_1 + m_2}{m_2} \right)^{1/2} \tag{29}$$

This expression for the limit of the mobility of the ions when the polarization attraction plays the essential role does not contain the charge e of the ion. This is because the force on the molecules which tends to retard the motion makes $\mathscr{B}(m_1 \xi_1)$ proportional to the charge, whereas the motive force in an electric field is itself proportional to the charge.

Let us now seek to deduce from our results the probable size of the ions. Denote by x the unknown ratio of the diameter of an ion to that of a molecule D_1. We have

$$D_{12} = D_1 \frac{x+1}{2} \quad \text{and} \quad \mu = \frac{e}{D_1^2} \left[\frac{2(K-1)}{\pi P} \right]^{1/2} \frac{1}{(x+1)^2}$$

and μ, and consequently $3/16 Y$, can be calculated as a function of x. Since

$$\frac{m_1 + m_2}{m_2} = 1 + \frac{1}{x^3}$$

$$\mathscr{K} = \frac{3}{16Y\sqrt{(K-1)\rho}} \left(\frac{m_1 + m_2}{m_2} \right)^{1/2} = \frac{3}{16Y\sqrt{(K-1)\rho}} \left(1 + \frac{1}{x^3} \right)^{1/2}$$

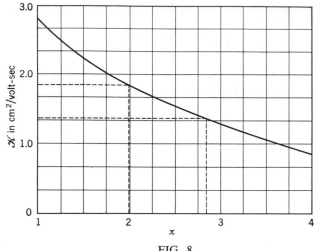

FIG. 8

Thus we have $\mathscr{K}$ as a function of x. We can then draw a curve showing x as the abscissa and the theoretical value of $\mathscr{K}$ as the ordinate (Fig. 8).

REFERENCES

1. R. D. Present, *Kinetic Theory of Gases*, McGraw-Hill, New York, 1958, Chapters 8 and 11.
2. L. Boltzmann, *Vorlesungen über Gastheorie*, Vol. 1, J. A. Barth, Leipzig, 1896, p. 119.
3. L. Boltzmann, *op. cit.*, p. 197.
4. L. Boltzmann, *op. cit.*, p. 96.
5. J. C. Maxwell, *Phil. Mag.* **19,** 19 (1860); **20,** ?1 (1860).

APPENDIX III

TABLES

TABLE I. Physical constants and conversion factors

*Fundamental constants**

Planck's constant	$h = 6.6257 \times 10^{-34}$ joule-sec $= 6.6257 \times 10^{-27}$ erg-sec
Rationalized Planck's constant	$\hbar = h/2\pi = 1.0544 \times 10^{-34}$ joule-sec $= 1.0544 \times 10^{-27}$ erg-sec
Velocity of light in vacuum	$c = 2.99793 \times 10^{8}$ m/sec
Charge of the electron (magnitude)	$e = 1.6021 \times 10^{-19}$ Coulomb $= 4.8029 \times 10^{-10}$ esu $= 1.6021 \times 10^{-20}$ emu
Rest mass of the electron	$m_e = 9.1091 \times 10^{-31}$ kg
Ratio of proton mass to m_e	$m_p/m_e = 1836.1$
Boltzmann constant	$k = 1.3806 \times 10^{-23}$ joule/°K $= 1.3806 \times 10^{-16}$ erg/°K
Avogadro's number	$N_A = 6.0224 \times 10^{26}$ molecules per kg molecular weight $= 6.0224 \times 10^{23}$ molecules per gm-mole

Other useful constants and relations

Unit mass on C¹² = 12.000000 scale 1 atomic mass unit (amu)	$= 1.6605 \times 10^{-27}$ kg $= 931.49$ Mev energy equivalent
Charge-to-mass ratio of electron	$e/m_e = 1.7588 \times 10^{11}$ coul/kg
Wavelength of photon with energy E ev	$\lambda = 12{,}398/E$ Å
Wavelength of electron with non-relativistic kinetic energy T ev	$\lambda = 12.26/T^{1/2}$ Å
Energy levels in hydrogenlike atoms	$E_n = -13.60 Z^2/n^2$ ev

Universal gas constant	$R = 8.314 \times 10^3$ joules/kilo-mole-°K $= 8.314 \times 10^7$ erg/gm-mole-°K
Thermal energy per °K	$k = 8.617 \times 10^{-5}$ ev/°K
Thermal energy at 290°K = 17°C	$kT = 1/40$ ev
Temperature associated with 1 ev	$T = 11,605°K$
Mksa units	$\varepsilon_0 = 8.8542 \times 10^{-12}$ farad/m
	$\mu_0 = 4\pi \times 10^{-7}$ henry/m
Loschmidt's number (the number density of an ideal gas at 760 mm Hg and 0°C)	$N_L = 2.69 \times 10^{19}$/cm^3
Number density of an ideal gas at 1 mm Hg and 0°C	$N_{1\,mm} = 3.54 \times 10^{16}$/cm^3
Atomic unit of cross section	$\pi a_0^2 = 0.88 \times 10^{-16}$ cm^2
1 joule = 10^7 erg	
1 electron volt (ev)	$= 1.602 \times 10^{-19}$ joule
	$= 1.602 \times 10^{-12}$ erg
	$= 23.069$ kcal/mole

1 Rydberg = 1 Hartree = 13.605 ev
1 Torr = 1 mm Hg pressure
1 angstrom (Å) = 10^{10} meter

* From J. A. Bearden and J. S. Thomsen, *Nuovo Cimento*, Vol. 5 Supplement No. 2, pp. 267–360 (1957), with later modifications by J. A. Bearden. See also E. R. Cohen, J. W. M. DuMond, T. W. Layton, and J. S. Rollett, *Rev. Mod. Phys.* **27**, 363 (1955).

TABLE II. Atomic units

Physical Quantity	Unit	Symbol	Numerical Magnitude
Mass	Electronic mass	m_e	9.108×10^{-28} gm
Charge	Electronic charge	e	4.8029×10^{-10} esu
Angular momentum	Rationalized Planck's constant	$\hbar$	1.0544×10^{-27} erg-sec
Length	$\hbar^2/m_e e^2$: radius of first Bohr orbit of hydrogen atom with nucleus of infinite mass	a_0	5.2917×10^{-9} cm
Energy	e^2/a_0: twice the ionization energy of hydrogen atom with nucleus of infinite mass	E_0	2 Rydbergs = 27.210 ev
Time	$\hbar/E_0$: time for electron in first Bohr orbit of hydrogen atom to describe one radian	t_0	2.4189×10^{-17} sec
Velocity	a_0/t_0: velocity of electron in first Bohr orbit of hydrogen atom	v_0	2.1877×10^8 cm/sec

The velocity of light in a vacuum c has the value $c/v_0 = 137.037$ in atomic units. The reciprocal of this quantity is Sommerfeld's fine structure constant, $\alpha = v_0/c = e^2/ch$.

TABLE III. The periodic table of the elements

	IA	IIA	IIIB	IVB	VB	VIB	VIIB	VIII	VIII	VIII	IB	IIB	IIIA	IVA	VA	VIA	VIIA	Noble Gases
1s	1 H																	2 He $1s^2$
2s / 2p	3 Li	4 Be											5 B	6 C	7 N	8 O	9 F	10 Ne
3s / 3p	11 Na	12 Mg											13 Al	14 Si	15 P	16 S	17 Cl	18 A
4s / 3d / 4p	19 K	20 Ca	21 Sc	22 Ti	23 V	24 Cr $4s^1 3d^5$	25 Mn	26 Fe	27 Co	28 Ni	29 Cu $4s^1 3d^{10}$	30 Zn	31 Ga	32 Ge	33 As	34 Se	35 Br	36 Kr
5s / 4d / 5p	37 Rb	38 Sr	39 Y	40 Zr	41 Nb $5s^1 4d^4$	42 Mo	43 Tc	44 Ru $5s^1 4d^7$	45 Rh $5s^1 4d^8$	46 Pd $5s^0 4d^{10}$	47 Ag $5s^1 4d^{10}$	48 Cd	49 In	50 Sn	51 Sb	52 Te	53 I	54 Xe
6s / 5d / 6p	55 Cs	56 Ba	57 La — (Lanthanides)	72 Hf	73 Ta	74 W	75 Re	76 Os	77 Ir	78 Pt $6s^1 5d^9$	79 Au $6s^1 5d^{10}$	80 Hg	81 Tl	82 Pb	83 Bi	84 Po	85 At	86 Rn
7s / 6d / 7p	87 Fr	88 Ra	89 Ac — (Actinides)															

Sub-shell labels: s^1 s^2 | d^1 d^2 d^3 d^4 d^5 d^6 d^7 d^8 d^9 d^{10} | p^1 p^2 p^3 p^4 p^5 p^6

Lanthanides 4f

f^1	f^2	f^3	f^4	f^5	f^6	f^7	f^8	f^9	f^{10}	f^{11}	f^{12}	f^{13}	f^{14}
58 Ce $5d^0 4f^1$	59 Pr $5d^0 4f^3$	60 Nd $5d^0 4f^4$	61 Pm ?	62 Sm $5d^0 4f^6$	63 Eu $5d^0 4f^7$	64 Gd $5d^1 4f^7$	65 Tb $5d^1 4f^8$	66 Dy ?	67 Ho ?	68 Er ?	69 Tm $5d^0 4f^{13}$	70 Yb $5d^0 4f^{14}$	71 Lu $5d^1 4f^{14}$

Actinides 5f

f^1	f^2	f^3	f^4	f^5	f^6	f^7	f^8	f^9	f^{10}	f^{11}	f^{12}	f^{13}	f^{14}
90 Th $6d^2 5f^0$	91 Pa ?	92 U $6d^1 5f^3$	93 Np ?	94 Pu ?	95 Am $6d^0 5f^7$	96 Cm $6d^1 5f^7$	97 Bk ?	98 Cf ?	99 Es ?	100 Fm ?	101 Md ?	102 No ?	103 Lw ?

Reprinted, with additions, from *Fundamentals of Modern Physics*, by R. M. Eisberg, John Wiley and Sons, Inc. New York, 1961.

TABLE IV. Excitation and ionization potentials of atoms in volts

Atomic Number	Element	V_m	V_r	V_{i1}	V_{i2}	V_{i3}
1	H		10.198	13.595		
2	He	19.80	21.21	24.580	54.400	
3	Li		1.85	5.390	75.62	122.42
4	Be		5.28	9.320	18.21	153.85
5	B		4.96	8.296	25.15	37.92
6	C	1.26	7.48	11.264	24.376	47.86
7	N	2.38	10.3	14.54	29.60	47.426
8	O	1.97	9.15	13.614	35.15	54.93
9	F		12.7	17.418	34.98	62.65
10	Ne	16.62	16.85	21.559	41.07	63.5 ±0.1
11	Na		2.1	5.138	47.29	71.8 ±0.1
12	Mg	2.709	2.712	7.644	15.03	78.2 ±0.1
13	Al		3.14	5.984	18.82	28.44
14	Si	0.78	4.93	8.149	16.34	33.46
15	P	0.91	6.95	10.55	19.65	30.16
16	S		6.52	10.357	23.4	34.8
17	Cl		8.92	13.01	23.80	39.9
18	A	11.55	11.61	15.755	27.6	40.90
19	K		1.61	4.339	31.81	45.9
20	Ca	1.880	1.886	6.111	11.87	51.21
21	Sc	1.43	1.98	6.56	12.89	24.75
22	Ti	0.81	1.97	6.83	13.57	28.14
23	V	0.26	2.03	6.74	14.2	29.7
24	Cr	0.94	2.89	6.764	16.49	31
25	Mn	2.11	2.28	7.432	15.64	33.69
26	Fe	0.85	2.40	7.90	16.18	30.64
27	Co	0.43	2.92	7.86	17.05	33.49
28	Ni	0.42	3.31	7.633	18.15	36.16
29	Cu	1.38	3.78	7.724	20.29	36.83
30	Zn	4.00	4.03	9.391	17.96	39.70
31	Ga		3.07	6.00	20.51	30.70
32	Ge	0.88	4.65	7.88	15.93	34.21
33	As	1.31	6.28	9.81	18.7 ±0.1	28.3
34	Se		6.10	9.75	21.5	32.0
35	Br		7.86	11.84	21.6	35.9
36	Kr	9.91	10.02	13.996	24.56	36.9
37	Rb		1.56	4.176	27.56	40

TABLE IV. (Continued)

Atomic Number	Element	V_m	V_r	V_{i1}	V_{i2}	V_{i3}
38	Sr	1.775	1.798	5.692	11.026	43.6
39	Y		1.305	6.38	12.23	20.5
40	Zr	0.52	1.83	6.835	12.92	24.8
41	Nb		2.97	6.88	13.90	28.1
42	Mo	1.34	3.18	7.131	15.72	29.6
43	Tc			7.23	14.87	31.9
44	Ru	0.81	3.16	7.36	16.60	30.3
45	Rh	0.41	3.36	7.46	15.92	32.8
46	Pd	0.81	4.48	8.33	19.42	
47	Ag		3.57	7.574	21.48	36.10
48	Cd	3.73	3.80	8.991	16.904	44.5
49	In		3.02	5.785	18.86	28.0
50	Sn	1.07	4.33	7.332	14.6	30.7
51	Sb	1.05	5.35	8.64	16.7 ±0.5	24.8
52	Te	1.31	5.49	9.01	18.8 ±0.5	31
53	I			10.44	19.0	33
54	Xe	8.32	8.45	12.127	21.2	32.1
55	Cs		1.39	3.893	25.1	34.6 ±0.7
56	Ba	1.13	1.57	5.810	10.00	37 ±1
57	La	0.37	1.84	5.61	11.43	19.17
58	Ce			(6.91)	12.3	19.5
59	Pr			(5.76)		
60	Nd			(6.31)		
61	Pm					
62	Sm			5.6	(11.2)	
63	Eu			5.67	11.24	
64	Gd			6.16	(12)	
65	Tb			(6.74)		
66	Dy			(6.82)		
67	Ho					
68	Er					
69	Tm					
70	Yb			6.2	12.10	
71	Lu			6.15	14.7	
72	Hf		2.19	5.5	14.9	
73	Ta			7.7	16.2 ±0.5	

TABLE IV. (Continued)

Atomic Number	Element	V_m	V_r	V_{i1}	V_{i2}	V_{i3}
74	W	0.37	2.3	7.98	17.7	
					±0.5	
75	Re		2.35	7.87	16.6	
					±0.5	
76	Os			8.7	17	
					±1	
77	Ir			9.2	17.0	
					±0.3	
78	Pt	0.102	3.74	8.96	18.54	
79	Au	1.14	4.63	9.223	20.5	
80	Hg	4.667	4.886	10.434	18.751	34.2
81	Tl		3.28	6.106	20.42	29.8
82	Pb	2.66	4.38	7.415	15.03	31.93
83	Bi	1.42	4.04	7.287	19.3	25.6
84	Po			8.2	19.4	27.3
				±0.4	±1.7	±0.8
85	At			9.2	20.1	29.3
				±0.4	±1.7	±0.9
86	Rn	6.77	8.41	10.745	21.4	29.4
					±1.8	±1.0
87	Fr			3.98	22.5	33.5
				±0.10	±1.8	±1.5
88	Ra			5.277	10.144	
89	Ac			6.89	11.5	
				±0.6	±0.4	
90	Th				11.5	20.0
					±1.0	
91	Pa					
92	U			4		

The *resonant level* V_r is the lowest excited level from which electric dipole radiation can take place. If there is an excited level, not part of the ground state multiplet, which is lower than V_r, it is a *metastable level* V_m. The *ionization potentials* of the neutral, singly charged and doubly charged atoms are denoted by V_{i1}, V_{i2}, and V_{i3}, respectively. These data were obtained from spectra by means of the conversion factor $V\lambda = hc/e = 1.2398 \times 10^{-4}$ v-cm. The ionization potentials are taken from W. Finkelnburg and W. Humbach, Naturwissenschaften, **42**, 35 (1955) and the remaining data from S. C. Brown and W. P. Allis, "Basic Data of Electrical Discharges," MIT Technical Report 283, June 9, 1958.

TABLE V. Dissociation, excitation, and ionization energies of molecules in electron volts

Molecule	E_d	E_r	E_{i1}	Molecule	E_d	E_r	E_{i1}
Br_2	1.971		12.8	HCl	4.430		13.8
CH_4			14.5	HF	6.40		17.7
CN			14	HI	3.056		12.8
CO	11.108	6.0	14.1	H_2O		7.6	12.6
CO_2		10.0	14.4	H_2S			10.4
CS			10.6	I_2	1.5417	2.3	9.7
CS_2			10.4	IBr	1.817		11.6
C_2H_2			11.6	ICl	2.152		11.9
C_2H_4			12.2	N_2	9.756	6.1	15.5
C_2H_6			12.8	NH_3			11.2
C_6H_6			9.6	NO	6.487	5.4	9.5
Cl_2	2.475		13.2	NO_2			11.0
F_2	2.75		17.8	N_2O			12.9
H_2	4.476	11.5	15.6	O_2	5.080	7.9	12.5
HBr	3.75		13.2	S_2	4.4		10.7
HCN			14.8	SO_2			13.1

These data are taken from S. C. Brown and W. P. Allis, "Basic Data of Electrical Discharges," MIT Technical Report No. 283, June 9, 1958, and from G. Herzberg, "Molecular Spectra and Molecular Structure," Second Edition, Van Nostrand, Princeton, N.J., 1950.

AUTHOR INDEX

SUBJECT INDEX